Klaus Grawe

Psychological Therapy

 Hogrefe & Huber

Library of Congress Cataloging-in-Publication Data

Library of Congress Control Number: 2002111974

National Library of Canada Cataloging-in-Publication Data

Grawe, Klaus
Psychological Therapy / Klaus Grawe
Translation of: Psychologische Therapie

Includes bibliographical references and index.
ISBN 0-88937-217-9

1. Psychotherapy. I. Title.

RC480.G713 2002   616.89'14   C2002-904376-X

Copyright © 2004 by Hogrefe & Huber Publishers

PUBLISHING OFFICES
USA: Hogrefe & Huber Publishers, 875 Massachusetts Avenue, 7th Floor, Cambridge, MA 02139,
             Phone: (866) 823-4726, Fax (617) 354-6875, E-mail info@hhpub.com
Europe: Hogrefe & Huber Publishers, Rohnsweg 25, D-37085 Göttingen, Germany,
             Phone +49 551 49609-0, Fax +49 551 49609-88, E-mail hh@hhpub.com

SALES & DISTRIBUTION
USA: Hogrefe & Huber Publishers, Customer Service Department, 30 Amberwood Parkway, Ashland, OH 44805,
             Phone (800) 228-3749, Fax (419) 281-6883, E-mail custserv@hhpub.com
Europe: Hogrefe & Huber Publishers, Rohnsweg 25, D-37085 Göttingen, Germany,
             Phone +49 551 49609-0, Fax +49 551 49609-88, E-mail hh@hhpub.com

OTHER OFFICES
Canda: Hogrefe & Huber Publishers, 1543 Bayview Avenue, Toronto, Ontario, M4G 3B5
Switzerland: Hogrefe & Huber Publishers, Länggass-Strasse 76, CH-3000 Bern 9

Hogrefe & Huber Publishers
Incorporated and Registered in the State of Washington, USA, and in Göttingen, Lower Saxony, Germany

Printed and bound in the USA
ISBN 0-88937-217-9

Cover image: Wassily Kandinsky, Durchgehender Strich, 1923
          Owner: Kunstsammlung Nordrhein-Westfalen, Düsseldorf
          Reproduction: Walter Klein, Düsseldorf
          © VG Bild-Kunst, Bonn 2002

Preface

This book was originally published in German, and despite its size quickly found a broad readership among psychiatrists, therapists and psychologists in Germany, Switzerland, and Austria. The concepts developed in that original edition, namely for an integrative form of psychological therapy with a consistent theoretical basis, have over recent years been presented — and at times heatedly discussed — at numerous congresses and meetings outside of those German-speaking countries, and have attracted considerable interest among colleagues of many different nationalities. With this English translation of the book, these colleagues and a broader international group of readers will, I hope, now have the opportunity to properly understand and get to grips with the concepts that we have not just been talking about, but also successfully putting into practice.

I would like to thank Robert Dimbleby from Hogrefe & Huber Publishers for his professional coordination of the work of translating and correction of the English edition. Brigitte Müller-Lankow and Jeof Spiro have translated the not always easy German text into English, and have shown great patience while we together tried to find the best English expressions for much of the specialist German terminology. In particular I am grateful to my psychotherapy research friend and colleague Dr. Björn Meier, who spent a great deal of time and effort in editing large parts of the book to make it as readable as possible for English-speaking and international readers. His contribution to the final quality of the text has been great, and with his willingness to take on this often difficult task he has been, for me, a model of exemplary collegiality. Dr. Anne Trösken has provided invaluable assistance in proofreading the final text; to her, too, I would like to extend my thanks and best wishes.

Finally, of course, I hope that this English edition of the book will attract just as much interest and attention as the original German edition did.

Klaus Grawe,
Bern, Spring 2004

Prologue

Psychotherapy denotes a healing that occurs via mental means. Psychological therapy, in contrast, means healing by using **psychologically based** procedures. This book deals with explanations of how mental processes can be influenced in a therapeutic manner. These explanations are rooted firmly in scientific psychology.

The psychological explanations developed herein contain ideas for how mental processes can be influenced most **effectively**. The psychological understanding of the psychotherapeutic process developed in this book yields specific suggestions for maximizing therapeutic effectiveness.

What I aimed for in this book is a vision of psychotherapy that is based on the principles of scientific psychology. It is a broad vision intended to include all of psychology and psychotherapy. Any procedures that can effectively alter mental processes are potential interventions for a psychological therapy. To arrive at a truly psychologically based psychotherapy, though, we must understand not only *that* something works but also *how* it works. Psychotherapy can well be conducted without comprehending the mechanisms of change. Conducting psychological therapy, by contrast, means strategically utilizing interventions whose psychological mechanisms are understood.

Psychology and psychotherapy have developed on somewhat separate trajectories. A person who knows a lot about psychology may not be an expert in psychotherapy and vice versa. Even within psychotherapy there has been a gap between the scientific research community and practitioners. Yet, all three areas of competence are needed to fully understand the mechanisms of psychotherapy and to be able to utilize this understanding in a therapeutic setting: The professional competence of the practitioner, that of the psychotherapy researcher, and that of the basic research psychologist. A psychological therapy in the sense of my definition can grow only from a mutually stimulating interchange, not from the continued separation of these areas. What is needed to develop this kind of a psychologically based psychotherapy, then, is a dialogue.

With this book I have tried to create such a dialogue. A practicing therapist, a psychotherapy researcher, and a basic research psychologist jointly explore the idea of a psychological therapy. Each of them contributes to and enriches this dialogue with his or her specific expertise.

The book is structured as a conversation among these three discussion partners. In the course of their conversation, they gradually develop the concept of a psychologically based psychotherapy. The discourse is divided into three dialogues. Each participant leads the discussion in one of the dialogues, which deals with his or her specific area of competence.

Each of the three dialogues is, in a sense, independent of the others because each focuses on a different perspective. However, these issues are generally interrelated and based on each other. Thus, the dialogues may be viewed as a sort of trilogy.

The first dialogue starts with issues primarily relevant for the practicing therapist. This discussion focuses on the question of which factors are responsible for producing outcome in psychotherapy. The psychotherapy researcher has much to say about this issue and does most of the talking in the first dialogue. Among the questions addressed here are: What can psychotherapy research tell us about the mechanisms by which psychotherapy exerts its effects? What are the conceptual implications of such findings? The conversation progresses well, and certain principles that account for the effects of the various therapeutic interventions emerge with increasing clarity.

Eventually, however, the discussants encounter a fundamental barrier: How can we truly understand changes in patients' mental functioning if our knowledge of these processes is in itself severely limited? In the second dialogue, therefore, the discussion focuses on the question of how the mechanisms of psychotherapy can be understood from a basic psychological perspective. This requires an excursion into the areas of basic perception and memory research. The research psychologist leads the discussion in this section and introduces the others to several basic psychological concepts that seem crucial for understanding the mechanisms of psychotherapy.

This second dialogue represents the core of the book in the sense that it establishes the foundations for the model of psychological therapy described in the third dialogue. Therefore, the second dialogue is subtitled "**Foundations of Psychological Therapy.**" This part is extensive, given that the foundations to be considered are indeed many. It would have been easy to discuss these foundations in even greater detail, or to consider additional psychological subfields, but the therapist and the therapy researcher make sure that the focus on issues relevant for psychotherapy is not entirely lost. In this second dialogue, the foundations are laid for an understanding of mental disorders, which then sets the stage for exploring the therapeutic implications of these ideas in the third dialogue.

This second dialogue may be of interest especially for therapists who either completed their degrees long ago or who never completed a regular degree in general psychology. The findings summarized in this part are often inaccessible to therapists because they tend to be scattered throughout the literature. For this dialogue alone, I reviewed over 500 publications from different areas of psychology and neurobiology. Writing this section was the most laborious and time-consuming, but it was also the most enjoyable part. I hope that I have managed to present this material in a way that conveys my own enthusiasm to the reader.

The third dialogue deals with the theoretical and practical implications of the concepts discussed in the first two dialogues. The previously discussed foundations are condensed into a three-component-model, which no longer has a merely descriptive character but also provides concrete guidance for therapeutic thought and action. In this part, it is the therapist who does most of the talking. She introduces a process model and a system of psychotherapy that can be viewed as a **theory of psychotherapy** and, at the same time, can serve as a **model for the practice of therapy**.

This model of a psychologically based therapy is then elaborated and rendered tangible via a case example. The conclusions suggested by this model are often at odds with conventional methods of therapeutic service provision. The question arises, then, if the psychological therapy developed here can be truly relevant for therapists practicing in the context of existing frameworks. Questions such as these are discussed in the chapter on "**Psychotherapy Training and Service Provision**" at the end of the third dialogue.

After the third dialogue, the three discussants leave the stage. In a short **epilogue** I then present a few more thoughts on my completed project. Specifically, I address the question of how **"Psychological Therapy"** is to be understood compared to the concept of a **"General psychotherapy,"** which I supported in earlier publications (Grawe, 1995).

On the Format of the Presentation

I had several good reasons for writing this book in a dialogue format. The three competence areas—that of the practitioner, the therapy researcher, and the basic scientist—suggested a natural fit with this style. Additionally, I wanted to illustrate that I do not regard psychological therapy as a finished product but rather as a continuing and evolving process. In the same way that psychology is in a state of continuous development, psychological therapy must also continue to evolve so that its concepts and methods remain linked to current principles within scientific psychology.

The dialogue format emphasizes that this book is not about absolute truths. What the three professionals say represents their opinions, which they try to substantiate to the best of their abilities. Everything they say is open to further discussion. The dialogue format illustrates that things could also have been said in different ways, and that the course of the discussion might have taken a different direction. At the same time, the dialogues could not have been completely different as long as the three discussants stick to their task of representing their respective domains of competence. I do not believe that any form of psychologically based psychotherapy could look entirely different from what is presented here, as long as such a therapy is built upon a sound scientific basis.

Finally, it was my hope that the dialogue format would make this rather thick book more entertaining. Several long sections deal with issues whose relevance for daily therapy practice may not be immediately apparent to practitioners. However, I found these issues important, which is why I chose to include them. It is the therapist's job in the first two dialogues to represent the practitioner's sphere of interest, thus preventing the conversation from drifting too far afield from topics that actually concern practitioners.

Despite its advantages, however, the dialogue format also added a particular presentational problem, for which I am asking the reader's forbearance. That is, in the first and third dialogue I could not help repeatedly referring to my own research work. After all, I have been concerned with these questions for almost thirty years. My practical experience and my own research have played a decisive role in shaping many of the views expressed in these dialogues. It would have seemed unnatural to me to deny these sources of my own views. Therefore, I let the participants in the discussion quote the author Grawe as if he were a third person. This would not be an inherent problem, except for the frequency of the citations in some parts of the book, which inevitably leads to the question of whether the author Grawe deserves this kind of attention.

As an author, I can certainly admit that what I think and write in the present has been influenced by what I thought and wrote in the past. This is all the more true considering that my writings have focused on a single major topic for many years. Nevertheless, there remains a certain element of awkwardness when the three professionals quote my work so frequently. I was tempted to reduce some of this awkwardness by having them attack some of my writings and point out inconsistencies in previous works. After all, as an author, one knows best when one is "guilty" of inaccuracies and inconsistencies. In the end I decided not to bother with this approach because it would not have contributed much to my overall goal.

There was a second presentational problem resulting from the dialogue format, for which I must also request the reader's understanding. In many cases, the ideas developed in the conversation needed to be illustrated with diagrams, and the reader might wonder, in light of the apparent spontaneity of the discussants' statements, how they could possibly come up so quickly with exactly the right diagram for each of their points. As the author, I functioned in these cases as a *deus ex machina*, so to speak. The same is true for the multitude of references that the professionals pull from their memories, seemingly without difficulty.

Furthermore, I thought it would be helpful for the reader to be referred to other points in the dialogue, where a specific topic is discussed in more detail. This allows the reader to jump from one part of the dialogue to another, where related issues are addressed in different contexts.

Acknowledgments

The majority of this book was written during a sabbatical year in San Francisco. I hope that the book conveys to the reader some of the stimulating, innovative, and optimistic atmosphere of this wonderful city. Psychology is an exciting, fascinating science, and psychological therapy is a world that remains rich with possibilities.

The constraints of my daily work would not have allowed me to write a book such as this. I am indebted to those who sheltered me from daily demands and provided me with the opportunity to concentrate on my reading, thinking, and writing. First and foremost, I owe thanks to my wife Mariann, who lovingly granted me exemption from so many responsibilities I should have attended to during that time. Thanks are also due to my longtime colleague and friend Franz Caspar, with whom I knew that my occupational duties and concerns were in the best of hands.

I thank my secretaries Heidi Rupprecht, Susanne Frischknecht, and Susanna Althaus for the sheltered niche they afforded me. I thank my staff, doctoral candidates, and master's students for respecting my need to concentrate on this book project for a longer period of time, for deferring legitimate and important matters, and for seeing that upon my return to the daily routine I was not overwhelmed by longstanding duties.

Several friends and colleagues in the field, whose opinions I value greatly, have read this manuscript during its development, giving valuable advice and suggestions on issues I would have otherwise disregarded or not given enough attention to. For that, I thank Claudia Baltensperger, Hinrich Bents, Franz Caspar, Martin Grosse Holtforth, Barbara Heiniger Haldimann, Mariann Grawe-Gerber, Dietmar Schulte, and Hansjörg Znoj. My special thanks to Mariann Grawe-Gerber for her suggestions on the interpersonal and resource perspectives.

Much of my own research this book is based on was supported by grants from the Swiss National Research Foundation (SNRF).

My relationship to this book would be different if t were not for the many daily experiences my colleagues and I have had in the practical implementation of a non-school oriented general psychotherapy over the last ten years. At the Psychotherapy Center of the University of Bern, approximately one hundred therapies are being performed over the course of a year, using a procedure that comes very close to the principles developed in this book. In the past years many therapists have completed their therapy training based on these methods, or are presently doing so. Those who participated in this experience know that a general (non-school-oriented) psychotherapy is indeed possible. Naturally, given our limited competence and capacities, we have not yet exhausted the full potential of this kind of psychotherapy.

For a long time I have been discontent with defining our common approach by demarcating it from what others do. General psychotherapy as a contrast to school-oriented therapy may reflect only a transitional stage, in the sense that this general approach to psychotherapy is currently replacing the therapy-school phase of psychotherapy.

Psychological therapy aims to contribute to a positive definition of our common identity as therapists. Our common work has its basis in scientific psychology. We are psychological therapists not so much based on our professional affiliations but by virtue of the common sources we draw from. Physicians can also be psychological therapists if they draw from the same sources. It is my hope that this book will also stimulate therapists who never completed a regular degree in general psychology to seek out the psychological foundations of psychotherapy.

For colleagues in the field who feel addressed by this book I have a request: Although I have reviewed a wide range of psychological research for this book, it is inevitable that I may have overlooked some areas and studies or not sufficiently acknowledged important programs of research. I would appreciate receiving suggestions on any areas, concepts, and studies that could supplement, correct, or constructively add to the ideas elaborated in this book, so that I can include them in an improved future edition. A common or general psychotherapy should be as good as it can possibly be. This can only be accomplished when many individuals contribute to this project.

San Francisco, October 1997   Klaus Grawe

Table of Contents

First Dialogue
How Does Psychotherapy
Achieve Its Effects?

Second Dialogue
Towards a Psychological Understanding of How Psychotherapy Works
Or:
Foundations of Psychological Therapy

Third Dialogue
A Psychological Model of Therapy

First Dialogue

How Does Psychotherapy
Achieve Its Effects?

Part 1: Entering Into Dialogue

1.1   The Participants Present Themselves

Therapist: I am pleased that both of you accepted my invitation to this discussion. I had already explained to you what this conversation is all about and I am glad you responded indicating your interest. I think as a start it might be a good idea for each of us to briefly explain what motivates him or her to take part in this discussion.

Psychologist: I would first like to offer my thanks for the invitation. I must say that at first I was somewhat surprised when you called me. I never thought that a practicing therapist would show an interest in basic psychology research, but after you explained the invitation to me, it made a lot more sense. It is, however, like "preaching to the converted," although I would probably not have had the idea myself to organize such a discussion group.

Therapy researcher: That is exactly how I felt. In fact, I was somewhat surprised that a practitioner would show an interest in the findings of therapy research of her own accord. This was somewhat unusual for me. I might add that, for a moment there, I was a bit suspicious of what motives might be hidden behind this invitation. However, once you began to explain your idea to me, I was all for it. What I liked in particular was your idea to include a basic researcher.

To be frank, not only do I have an interest in an intensive exchange with the practice of therapy, but in my development as a therapy researcher, I have come to a point where I am afraid that without stronger ties to basic psychology research my work might stagnate. I too would have not come up with this idea for a three-party discussion myself.

Therapist: I noticed from your reaction before that both of you have a self-interest in taking part in such an exchange and that is a perfect ground upon which to begin. So, let me give you a detailed account of what motivates me to seek such a discussion.

After having worked as a therapist for over twenty years, I have reached a point at which I feel a strong need to reorient myself. Of course, I know my business as a therapist, but by the same token, I see myself confronted with more unanswered therapy-related questions than ever before.

I studied psychology and became a therapist because I wanted to understand more about human life. My desire to help and to do something beneficial has always been closely tied to this objective.

In this respect, my psychology studies in the sixties could be seen as a serious disappointment to me. What was offered to us, was so far removed from real life! We considered ourselves happy when the research hypotheses were supported by data collected among college students and not among animals. Only observable behavior was a legitimate research subject, and all personal experiences were excluded since they were considered taboo or declared irrelevant epiphenomena. Consciousness, the relationship between conscious and unconscious processes, the question of the self, feelings of self-esteem, and identity, or questions of how feelings, thoughts and motives are interrelated; all these questions which truly would have provoked my interest were not even addressed.

The question of how people can change themselves was reduced to two learning principles: classical and operant conditioning. Although I was ready to accept that temporal contingencies must play an important role in individuals' mental lives, I simply could not acquiesce to the implications such a—in my view—simplistic and reductionist psychology has for the concept of humans.

At that time, I would have been willing to also familiarize myself with more complicated methods, had I seen the necessity for this. But I simply could not imagine what all this had to do with a person's real life and with my own private experiences. More and more, I began to doubt the explanatory value and the use of such a psychology, particularly with the prospect of wanting to become a therapist. So I eventually completed my psychology studies more or less only because it was the proper and reasonable thing to do.

In the meantime I had learned about a different kind of psychology, which was more tangible, more exciting, and appeared more useful, and by which I was absolutely enthralled. Via a student encounter group I had come into contact with therapists using client-centered therapy and gestalt therapy approaches, and I had also completed a practical course at a psychoanalytically oriented clinic for psychosomatic illnesses. There I found everything I had missed in my psychology studies. From then on, the kind of psychology I had encountered before became far less interesting to me. In the course of the years I completed many therapy training courses, allowing myself to be guided by my active interests, and as a result, ended up benefiting from each of them. Yet, I am not a person who can be considered a loyal supporter of any one school of therapy.

By the way, I think a lot of therapists have gone through a similar development and by now have reached a similar point. Whenever I get together with other therapists, the conversations reflect a mixture of terminology from all kinds of different schools of therapy. Somehow it has become obvious that none of the schools can ever cover all the experiences and observations made by therapists, which then results in us simply applying the concept that is best suited to a specific situation.

One can easily live with that, but—as I said before—the longer the current situation lasts, the more displeased I become with it. Without a doubt, I have achieved a certain virtuosity in the application of the different therapeutic concepts. However, I see these concepts as more like playing with words rather than as accurate descriptions or explanations of what is really going on. I use them for communication regardless of whether I believe in them. At the same time, as I also stated earlier, I feel sure and competent in my practical routine.

So, where do I stand today with my desire to better understand peoples' mental lives, something that was so important for me in the beginning of my career as a psychologist and therapist? In the interim, I have learned a great deal more than I knew way back then, and I could certainly pretend in one of the many word games, both with myself and in front of others, that I do indeed understand patients and how they function. I find it easy enough to write a convincing patient report for a health insurance company, conveying that it makes sense, or that it is even necessary, for a patient to receive this or that treatment. But even I do not believe in my own explanations any more. On a much higher level, I have somehow returned to the same initial questions: How am I to conceive mental functioning? How am I to conceive the overall interaction between motivations, emotions, perceptions, cognitions, actions, conscious and unconscious processes, and the emergence of psychological disorders? How am I to conceive how people can best accomplish long-term changes?

As an ideal situation for my professional work I imagine operating within a conceptual sphere, the dimensions of which correspond to the current state of psychological knowledge as well as to the peculiar nature of psychotherapy. These concepts ought to be—even if this sounds somewhat strange—as true and useful as possible.

So, as you can infer from above, I no longer have the urge for absolute truths. In fact, after having been flooded with absolute truths for many years, I have become impervious to them. As a result, I am in pursuit of concepts that can claim an adequate explanatory power for themselves **today**. The possibility that at some point these concepts might be in need of revision, as psychology and its neighboring sciences progress, is not a problem for me at all. On the contrary, this is exactly the goal, at least in my eyes. Along with my desire for a better understanding of the therapeutic process today, I have a strong interest in an ever advancing knowledge, in a continuous learning process; I do not want to cling to certain concepts forever.

This is why, with my desire for better understanding, I am once again turning to psychology, because I have noticed that such a learning process is under way there. After my experiences with all the different schools of therapy and with their certainties about their approaches, I have now, at this stage of my life, a greater appreciation of empirical psychology and of the provisional nature of its knowledge than I had during my student days. Today I would actually gladly choose to study psychology again, but I am realistic enough to see that a regular psychology program could not possibly answer all my current questions. This is how I came up with the idea of starting a discussion group set up in a way that allows me to address my own questions.

Since completing my studies, my trust in psychology has increased because it has proven that it can develop further. Through my daughter, who also is a psychology major, I have been able to reestablish a contact with academic psychology that I had almost lost. My daughter's reports about her lectures lead me to believe that, aside from certain methodology courses, most topics have little to do with what I was taught way back. The program my daughter is enrolled in deals with the relationships between motivation and emotion, motivation and action, emotion and cognition, with determinants of self-esteem, unconscious information processing, functions of consciousness, non-verbal communication, determinants of personal commitment, even with issues such as free will, and a variety of other questions that have tremendous significance for my daily practical work as a therapist. On top of that, there is the entire field of clinical psychology with all the basic knowledge of psychological disorders, which is something the discipline essentially has only begun to focus on within the last two decades.

My daughter would also like to become a therapist, but she dreads the thought of doing her therapist training in one of these therapy schools. She maintains that this would be like living in the age of Enlightenment and then being thrown back into the Middle Ages. She prefers to complete a therapist training that carries on with the state of knowledge where her psychology studies left off. Something really must have changed in psychology, since the attitudes among students have definitely changed in comparison to my time. So, many of my questions will be addressed to you in your capacity as a basic researcher.

Therapy researcher: I can understand your motivation for convening this discussion group. I too have the feeling that psychology today has more to offer for psychotherapy than it did in our era. For over twenty years I have tried hard to gain a better understanding of what is going on in therapy. As for methods, I draw on the repository of psychology, but the concepts directing my research are mostly taken from one of the many therapeutic approaches, which for the most part were developed irrespective of the current state of psychological knowledge.

Lately, I find myself coming more to the view that only through a better understanding of my patients' mental processes will I be able to really comprehend what is going on in therapy. I know enough about today's psychology to see that the concepts developed by the different schools of therapy have little to do with the current state of psychological knowledge: in fact, some are even completely contradictory to it. Of course, in this regard, you cannot lump all these concepts together. Some therapeutic concepts are more congruent with today's psychological views than others. But I see no therapeutic approach which continuously draws from psychology in its full range. There is really no therapeutic approach that deserves to be called psychological therapy or psychologically based therapy.

Although in my research I attempt to consider the full spectrum of psychotherapy, I feel actually overtaxed to consider the full spectrum of psychology too, because my knowledge of today's psychological research is insufficient. That is why, when you called me, and you mentioned that for this discussion you wished to include someone with an intimate knowledge of basic psychological research, I was immediately very excited.

Again an impetus through contemporary concepts of psychology is—in my view— exactly what therapy research needs. Without a scientifically based notion of the mental processes and the emergence of psychological disorders, one will always reach a basic barrier in therapy research. We can make sure that our interventions work, but we often do not know why. I find this increasingly unsatisfactory.

I have never conceived of psychotherapy research as pure technological research. For me it also always had the character of basic scientific research about it. Clearly, the main focus of therapy research is on investigating the processes of personal change. The patterns with which changes in experience and behavior take place are also the focus of core areas in basic psychological research such as memory research, psychology of learning, psychology of action, developmental psychology, and many broader areas such as personality psychology or social psychology. Thus, psychotherapy research shares a central interest with a large portion of basic psychology.

Although generally considered to be part of the applied sciences, psychotherapy research can also be viewed as a sub-field of basic psychology. The therapeutic setting creates a unique laboratory for studying the processes of human change. Freud took great advantage of this laboratory to pursue his pronounced interest in basic research. Those reading one of his first psychological publications, the *Draft of a Psychology* written in 1895, and observing in his correspondence with Fliess (both published by Bonaparte, Freud & Kris, 1950) with what feverish thirst for knowledge he worked on this draft, will have no doubt that his main motive was an extraordinarily strong intellectual interest in basic science rather than the effort to develop an effective therapeutic approach. Freud was first of all a psychologist, and only secondly a physician. For him, his kind of psychology, psychoanalysis, was both a basic and an applied science, in exactly this order. He was convinced that a proper understanding of the psychological processes would provide the basis required in order to change them. In the kind of therapy he developed, this conviction led to a strong preponderance of analysis as opposed to active intervention. For the efficacy of the therapy this balance does not seem to be very promising. On the other hand, this kind of therapy is not at all a strict conclusion from the assumption that effective change of mental processes should be based on a scientific understanding of these processes. I think we should honor as one of Freud's greatest accomplishments his basic idea to closely link basic and applied science, and his assumption that true knowledge and useful application do not exist separately but complement each other by providing reciprocally valuable information. We should indeed be able to base our therapeutic efforts towards change on a thorough understanding of mental functioning.

I am convinced that in the long run this is the best way towards an optimal psychotherapy, even if the current state of therapy research forces us to recognize that we can also perform effective therapy without a well founded scientific understanding of mental processes. Ultimately, we will only get beyond today's situation in psychotherapy if we acquire a better comprehension of the psychological disorders and the psychological processes underlying therapeutic change. For this, we need basic psychology, because that is where the foundations for this understanding are laid.

It is, therefore, essential to have somebody in our sessions who can tell us where basic psychology can contribute to the questions addressed here. Our goal is not to receive a complete overview on basic psychology, but to obtain valuable stimulating ideas that might give us an improved understanding of psychotherapy.

Psychologist: I am actually a bit intimidated that you as therapists demonstrate this concentrated interest in scientific psychology. I have to first become accustomed to this. After all, this has not always been so. Hopefully, I will not disappoint you.

Of course, it is my turn now to give a brief account of what motivated me to participate in this discussion. But before doing so, let me ask, what is it that you actually expect from one another? As a practicing therapist, what made you invite a therapy researcher to our discussion?

Therapy researcher: This is also something I wish to ask you. Until now, you have displayed only your interest in basic psychology, but what made you include a therapy researcher? It is not exactly typical that a practicing therapist takes an interest in the results of therapy research.

Therapist: I understand that you are surprised. Admittedly, for the longest time I had no interest in the results of therapy research, because the little I knew about it appeared more or less irrelevant to my daily practice. By now I recognize that there have always been research results which were anything but irrelevant for my therapeutic practice. On the other hand, I never found out much about this research. In the various therapist training programs I have completed over the years, I have heard or read little or nothing on therapy research. Self-critically, however, I must admit that I was not especially open to such issues. I was eager for truths and security, and they were offered to me. Research, however, always produces questions, expresses doubt, and demands testing and scrutiny. This is why, at the time, I was not in favor of it at all.

Feeling more secure and competent in my practical work, I can now allow myself to raise more questions and doubts which might actually challenge the foundations of my methods. Strangely enough, I find that I do not feel any more unsure of my work. Sometimes I wonder how much distance I have gained to the concepts imparted to me by my education. Somehow over time it has become obvious that these concepts have very little to do with what is really going on in my daily practical work. It is as though they had lost their original function. In fact, I do not need them anymore, and I have come to realize that I no longer believe in them.

I know now, from experience, that the concepts imparted to me in my therapist training do not effectively explain the changes I observe in my patients. All too often, positive changes take place that cannot be directly traced to a certain therapeutic intervention, and equally often, particular interventions do not have the desired effect or have a completely unintended effect. By now, of course, I attempt to make my own sense of what actually happens in my therapeutic work. But I realize that I am reaching my limits. My explanations are too "homemade" for me.

I have, therefore, recently begun to look around for appropriate readings. I came across two articles in one of the journals also read by practitioners that appealed to me. One is by Orlinsky (1994), the other from Grawe (1995). They both outline a comprehensive perspective across the schools of therapy, based on hundreds of research findings. These concepts derived from various research results appealed to me, because they reflected my own experiences. Until then, I had not expected therapy research to produce such plausible and practice-relevant results. This made me curious. Both articles continuously referenced the *Handbook of Psychotherapy and Behavior Change* by Bergin and Garfield (1994). This did it for me, I bought the book and I began to read it. Though eventually I lost my courage, because there was such an overpowering amount of research findings that soon I no longer knew whether I was coming or going.

This enormous flood of research results was too much for me to digest on my own. I could no longer see the forest for the trees. What I needed was someone with an overview, someone who could mediate between my questions and the extant knowledge of therapy research. I then asked around and heard of you. I had little hope that you would accept my invitation. I thought, what interest should a therapy researcher have in one of those practitioners? I was very surprised by how much interest you showed. After what you just said, it is obvious that I was simply very lucky. My proposition to invite a psychologist concerned with basic research had obviously only awakened an already existing interest in you.

Therapy researcher: It was not just that. It was also your open and uninhibited nature, your curiosity that attracted me and made me accept your offer. Just like you, I am always in search of something. In addition, you made a competent impression. It seemed to me that your curiosity stemmed from true practical experience. The abundance of your practical experience is far above that which I have as a therapist. I thought that you could be a real source of help for my efforts to examine psychotherapy in its full scope. When you suggested also inviting someone who is able to envisage psychology in its entirety, it seemed that fate smiled upon us. So, I am not here only for the sake of our basic researcher, of whom we both obviously have high expectations, but also to benefit from your in-depth knowledge of the practice of therapy.

Psychologist: Now that we know what your interests are in each other, it falls upon me to say what motivated me to participate in this discussion, which I view as a great challenge.

It is my belief that academic psychology is in part responsible for the deplorable state of affairs in the area of psychotherapy. If, for decades, psychology students were running away from us only to fall into bed with a particular school of therapy and to forget everything they learned before, then we cannot blame everything on our students. Psychology itself and the way it was taught must have had something to do with this. The example of your daughter demonstrates that there must be a better way.

Her example illustrates that psychology as a science has something to offer today that it could not offer two or three decades ago, namely research results and concepts concerning those subjects which most psychology students, and also laymen are highly interested in. A number of these areas and questions you already addressed.

All of this certainly had something to do with psychology's liberation from behaviorism, and we have Miller, Galanter and Pribram (1960) and other pioneers of the "cognitive turn" to thank for this. Until then the methods allowed by the codex of behaviorism determined which questions could be investigated and which could not. The liberation from this yoke had an unbelievably stimulating effect on psychological research and theory formation, something that can still be felt now. For a while after 1960, psychology seemed initially to be rather cognitively oriented. But this time is long over. Emotion, motivation, will, conscious and unconscious processes, the self and the regulation of self-esteem, just to mention a few examples, are nowadays just as much legitimate subjects of psychological research and theory formation as are traditional areas such as perception, memory, and learning. Undoubtedly, cognitions play a large role in all these aspects of mental activity, but that is no reason for any psychology concerned with these processes to be labeled "cognitive." In all of these processes, emotions play an important role, but luckily so far nobody has come up with the idea of speaking of an "emotional psychology."

The concept of cognitive psychology was, for a while, a historically useful tool in order to distinguish itself from the preceding constraints put upon psychology by behaviorism. In your field, in psychotherapy, this historical process has manifested itself as the unpleasant concept of cognitive-behavioral therapy. Does this term truly mean that this therapy approach takes into account nothing but behavior and cognition, and ignores emotions or motivations, etc.? If this were true, this approach could not possibly claim to be grounded in today's empirical psychology which, in fact, views emotions, cognitions, motivation, and other aspects of the mental processes as interrelated without granting a principle primacy to any one over the other. A good example for that is Richard Lazarus' "cognitive-motivational-relational theory" of emotions (Lazarus,

1991). The term "cognitive" was historically a tool to reintroduce the concept of the experience, something that is unobservable from the outside, as a legitimate subject of psychological research in addition to behavior. The term has survived until today. A demarcation with respect to behaviorism is no longer necessary and a new restrictive "cognitive codex" analogous to behaviorism does not exist. Today, the application of the cognitive concept runs the danger of being misunderstood—in the sense that other crucial aspects of mental functioning might be excluded—as being part of a psychology that places no significant value on feelings, motives, and other determinants of mental processes, but only on cognitions. In many research areas this is undoubtedly not the case, even if cognitions are expressly acknowledged.

To label a psychotherapy based on today's psychology as cognitive or cognitive-behavioral would be inappropriate. It would be more correct to speak of a psychotherapy based on empirical psychology or of **psychological therapy** for short. Such a psychotherapy does not yet exist, as you already mentioned. My opinion is, however, that it should exist.

I view psychotherapy as one of the natural fields of application in psychology. As a psychologist, I feel jointly responsible for what happens in psychotherapy. In Grawe's book *Psychotherapy in Transition*, which concludes with him suggesting a general psychotherapy, he opens up with the statement: "Those who love psychology have frequently had the occasion to be ashamed of psychotherapy" (Grawe et al., 1994, p. V). This is exactly how I feel. If I consider psychotherapy to be a field of application of psychology, then I, as a psychologist, cannot agree with what is happening in this field. What is the purpose of acquiring all this knowledge in psychology if it is not implemented in one of the most important fields of application?

In the past two decades, psychology has generated a number of topics which are highly relevant to the three of us. Moreover, it has supplied a large quantity of research findings and more or less well-supported theoretical concepts. I find it to be long overdue that all this acquired psychological knowledge finally exerts an influence on psychotherapy.

Of course, I do not mean this in the sense of direct application. Nevertheless, psychology could provide valuable suggestions on how to conceive various clinical phenomena and for resolving practical problems in psychotherapy.

It is clear to me that the ignorance with which psychological knowledge is treated in psychotherapy cannot simply be ascribed to therapists' malevolence. There is a real problem with transfer. Research findings in the various areas of psychology are presented in a way that makes it difficult for people who are not involved in the research process themselves to understand. The results would have to first undergo a preparatory process before their relevance to many aspects of psychotherapy becomes clear. Such preparation would essentially include an abstraction from the specific conditions under which certain research results emerged, since the results have to be transferred to a different area. The conscience of the basic researcher resists such a detachment from the conditions under which the validity of certain findings was examined, because it is exactly this meticulous observation of conditions that constitutes one of the most important virtues of empirical research.

As a basic researcher you cannot gain a reputation among your colleagues by coming up with generalizations beyond the area in which certain findings were truly proven.

This is, however, necessary when one wishes to draw conclusions from basic science for psychotherapy. Such conclusions are inevitably of a somewhat speculative nature.

So, as soon as I become engaged in a discussion with you about what basic psychology has to offer for psychotherapy, I expect some of my colleagues to become somewhat suspicious of me. Beyond that, it is inevitable that some of the remarks and explanations will contain assessments that are not shared by all of them. In each individual area there are different conceptions and research approaches as well as various ways of interpreting research findings, which I am unable to give a complete and balanced report on in this setting, because we would otherwise lose sight of our original goal.

Your interest is in having clear propositions and comments on the areas of psychology that are of particular interest to you. I see this interest as justified and would, therefore, venture to provide the necessary selective interpretation of the respective results, even if—in the eyes of some colleagues—this might be a risky endeavor. When all are in agreement that this is not a matter of unshakable truths but explicitly of selective interpretations of results for a certain purpose, I personally do not see the possible damage as so great. Those opposing this assessment are entitled to their own opinion. Every potentially wrong assessment of results is, in my eyes, not as bad as not coming up with any interpretations, because this would mean that the findings of basic psychology remain cut off from psychotherapy. As a result, we would have a perpetuation of the status quo, and our declared goal is to jointly overcome that. Thus, my participation in this discussion carries with it a certain risk for me.

An even greater challenge, and thereby greater risk, is, in my eyes, the necessary attempt to bring together the results from the various sub-fields of basic psychology into a consistent concept, one that could be called a psychological image of man that is based in empirical psychology. With this, I do not mean a theory whose truth can be substantiated by particular experiments. Rather, such a theoretical view should refer exactly to mental functioning in its overall life context. A researcher who seeks to explain the entire mental life with only one theory, however, has definitely taken on too much. In any case, he or she would have given too little thought to the relationship between scientific explanatory theories and empirical facts.

Explanatory theories must remain closer to the data than the conception I just mentioned can be. I am referring to a concept which selects and integrates theories and findings from all the different sub-fields of psychology. An essential criterion for the selection of such theories and findings would be the extent to which they are compatible and complement one another. In answering your questions about particular psychological sub-fields, I will make an effort to give an interpretation of just those results that taken together give a holistic, and thus consistent, view of mental processes.

It is quite possible these ventures of mine will have many of my colleagues in the field beginning to shake their heads. As far as I can see there is agreement among scientific psychologists that in psychology we are far away from a "grand theory" such as scientists in physics are seriously aiming for. Many even believe that such a theory is, in principle, unattainable. For me too, it is hard to imagine just how we could ever arrive at such a theory. Anyone even currently going so far as to attempt the formulation of such a theory I would find eccentric.

Up until now in psychology we can tell with more certainty how mental processes are not to be conceived than how they can be adequately conceptualized. With some certainty, one can, therefore, maintain that the theoretical foundations—if one should even speak in such sophisticated terms—underlying most therapeutic approaches are untenable. To support this in detail, one would have to refer to proven empirical research findings that are incompatible with these theoretical assumptions. One could go through this exercise for a large number of therapeutic approaches. But what would be left? What would one make of a scientist who can only say what is wrong, but can never say how something could be done better? This is exactly what we as basic researchers do, jokingly commenting on the many inept concepts underlying the various therapeutic approaches, instead of coming up with suggestions as to which concepts might be more compatible with current scientific knowledge.

Psychotherapists cannot afford the luxury of restricting themselves to a single aspect of mental life in the way that basic scientists do. They are always confronted with the psychological versatility of the entire person. Unlike what can be done in a research paradigm, they are not able to pigeonhole a person, because in different patients different areas of mental functioning are affected. In addition, psychotherapists cannot ignore the fact that the various aspects of the mental processes are intertwined.

A therapist, therefore, needs to have a scientific view on psychological processes in their entirety if she wants to base the treatment of her patient's problems on scientific knowledge. This view cannot be taken from any of the existing basic psychological theories, because they only refer to partial aspects of the mental life. The essential reason why nobody has yet developed a psychological therapy as outlined earlier, lies in the discrepancy caused by the therapist's need for a foundation upon which to base her professional perceptions, thoughts and actions, versus what basic psychology with its partial theories and knowledge has to offer.

For me the point of this discussion is to jointly find a level which will provide a meeting ground for both psychotherapy and its need for a holistic view of mental processes and basic psychology with its present state of knowledge. How successful we will be, and just how satisfied the three of us will be with the discussion, I cannot foresee at this point. I only know that the attempt must be made. Either we come up with some constructive inspirations and results, or we will find out what we aspired to do is not possible at the moment. Both of these possibilities represent a gain in knowledge, but the latter would be a disappointment. For now, I remain optimistic that we will be able to increase our knowledge. Let us then begin with our discussion.

I think it is appropriate that, since you invited us, you open our discussion with the most pressing questions.

1.2   Mysteries of Therapeutic Change

Therapist: The most pressing question I have is how therapeutic changes are to be understood. As a therapist, people view me as an expert for helping bring about changes in the patient's experiences and behavior. My practical experience confirms my status as an expert. I have often helped people to change their behaviors, to be less hindered by psychological disorders and problems, and to generally feel happier. But to be completely honest, in many cases I am unable to explain what brought about these changes.

I am also occupied with questions going far beyond what is immediately happening in my therapy sessions. The reasons for someone to seek help in a therapy also have to do with changes. Many patients enter into therapy because they have gone through changes in their experience and behavior which they consider to be not normal and outside of the realm of normal mental functioning. Many psychopathological symptoms are something entirely new for most patients, something most other people do not experience in this form. Yet, also for these unusual manifestations of mental activity there seems to be something like prepared patterns. This is the basis for diagnostic systems such as the DSM or ICD which describe the routines of these patterns. How can the emergence of such qualitatively new experiential and behavior patterns be explained? What influences which of these new possible patterns evolve, and which do not? Why do, for instance, eating disorders occur much more frequently today than three decades ago? Obviously, outside the realm of therapy, there are changes taking place that I, as the expert, should understand better than I actually do.

By the same token, one can also say that it is usually the absence of change which marks the beginning of psychotherapy. All people who are affected by emotional disorders initially try to come to terms with the problems themselves, turning to friends or other trusted persons, thinking about the possible causes, trying out all available strategies that have proven effective in overcoming difficulties in previous situations, etc. Some succeed in getting rid of their problems—this has been designated spontaneous remission, which does not explain much—others do not. In these persons it is often the inalterability of their problems that causes them to seek help. What is the difference between these two groups of people? The success or failure to change without therapeutic help, what does it depend upon?

For still other patients, the reason to begin therapy is not the incidence of entirely new experiences such as previously unknown psychopathological symptoms, but rather the persistence of long known problems. It could for instance be the fact that they are simply not successful in establishing the kind of interpersonal relationships they desire. Those individuals with a strong wish for a trusting, harmonious partner relationship, but who instead find themselves continuously tangled up in conflict-ridden and unhappy relationships, can develop a heavy burden of suffering, without demonstrating psychopathological symptoms in the sense of totally new experiences or behaviors. Such people are moving around on all too familiar grounds. Their malady consists of their being like a captive; they simply do not succeed in finding new ground, although this is what they really want, and although they invest all their conscious energy trying to achieve it. How can this lack of potential for change be expainded a captive within oneself? In my experience, these patients have difficulties in opening themselves to a new world of experience and behavior. They always fall back into their old patterns. In any case, the therapy with these patients often takes longer than with patients presenting mainly psychopathological symptoms.

Luckily, there is also a completely different and more frequently occurring case, in which the patient shows signs of improvement shortly after beginning his or her therapy. Perhaps therapists should not mull this over and just simply be happy with it. For a long time, I stuck to this principle, but today I believe that I deceived myself for too long. At an earlier stage in my career, I was personally very quick to give myself credit for such quick improvements. For one thing, I attributed the success to my personal beneficial influence, for another, to my special art, my approach. Now, I have my doubts. For a while now, I have observed this more consciously: It is not exceptional for a patient to improve within a few therapy sessions, without a single thing happening to which I could ascribe these improvements. There are patients who did not have the opportunity to make important corrective experiences, nor did they gain meaningful insights about themselves, with whom I did not try to work on particular irrational convictions or to promote any particular learning processes, and where there were no important changes taking place in their environments. In short: None of the concepts that I am familiar with through my training as a therapist could explain these improvements. All I can say is that such quick improvements came only when I was able to establish a good trusting therapeutic relationship with the patient, if one can even speak of that after just a few sessions.

There are advocates of extremely short therapies out there, who promise their patients quick results after only a few therapy sessions and claim that they can achieve such improvements on a regular basis due to their approach. I do not believe this. It contradicts my experience. Regardless of this, instances of unexplainable, quick, clear improvements also occur in my therapies. Most irritating to me is that I cannot say that these quick improvements are "superficial" changes. My impression is that frequently they are real long-term positive changes. In patients who are very receptive to therapy from the beginning, further valuable changes may occur later, which I can, at least in part, ascribe to the concepts mentioned above. Nevertheless, both the speed and the extent of the changes remain a mystery to me. Both are, however, such an essential part of the therapeutic reality that I truly wish to understand what exactly takes place in these rooms.

In my practice I also encounter change processes which are very different from those just mentioned. It would, of course, be great if all patients began to show improvement shortly after beginning therapy, but at least for me, this is unfortunately not so. With some patients, I must work for a very long time before I see a gradual, sometimes even an unexpected change. It is almost as if the ground for these patients has to first be prepared for observable or perceptible positive changes to come. Also, when such changes suddenly appear, I am unable to trace them directly back to a particular event in the session. Rather, my impression is that I spent a long time working on something without visible results before seeing it bear fruit, oftentimes without the patient understanding the connection to what, I believe, the forms of our work was. What is the difference between the quickly occurring improvements and those which require more time? Why do some changes require so much longer than others? Didn't I do a good job in these instances? I do not believe this to be the right answer. On the contrary, it is my impression that in these cases my therapeutic technique is often more important than in those with rapid improvements.

Lastly, there are cases, of course, where I do not achieve any positive results, regardless of how much effort I put in. Some of these patients have had me practically tearing my hair out, and eventually I had to admit that I was unable to help them. I know that even the best therapist comes across patients like that. This is why I do not completely attribute these unsuccessful therapeutic attempts to my insufficient personal performance, conceding that some of these patients might possibly have been helped by another therapist. However, there are occasionally patients who defeat the efforts of one therapist after another, so that the reasons for the lack of change are likely to lie with the patient rather than with the therapist. What is it that makes some patients so resistant to all efforts towards change?

Admittedly, this is quite a load of questions. Some are, of course, interrelated. I do not expect that we can completely solve all these puzzles. Nevertheless, I would be satisfied if I only received some advice on how to view the multitude of phenomena that need further explanation in a new perspective, so that I can make systematic use of them in my daily practice.

Therapy researcher: That is truly an imposing collection of questions. I do not believe that anyone can give you an empirically based answer to all of these questions. I myself find that with some of your questions I must rely on speculations rather than on well established knowledge. But by pooling our understanding and knowledge, we may be able to jointly arrive at better answers than each of us could working alone. To begin, let me pick one of your questions to which psychotherapy research can already contribute significantly. I am referring to an explanation of the patient's rapid improvement shortly after therapy begins.

1.3　The Phenomenon of Rapid Improvements at the Beginning of Therapy

First of all, research confirms that it is not just your personal impression in your individual practice but a wide-spread phenomenon. Howard et al. (1986) did a study on a sample of over a thousand patients treated predominantly with a psychodynamic approach. He found that the majority of these patients already showed distinct improvements after very few initial therapy sessions. The improvement curve rises very steeply at the beginning of therapy and then gradually rises more slowly until it eventually reaches an asymptote. Of course, a curve which results from averaging approximately a thousand patients, and which is based on a very general criterion for improvement, tells us very little about the process of individual change in a single patient. Also, it does not tell us anything about the qualitative differences between the changes taking place in different patients and at different points throughout the process of therapy. But the curve demonstrates that for many patients, with many different therapists, there are rapid improvements right at the outset of therapy, just like you have reported seeing in your practice.

Some time later, the same research group (Howard et al., 1992) presented empirical findings on a differentiated "phase model" of psychotherapy, which distinguishes between three different aspects of improvement:
1. Improved psychological well-being
2. Improved symptoms
3. Improved psychosocial adaptation.

The empirical findings indicate that the improvements in these three criteria generally do not occur simultaneously, but in a temporally postponed fashion. First come improvements in psychological well-being, then improvements of the symptoms and finally improved psychosocial adaptation. The findings show that different types of changes require different lengths of time and that the different changes are not independent of one another. The patient who begins to notice a distinct improvement in psychological well-being has a better chance of experiencing a subsequent improvement in his symptoms. Improvements in psychosocial adaptation take even longer than symptom improvements, and are more likely to appear in those patients who already went through distinct improvements of the other two kinds. The fact that improvements of psychological well-being frequently occur at the beginning of therapy, even before improvements of the symptoms and social adaptation, has, in the meantime, been confirmed in an independent study with different patients and other forms of therapy (Bieri, 1996).

As a result, it is safe to assume that these quick improvements observed by you right after the beginning of therapy represent a common phenomenon in psychotherapy and need more explanation.

Part 2: Psychotherapy Seen From the Expectancy-Value Perspective

1.4   Change of Expectations as a General Change Mechanism in Therapy

I wish that I had such well supported explanations for all the phenomena of psychotherapy as we have for this. My view on how these rather quick improvements are brought about, is based on a large number of studies from different areas of therapy research, most of it done recently but dating back to as early as 1961, namely to Jerome Frank's book *Persuasion and Healing*. Frank's assumptions grew from the idea that most patients enter psychotherapeutic treatment upon finding themselves in a hopeless and demoralized state (Frank, 1961, 1971, 1973, 1982). According to him, therapy produces improvements when it gives rise to hope, i.e., brings about a positive expectation for improvement, and when it imparts to the patient a belief in a better future. Thus, the crucial mechanism for effective therapeutic change is assumed to be a **change in expectations**. Regardless of what theoretical concept it is based on, every type of psychotherapy is seen as useful in inducing hope for improvement, and that is because all therapies share certain features which can be viewed as common change factors independent of the form of therapy. These are:

1. A therapeutic relationship defined as a relationship between the recipient of help and a specifically educated, socially sanctioned provider, who is thereby qualified and appears competent in the eyes of the patient.
2. A formalized offer of treatment in a recognized institutional setting, such as a clinic, counseling center, emergency room, therapy practice, etc. The setting itself, according to Frank, contributes to the expectation of receiving competent help.
3. A certain rationale for treatment. This imparts to the patient that there is a specific assessment of his condition for which a certain method is indicated.
4. The implementation of a treatment ritual or method consistent with the treatment rationale.

These four conditions can be basically accomplished by any type of psychotherapy regardless of how exotic it may be. That is why, according to Frank, every therapy has the potential to induce improvements. The deciding factor for the efficacy lies in how credibly the four conditions are met in every individual case. A therapist not appearing competent in the eyes of his patient, a therapeutic setting which appears suspect, or a treatment rationale not being plausible, causing the method to seem inconsistent, will, according to Frank, not lead to improvement. For therapy to be effective, it is of vital importance that the conditions created to induce hope in the patient be credible. This part of Frank's view has, in the meantime, been empirically confirmed. The competence and credibility of the therapist belong to those features of the therapeutic process which are scientifically confirmed to exert a positive influence on the therapeutic outcome (Orlinsky, Grawe, & Parks, 1994). Although, one must add here that the same is true for many other features of the therapeutic process, not included in Frank's four change factors. These well confirmed findings on the functional significance of many more features demonstrate that Frank's ideas cover only a partial aspect of the change mechanism of psychotherapy. Thus, the efficacy of psychotherapy cannot just be reduced to Frank's four factors. This has been empirically proven.

However it is enticing to make use of Frank's ideas in explaining the difficulties one has in therapy research to locate differences in therapeutic efficacy when comparing various forms of therapy, despite obvious differences in the treatment rationale and methods (Stiles, Shapiro & Elliott, 1986). When all of these somewhat credibly performed therapies share some common change factors, then it is quite possible that a considerable portion of the effect achieved in the individual cases can be linked to these common factors; and the remaining therapy-specific portion of the overall effect may not be large enough that therapy researchers are able to detect it as significantly different from the specific effects of another therapy included in the comparison, especially with the relatively small sample sizes in most psychotherapy outcome studies.

Frank wanted to ascribe all of the efficacy of psychotherapy to his four common factors, and to one central psychological mechanism, the induction of positive expectations, activated by these factors. I believe this view to be empirically untenable. But perhaps the induction of a positive expectancy might indeed play a decisive role for these rapid improvements in well-being right after the beginning of therapy observed by you, the practitioner, and by us researchers.

In my opinion, Frank pointed to a psychological mechanism which actually plays a very important role in therapies. The hypothesis that psychotherapeutic effects have nothing to do at all with the assumptions of the various schools of therapy was a constructive provocation. Nowadays, it is clear that indeed not all effects of psychotherapy can be explained by this one single mechanism. The significance of changes in expectation for psychotherapy must be embedded and differentiated in a broader context.

But before I give this a try, I am tempted to play with the thought of what the consequences might be for both practice and training in psychotherapy if Frank were right. Therapists would have to be trained in a way that would enable them to develop and implement a treatment plan viewed as a convincing and appropriate path to improvement by the individual patient with his or her individual preconditions, especially his or her personal attitudes and convictions brought along to the therapy. The therapist would have to mainly focus on the patient's ideas about his or her problem, or what other opinions he or she might have, in order to develop a treatment rationale and "treatment ritual" optimally tailored to the patient's idiosyncrasies. The therapist would have to be able to convincingly explain his approach to the patient and to apply the method warranted by his rationale in such a fashion that the patient is given the impression of being in competent hands. There would be no fixed set of therapeutic methods and theories. These would only serve as prototypes, from which the therapist could take suggestions for creating optimal rituals. The treatment would not be directed by the therapist's beliefs but by those of the patient.

This scenario would represent the extreme side of a patient-oriented psychotherapy and at the same time the abandoning of all forms of therapy for the benefit of a single uniform psychotherapy. All forms of therapy would be mere variations of one and the same concept, more or less well suited for different patients depending on how it fits with the patient's convictions, but all without any claim to truth. For us therapy researchers it would then be superfluous to compare the mechanisms of different therapies with respect to their efficacy. Only the question of indication would remain relevant: Which rationale has the greatest persuasive value for which patient? In terms of variance analysis: All that would be left for research would be interactions, but no more main effects.

I assume that this is quite a horrific vision for most therapists, especially for convinced supporters of a particular school of therapy. But even I as a therapy researcher and you as a basse psychologist would not be exactly thrilled with such a consequence. What connects us all in this case is the conviction that there are indeed true and false assumptions about individuals' mental functioning and about the nature of mental disorders, and how best to treat them. If the mechanism of psychotherapy were sufficiently explained by Frank's theory, then we would not need this forum. In particular, your presence here as a basic researcher, I think, would then be unnecessary.

Nevertheless there are, in my eyes, reasons to take Frank's provocation seriously instead of sweeping it aside just because we find its consequences unpalatable. I have purposefully portrayed Frank's quite popular conclusions and ideas in a rather gross fashion. By doing so, I wanted to emphasize what could happen to psychotherapy if one gave up all claim to truth and instead developed psychotherapy merely according to criteria of utility in the sense of a "systematic technical eclecticism" (Beutler, 1986). The questions is, can psychotherapy, in the long run, really exist without a scientifically founded conception of mental functioning, to be evaluated by criteria of truth?

My answer to this is no, and that is why I am participating in this discussion. But there are respected colleagues of the opposite opinion, therapy researchers (Beutler, 1986; Beutler & Consoli, 1992; Garfield, 1992), as well as therapy practitioners (Lazarus, 1992). It therefore seems worthwhile to me to take a closer look at this vision of a psychotherapy bearing no claim to truth.

First one has to realize that this is not merely a vision, but that this vision has taken shape in the form of a concrete therapeutic concept. Fish (1973), reformulating Frank's description of the change mechanisms in psychotherapy, came up with concrete instructions for therapy implementation by virtue of a consequent materialization of Frank's previously mentioned four common factors. In a deliberately provocative manner, he named this therapeutic concept "placebo therapy." The therapist initially comes up with an assessment of the patient's beliefs and views and of his problems. Next, a treatment contract is worked out listing the goals of the therapy. Based on this, the therapist develops a ritual which appears most convincing to the patient with regard to his beliefs and problems. The criterion for choosing the ritual is solely the question of whether the patient is convinced it will help him. Most importantly, special attention is paid to the patient becoming convinced that he himself can do something so that he feels better. Every small change will stand as proof that change is possible and will be used to reinforce hope for further improvement.

Positive expectancy induction—that is the declared mechanism of this "placebo therapy," and very likely an important mechanism in most psychotherapies with a positive outcome—causes something like a chain reaction that could also be considered a self-fulfilling prophecy. When the therapist succeeds in inducing positive expectations for "effective help" and rapid improvement in the patient, he will feel more confident and will approach things with more courage, élan, and trust, leading to small experiences of success. These will strengthen his confidence that change is possible. This improves and lifts his mood further, producing more positive expectations for the future, which serves to further improve the basis for more successful experiences. The positive changes the patient experiences will be interpreted by him as signs that the therapy is taking effect. It is precisely this conviction that actually makes the therapy work, and the therapy is so convincingly effective because his own first-hand experience confirms its credibility.

The realization that the therapy is taking effect raises the patient's receptiveness for the input coming from the therapist and increases his willingness to cooperate and actively engage in the therapy. This serves to improve the conditions for an effective outcome of all other specific influences inherent in the therapeutic approach. Also the patient's willingness to open up to new experiences will be reinforced by these initial positive changes. All of this will also lead to increased involvement on the part of the therapist, giving him the impression that he is on the right path, boosting his confidence. This in turn will reassure the patient's expectations that the therapist can and will help him. The positive experiences on both sides have beneficial effects on the quality of the therapeutic relationship. The patient has ever increasing trust in the therapist, who then feels appreciated and confirmed in his own competence. In turn, both his respect for the patient as well as his commitment towards supporting him will rise, and along with it, his conviction of being able to help this patient effectively.

All the characteristics of the therapy process portrayed above as well as those of the therapeutic interaction belong to those variables whose positive influence on the therapeutic outcome is most well supported by research (Orlinsky, Grawe & Parks, 1994; Schulte, 1996). The reciprocal influence between these variables just described agrees with the respective assumptions in the "Generic Model of Psychotherapy" by Orlinsky and Howard (1986), formulated independently of the question of the significance of expectations for positive improvement. Hence, this view of the processes happening right at the beginning of therapy is substantiated by a broad array of empirical findings.

Through positive expectancy induction, a self-perpetuating process of positive feedback is set in motion, leading to the fact that after some time the patient really finds himself in a new place. He does not just imagine he is better, he really is doing better. Something has happened. The patient senses that he feels better and behaves differently. This is exactly the goal a therapy strives for. These are "true" effects of therapy, not just changes of a lesser quality that are in danger of popping like a soap bubble. These effects are based in felt changes of experience and behavior achieved by the patient step by step. More real than this, changes cannot be.

I do not see why such changes should not be lasting, since, in the course of the positive feedback process, the patient has actually made real experiences which have gradually led to increased self confidence. These experiences and this self confidence can be a solid basis for a lasting, better future, unless there are certain unfavorable sources of influence emerging or persisting that were originally not included in this process, and that continue or begin to undermine the positive changes over time. One example of this could be a conflict-ridden partnership.

Your impression that the rapid improvement at the beginning of a therapy does not consist merely of "superficial" changes of short duration, is definitely confirmed by such a view. The point is that these are "true" therapeutic effects which would not have been established without therapy, and the cause can even be traced back to a particularly strong psychological mechanism.

1.5   Placebo Effects and Expectancy Induction

Why am I emphasizing this so much? Because of the term "placebo" used by Fish in conjunction with his therapeutic concept. In speaking about the placebo effect, we are generally talking about effects that cannot be ascribed to a "real," specific change mechanism. In drug research, placebo is understood as "pseudo medication," a pill that looks like and is prescribed in the same manner as a "real" pill but does not contain the active substance which produces a specific metabolic physiological effect, but rather an inert substance known to have no physiological effect whatsoever.

In pharmacological research placebos are used because it has long been known that drugs do not work only via their active chemical substances, but that the psychological impact of taking medicine also plays a very important role. In the context of pharmacological questions it is a fairly logical approach to regard these psychological factors as irrelevant for the purely metabolic effects which are the focus of the research question. That is why, in a controlled trial, one group of patients is given the placebo and another group is given the similar looking drug containing the active substance. It has been understood in pharmacological research for quite some time that the patient's belief in getting effective help represents an essential part of the observable therapeutic effect (Shapiro, 1971; Shapiro & Morris, 1978). Further still, it has also long been known that both the patient's and the therapist's beliefs must also be considered as a source of influence. The experimenter's expectancy has an effect on the test results, much like the expectations of a teacher on his student's performance, and the therapist's expectations for success on his patient's actual achievements. In psychology, we refer to this as the "interpersonal expectancy effect," also known as the "Rosenthal effect" (Rosenthal, 1969; Rosenthal & Rubin, 1978). In pharmacology, researchers attempt to control this interpersonal expectancy effect by conducting double blind studies. More and more, therapy researchers have been expressing the need for such studies in psychotherapy, while at the same time regretting that unfortunately, due to the nature of things, double blind studies are just not possible, as the therapist naturally knows which therapy he is performing.

This hard to argue fact has pretty much made double blind studies in psychotherapy impossible. On the other hand, predominantly methodically thinking therapy researchers have vigorously demanded that every psychotherapy outcomes study must also include a placebo control group. I suppose this demand evolves out of insufficient clarification of what the so-called placebo effect entails psychologically.

Using the term placebo in the context of psychological therapies is a completely different issue than in drug research. Can we really speak of "pseudo-therapy" the same way as we speak of a "pseudo-medicine" if a psychological therapy systematically makes usage of one of the most important mechanisms of psychological change? The application of the term placebo in psychotherapy seems closely tied to very questionable assumptions put forth by the various therapeutic approaches. All those influences not attached to the particular theory of a particular school are pronounced to be a placebo or an unspecific factor suggesting something of lesser importance. Only the specific change mechanisms presumed by the respective therapy theory are considered to be really important influences.

Why, however, should this positive feedback process described by me before, initiated by positive expectancy induction for change, be classified as an unspecific or even second class mechanism if in reality it indeed does lead to positive improvements, as it appears? Given the extent of its effectiveness, this mechanism obviously plays a significant role in almost all therapies, obviously a more important one than many other mechanisms assumed to be significant by most therapy school theories. This is a major, by virtue of being almost omnipresent, mechanism, which, in my view, is not by any means more unspecific than any of the mechanisms assumed by the various therapy approaches. It can be specified very precisely, and it can be implemented for better or worse depending on how much attention one pays to it.

As for the presumed mechanism I previously described, a placebo therapy and thereby also a placebo control group could be quite different in their effects. If in a placebo control group Frank's aforementioned four change factors are implemented in a convincing and competent manner, one could expect rather favorable therapeutic effects. If no attention is given to the credibility of the placebo control group, you can hardly expect positive therapeutic effects.

Those in psychotherapy research have so far demonstrated a lack of consciousness for these issues. For instance, activities without any convincing therapeutic value such as listening to stories, reading books, attending language classes, watching movies, playing with puzzles, sitting quietly with a silent therapist, or going over the day's issues are all lumped together as placebo control groups with ones that come very close to the particular placebo therapy by Fish or other convincing therapy procedures such as the one described in the study by Kirsch et al. (1983). In some studies, like the well known comparative outcome study by Sloane et al. (1975), putting the patient on a waiting list is already reason enough to refer to the treatment conditions as being placebo controlled. So one should not be surprised when very different effect sizes were found in meta-analyses of placebo conditions, and when those for placebo control groups were significantly weaker than those for the true therapy conditions, namely somewhere in the medium range between untreated control groups and actually treated groups (Bowers & Clum, 1988; Prioleau, Murdoch & Brody, 1983).

One cannot but assume that the moderate effect sizes found thus far for placebo control groups result in a systematic underestimation of the effects achieved by expectancy induction as an independent specific therapeutic mechanism. A great deal of research findings exist demonstrating that the effectiveness and the significance of this particular mechanism should be rated higher.

Systematic desensitization can be seen as one of the therapies with an undoubtedly proven effectiveness (see also Grawe, Donati & Bernauer, 1994, pp. 247—274). In fifteen studies, systematic desensitization was compared with placebo control groups that all credibly aroused hope for improvement (see also Kirsch 1990, pp. 64). These studies produced results quite different than what was found in other control group comparisons where systematic desensitization was almost always found to be superior.

In thirteen comparisons the placebo treatment was just as effective as systematic desensitization. In only one study was it found to be slightly inferior and in another, in fact, it turned out to be highly superior. In that particular study (Tori & Worell, 1973), the patients under placebo conditions, unlike the patients under systematic desensitization, were informed that they were undergoing a very effective treatment.

Considering that systematic desensitization can be viewed as a very credible procedure for the treatment of phobias—proven more credible than the usual placebo control groups (Borkovec & Nau, 1972) and also more credible than client-centered therapy and rational-emotive therapy (Shapiro, 1981)—then one has to seriously ask whether, in light of all these findings, the good results achieved by systematic desensitization are not predominantly due to the credible induction of high improvement expectations and the positive feedback processes initiated thereby. At least, systematic desensitization actualizes Frank's four change factors in a very credible way.

This hypothesis garners extra support from the fact that the particular parameters of the procedure (relaxation, gradual presentation of stimuli in increasing order, etc.) which, according to the underlying theoretical assumptions, are supposed to be crucial for the impact of systematic desensitization, have proven insignificant for the therapeutic outcome in experimental testing (Emmelkamp, 1982). Thus, a therapist performing a "school-oriented" systematic desensitization does, according to the current state of knowledge, in fact celebrate a ritual, whose effectiveness is essentially based on its credibility, but not on its particular procedural components.

I find this to be a good example for the utility of empirical and especially experimental psychotherapy research. A long series of studies stretching across three decades has in this case radically challenged the former assumptions about the mechanisms of the therapeutic method. Instead, it facilitates a completely new conception that, although not questioning the utility of the therapeutic method, opens a new horizon for possible explanations, suggesting new questions and practical conclusions beyond this one therapeutic method.

If expectancy induction carries such a high explanatory value for the mechanism of systematic desensitization, we can assume that this mechanism is likely to play an important role in other forms of therapy as well. And exactly that seems to be the case.

In this connection, Southworth and Kirsch (1988) have performed a very interesting study with agoraphobics. Two groups of patients suffering from severe agoraphobia were instructed to go as far away from their homes until they become anxious and then return home. Over two weeks, this was repeated ten times. One group had this explained to them as the beginning of their treatment. The other group was told that this would be a diagnostic measure used to gauge their fear and that the actual treatment would begin after these two weeks. In both groups, the level of fear decreased compared with an untreated control group. In the group with therapeutic instruction, however, the reduction of fear was more marked than in those patients exposed to the phobic situation for the same amount of time, but without therapeutic instruction (the duration of the stimulus confrontation was controlled for in the statistical analysis).

Hence, it is not just the in vivo exposure that leads to the sharp reduction of fear in stimulus confrontation therapies. In the case of the in vivo exposure as well, the expectation to receive effective therapy plays a very essential part. Due to the higher content of reality, the credibility of the treatment method is even greater than in systematic desensitization. That is why it agrees so well with the view that positive expectancy induction is a crucial component in such treatments, that the in vivo stimulus confrontation treatment has been proven more effective than the mere imagining of anxiety arousing situations in systematic desensitization and implosion therapy (see also Grawe, Donati & Bernauer, 1994).

Regarding most other therapeutic approaches, such as those from the psychodynamic or humanistic domain, I do not know of any studies which directly address the question of the induction of positive improvement expectations. I see no reason, however, why the previously described positive feedback processes, which are set in motion by inducing expectations for positive improvement, should not also play a significant role in these therapies, if the conditions are credible to the patient in giving the outlook for a speedy improvement.

The majority of findings on process-outcome correlations, upon which the "Generic Model of Psychotherapy" (Orlinsky, Grawe & Parks, 1994)—and my preceding description of the positive feedback process are based—generally do not refer to behavioral therapy but to psychodynamic and humanistic therapies. I find it to be most likely then, that also in these therapies a successful outcome can largely be credited to expectancy induction for improvement. These therapies, however, often do not promise a fast therapeutic success, but the patients are informed that in order for therapy to be successful, there has to first be a better understanding of the causes underlying their problems. In such therapies one can then expect that the improvement—conforming to the therapy rationale—will only take place after undergoing a lengthy therapy. I will return to this assumption at a later point.

None of the aforementioned therapeutic concepts have expectancy induction built in as an expressly essential or central change mechanism. This is different for hypnosis and hypnotherapy. Hypnotic induction is essentially an expectancy induction. I do not want to go any deeper here into the numerous studies providing evidence that expectancy induction is the central working mechanism of hypnosis and the most important instrument of hypnotherapists. This would detour us too far from your question. A very thorough and detailed overview is given by Kirsch (1990, pp. 127—181). Expectancy induction is "the" specific mechanism in hypnotherapy. Kirsch sees quite a direct analogy between hypnosis and psychotherapy. "Hypnosis is psychotherapy in miniature. It begins with the establishment of rapport, proceeds to an assessment of the individual's beliefs and expectations, continues with the presentation of a rationale that corrects misconceptions, and utilizes individually tailored and flexibly administered rituals for producing changes in experience and behavior" (pp. 180/181). The hypnotherapist Milton Erickson was perhaps the best model for proficient control and implementation of a flexible, patient-oriented expectancy induction. His "utilization technique" (Erickson, 1980) can serve as a model of how to accept and utilize the attitudes, convictions and habits the patient brings along in order to produce expectations tailored to a specific therapeutic purpose. In light of the fact that in hypnotherapy one is likely to easily agree with the assumption that the expectancy induction is the main mechanism applied, the good results found for hypnotherapy in controlled studies (see Grawe, Donati & Bernauer, 1994, pp. 626—637) substantiate the aforementioned evidence that expectancy induction can be considered one of the most important factors for the effectiveness of psychotherapy.

Thus, I explain these rather quick improvements oftentimes occurring right at the beginning of therapy by the previously mentioned positive feedback process, through which one can reliably produce an induction of positive expectations for improvement. In this process, considerably more variables play a role than Frank himself had assumed. I have listed some of these variables in describing this process. I am far from contending that expectancy induction would represent the sole working mechanism that could produce improvements shortly after the beginning of therapy. Other influential factors can crop up and have their own impact. But the conditions for just how effective such other influences will be improve if the ground is already prepared by positive expectancy induction.

The positive feedback process put forth by me is likely to play a role in most therapies with a positive outcome regardless of the therapist's particular theory of change. That, however, does not mean that this feedback process has something unspecific about it. The process unites many active variables up on which the therapist can exercise a calculated influence. This also holds true for the conditions that must be fulfilled for credible positive expectancy induction. These conditions are not simply given in a therapy setting, but they can be created for better or for worse, which will quite possibly be reflected in the therapeutic result. Creating optimal, patient-centered conditions must, therefore, be seen as one of the therapist's most important tasks, particularly in the opening stages of therapy. For this, as for all other challenging therapeutic tasks, special competencies are needed that should have been acquired during therapy training. A therapist who thinks he can plan his therapy without a proper idea of the patient's individual expectations, going simply by his own concepts will, on average, achieve worse therapeutic results than he would have by explicit observation and competent command of the aforementioned change principles. In my eyes, this alone is reason enough to question a school-oriented training for therapists.

As my comments have demonstrated, doing without the assumptions about the working principles of psychotherapy of the specific schools of therapy need not necessarily lead to a loss of orientation and to arbitrariness. What I imagine for the future of psychotherapy is that therapists can orient themselves towards working principles that have a solid foundation in empirical research findings, which means not just towards those based on psychotherapy research in the narrower sense, but especially towards those coming from basic psychology. I am sure that we can derive valuable suggestions for our understanding of how psychotherapy works from it. Maybe you, as a psychologist engaged in basic research, could tell us, for example, which role is attributed to expectations in general psychology.

Assumptions such as these derived from empirical research are no less specific than those of the different schools of therapy and demand no less introduction and instruction for their competent therapeutic application. It would be hubris to assume that one could be in full command of such complex principles as the changing of expectations without specific training. But where do we have institutions offering psychotherapy training that keep track of and incorporate these research findings into their programs, thereby carrying them into the field of practice? Here is, in my eyes, a still wide open field for a new type of cooperation between psychotherapy research and practice.

Therapist: That was an interesting excursion into psychotherapy research. Most of that was so far unknown to me. I am surprised at how much the research reslts agree with my practical experiences. Obviously out of habit, not so much due to conscious planning, I am normally doing a lot to induce positive expectations for improvement in my patients, more so today than at the beginning of my career as a therapist.

I used to actually believe that having a correct understanding of the patient's problem was of primary importance in order to use the appropriate means to guide him or her towards corrective experiences. The patient's problem was obviously the central focus for me. There was a "right" way to successfully treat the problem and I saw it as my duty as a therapist to figure out the right way, to guide the patient to it and keep him there. In my opinion, extraneous factors like clothing, appearance, office furnishings, etc., had no significant influence on the contents of my therapeutic work. Today, I have a different professional consciousness regarding all that. I imagine how my actions, my clothing, the location of my practice, the interior of my office and how it is organized, in short: how its total presentation down to the most minute details such as letterhead, invoicing, etc. might affect the patient. I place specific value on all these aspects so as to contribute to making an overall professional impression. The patient should understand that I know my business, and he is seeing a successful therapist. So, if I have correctly understood you, all of these "extraneous details" are not menial factors at all with respect to expectancy induction, but they all contribute to the patient's impression that he can obtain competent help from me.

Since I have undergone several therapy training programs in the past and have, by now, gathered extensive experiences with many different therapeutic techniques, today I no longer feel that I have to strictly adhere to certain technical rules. I have long become accustomed to making my concrete method dependent on the respective patient and his personal idiosyncrasies in each individual case. I choose the procedures and expressions that seem well matched to each individual patient. I also work only with methods that I feel absolutely sure about, because only these can I manage in a flexible manner. I am confident that I can impart to every patient a plausible interpretation of his condition and explain to him how we must approach his problem together. There have often been times when I did not believe in my own explanations, something I conceded already in the beginning, but this in no way makes me insecure in front of my patient.

Considering all of this with respect to your comments as to what is important for credible expectancy induction for improvements, I seem to be doing quite well in my practice. Obviously, experiences in my daily practice have guided me gradually in a direction similar to therapy research, and that is away from the assumptions of a particular school of therapy and towards a more patient-oriented method. I find it reassuring that one can arrive at such similar conclusions in such different ways but I must admit, however, that my conclusions did not have the same explicit character as did yours in research. Mine have developed more implicitly and gradually through actions without me having had a clear concept for them.

I mentioned to you previously that for a while now I have begun to take an interest in the results of therapy research, reading a few artic les. Among those was an article by Grawe (1995) in which he ascribes the psychological effects of various forms of therapy to four therapeutic working principles, namely: mastery/coping, motivational clarification, problem actuation, and resource activation. This explanation made sense to me, because I was able to fit my own therapeutic methods nicely into this model. The concept of "resource activation" I found especially useful. I found much of what I already do in my practice, without a clear awareness of why I do it, described and explained within this concept. Since that time, I pay much more conscious attention to this factor. This clearer, more explicit awareness towards the importance of resource activation has changed my therapeutic practice quite a bit. I have found such a compact and practical concept for the reflection and planning of my therapeutic actions to be very helpful.

Still, your comments have left me somehow confused. Much of what you stated to be useful for positive expectancy induction, I had formerly attributed to resource activation, such as the utilization techniques by Milton Erickson. Are expectancy induction and resource activation basically the same concept under a different name, or are they entirely different concepts with somewhat of an overlap? In short: How are these two interrelated?

1.6   Expectancy Induction and Resource Activation

Therapy researcher: I am glad that you are addressing this problem. Perhaps I should have referred earlier to the concept of resource activation in order to stave off confusion. I will take the occasion now to offer my opinion about how these two constructs are interrelated.

The concept of resource activation is essentially a much more comprehensive concept than expectancy induction. Every aspect of the patient's mental functioning, and even beyond that, the patient's entire life situation can be seen as resources, for instance: motivational willingness, goals, desires, aversions, interests, convictions, values, tastes, attitudes, knowledge, education, capabilities, habits, interaction styles, physical characteristics such as appearance and general fitness, financial possibilities and the entire potential of the individual's interpersonal relationships. Seen from the resource perspective, all of this in its entirety represents the patient's potential arena in which he or she can presently move around, or in other words, his or her positive potential which can be used for the process of change. Conversely from a negative or problem perspective, however, these same characteristics can be viewed as constraints on the patient back.

Viewed as resources, the characteristics listed above represent the sources from which a person draws his feelings of self-esteem. Resource activation then means tracing those among the multitude of individual characteristics, which strongly engage the patient's motivation, and which are especially important for his self-esteem, and mobilizing these as resources for the process of change in therapy. The more the therapist succeeds in activating these pre-existing resources through his therapeutic offer, the more the patient will see himself reflected in his positive capacities, his own goals and values, and feel an increased self-esteem. Resource activation attempts to pick up on the patient's extant goals, values, and possibilities, seeking to give these individual characteristics as much space within the therapy as possible. After all, it is not exactly "honey" for one's self-esteem being in a demoralized state due to problems one is unable to solve and turning to a therapist or institution for help. The therapeutic situation is much the same: The patient is mostly confronted with his problematic sides.

Apart from working on his problems, the more the patient feels recognized also in his positive sides by the therapist during the course of a successful resource activation, the more he or she will have perceptions that are compatible with his or her goals and positive self. Perceptions like these are accompanied by positive feelings and will lead to increased self-esteem and improved well-being. The patient will most likely ascribe these positive changes to the therapy without having any idea about the specific methods the therapist utilized to contribute to this improvement. The perception of the therapy starting to take effect will strengthen his hope for further improvement and will raise his receptiveness and involvement in the therapy. This has a positive impact on the therapist himself, and this in turn ... We find ourselves in the midst of the previously expounded positive feedback process, which can eventually lead to the rapid therapeutic successes that we still wanted to explain.

By the way, I would like to point to the fact that in this self-sustaining therapeutic process sparked by resource activation and/or expectancy induction, a second of Grawe's four working principles also plays a significant role, namely that of mastery/coping, because in the course of this process, the patient goes through many small and perhaps even bigger mastery experiences. During the course of resource activation as well as through the experiences of mastery, he has perceptions according to his existing goals and desires. These are not questioned or analyzed, but supported and promoted. Both working principles are directed towards supporting the patient in his becoming more the way he would like to be in the sense of his existing goals and desires. This appears to be an essential, shared characteristic of both resource activation and mastery. I point to this fact, because it might be one of the causes, among others, why the realization of these two working principles can produce quick improvements in well-being and symptoms. Changing a goal is likely to require more time and is not accompanied by an improvement in well-being for the entire time. It seems plausible that changes in social adaptation possibly require changes in motivational goals. Perhaps that is why Howard and his colleagues (see above) found that such changes generally only take place after prolonged therapy.

Strictly speaking, positive expectancy induction for improvement is only one aspect of resource activation. Expectations are global assessments of the situation. When this global assessment promises an approximation of the fulfillment of an important goal, then we can speak of hope. Expectations are special kinds of cognitions. In contrast to attitudes and convictions, many expectations are temporally unstable as they depend on the specific situation. We can assume that they are for the most part a result of unconscious information processing. They also need not be cognitively represented in communicable form. Like many cognitions, their function is not only to reflect the situation and to have an evaluating and interpreting function with respect to actuated goals, but they also exercise a controlling influence on experience and behavior. Hence, expectations mediate between the subjectively perceived present and the desired or dreaded future. Since successful resource activation positively impacts the subjectively perceived present, it also leads to more positive expectations and thereby exerts influence in the direction of a positive future.

Since cognitions accompany mental processes in a permanently reflecting, evaluating and controlling fashion, expectations are an ever-present part of mental functioning. They, therefore, inevitably play a very important role in each of Grawe's four working principles.

Resource activation is one of the best means of positive expectancy induction, but positive expectations can also happen without preceding resource activation. Many studies have demonstrated that patients often began to clearly improve, even before the actual treatment had begun. A diagnostic interview (for example: Frank et al., 1963) or just a psychological testing to obtain information about the patient's initial condition (Shapiro, 1995) can in itself induce positive expectations for improvement and lead to significant claupes.

Expectancy induction is thus an integral component of the positive feedback process, which is supposed to be initiated and promoted by resource activation. It can, however, also take place and initiate a similar process without the therapist performing resource activation. A person who suffers severely develops a strong desire for improvement that influences his perceptions, cognitions, emotions, actions, etc. Everything happening around the patient will be assessed by him in terms of his desire for improvement, even when he is not necessarily focusing all his conscious attention towards the interpretative assessments of his situation. These assessments form his expectations. This is why expectations always play a role in psychotherapies whether or not the therapist exerts a resource-oriented influence and regardless of whether this was expressly stated or not. The likelihood that a situational assessment will lead to positive expectations for improvement is, however, essentially raised by successful resource activation.

I have previously mentioned that many expectations are markedly situation-dependent. That is why I did not discuss them in conjunction with the patients' characteristic features, which are the ones that are relevant for resource activation. These are more temporally stable features. However, being able to hope and other characteristics, which may have a facilitating effect on the induction of positive expectations, such as suggestibility, are a whole other story. The ability to hope and to allow oneself to engage in a trusting relationship with a therapist varies, of course, greatly from person to person. Individuals who are basically mistrustful on the basis of previous relationships are less easily inclined to draw hope from someone explicitly or implicitly promising them improvement. The same is true for persons who normally react to any attempts to influence them with "reactance," that is a tendency to be opposed to the influences (Beutler & Clarkin 1990; Beutler et al., 1991). For those patients who are able to contribute to the therapy with the resources of hope and trust, the therapist can easily make use of these resources in order to induce positive expectations through the measures that initiate the positive feedback process discussed earlier.

Not all patients bring these resources with them and these are the "difficult" patients. We are likely to find them frequently among those patients displaying little or no improvement shortly after the onset of therapy. Here the concept of expectancy induction leaves the therapist at a loss as to what to do next. While the concept can easily explain why positive improvements cannot be brought about, it does not tell us how to effectively help these patients. Especially for such "difficult" patients, the concept of resource activation can offer attractive therapeutic solutions by grasping the reactance in these patients as a resource and making targeted use of it as a motivational force through paradoxical intervention strategies (Shoham-Salomon & Rosenthal, 1987; Shoham-Salomon, Avner & Neeman, 1989; Shoham-Salomon & Hannah, 1991). Another example of the explicit use of the principle of resource activation with such difficult patients is Grawe's concept of a "complimentary relationship strategy" (Grawe,

1992; Grawe et al., 1996), that means the therapist explicitly behaving in the interaction with the patient in such a way that the patient feels recognized and accepted in his most important, but not openly expressed, wishes.

Resource activation is thus a much more far-reaching concept in terms of its therapeutic consequences than is expectancy induction. I still believe that the concept of changing expectations is very useful for psychotherapy both in research and in practice, and should not just simply be absorbed by resource activation. In research this concept has led us to very constructive research questions as well as empirically verifiable assumptions and has so far generated a valuable gain in knowledge. The concept of expectancy induction leads to concrete conclusions for therapeutic practice and training alike, which are plausible, but not banal. Expectancy induction and resource activation are both useful constructs for psychotherapy. Where the first one reaches its limits, the second continues; and where the second one stays somewhat on a rather general level, the first one enables verifiable prognoses and leads to concrete conclusions that can be considered as a specification of one of the many facets of resource activation.

I could clarify the benefit of the expectancy concept for psychotherapy in more depth by being less general and by trying to exemplify the question of how psychotherapy works for a specific mental disorder. By doing so, I could more easily explain the relative importance of expectancy changes, resource activation and other working principles, within the framework of an overall conception for the treatment of specific disorders. Agoraphobia would be an especially well suited example for this because expectations and their influence play an especially important role in the explanation and treatment of this particular disorder.

Psychologist: If I might just hook into that point. For a while now, I have been at the edge of my seat. As a fundamental psychologist, hearing the term "expectation" makes it difficult for me to just sit here silently. Psychology has a great deal to say about expectations, and that is regardless of the question of what the mechanisms of psychotherapy are, but of course with some relevance for it. Following the cognitive turn of psychology, expectations have become one of the pivotal constructs in psychology. To many of the issues brought up by you, I actually might have something to contribute, or I might add some differentiating comments. What I have to contribute, however, will contain some very fundamental conceptual thoughts that might lead us far beyond the subject of expectations.

You indicated before that you would give us an account of the role of expectations in an overall concept for the treatment of a particular psychological disorder such as agoraphobia. So I would like to hear that first. I would also be very interested in your overall assessment of the relationship between general and disorder-specific working principles. Maybe it would make sense to say something about these questions directly after this. I would then postpone my own contribution for now and switch over to some thoughts later that might contribute to the clarification of the initial questions regarding how changes can be brought about in psychotherapy.

Therapy researcher: You make me curious with your announcement to bring in some fundamental conceptual thoughts, but I find myself unable to leave the question about the role of expectations for therapeutic changes answered so incompletely. Also, your question regarding the relative importance of general and disorder-specific working principles appears justified and important to me. I would prefer, therefore, to first finish winding up the thread that I had already spun out to you.

It goes without saying that I can only discuss the question of how general and disorder-specific working principles are interrelated in reference to specific disorders. In order for us not to get tangled up in too many things at once, I suggest that we discuss these principals in the form of an example for a single disorder and the example of agoraphobia seems especially well suited for that. Exactly why, we will see in a minute.

1.7 The Interplay of General and Disorder-Specific Working Principles

So far, I have only discussed general working principles, because we were interested in a specific phenomenon, namely: the frequent occurrence of rapid improvements shortly after the beginning of therapy, something which seems to appear in a number of patients presenting different symptoms as well as with different forms of therapy. This fact would suggest an explanation of such a wide spread phenomenon with general working principles. Of course that does not mean that there could not be any disorder-specific working principles contributing to rapid improvements, in which case we would have to allocate different working principles to patients suffering from different disorders. The lack of convincing evidence for working mechanisms that are specific for the treatment of phobias with the technique of systematic desensitization cannot simply be generalized to the treatment of other disorders with other therapeutic methods.

I can see that the formulation of general therapeutic working principles could lead to the misunderstanding that disorder-specific factors are not important for achieving good therapeutic outcomes. I see the danger in such misunderstandings also in Grawe's general working principles, especially since we just spoke about the one factor of these for whose realization disorder-specific aspects actually did not play such an important role. That was the case because we focused on the resources, and not on the disorders. Resources must be activated specifically with respect to the individual and his or her life situation, and to a much lesser degree with respect to the specific disorder. To a lesser extent, this also holds true for Grawe's working principle of motivational clarification. The possibility to initiate and promote a clarification process is not so much dependent on the type of disorder, but on other individual traits of the patients, such as their capacity to deal with uncomfortable emotions, their extant ability for self-reflection, and many more.

As for the two remaining working principles supposed by Grawe, problem actuation and mastery, part of their essential nature is that they must be realized in a disorder-specific way. Fear of closeness cannot be actuated in the same fashion as fear of heights, nor can obsessive rumination be actuated in the same way as compulsive eating. The situations in which the distinct disorders manifest themselves each contain their own specific constraints and possibilities. These conditions not only determine in which form these problems can be best actuated, but also which mastery experiences are possible and necessary, and how they can be imparted.

The implementation of the principle of mastery will be handled quite differently in agoraphobia than it would in the treatment of depression. It would go against my convictions if my elaboration on the overarching role of positive expectations for improvement and on resource activation created the impression that I had scant regard for the significance of disorder-specific knowledge and know-how in the treatment of mental disorders. Quite the contrary, I interpret the current state of psychotherapy research such that therapists essentially should plan their actions based on a sound knowledge of general **and** disorder-specific mental functioning as well as empirically founded general **and** disorder-specific working principles. The individual characteristics of a patient also include, of course, the specific disorders of his mental functioning. That is why a patient-oriented as opposed to a method-oriented psychotherapy must also always be a disorder-specific therapy, but without reducing the patient to his disorders.

I will now attempt to illustrate this, using the example of agoraphobia. There are several reasons why this disorder is ideally suited for this purpose:

First, there is sufficient evidence that agoraphobics frequently go through a quick recovery, which leads us back to our initial discussion on improvements. Second, we have a large number of relevant research findings for this disorder. Third, expectations are well researched with respect to their functional role for this particular disorder. Therefore, via the construct of expectations, agoraphobia is especially well suited for assessing the relative importance of general and disorder-specific influences. Fourth, especially because the disorder-specific approach has been proven to be so successful with agoraphobia, it is also well suited for demonstrating the limits of a purely disorder-specific conception.

With agoraphobia there is good reason to assume that expectations play a specific role in the development, the perpetuation, and the treatment of the disorder, which goes beyond the functions that changes in expectations generally have for psychotherapy.

1.8   Each Mental Disorder Has Its Own Disorder-Specific Dynamics: Agoraphobia as an Example

The traditional classification of phobias points to certain objects or situations as eliciting phobic fears: fear of open spaces (agoraphobia), spiders (arachnophobia), closed in or narrow spaces (claustrophobia), heights (acrophobia) etc. The usage of Greek terminology awakens the impression of sophistication and lends a certain dignity to the diagnosis related to the situation. However, it was already acknowledged by Freud that these designations do not get at the essence of such fears. Those suffering from phobias know, just as well as others, that the situation in which they become fearful is objectively not dangerous. They do not actually fear situations or objects. The real trigger for their anxiety is much more the anticipation of finding oneself in a condition of uncontrollable fear. "In the case of agoraphobia etc., we often find the recollection of a state of panic; and what the patient actually fears is a repetition of such an attack under those special conditions in which he believes he cannot escape it" (Freud, 1895/1959).

Phobic anxieties contain what is essentially a self-fulfilling prophecy. Being apprehensive about getting into a state of panic helps bring it on. In recent years, notably Goldstein and Chambless (1978) have reexamined this view of agoraphobia and have given it a more in-depth elaboration.

The development of agoraphobia is almost always preceded by a series of panic attacks. Experiencing panic is a very uncomfortable condition, justifiably dreaded. It begins with sensations that in themselves can be uncomfortable but need not singularly trigger panic such as dizziness, racing heart beat, shortness of breath, sweating, feeling weak, etc. Shortness of breath often leads to hyperventilation which in turn contributes even more to these sensations. But it is really the interpretation of these sensations which leads to the actual panic. Needless to say, experiencing the sensation as a sign of a dangerous, life threatening condition—a heart attack or stroke—or as a sign of being completely insane and out of control, might put one in a state of panic. Equally understandable is that a person might fear a future recurrence of these sensations and do whatever he or she can in order to avoid the situations in which they appear. Cognitions which anticipate the worst occur much more frequently among agoraphobics than among normal people (Chambless, et al., 1984) and seem to play a crucial role in the development of agoraphobia. Breier, Charney and Heninger (1986) found in an epidemiological study of agoraphobia that persons perceiving their first panic attack as a life threatening event developed agoraphobia rather quickly, in that they began to avoid those situations in which they had experienced a panic attack. Most of the other patients who experienced their anxiety attack for what it was, namely an anxiety attack, only developed the agoraphobic symptoms years later if at all.

According to Goldstein and Chambless, people perceiving their panic attacks as a sign of utmost danger may, after only one or possibly several panic attacks, develop an already increased awareness for the physiological sensations associated with the condition of anxiety. They are inclined to interpret any future feelings of moderate anxiety as a precursor of a panic attack and react with such pronounced fear that the dreaded attack is almost bound to happen.

Agoraphobics easily get into an aroused or anxious state as soon as they begin to experience the above mentioned physiological sensations. Of all anxiety disorders, those suffering from agoraphobia exhibit the highest scores in the anxiety sensitivity index by Reiss et al. (1986). Even non-clinical groups of persons with high levels on this scale perceive the accompanying physiological symptom of hyperventilation in a much stronger fashion and react with greater anxiety levels than persons with lower ratings (Holloway & McNally, 1987).

Individuals with a panic disorder and/or agoraphobia thus get caught in a vicious circle, in which the self-fulfilling prophecy plays a disorder-specific role. An initial panic attack is elicited by a specific constellation of conditions, meeting together in this exact constellation at this point for the very first time. The components of such a circumstantial constellation could be: stressful life events, a particular conflict constellation, observational learning involving another individual, hyperventilation, mitral valve prolapse, and many more. Later I will give an in-depth explanation of the psychological breeding ground for an initial panic attack and for its development towards agoraphobia (section 1.25, see also section 2.51), but at this point this would lead us too far away from the question of agoraphobia's own disorder-specific dynamics, which I prefer to describe first. It will suffice for now to say that every mental disorder must be understood in the context of a specific psychological constellation encompassing as combined determinants the developmental history of the individual, his or her life situation, personality traits, and biological parameters. The person developing a mental disorder usually has, at its onset, reached a stage in his or her development, which prepares the ground for the emergence of a qualitatively new mental condition. For agoraphobia there are well elaborated conceptions for that, I will address these later. Although the psychological breeding ground in which agoraphobia takes root can also exert influence on the course of a disorder-specific treatment by essentially defining the meanings with which the patient processes the events, I will ignore this right now for the sake of simplification. This will better enable me to explain the disorder-specific dynamics of agoraphobia. In the following, I will examine an initial panic attack without respect to its origins, and I will limit myself to explaining the ensuing individual dynamics of agoraphobia.

When an initial panic attack takes place, its further development is largely dependent on how it was perceived. This in turn is influenced by the individual's personality traits and life situation, and is, therefore, also associated with the overall conditions which led to the first attack. Experiencing a panic attack as a legitimate fear for which there is an obvious reason—even if the reason is not known in that particular moment—and without expecting something worse, will most likely not result in a panic disorder or agoraphobia. If, however, this panic attack is associated with the worst apprehensions, as is the case with most agoraphobics, it will have the effect that perceptions similar to those in the initial attack will arouse such a strong fear in a future situation that another terrible attack will inevitably recur. This fear of fear is linked to the dreaded precursors of something terrible that might happen. The perceived anxiety symptoms become stronger and lead to cognitions of the worst kind, etc., in short: The person finds himself in the midst of the next panic attack, and it was largely his expectation that triggered it.

Kirsch (1990) calls the self-fulfilling expectations in this process "response expectations" distinguishing them from Bandura's (1977 a) "self-efficacy expectations." Response expectations typically refer to one's own involuntary reactions such as physiological reactions and emotions. The expectation of fear leads directly to the occurrence of fear. Self-efficacy expectation refers to voluntary behavior. It has an impact on whether or not the person exposes himself to the feared situation, and how he behaves in it.

Measured according to their respective scales, response expectancy and self-efficacy expectations have a correlation of $r = -.89$ (Kirsch, 1986), so high that one could assume them ultimately to be one and the same. Kirsch (1990), however, justifiably points to the possibility that this might well be an artifact of the circumstances under which they were measured. The agoraphobic person can cross the street. He has not unlearned how to walk. He prefers not to walk due to the feelings of anxiety he expects. He is unable to willfully choose to walk without having feelings of anxiety. But he is, however, capable of willfully deciding to go out on the street and expose himself to his anxiety feeling. According to the different variants of expectancy-value theories (Heckhausen, 1980; Feather, 1981), voluntary behavior is influenced by two components: the expectations and the values connected with the behavior and its expected consequences. If the expectation of fear remains constant and the positive incentives for abandoning the current avoidance behavior increase, there comes a point where even the agoraphobic all of a sudden trusts himself to be out on the street. If the safety of her child were at stake, every agoraphobic mother would probably run across the largest market place in the world to rescue her child, and would assess her self-efficacy expectation accordingly high no matter how great the anticipated anxiety. In a trial by Valins and Ray (1967), students suffering from fear of snakes were given a small financial incentive. The incentive of two dollars was sufficient enough to cause 13 of 17 test persons to touch the snake, although they previously declared that they were incapable of doing so.

Based on what we have said thus far, considering only the symptomatology and the particular dynamics of agoraphobia, not the context from which it emerged, allows us to come up with the following picture for an effective treatment of this disorder: Treatment success has been achieved when the patient is able to re-expose himself to the situation previously avoided due to his fear, and if he in fact experiences no more fear. In order to achieve that he has to expose himself to the situation previously avoided, even if he experiences fear. As shown by Southworth and Kirsch (1988, see above), this exposure in and of itself, however, is not sufficient for achieving far-reaching therapeutic effects as can be accomplished in exposure therapy. In order to produce a clear reduction in fear the exposure must be linked to a positive therapeutic expectation: Therefore, one needs a credible rationale for the patient to expose himself to the fear inducing situation. The most convincing rationale is the prediction that the exposure will diminish his fear.

One of the mechanisms for making the prediction come true is habituation, a tendency for repeated involuntary reactions to decrease over time. In exposure therapy, this habituation tendency, which is based within the functioning of our nervous system, leads to a reduction of anxiety over time, provided that the patient remains in the situation long enough without fleeing and/or avoidance. Anxiety reduction in the feared situation is in itself the most credible evidence imaginable that the treatment is effective in the way predicted. Thus, habituation—apart from diminishing the disorder-specific fear of the fear—rather effectively reinforces the patient's expectations for improvement, hence activating the general therapeutic working mechanism discussed before. This is most likely also part of the credibility of systematic desensitization. Repeated imaginary presentation of the feared situation within the same therapeutic session leads to a diminished reaction through habituation, thereby confirming the credibility of the treatment rationale. However, experiencing reduction of fear in the real situation is certainly even more reinforcing, and that is why the *in vivo* exposure therapies are even more effective than those working with an exposure *in sensu* (see Grawe, Donati & Bernauer, 1994).

Yet habituation **in** the situation is not the only reinforcement possible. An analogue feedback, although less direct, can also happen through habituation **between** successful courses of exposure. Rachman et al. (1986) discovered that agoraphobic patients exposing themselves to the situation for only as long as it took to reach a certain level of fear and then discontinuing the exposure showed an equally strong reduction in fear as patients who remained in the situation until the fear diminished to half of its previous peak level. For many behavior therapists, the latter is still an important part of *lege artis* exposure therapy. Underlying this is the fear that premature discontinuation of exposure would lead to negative reinforcement of the flight behavior, changing the symptomatology for the worse. In reality, it seems to depend on the interpretative context. If the patient receives the instruction to remain in the situation until his fear has the situation prematurely while still at the peak of his fear, then consequently he must experience this as a failure and defeat. How should he be able to perceive this failure as a positive step towards his improvement? But when the therapist tells him to go as far as he can manage until he reaches a certain level of fear, he can then experience his next attempt as a step towards improvement if he achieves a bit more, which is what one can expect due to habituation, the beginning reduction of the fear of fear and the positive impact of expectancy induction.

The effect of exposure thus depends on the interpretative context in which it takes place, and this context is largely defined by the patient's expectations.

Whether or not the patient exposes himself to the situation at all is again dependent on whether he trusts himself to take this step (self-efficacy expectation). This would seem to indicate a step-by-step procedure for those patients with a very low self-efficacy expectation, both in terms of time duration and level of fear. Most patients will be more confident about a shorter exposure to a less fear inducing situation than about a step straight into the lion's den. The self-efficacy expectation is also dependent on the patient's general confidence level at the time. Through the convincing induction of positive expectations for improvement and other ways of resource activation the self-efficacy expectations of the patient could already be increased at the time of the first exposure to the point where he might feel confident enough, with the help of his therapist, to immediately expose himself to the fear inducing situation, because he is expecting this to be the quickest and most efficient method for getting over his fear.

Increasing self-efficacy expectations is focused primarily on diminishing previously learned avoidance behavior and boosting self-confidence in order to expose oneself to these situations and cope with them. It is, therefore, important for the patient to be able to ascribe any progress to his own accomplishments by experiencing it as an effect of his own behavior. Ultimately, he can only achieve that by making a self-determined choice to expose himself to the feared situation and proving to himself that he can cope with it.

Another component in the treatment is diminishing the fear of fear. Self-efficacy expectation and fear expectancy, as previously indicated, are two aspects of expectation that, while separate from one another, are still strongly interrelated. Without a simultaneous or ensuing reduction in fear expectancy in the course of relinquishing avoidance behavior, no improved self-efficacy expectation will be achieved in the long run. For this, it is crucial to alter the interpretation of the indicators of inchoate fear, i.e., especially those sensations which can be associated with an anxiety attack. The goal is to replace the catastrophizing cognitions with more realistic ones and to lower the excess attention devoted to such sensations. In their concept for the treatment of panic disorders, Margraf and Schneider (1990) have devoted special attention to this particular component. By using a vicious-circle model, many of these perspectives are explained to the patient in order to create a basis for achieving a change in their fear expectations. By deliberately inducing fear arousing sensations, for instance, via hyperventilation and exposure exercises, very real situations can be created which allow an actuation of the problematic cognitions ("processual activation") and their replacement by cognitions that are more appropriate and less fear arousing (coping).

1.9   The Significance of Expectancy-Value Theories for the Understanding of the Mechanisms of Psychotherapy

I already referred to expectancy-value theories earlier. According to this group of theories—I am not going to give an in-depth account of the differences between the diverse theories, as they are not so important for my point—intentional behavior can be defined as the product of the expectations related to the respective behavior and its consequences, and of the associated values (evaluations). Since in agoraphobia we are dealing not only with problematic willful behavior, such as avoidance behavior, but with problematic involuntary behavior as well, such as feelings of fear, I would like to point out, without elaborating this, the parallel aspects in both the expectancy-value conception for intentional behavior and the theory of emotion by Lazarus (1991). According to Lazarus, feelings of fear emerge out of the interaction between two evaluative processes. One, the "primary appraisal," evaluates the situation with respect to its significance for current motivations—this would be the value component in the expectancy-value theories—the other, the "secondary appraisal," refers to the assessment of how well the person expects to be able to cope with the situation and with the feelings of fear, which could also be defined as self-efficacy expectation (see also section 2.21). Secondary appraisal thus correlates with the expectancy component of the expectancy-value theories. According to more recent psychological theories, motivational evaluations and expectations (outcome expectations, self-efficacy expectations, response expectations) and their interrelatedness play a decisive role for both intentional and unintentional behavior and experience.

Therapist: I am not quite sure what this actually means. Could I ask you to relate all this a little more to what is actually happening in therapy?

Therapy researcher: I will try. With respect to what has been discussed so far, it is crucial for the treatment of agoraphobia that the patient chooses to expose himself to situations avoided in the past. Whether and how actively he will do so is, according to the expectancy-value theories, determined by expectations on the one hand, and by a motivational or value component, on the other. So far, we have discussed expectations at great length, but we have not really discussed the motivational component yet. My following comments will now focus on this. The motivational component will eventually also lead us from the symptomatology and the disorder-specific dynamics to the preconditions of mental disorders.

The stronger the patient's motivation for freeing himself of the phobia and for again being able to do what he had hitherto avoided due to his fear, the firmer his intention and his self-commitment to expose himself to the feared situation, the sooner he or she will do so, and thereby contribute whatever he or she intentionally can to the treatment success. It is, therefore, a very specific therapeutic task in exposure therapy to build up and sustain a sufficiently firm intention. The whole treatment success can depend on how well this task is accomplished (Fiegenbaum, Freitag & Frank, 1992 a).

According to Kuhl's action control theory (Kuhl, 1983, 1987 a, 1987 b; Kuhl & Beckmann, 1994; Kuhl, 1996), the self-commitment to certain goals, the forming of intentions, and the decision to stick to them requires a certain mode of action control, which Kuhl terms "action orientation." This control mode is primarily characterized by the forming, sustaining and implementing of firm intentions and resolutions. The action-oriented control mode is set apart from a "state-oriented" control mode, which is predominantly marked by a continuous preoccupation with one's own state. What an agoraphobic person would have to accomplish in exposure therapy, requires, according to Kuhl, an action-oriented control mode. In his terminology, it is crucial for exposure therapy to bring the patient into an action-oriented control mode and to keep him there.

In fact, Schulte and his colleagues (Hartung, 1990; Hartung & Schulte, 1991, 1994; Schulte, Hartung & Wilke, 1996) were able to show that an action-oriented control mode has a significant positive impact on the treatment success in exposure therapies with agoraphobics. The more action oriented the patient is at the onset of therapy, the better his prospects for a good treatment outcome. The ability to get into an action-oriented control mode can be considered a resource in the agoraphobic person, effectively activated by exposure therapy and its preparations. Furthermore, a successful therapeutic outcome in exposure therapy goes hand in hand with an increase in action orientation over the course of the therapy. Action orientation is, therefore, a favorable prerequisite for exposure therapy and in turn will be simultaneously supported by it. Both speak for a specific functional significance of an action-oriented control mode for precisely this form of therapy. It makes immediate sense. One must have a clear intention and firm resolution to not be controlled by one's fears, but to actively stand up against them, endure them, and to cope with them, in order to actively participate in and successfully complete an exposure therapy. The formation of intentions and resolutions and their successful protection from other "intrusive" intentions are the defining characteristics of an action-oriented control mode. As the firm intention to not get involved in any kind of avoidance behavior is a *conditio sine qua non* for successful exposure therapy, an action-oriented control mode has a specific functional importance for this kind of procedure. The findings by Schulte and his colleagues have been corroborated by similar findings by de Jong-Meier et al. (1997) for cognitive behavioral treatment of depressed patients.

Given the plausibility of these findings, one could be tempted to ascribe a general significance to action orientation for bringing about therapeutic changes. This generalization is not justified however, because there are empirical indications that other therapies achieve their results in different ways.

1.10 Differences in the Mechanisms of Mastery- Versus Clarification-Oriented Therapies

A study comparing four different types of therapies performed at the University of Bern (Jeger, 1996) found in a sample of patients with mixed anxiety, affective, and personality disorders that action orientation and state orientation played entirely different functional roles in the four therapies compared. For a mastery-oriented behavior therapy treatment condition, a similarly positive significance of action orientation for therapeutic outcome was found as that seen in the Bochum studies by Schulte and his colleagues. Yet among patients undergoing client-centered therapy, treatment success was, to the contrary, related to a marked increase in state orientation. Generally, in this study there were more significant correlations between the state-oriented control mode and therapeutic outcome than between the action-oriented control mode and therapeutic outcome. It is noteworthy that on average no significant differences in outcome were observed between the successfully treated behavior therapy and client-centered therapy patients. Thus, there seem to be different ways to achieve a positive therapeutic outcome.

How are such different patterns of change to be understood? Could the sole reason be that the Bochum studies included only agoraphobics, whereas the Bern study dealt with a more heterogeneous patient group? What argues against this is that in the Bern study, which used procedures similar to the exposure therapies examined in Bochum, for the mastery-oriented behavior therapy a similarly positive connection was found between action orientation and therapeutic outcome. The differences found appear to have more to do with the therapeutic procedure rather than with the kinds of patients studied. They point to clear differences in the mechanisms of behavior and client-centered therapy, for which there are a whole series of indicators.

Figure 1.1 illustrates the changes in the patients' emotional well-being in the four different treatment conditions over the course of treatment in the Bern comparative treatment study already mentioned above (Grawe, Caspar & Ambühl, 1990 b). This study compared the processes and effects of three behavior therapy conditions and one client-centered therapy condition among a sample of patients suffering from various neurotic and personality disorders. The figure shows very different changes in well-being over the course of the four therapies. It demonstrates that even in therapies that might prove to be very successful later on, the changes may evolve differently than my descriptions have suggested so far. Of the four treatment conditions, only two show patterns of change that correspond more or less with the understanding developed up to this time of how psychotherapy achieves its effects. For "broad spectrum behavior therapy" (BBT) and "interactional group therapy" (IGT) we found clear improvements even during the first ten sessions, which then later continued. These patterns of change can be well explained by the positive feedback process, which can be initiated by the induction of positive expectation for improvement, resource activation and initial mastery experiences.

Therapist: I like the fact that you have used a figure to illustrate this to us. That is a first in our conversation! However, I do not immediately understand this figure. Could you please explain how these curves were arrived at?

Therapy researcher: These curves show average effect sizes for changes in emotional well-being. The well-being was measured every ten sessions with the emotionality inventory by Ullrich and Ullrich (1978). High values indicate an improvement in emotional well-being. Four therapy conditions were compared: individual interactional behavior therapy (IBT), interactional group therapy (IGT), broad spectrum behavior therapy (BBT), and client-centered therapy (CCT). Noteworthy here are the very different changes in the well-being that took place in these four types of therapies up to the twentieth therapy session.

For those patients undergoing client-centered therapy, i.e. those who received a clarification-oriented treatment, only weak improvements in well-being can be observed at the beginning of therapy, and these improvements do not continue; they are only temporary. In fact, between the tenth and twentieth session, the emotional well-being becomes coe:nsiderably worse. After over half of the sessions—the client-centered psychotherapies lasted on average 32 sessions—the average patient's well-being is worse than at the beginning of therapy. Only after that, in the second half of the therapy, can distinct improvements in well-being be seen. While the improvement in emotional well-being still does not reach the positive level of the other therapies, the overall therapeutic outcome for the patients undergoing client-centered therapy was essentially no worse than in the three behavioral therapies at treatment termination. These developments seem to indicate that while having clear improvements already right at the beginning of therapy may be favorable for a positive therapeutic outcome, it is not absolutely necessary.

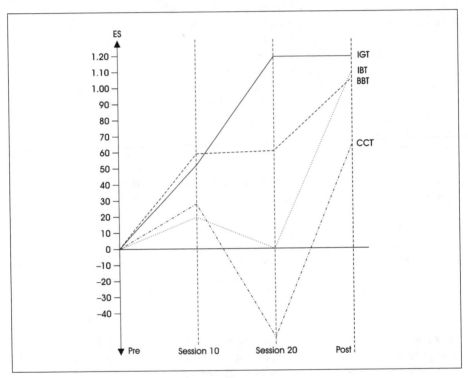

Figure 1.1:
Different patterns of change achieved by four different types of therapy in the Bern Comparative Treatment Study by Grawe, Caspar and Ambühl (1990 b). The four curves refer to the integrated effect sizes (ES) obtained by averaging across seven different scales for emotional well-being. The changes up to the tenth, the twentieth therapy session, and at post-test are represented. The duration of therapy for the four treatment conditions varied between 30 and 40 sessions.
Interactional Group Therapy = IGT; Interactional Behavior Therapy = IBT;
Broad Spectrum Behavior Therapy = BBT; Client-Centered Therapy = CCT
The values for the figures were taken from Grawe, Caspar and Ambühl (1990 b, p. 353).

In one of the three behavior therapies, the "individual interactional behavior therapy" (IBT), the pattern of change is similar to that of client-centered therapy even if the worsening in emotional well-being is not as strong between the tenth and twentieth sessions. Here also, distinct improvements only appear in the second half of therapy—these therapies lasted on average 38 sessions—but they are so strong and lasting that patients undergoing this therapy, by the time they completed their treatment, eventually ended up having achieved the second strongest improvement of all four therapies.

What distinguishes this particular therapy from the other two behavior therapies? In the individual interactional therapy, unlike the other two behavior therapies, great emphasis was put on obtaining a differentiated understanding of the problem, before treating it with a problem solving approach. The emphasis of this clarification-oriented treatment phase was to detail the most important goals determining the patient's interpersonal behavior. A structured method of analysis, a "plan analysis" (Grawe & Caspar, 1984; Caspar, 1996) was used for this. Therapy began with a structured phase of motivational clarification with the explicit understanding that in this way the best conditions for targeted problem solving could be created. In CCT as well, the focus was on learning to better understand one's own experience and behavior, which commonly means relating it to its underlying motives. Yet motivational clarification happened here in a more unstructured fashion than in interactional behavior therapy and was not followed up by systematic problem solving.

The patients in these two treatment conditions were not promised quick therapeutic success. Instead, they were told that in order for them to arrive at long-term improvements, a better understanding of the problems first had to be elaborated. From what we have set forth so far about expectancy induction it is understandable that these patients did not have strong improvement reactions directly following the beginning of therapy. In fact, it was never suggested to them that they should expect such a rapid improvement.

Patients undergoing psychodynamically and humanistically oriented therapies are generally given the message that their changes must arise from understanding (Biermann-Ratjen, Eckert & Schwartz, 1979), and understanding takes time. The actual process of change in these patients happens according to this induced expectation. From that angle, we could maybe even interpret their patterns of change as evidence for the powerful impact expectations have in psychotherapy. One might perhaps speculate about which kind of expectations are induced in a psychoanalysis patient who is given the perspective by his therapist that the therapeutic goals can only be reached years from now.

If you wish to achieve rapid improvements in your patients, then you must give them a plausible rationale according to which these rapid improvements can be achieved, and the method must be consistent with this rationale. Looking at the above mentioned patterns of change, not every therapy leads to expectations for a rapid improvement and, therefore, to the positive feedback process in the early stages of therapy, from which this rapid improvement can emerge. In fact, through his or her own specific method or instruction, a therapist can just about block the emergence of positive expectations by making the patient think that such rapid changes would be very unlikely, or should they evolve, not be of long-term duration. Therapists who are convinced that true and long-term changes require a long time will most likely not notice positive effects until relatively late in their therapy, because in one way or another they impart their own convictions to the patient. Their experiences are the result of a self-fulfilling prophecy.

Looking at research on psychotherapy outcomes from that perspective, it should be expected that problem-solving-oriented therapies with a short duration, in which the patient is clearly told how his problems should be solved and exactly why this method is the most adequate one, and which plausibly convey to the patient that all this can be achieved in a short period of time, do much better than those therapies in which the patient is implicitly or explicitly told that treatment successes are only to be expected as a result of a longer process of understanding. This advantage is germane specifically to cognitive-behavioral therapies, but also to hypnotherapy, relaxation techniques as well as problem-solving-oriented family therapies. If, in addition to the structuring of expectations, a convincing and understandable disorder-specific view of the respective symptomatology can be imparted to the patient, then the credibility of the positive expectancy induction is even higher. When in addition, this view is based on well-founded disorder-specific knowledge, then the patient will most likely come to realize that his experiences are congruent with what the therapist predicts.

All these characteristics of a positive expectancy induction apply very specifically to cognitive-behavioral therapies. If the induction of positive expectations for success plays a significant role for psychotherapies, this could explain why this group of therapies has been shown to be consistently and statistically significantly superior to other therapies in controlled outcome studies—even if the difference is not very large in absolute terms (Grawe, Donati & Bernauer, 1994). The advantage should be even greater, the shorter the therapies, because those therapies achieving their effects predominantly through other mechanisms could not unfold their specific mechanisms in a short period of time. Unfortunately, there are hardly any controlled trials in therapy research comparing courses of different therapies for long enough to separate the quick improvements caused by induction of positive expectations from other positive therapeutic effects.

Psychologist: Isn't it possible that the representatives of humanistic and psychodynamic therapies could use your view for arguing in favor of their own therapies? They might say: If we use the possibilities of positive expectancy induction and the targeted precipitation of coping experiences so little, but they are, on the other hand, according to you, the predominant working mechanisms for successful therapy, then how do you explain the positive therapeutic effects we achieve in our therapies? This is a good question, in my eyes. I wonder how you would respond to this argument.

Therapy researcher: To explain that I have to go back a bit. Earlier on, I made an attempt to explain the mechanisms of psychotherapy using the example of agoraphobia. Admittedly, I left out a few facts, because they would not have fit so well into the picture I was drawing for you. Not that I would have deliberately drawn a wrong picture. It was, however, incomplete, and I would like to make an attempt to complete it now.

To complete the picture of how psychotherapy works in the treatment of agoraphobia, I would like to start by quoting the results of a, now older, study that gives us something to think about. These results stem from the comparative outcome study by

Grawe (1976), in which psychiatric patients with severe phobias were treated. Most patients were suffering from agoraphobia, but there were also a few social phobics and a few cases of particularly severe and specific phobias of the kind that really get in the way of the patient's everyday life functioning, such as phobias relating to injections and animals. Today all these different phobias would not be included in one and the same study any more, but at the end of the sixties, when this study was planned, a different opinion on this prevailed. However, this is not so important for what I would like to explain right now. More than two thirds of the patients suffered from severe agoraphobia, so we have a connection here to what I previously said about the treatment of agoraphobics.

The patients were randomly distributed among three treatment conditions. One group of patients served as a control group for the two other treatment groups. They remained in the care of their former psychiatrist where they were treated with medication. This treatment was not new, but a continuation of the treatment they had been receiving previously. We can, therefore, assume that in these patients no strong expectations for improvement were aroused at the beginning of the experiment.

This was different for the other two treatment conditions. To these patients, their treatment was presented as the method of choice specifically indicated for their symptomatology. This must have been very convincing for these patients, as the indication was presented following a careful diagnostic examination.

One group of patients received behavior therapy as it was developed at that time. Systematic desensitization, relaxation training, assertiveness training, and self-control techniques were applied with most patients, and exposure therapy (flooding) in all those for whom the other techniques did not produce sufficient positive effects. That was particularly the case among the agoraphobics. At the time, exposure therapies were brand new and had something intriguing and pioneering about them. They were not part of the behavior therapists' routine repertoire. I mention this, because given today's experience with performing exposure therapies, some agoraphobic patients could have been treated somewhat better today than was the case at the time. Perhaps the potential of this therapy may not have been fully realized in this study.

The second treatment condition with a high expectancy for improvement was client-centered psychotherapy according to Tausch and Tausch (1971). Client-centered psychotherapy was in its heyday at that time. In Hamburg, where this study took place, a center for client-centered psychotherapy had been established around Reinhard Tausch, and there was great enthusiasm for this, then new form of therapy in German-speaking areas. Therapists educated by him were confident about almost everything. They strongly believed in the credo of nondirectivity and in the healing and sufficient effect of the Rogerian triad: genuineness, acceptance, and empathy. According to that, no disorder-specific knowledge and methods were applied in the client-centered therapy condition. The patients were neither asked by their therapists to expose themselves to the feared situations, nor were they in any way supported by them through active problem solving. The therapists confined themselves to supporting the patient's self-reflective process labeled by Rogers as the process of self-exploration.

Astonishingly, this method, which was not expressly focused on the phobic symptomatology, on average led to similar symptomatic improvements as the explicitly disorder-oriented behavior therapy. This was not just the case according to the patients' judgments, but also according to those of an independent psychiatric expert. Figure 1.2 shows the average changes in fear in the individually most important phobic situations for the patients undergoing symptom-oriented behavior therapy compared to those undergoing client-centered therapy and the control condition.

This finding from Grawe's study (1976) is not an isolated result. A controlled study by Teusch (1995) also found a highly significant reduction in agoraphobic symptoms through client-centered therapy among patients with panic disorder and agoraphobia. Treatment was performed predominantly in a group setting for inpatients. In this study, Teusch compared pure client-centered psychotherapy with one that was supplemented by a behavior therapy exposure treatment. Overall, this combination therapy had some advantages; however, especially with regard to the reduction of agoraphobic fear, the pure client-centered psychotherapy was just as effective as the combination treatment. These facts are difficult to reconcile with the beliefs of many behavior therapists according to whom agoraphobic fear can only be effectively treated with exposure therapy. What exactly in client-centered therapy is capable of causing this effect? Could it be that the symptomatic improvements are, in fact, related only to the induction of positive expectations for improvements?

This is very unlikely, for many reasons. First, as I pointed out earlier, according to a study by Shapiro (1981), the explanatory and treatment concepts for phobias in behavior therapy are much more convincing and plausible for the patient than are the ones in client-centered therapy. Therefore, in terms of expectancy effects, behavior therapies should have an overall advantage and should have achieved better results. Second, we know from the Bern comparative study of treatment by Grawe, Caspar and Ambühl (1990), from which I took the figure on the course of change in emotional well-being, that behavior therapy and client-centered therapy produced changes in emotional well-being in quite a different fashion. While we do not have any analogous description for the course of therapy from the earlier study by Grawe (1976), there are also indicators in this older study that behavior therapy and client-centered therapy produce their therapeutic effects in a different fashion.

That is to say, this study did not just report on the average changes, according to which there was more or less an equally successful outcome for both therapies, but it explicitly took a closer look at how the changes in the different areas were interrelated. And something interesting turned up there for our question about the mechanisms of psychotherapy: In behavior therapy improvements in symptomatology and emotional well-being were closely interrelated, i.e. those patients experiencing improved symptoms felt better and vice versa. This is not at all surprising, because it fits the rationale underlying the therapy.

The correlation can also be interpreted the other way around. It is in agreement with the phase model developed by Howard et al., according to which a patient experiencing an improvement in well-being will have a better chance for improved symptoms. It is remarkable that this connection was only found for behavior therapy.

On the other hand, the findings for client-centered therapy were somewhat surprising and less comprehensible in that the patients' phobic symptoms and emotional well-being changed independently of one another. There were patients whose phobic symptoms had not improved significantly, but who felt better nonetheless, and also patients experiencing less phobia without this having any effect on their overall emotional state.

Altogether, the improvements in the symptoms and emotional well-being in these patients were equally strong as in those undergoing behavior therapy. It is not that the average magnitude of these changes was different for the two therapies, but the way these changes were interrelated. One can, therefore, maintain that the two therapies produce qualitatively different results, which remain hidden in a figure illustrating just the average quantitative changes. Furthermore: There were different patient groups successfully treated by these therapies. Symptom-oriented behavior therapy was especially effective in patients who suffered most severely from their phobic symptoms, who experienced them as the central cause of their malady. Those experiencing their phobic symptoms in a different way, who did not view them as the sole cause of that suffering, showed better results under client-centered therapy. This also makes sense, since client-centered therapists explicitly focused on the patient's most pressing issues, which even in phobic patients can be aspects of their lives other than their phobic

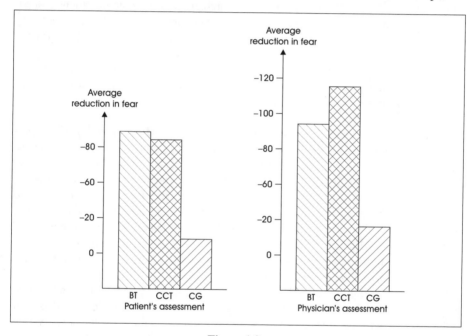

Figure 1.2:
Changes in the phobic symptomatology in behavior therapy (BT), client-centered therapy
(CCT), and in a control group (CG) from the comparative study by Grawe (1976).
On the left, the reduction in fear for the individual main phobias as assessed by the patients;
on the right, as assessed by an independent physician.
Figures taken from Grawe (1976, p. 89 and p. 98).

symptoms. A diagnostic classification must not necessarily be congruent with the patient's most burning agendas. Evidently, behavior therapists who generally focused on the phobic symptomatology were less able to handle these other matters in their patients than were client-centered therapists.

The exciting thing about these findings is that even a therapy which is not focused on the treatment of the predominant symptoms can lead to pronounced improvements in symptoms or well-being that are a close second to those achieved by a disorder-specific treatment. Although the study still suggests that agoraphobic patients are best treated with behavior therapy—nowadays we can be even more specific: with exposure therapy—there are nevertheless patients with the same diagnosis whose needs are obviously better met by a method that is less focused on symptomatology. Thus, the diagnosis alone is not a sufficient indicator for choosing the treatment method.

We already have two phenomena that require explanation which were not covered by the previous ideas about the mechanisms of psychotherapy. First is the fact that psychotherapies which do not apply a disorder-specific method, and which do not offer active help for the mastery of problems, can also produce good therapeutic results. Second is the fact that therapies can lead to clearly positive results at a relatively late stage in their course, even if there were not any of these improvements of well-being, so typical of other therapies, at the very beginning. Both phenomena are not just typical for one or the other single therapy, but are characteristic for whole treatment groups. Consequently, they have something to do with the therapeutic method. We are actually faced with the necessity of extending the range of working mechanisms thus far considered. This is true in a general sense, but also specifically with respect to agoraphobia, which we used as an example. Clarification-oriented therapies, such as client-centered therapy, in part work differently than mastery-oriented therapies, and this other mechanism is not yet sufficiently clarified.

Therapist: I can follow your conclusions. They fit observations from my daily practice. There have to be therapeutic factors other than those proposed by you. However, for me, there is yet another fact that limits the extent of the explanatory power of the therapeutic factors detailed by you earlier, although I found your arguments for the significance of these therapeutic principles very convincing. Even the most optimistic assessments with regard to the efficacy of exposure therapy in agoraphobia (Fiegenbaum, Freitag & Frank, 1992 a; Fiegenbaum & Tuschen, 1996) show that the proportion of successfully treated patients does not reach one hundred percent, but only seventy-five. What about the remaining twenty-five percent of the patients, in whom the treatment did not achieve the desired success?

I cannot quite bring myself to believe that the twenty-five percent failure rate is due to the fact that the above mentioned therapeutic factors were not implemented as well in the unsuccessful therapies as in the successful ones. Even among the seventy-five percent in whom treatment was regarded as successful, there are therapies with a more or less positive result that can be linked to a better or worse implementation of the therapeutic principles. But if a therapy does not work at all in a patient, one has reason to believe that this therapy was basically not launched from the correct point and that it did not account for those crucial conditions which sustain the patient's problem.

You mentioned earlier that there is evidence for believing that client-centered therapy and behavior therapy work for different kinds of patients. Could it be that client-centered therapy could achieve good results in those twenty-five percent of patients among whom exposure therapy is not working, or at least in a few of them? It could very well be that therapies working with totally different therapeutic factors could influence exactly those factors responsible for the perpetuation of the disorder that exposure therapy is unable to target.

Therapy researcher: You mention a very interesting possibility here, which could actually be the foundation for future pioneering research projects. Maybe it would be a good idea for those of us in therapy research to systematically treat any patients who fail to improve with one form of therapy within a controlled comparative outcome study with a totally different approach, and that is to say reciprocally. In the study by Grawe (1976) quoted earlier, for instance, those patients for whom behavior therapy did not work could have been treated with client-centered therapy right afterwards, and vice versa. Giving it some thought in the context of our discussion, I am actually surprised that such studies do not yet exist. We would most likely be able to find out more about the differential indicators and mechanisms of various kinds of therapies than we have in the past, especially if additional attempts were made by us to document or measure the presumed working mechanisms in the course of the therapeutic process.

Psychologist: I noticed that whenever you mention client-centered therapy and its mechanisms, or other therapies more oriented towards understanding, your comments become a little more vague than they were in your previous introduction about the role of expectancy and the mechanisms of exposure therapy etc. Is it because there are fewer sound studies and substantiated results, or do you have other reasons?

Therapy researcher: Both are the case. There are a great deal of experimentally designed studies of those influential factors introduced by me earlier that have saved us from many misconceptions. Taking them all together, one gets a pretty clear picture. At least one can derive a few lasting, reliable ideas that will be of value for us tomorrow as well. This is different for the mechanisms of psychodynamic and humanistic therapies, since they have been studied relatively rarely within experimental designs. Our empirically-based knowledge of the mechanisms of these therapies draws largely upon correlative studies that can be interpreted one way or the other (Orlinsky, Grawe & Parks, 1994). Very often in these studies, the measuring instruments used were developed ad hoc and their relation to the respective therapy theory remains unclear, especially since the theories themselves are not at all stringently formulated. The experimental thinking is lacking. The study conditions vary from one study to the next, so it is not possible to draw clear conclusions that are consistent from one study to the next. The reasons for that are obvious. We are talking about concepts that were initially developed for the clinical context and not for research purposes. Therefore, there are hardly any connections to research areas of fundamental psychology. This all has to do with the nature of the research subject. Concepts such as resistance, transference and insight are difficult to operationalize, let alone to control experimentally. That is a huge disadvantage for the progress of scientific knowledge. Assumptions that are essentially not tenable are maintained for much too long because they have not been proven wrong. As we saw with systematic desensitization however, the progress of knowledge is largely based on the realization of errors and not on the confirmation of what is considered to be true.

All this leads to the situation that, although I have my own ideas about the mechanisms of these therapies, I am unable to back up their assumptions with such sound research findings as those found on the role of expectations for improvements. Therefore, by comparison, I hesi??? to offer specific statements.

Another reason is that I lack the theoretical background for such statements which would enable me to bridge the gap to what I have stated before about the mechanisms of exposure therapy. It is like moving in two separate worlds. I would like to combine these two worlds—in accordance with Grawe's therapeutic factors, I name them the world of mastery-oriented therapies and the world of clarification-oriented therapies—into a consistent view, but I lack the link. I have vague ideas about how to conceptualize it, but these concepts could not be supported by sound empirical findings, and that is why I probably hesitate to come forward with these ideas.

Psychologist: My opinion is that we should not be too scrupulous about this. I think I mentioned before that there would be various reasons for me not to participate in such a forum, and I had already made clear why I had overcome my reservations. I would like to encourage you to do the same, and just share with us your opinion which has built up after years of having been confronted with these issues. You have convinced us by now that you have expert knowledge in the field of therapy research and do not lean towards unsubstantiated speculation. The fact that there are not always sound results for some questions should not lead to us excluding these questions from our discussion. It is natural that there are not a lot of research findings yet on novel ideas and research approaches. But it is exactly these new ideas that are interesting for us. They are bred from the realization that other ideas that have been studied in-depth cannot be maintained any longer. Behaviorism is a perfect example of this. After thousands of empirical investigations, we know today that the concepts of behaviorism lead us nowhere. It has been proved that far too much that needs to be explained cannot be satisfactorily explained by these concepts. This is also a finding, in fact a very sound one. If we are able to draw the correct conceptual conclusions from this, the questions we are asking on this new basis will most likely lead us much further, because they are more informed than the ones previously researched. We should definitely, whenever possible, make an effort to refer to well replicated research results where they exist. But "softer" grounds should not keep us from thinking further in that direction. As long as we are aware of the provisional nature of our views, I see no danger in that whatever we are developing here goes beyond what has been generally well predicated so far.

I am about to give you an example of what I mean. While listening to you earlier, the word "Rubicon" went through my mind several times. Presumably, this will not tell you much. But I wish to tell you what it is about. It represents an idea of how to combine these two worlds. Of course, none of this is based on any empirical findings, but the more I apply this idea to what you said, the more it seems worthwhile to think about it.

1.11   Therapy This Side and That Side of the Rubicon

The Rubicon is a river in Italy. If you are familiar with it at all it is probably more from history than from geography lessons. In reality, it is more a stream or brook, than a river. The fact that it is known at all is due solely to Julius Caesar. When, on the eleventh of January in 49 B.C. he decided to cross the river Rubicon with his legions and documented for posterity the fact that he thought this was an extraordinary decision with far-reaching consequences by saying: "*Alea jacta est*" (the die is cast), he had made a final decision in favor of civil war at that moment, and there was no way back for him. From that moment on he was determined to wage this war and win it. The time for hesitation and for weighing decisions was finally over.

Heckhausen (1987 a, b) chose this historical event as the metaphor for an "action phase model" that describes the process from wishing via choosing to forming intentions and acting. The psychological Rubicon is crossed in the bridging from choosing to willing, when out of wishes and fears, intentions emerge and take the shape of concrete action plans that are intently followed up and then begin to direct actions. Figure 1.3 shows Heckhausen's diagram of the Rubicon model.

According to Heckhausen and his colleagues (see Heckhausen, Gollwitzer & Weinert, 1987), the psychological worlds, or the processes, respectively, on this side and the other side of the Rubicon look very different and follow different principles. This model comes to my mind in this context because I see that the therapeutic procedures we have spoken about seem to work on different banks of the river. Problem solving or mastery-oriented therapies, such as exposure therapy for the treatment of agoraphobias, for instance, predominantly work on the right side of the Rubicon. They presume certain goal intentions as already existing and aimed at supporting the process of realization of these intentions via suitable means. There is an initial definition and specification of treatment goals that can be viewed as a realization of intentions the patient brought along with him; for instance, the intention "I would like to be able to move around without fear again." In a first step, the intention has to be transformed into a volition. The volitional strength is a result of both the **desirability** and the perceived **realizability** of the treatment goal (Gollwitzer, 1987). The desirability corresponds to the value component of the "expectancy-value-theories" addressed by you earlier; the realizability refers to the possibilities the patient sees for putting his wish into practice and thus to the expectations he has regarding the realizability.

The therapist can exert direct influence on both components. To raise the level of desirability, he can guide the patient into detailed fantasies about all the wonderful and interesting activities she could resume if she were in a position to move around freely again. Just the exercise of imagining she would actually be doing all these things can strengthen her intent to take action in that direction. In a study by Gollwitzer, Heckhausen and Ratajczak (1987), female students faced with the decision of whether or not they should switch to another major made more and more concrete plans in that direction following an exercise in which they were asked to envision how they would actually put such a decision, one that they had not yet made, into practice.

Therapist: As therapists we have an arsenal of techniques available for strengthening desirability, as you termed it. In addition to guided imagery directed towards the positive treatment goals, the formation of a firm intention can also be fostered by having the patient specifically imagine all the negative consequences should he or she not do anything about the condition. The therapist can play the role of *advocatus diaboli* listing for the patient all that speaks against his taking such uncomfortable steps in order to activate everything that speaks in favor of it. We have here a smooth transition to the so-called "paradoxical intervention strategies." These seem to work mainly by contributing to the development of a firm, clear-cut intention in a situation where an ambivalence of intentions prevails. The "magic question" in the solution-oriented short-term therapy concept of De Shazer (1985) could also be taken as a way for increasing desirability.

Psychologist: Apart from the desirability component, the therapist can also directly influence the expectancy component as well. All measures inducing positive expectations for improvement contribute to that. The same is true for all measures which increase the patient's self-efficacy expectation as well as those suitable for diminishing his fear of fear.

If I understood you correctly: What typically occurs in an exposure therapy contributes to the fortification of the volitional strength so that the patient can expose himself to feared situations. In behavior therapy the formation of concrete intentions is supported by the fact that the intentions are linked to concrete situational behaviors. Substantive talking about the how, when and where promotes the formation of binding intentions (Heckhausen, 1987 a).

A person's firm intention to give up old behavior and to behave in a different way from now on does not necessarily lead to the realization of that intention. Instead, the

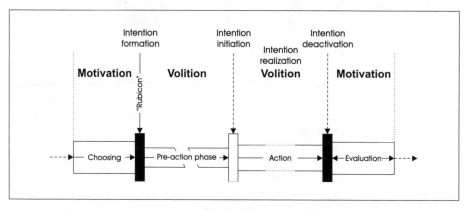

Figure 1.3:
The action phase model (Rubicon model) by Heckhausen.
The figure was taken, slightly adjusted, from Gollwitzer (1987, pp. 180).

new intention has to be constantly protected from invasion by competing intentions whose volitional strength, as a product of desirability and realizability, allows them to easily overtake and defeat the newly formed intention. A wonderful smelling roast, an inviting cocktail lounge, a one-armed bandit spitting out coins, a tempting woman or attractive man has melted the strong will of many who have made the resolution to lose weight, stop drinking or gambling, or to be faithful. That is why panic disorders are so much easier to change than excessive smoking, eating, or gambling habits etc. Once fear has diminished as a result of exposure, the desirability of the avoidance behavior, and thereby its volitional strength is constantly reduced. It has made room for other intentions. With consumption behaviors, the desirability, and thereby the intentional strength remains high, and normally there are also plenty of occasions. The volitional strengths of new "positive" resolutions need regular care and nurturing to defend these intentions against intrusions from old established intentions. The members of Alcoholics Anonymous have drawn logical consequences from that.

Kuhl (1983, Kuhl & Beckmann, 1994) a former associate of Heckhausen, in particular, has concerned himself in great detail with the volitional process in the realization of intentions. Earlier, in your report on studies of the therapeutic process from Bochum and Bern, you mentioned Kuhl's concept of action and state orientation, which revolves around the transformation of intentions into actions. Under which conditions is an intention efficiently realized; which conditions are detrimental to this? Kuhl defines the first successful mode of action control as action orientation; the second mode which is detrimental for an efficient realization of intentions is designated state orientation. Kuhl's action control strategies overlap significantly with the concepts of self-regulation and self-control (Kanfer, 1987). That is why it is not surprising that many of Kuhl's action control strategies already have a longer tradition in behavior therapy, albeit under different terms, such as self monitoring, stimulus control and many more. Kuhl also mentions other action control strategies, such as intention control, emotion control, motivational control, and encoding control, and many more that perhaps can offer new suggestions for therapeutic practice.

I do not want to go deeper into Kuhl's complex approach which is still being further developed (Kuhl, 1994; Kuhl & Beckmann, 1994). My point is to make you aware that in today's psychology appreciable amounts of research have become established around the term volition, which can be related to therapeutic practice and can help to address questions which are of obvious relevance for therapists. Recently a book appeared in which a number of prominent psychologists who are mainly active in basic research like Dörner, Herrmann, Kornadt, Kuhl, Prinz, and others, addressed the problem of freedom of will (von Cranach & Foppa, 1996); only ten years ago this would have been unthinkable in psychology. These new concepts taken from the psychology of volition have already had, as you know, a stimulating effect on the questions and methods of psychotherapy research. Vogel (1993) conducted a study on changes in intention and treatment strategy of therapists in the course of their therapies that was largely inspired by Kuhl's basic research concepts. You have already mentioned Hartung's "translation" of Kuhl's conception of action and state orientation into a system for coding therapeutic interactions (Hartung, 1990) and the ensuing results obtained from the system (Hartung,1990; Hartung & Schulte, 1994; Schulte, Hartung & Wilke, 1996; de Jong-Meier et al., 1997; Jeger, 1996).

Therapy researcher: I have no problem seeing the parallels between Heckhausen's and Kuhl's conceptions of what is taking place on the right bank of the Rubicon and the behavior therapeutic approach as illustrated by you. In exposure therapy these parallels are obvious but Kanfer's self management approach (Kanfer, Reinecker & Schmelzer, 1991) can also be related to this part of the Rubicon model right down to its details. Kanfer et al. put the greatest emphasis on the patient's firm commitment towards implementing the steps necessary for problem solving before starting with it. In the theory and practice of psychodynamic and humanistic therapies, on the contrary, little attention is paid to the processes leading from intention to action realization. What remains as a question for me, however, is understanding how a connection between the psychological processes left of the Rubicon and the humanistic and psychodynamic approaches can be established. From what I know about the academic psychology of motivation and the various expectancy-value-models, studies performed on these processes have rather little to do with the issues typically addressed in such therapies.

Psychologist: Unfortunately your last statement is quite correct, although I would prefer it were not otherwise. The research questions guided by the expectancy-value model belong to those subjects in psychology which are among the best overall researched since the breakthrough approaches by Tolman (1951, 1952), Rotter (1954, 1966) and Atkinson (1957; Atkinson & Birch, 1970). However, you are right: the research paradigms used in this research are often far removed from everyday life and even more foreign to psychotherapy. The question as to how motivation and action are interrelated (Heckhausen, 1980) points directly to the center of therapeutic questions. Nonetheless, a therapist will usually find few answers to his questions on this topic in psychology textbooks and this includes even those dealing directly with "social learning and clinical psychology" such as the book by Rotter (1954). Those issues on human motivations, which are generally of special interest to therapists, have received little attention in social learning theories. I find this to be regrettable because the expectancy-value paradigm can be easily utilized for the analysis of practical problems. It has, for instance, proved to be very useful in analyzing consumer purchasing behavior or political decision making processes (Janis, 1972).

For me the value the "Rubicon-model" and the psychological expectancy-value models have for psychotherapy lies less in the abundance of research results collected on conditions capable of influencing the two components "value" and "expectancy" (Feather, 1981). It is rather the fundamental idea—one which in fact has been frequently confirmed for the areas researched—that the likelihood of a behavior is dependent upon first, its value with respect to the individual's wishes and fears, and second, its perceived realizability and the expected consequences, which appears to be very promising for psychotherapy. As I mentioned earlier, even if there is a lack of sound empirical research results on a new concept so far, or on the transfer of a proven concept from another domain to a new application field, letting ourselves be inspired by this new fundamental idea to view certain phenomena and questions in a new light I feel to be quite legitimate. It seems to me that the Rubicon model is well suited for creating a link between the world of wishes and fears on the left bank of the Rubicon and the world of the realization of intentions on the right.

In reality, crossing the Rubicon is a fairly common everyday life event. The Rubicon, as I said before, is more of a brook than a river, and the bridge where Caesar crossed, is wide and can handle a lot of traffic. It is said to have already been that way during his time. There is quite some traffic across the psychological Rubicon as well, from left to right, from the superior goal intentions to the realization of action plans. In Figure 1.3, if we imagine curving the band into a circle, it becomes clear that the assessment of the realized action in turn leads to changes in the motivation of landscape to the left of the Rubicon. Processes on the right bank of the Rubicon thus affect those on the left; as a matter of fact, the reverse process is even more obvious. What happens in the world of wishes and fears has, by virtue of goal intentions and action plans, direct effects on actions.

Consequently, the assessment of the action results has an impact on the activation level (volitional strength) of the intentions. The successful realization of an action plan will most likely lead to a decrease in the activation level of the respective intention and, therefore, possibly to a switch in intentions. If the individual had to choose among a variety of equally strong goal intentions in the preceding formation of action plans, then the realization of the chosen action plan will most likely lead to one of the competing intentions becoming dominant and relevant for action. One example for this might be a working mother whose deliberate actions are constantly switching back and forth between two equally strong goal intentions. Just as she has managed to have her children somewhat taken care of, competing vocational goal intentions emerge, and vice versa. The actualization level of the goal intentions determines which aspects of life's complex demands will emerge as objects of intentions.

Gollwitzer (1987) terms such largely superior goal intentions: identity goals. Identity goals are so to speak "unsatisfiable." They are constantly activated and just waiting for an occasion to realize action plans initiated by these goal intentions. Through the realization of action plans—so goes Gollwitzer's assumptions—the goal intentions are temporarily deactivated and have less impact on the behavior. Other competing motivations may arise and gain control over the behavior. Exactly the opposite is happening if the respective goal intentions are not given their turn or are being kept from becoming active. In that case, the intention level should increase and increasingly determine the behavior.

Several interesting findings confirm these assumptions. Psychology students with the identity goal "becoming a psychotherapist" were encouraged to express their intention to watch films on therapy. In one group of students this intention was expressly acknowledged while in another group it was ignored. Upon receiving the opportunity to put their goal into action, those students whose intention had been acknowledged actually took less advantage of the occasion than did those students whose intent had been ignored. The confirmation of an important identity goal evidently leads in fact to a temporary decrease in the volitional strength and vice versa. For students without the identity goal "psychotherapist" the same experimental influence led to exactly the opposite effect. They were more likely to look at these films after their intent had been acknowledged (Gollwitzer, 1987).

Wicklund and Gollwitzer (1982) performed another study confirming these assumptions: "The procedure used here was as follows: test persons with definite identity goals (e.g. manager) were first confronted with not having an important identity indicator (e.g. it was imparted to them in a credible way that their personality characteristics would be distinctly different from those of successful managers). Then they were given the opportunity to acquire alternative identity indicators (e.g., to give themselves relevant vocational titles, to become active as a trainer or instructor in a relevant specific field or to solve typical tasks crucial for the aspired identity). In comparison to a control group which had not undergone these manipulations (incompleteness manipulations), it was always demonstrated that the 'incomplete' group of test persons made increased usage of the opportunity to acquire identity indicators" (Gollwitzer, 1987, pp. 180—181).

I could imagine that the possibilities suggested by these results, to use important identity goals for the purpose of achieving a certain influence on behavior, could also be employed for therapeutic purposes.

1.12 Therapeutic Effects Via Activation and Deactivation of Intentions

Therapist: Quite spontaneously something comes to mind. For a long time in my practical work I have made use of a relational strategy that I once learned in a training course by Grawe on the topic "Forming the Therapeutic Relationship." He calls this strategy "Complementary Relationship Formation." This strategy is predominantly employed with patients who behave in ways that seem to be not in their best interests, with the eventual result that everybody turns away from them. This could be, for instance, an extremly complaining, self-pitying behavior, with a denial of all self-responsibility leading soon to the situation in which the therapist can barely restrain himself from more or less bluntly making the point to the patient that he or she also has a part in his or her own situation. It is exactly this rejection and these underlying feelings of anger from his interaction partners that the patient experiences over and over again. The patient finds himself in a very familiar interaction pattern with even his therapist reacting the same way as everyone else. This is not exactly helpful for solving his problems; as a matter of fact, it will most likely contribute to them. Needless to say, the therapist is unlikely to be able to help the patient if even he or she gets involved in this interaction pattern.

Grawe assumes that such interpersonal behavior serves an important overall goal or a relational schema, which may not be obvious or conscious to the patient (Grawe, 1992; Grawe et al., 1996). In the terminology you used before, one would instead speak of an important identity goal. Grawe infers this "actual" behavioral intention predominantly from the patient's non-verbal behavior. He then forms a relationship to this patient in which he very systematically puts himself in a complementary position, which means deliberately confirming the patient's identity goal. The effect is often absolutely stunning. After a short time, sometimes in the same session, but almost always after no more than a few therapy sessions, the patient's behavior is hardly recognizable. Within only a short period of time, the same "spineless jellyfish in constant search of pity" from before, has transformed into a person with whom one can actually have a reasonable exchange about his problems and who, in fact, is capable of feeling responsible for himself.

According to your interpretation of the Rubicon model, I suppose one would have to explain this drastic change in interpersonal behavior by the fact that the previously behavior-controlling goal intention was finally being realized through the therapist's complementary behavior, and that its intentional strength thereby decreased so much that other goal intentions were able to achieve a higher volitional strength and became behavior-controlling. Of course these identity goals will not have disappeared once and forever through this. According to Gollwitzer they are indeed ultimately "unsatisfiable," as you mentioned. These are also the experiences made in practice. After all, such a relational strategy is no "therapeutic trick" which the therapist can use to achieve a magical cure, even if the immediate effects can be quite impressive. It is more like a basic attitude towards the patient. The patient has to principally feel that he is recognized and accepted in this identity goal, which is something that has to be imparted to him over and over again so that other intentions will get the chance to control his behavior during therapy. By pursuing these other intentions, the patient may then reach a point where it is possible to identify, to reflect upon, and to change the conditions underlying these problematic identity goals in the motivational landscape left of the Rubicon. Changing a problematic identity goal in the long run, may require the fulfillment of this goal in therapy first.

Many therapists initially have strong reservations against such a strategic approach to the therapy relationship. They feel a therapist should not be invilved in supporting problematic behaviors. However, this argument would seem valid only if people did in fact function according to a simple principle of reinforcement, but I have never been a fan of such a theory. I am really happy to hear that your basic science conception confirms that people are a little more complex after all, which concurs more with my therapeutic experiences. Could the extraordinarily positive effect of so-called "paradoxical interventions" observed in some cases not also be understood as a deactivation of intentions? Is it not possible that in those patients with a permanently activated intention to deny any influence from others, a paradoxical message from the therapist, one which in fact at its core represents a "declaration of non-changeability," might fulfill and thereby deactivate the patient's intention so that other intentions may emerge and gain control over the patient's behavior (Shoham-Salomon, Avner & Neeman, 1989)?

But I interrupted you earlier, maybe I do this too often with my need to relate everything to my practice. What you actually still wanted to do was to create the bridge to the left bank of the Rubicon.

Psychologist: That does not bother me at all, on the contrary, I find it interesting how you related my theoretical conceptions to your practice. This brings up new aspects for me. But of course, you are right, I have not yet brought my thoughts quite to where I wish them to be as my actual goal was to show some of the possibilities for how the world of mastery-oriented therapies could be connected to that of clarification-oriented therapies. I will get to this now.

1.13 The Formation and Realization of Intentions as Different Goals of Clarification- and Mastery-Oriented Therapies

Why do both the action phase model by Heckhausen and associates, as well as the Rubicon metaphor put so much weight on the transition from the motivational to the volitional phase in the course of action? Because of the assumption that the processes on this side and the other side of the Rubicon differ fundamentally in one specific feature. On the right side of the Rubicon, partisanship prevails. Everything is focused on realizing the intention with the highest volitional strength. Situations are not perceived in a neutral or reality-oriented fashion but according to their meaning for the intention actuated at the moment. Situations offering the opportunity for intention realization are acknowledged and given preference, called on and taken advantage of. Perceptions, emotions, thoughts, and actions stand in the service of the respective intention. They are **realization-oriented**, not reality-oriented.

The processes left of the Rubicon are—according to the assumptions of the model— **reality-oriented**. These reality-oriented processes mean carefully weighing and choosing between the different alternatives, not the wishes and fears themselves towards which they are directed. These represent the object of the reality-oriented processes. Heckhausen writes: "...the special mindset when choosing. It is an emotional mindset that is sharply distinguished from the one of wishing. It is characterized on the one hand by additional attention for all that could be of interest and, on the other hand, is unerring in the evaluation of negative aspects as well. In short: a remarkable reality orientation of a cognitive apparatus running at 'full tilt,' whose willingness and capacity to receive and process information was maximal" (Heckhausen, 1987 a, p. 5). These statements sum up the results of a study investigating the decision making processes among students faced with the question of whether or not they should move out of their parents' home (Gollwitzer & Heckhausen, 1987). Contrary to the researchers' expectations the students did not waste much time with the question of what their most desired wish was, but mainly focused on which pros and cons regarding the desirability and realizability of their actual wish they could put forward as an argument. Even negative consequences if their wish was not realized were also given in-depth and down-to-earth consideration. Only after the wish had withstood this acid test did the students reconsider the more positive sides of their wish.

Another study by Beckmann and Gollwitzer (1987, here cited according to Gollwitzer, 1987) on an experimentally induced decision conflict, also confirmed the unbiased nature of information receiving and processing in such a decision making situation prior to intention formation. Evidence for such a self-critical, reality-oriented approach to such important decision making conflicts in the phase prior to intention formation can also be found in studies performed in conjunction with the investigation of quite different questions, such as the study by Marcia and associates on identity develop-ment in adolescents (Marcia, 1980). Young people having difficulty in deciding on a particular profession who got into a real identity crisis over this decision used all avail-able sources of information and weighed all the different aspects with great care. One could even say it is exactly the continuous reality orientation and lack of bias that may produce a problem in the long run in such cases of motivational conflicts. Such con-tinuous motivational conflicts may prevent the formation of a dominant intention, in this case, the formation of clear identity goals (Gollwitzer, 1987). This may result in conflictual intentions with the consequence that none of the intentions is effectively realized. The intentions then remain constantly activated and impede each other.

Therapist: I must admit that I have some difficulties with the concept of reality orien-tation. It makes sense to me to refer to the processes on the right side of the Rubicon as realization-oriented, however, I doubt that the most important distinguishing property of the processes right and left of the Rubicon should be that of reality orientation. Heckhausen talks about the process of choice and I believe this represents only a small portion of the intra-psychological processes left of the Rubicon. On the left bank of the Rubicon landscape we are faced with wishes and fears that need not even be conscious and reality orientation is definitely not among their striking properties.

Psychologist: This distinction was a central focus for Heckhausen and I have only summarized him here. Perhaps we could find a more suitable characterization of the processes to the left of the Rubicon for ourselves. I can then leave out reality orienta-tion for now.

If wishes are not transformed into intentions, goals and actions, or if they cross the Rubicon with only a low volitional strength, they remain unsatisfied. The volitional strength results from the product of **desirability** and perceived **realizability**.

The realizability component can be therapeutically influenced by manipulating the expectancy. Since expectations are based on the interpretation of the actual situation, all improvements to the prevailing life situation, that is actual changes in the behavior of interaction partners, actual changes in work conditions etc., contribute to changes in expectations as well and it is these changes in the real life situation that can change expectations particularly effectively. This explains the positive effects of therapies not so much focused on changing something in the patient's mind, but in the conditions of his actual everyday life. When, in the course of family therapy, familial interactions actually change, the expectations of all family members and their experiences and behaviors, including, of course, those of the "identified" patient are all influenced. A patient's expectations can also be changed by extending his actual behavioral repertoire, as is the goal of social skills training for instance. Changing expectations is then not just a purely cognitive matter. More positive expectations, that is a better appraisal of the realizability of intentions, lead to a higher volitional strength and thereby to a more efficient realizability of intentions, and ultimately to a greater fulfillment of wishes or satisfaction of needs.

Therapist: The connection between the realizability expectation and the satisfaction of needs seems important to me. If I am successful in improving the patient's realizability expectation in therapy, I can then contribute to a greater satisfaction of needs. Intentions are based on the person's needs, and increased satisfaction of needs will most likely find its expression in an improved well-being. So ultimately, improved realizability expectations should also manifest themselves in improved well-being.

Psychologist: Your conclusion appears consistent with my previous statements. These functional relations are not what I immediately had in mind, but these are basically a logical consequence from the assumptions of the Rubicon model.

The **desirability component** depends on the one hand, upon the wishes and fears flowing into the process of weighing and choosing, and on the other hand, upon the very process of weighing alone. The Rubicon model does not tell us where the wishes and fears stem from. Their existence is just presumed and herein lies a weakness if we wish to apply the model to therapeutic problems. What we can do, however, is extend the model to the left by means of a concept specifying how a certain individual has exactly these wishes and fears; a concept that specifies which determinants actually exert an influence on their development. Therapeutic influencing of these determinants should then also change the wishes and fears. As a result, the variables significant for the process of choice would be changed, leading to different intentions and volitional strengths as a result of the process of choice, and this in turn would manifest itself in changed behavior.

Therapist: That we have no clue as to where the wishes and fears emanate from is indeed a shortcoming for the application of the model in psychotherapy. I think we must complete the model ourselves, otherwise we will not get any further as far as the processes on the left bank of the Rubicon are concerned.

Psychologist: Agreed. Later we will have to delve deeply into the question of motivations (second dialogue, part 3). Once there, we will have to go beyond the Rubicon model. For now, however, let us stay with the model and see how far we get.

If no formation of clear intentional goals is achieved, it may be attributable to an inefficient process of weighing and choosing or to a particular conflictual constellation of wishes and fears worked on in this process. Both can be therapeutically influenced. I imagine this to be the kind of influence that constitutes the special approach of psychodynamic and humanistic therapies which distinguishes them from cognitive behaviorial therapies. Both of you probably know more than I do about how such influences on the process of weighing and choosing, as well as on the constellation of wishes, fears and conflicts, can be implemented in practice. Perhaps one of you can try later to pick up this thread and run with it but I can conclude:

If a therapy is successful in exerting a positive influence on both of these motivational components, i.e. the content component, the constellation of wishes and fears, and on the process-component, the process of weighing and choosing, then one should expect far reaching effects on all subsequent processes in the action phase model and thereby also on the patient's behavior and well-being. Ultimately, these effects do not necessarily differ very much from those achieved by therapeutic work on the right bank of the Rubicon. While the working mechanisms of the different therapies and the processes initiated thereby, might be very different, the end result might not. At the most, the outcome would reveal some traces of the various processes which led to these end results. Would that not be a solution to the so-called "equivalence paradox" (Stiles, Shapiro & Elliott, 1986) you referred to earlier? Would this not truly explain the fact that, when comparing different therapies, there are consistently more pronounced differences in the therapeutic approaches and processes than in therapeutic outcome, where there are fewer differences than one should actually expect given such different procedures?

Therapy researcher: I like that. This can be very nicely combined with what I said about the different mechanisms of clarification- and mastery-oriented therapies. The Rubicon model is really quite well suited for that.

Therapist: I find this model astonishingly inspiring. All sorts of references to my therapeutic practice spring to mind. I can actually find equivalencies in my therapy practice for all phases of the Rubicon model, including its expansion towards the explanation of wishes and fears. I have a strong urge to think this through in peace and quiet for myself, and to reflect on my own work with regard to this perspective, but that will have to wait. Now I would like to pick up one of the threads you left for us and try to take it somewhere.

I am tempted to go all the way to the very left edge of the motivation of landscape left of the Rubicon laid out by you, to where wishes and fears emerge. I believe this is presently territory mostly covered by psychoanalysis. It is perhaps no coincidence that in Heckhausen's original Rubicon model wishes and fears are simply presumed to exist, and that scientific examination begins with the process of choosing. It still has something of the old "sterile," academic psychology about it, which we, as therapists, can do so little about, even if I must admit that the image of man implied by this model is still more appealing to me than that conveyed to me during my psychology studies. After all, man can now reflect and want, be conscious of himself, act deliberately, or unconsciously pursue certain intentions. All those are definitely qualities required by us as a basis for our therapeutic work. This is why only a kind of scientific psychology is acceptable as a basis for psychotherapy that is able to give an account of these qualities of mental life which goes beyond common sense.

I find the Rubicon model offers many of these qualities. What I still miss is an elaborated conception of what the most important human motives are, how they develop, how they can come into conflict with each other and how they are connected with the emotions. My mentioning this here is no coincidence because the qualities of mental life we just talked about are exactly the ones given priority in psychodynamic and humanistic therapies. In order to explain their mechanisms, we will have to go more deeply into the motivational-emotional aspects of mental life. Most pressing, it seems to me, is that we come up with ideas as to how those factors constituting the process of choice, namely the wishes and fears, can be altered through psychotherapy.

Therapy researcher: Please excuse my interrupting you but from what you just said I imagine that our occupying ourselves with wishes and fears will lead us far beyond the original Rubicon model. I do, however, have another question which I would like to address before we go on and that is on the model itself concerning the phase from the process of choice to the formation of goal intentions.

Therapist: Of course, we can always return to the wishes and fears later. It's no problem for me to postpone what I wanted to say. We could focus on the process of choice for now as this was an issue I wanted to address anyway.

Therapy researcher: The Rubicon model is in fact an action **phase** model, that is, a process model. Is it truly realistic that this process has to be run through completely for each action? Do superordinated goal intentions have to be regenerated anew every time? Is it realistic to assume that in the action process every volitional step is preceded by a reality-oriented process of choice? Isn't it rather that everyday actions are marked by a continuous bias in that they are consistently directed towards the realization of long-term existing superordinated goal intentions? It was you who mentioned the example of the working mother. The action plans and their realization which she is ultimately concerned with are, in fact, based on long-term fixations and not on constantly changing new decisions.

Apart from that, it appears doubtful to me that there is always only one intention being pursued at a given moment. I might agree with the assumption that conscious action control is mostly dedicated to one goal at a time, although in well established routine actions even that seems doubtful to me. I definitely do not share the opinion that individuals can essentially only pursue one intention at a time. Particularly in psychotherapy, I think, we frequently deal with the fact that individuals pursue several intentions simultaneously, which are actually incompatible with one another and impede each other's realization; we are speaking of conflicts. It is typical, however, that such contradictory intentions are very often not consciously experienced as conflicts. It would then seem correct when psychodynamic therapists speak of unconscious conflicts and accredit a crucial role to their processing and resolution for achieving successful therapy outcomes.

Therapist: Hearing such words from you is rather surprising. How can you, as a therapy researcher, talk about unconscious conflicts? I thought the unconscious does not exist for you at all. Isn't the possibility of operationalizing and measuring of the theoretical constructs you work with of utmost importance for you? How then would you measure the unconscious?

Therapy researcher: Whether it makes sense to talk of "the" unconscious remains open for discussion. I take it for granted that the majority of psychological processes happen unconsciously. In my eyes no one can seriously question that we must assume many psychological processes to be happening simultaneously, and why should all these processes be completely matched with one another and serve the same goal? That is rather unlikely. In any case, if this were so, one would have to explain how this could be achieved; and this may not be any simpler than explaining how conflicts come into being. For me it seems more adequate to put the question the other way around: Which distinct functions does the consciousness have for the mental process? This is a question I would very much like to discuss in greater detail with both of you.

Most likely you probably meant rather the measurement of unconscious motivational conflicts, as measuring unconscious processes is not fundamentally a problem at all, a large part of the psychology of perception is concerned with that. Methods for the measurement of unconscious conflicts have also been developed in psychotherapy research over the last two decades. A whole volume of the journal "Psychotherapy Research" was recently dedicated to the description of such methods (Luborsky & Barber, 1994). You must consider that of all the empirically-oriented therapy researchers from all over the world who are affiliated with the Society for Psychotherapy Research the majority have a psychodynamic background and have taken psychodynamic assumptions as the basis for their research work. We have been seeing an increase in methodically challenging research activity for quite some time now. Unfortunately, not much about these methods and their findings (see for example Dahl, Kächele & Thomä, 1988; Henry et al., 1994) is known in the world of therapy practice. Understandably, therapy training institutes are not incorporating these results into their curriculum because if they were to draw the suggested consequences from these research findings they would be unable to continue on as they have. You already made reference to these deplorable conditions in our opening round. I do not think we should get too caught up in this right now.

I think it would be better to remain disciplined and stick for now with the Rubicon model. Later on we can return to all the other topics and I would be very happy if you could address the two questions I brought up for you first.

Psychologist: Both of your questions are legitimate, but they must be further clarified so that my previous thoughts are not misunderstood. Maybe we let Heckhausen himself speak to us on that topic. His own assessment of the Rubicon model within psychology will then become much clearer.

"Desires. This breeding ground of restlessness, has so far been barely researched in psychology. We have no idea, how many wishes emerge, wilt, and eventually die out each day throughout the various phases of life, but above all, how some of them ripen to bear fruit. Freud's dictum (1915) according to which every wish remains active in mental life until it is fulfilled, seems questionable. So many wishes could hardly be hosted and held in storage for such a length of time. ...

"Wishing is not enough. Many wishes remain platonic because we consider their fulfillment—justifiably or not—as something not within our own power. But there is a remainder—from the flow of wishes a small trickle is left over—which not only appears worth fulfilling but actually fulfillable. This introduces a different state of mind where careful consideration is given in order to choose. There are three reasons why we must choose. First, many more wishes than we could ever handle are still left over. Second, many wishes are competing with each other; you cannot eat the cake and also hold on to it. Third, and most importantly, the actual desirability and also the realizability of a wish must be critically evaluated. Many a wish does not survive such scrutiny. The process of choosing will then result in abandoning the attempt to realize this wish. ...

After all choices have been examined, even more wishes fall by the wayside. For others, the choice leads to indecision. They are stored somewhere and can be picked up and reexamined some other time. Perhaps those are the ones that Freud (1915) referred to as remaining effective until fulfilled. We speculate that one could also have too many wishes stored and then be disturbed by those in the process of choosing and willing. This remains to be clarified. At any rate, one wish or the other is eventually left over, waiting to be realized now, or when the right occasion presents itself. With the transition from choosing to willing, another state of mind is reached. ...

Wishing—Choosing—Willing. After all this, some might think that people are more or less constantly so occupied with these three things that they tumble from one state of mind to the other. Nothing would be more wrong! Anyhow, choosing and decision making are rather rare processes. Sometimes days pass by before something like that happens in a person's mental life. ... Our existence could not be maintained with wishing, choosing and willing alone. They are only the upper most thin layer on top of a series of basal motivation systems that have established themselves over millions of years and have situated themselves hierarchically on top of each other (Buck, 1984). But they remain the upper most level, the pinnacle of the hierarchy. ...

On the lowest level there is a set of automatic reactions of the autonomous nervous system, of the endocrine and the immune system. On top of that we find pre-established patterns of movement for specific innate behaviors. On top of that there are primary drives, leveling out the disturbances in the body's equilibrium. And on top of that, learned needs have formed, derived from primary drives, but which have become independent. And again, on top of that, are located all the primary affects, such as happiness, sadness, fear, anger, surprise, and disgust as part of our experience. Although physiologically anchored deep in the brain, they relate to the entire internal and external world of impressions and experiences, or can even be conditioned. Additionally, we are accompanied by a constant striving to be efficacious in our close environment. And only on top of all this our higher motives, the social and cultural ones emerge, from which the majority of our wishes originate, when the systems at the lower levels are not too much occupied with the elimination of homeostatic crises of our organism. And finally these wishes are sometimes followed by some choosing and some willing" (Heckhausen, 1987 a, pp. 3—8).

1.14   Psychotherapy as a Process of Motivational Clarification for the Formation of Clear Intentions

The previous passages demonstrate that Heckhausen views the conscious weighing and choosing between different wishes and action possibilities and conscious decision making as rather rare psychological processes. Most of the time a person is occupied with the realization of action plans as a result of goal intentions that have existed for quite some time and that he is not aware of as goals at the moment of action. The consciousness is rather focused on the concrete conditions of the when, where and how under which the realization of intentions must be planned and executed. By far the greatest part of psychological processes is in fact realization-oriented in the service of superordinated identity goals which are pursued in an automated mode of perception, information processing and action regulation. One does not have to consciously scan the environment for opportunities to realize action plans according to these goals, one perceives such occasions automatically and utilizes one's action repertoire for the realization accordingly, similar to driving a car in order to get somewhere.

Heckhausen does not make any explicit statements on the simultaneous pursuit of several intentions in his action phase model. I have some ideas on that which go far beyond the Rubicon model. In my view an appropriate conception for the fact that so many goal-oriented processes are simultaneously happening in a person, and how this is possible, is virtually the key to understanding human mental life. Heckhausen gave a few examples of these processes at the end of the previously quoted text.

The Rubicon model offers no explicit ideas on that. Nonetheless, the assumption that the simultaneous pursuit of several intentions is the rule rather than the exception, certainly appears to be compatible with the model. Basically, a person can implement the action plan to drive to a specific location with his car and at the same time pursue the intention to portray himself as a considerate driver to one passenger and impress another one with sophisticated remarks. According to the logic of the Rubicon model each action plan would have certain volitional strengths that result from the combination of its desirability and realizability. Many action plans can be simultaneously realized this way. The more extensive a person's goal intentions have become and the more differentiated his behavior repertoire, the more a simultaneous realization of several action plans will be the rule.

When the intentions are in conflict with one another, it becomes more complicated. Even then one can still attempt to simultaneously realize both or all. The behavior, however, may no longer be unambiguous, leading to a situation in which the realization of all intentions will suffer and none will be very satisfactorily realized. In such situations it would be necessary to leave the automated mode of intention realization and to get over to the left bank of the Rubicon to reflect upon the situation in a reality-oriented manner, to weigh the different conflict components against one another in order to arrive at a conscious decision. This would result in a new constellation of intentions with newly distributed volitional strengths. The newly formed dominant intention acquired through the process of weighing and choosing has to be protected against competing intentions in subsequent situations. These are above all the consciously "discarded" intentions previously involved in the conflict. Concrete action plans have to be decided upon and a new sort of perception and behavior will have to be practiced.

All this does not necessarily have anything to do with therapy, it belongs to normal life. What I mean is that psychotherapy offers an institutionalized setting for developing an awareness about oneself and about what one does, how one does it and why. Out of the awareness of something previously happening without awareness, new consciousness emerges. This applies to all forms of psychotherapy including those working predominantly on the right bank of the Rubicon. The volitional and action control processes for the realization of extant intentions, as we have seen, are given special attention in behavior therapies and other problem solving oriented therapies. In the course of the problem analysis preceding intervention, as well as during the actual intervention, the patient learns, for example, in the form of self observation tasks, to reflection his own experience and behavior from new angles. While trying to change his behavior, he gains new insights about himself. All these interventions are geared towards the change of volitional and action control processes which previously happened largely automatically. Included in these automated processes are also cognitions accompanying, interpreting and controlling the behavior. Reflecting the attention to these realization-oriented processes creates a new consciousness. One should, therefore, not be surprised if patients undergoing behavior therapy also have the feeling that they are learning to understand themselves better. In fact, they are learning to understand better how they have previously involuntarily blocked realization of their own intentions, and how to better realize them in the future.

In the case of an automated pursuit of conflictual intentions, a therapy focusing on only one of these intentions, perhaps the one closer to consciousness, and attempting to improve its realization with targeted measures, would proceed from false premises. It would work against the volitional strength—we could also say against the resistance—of the other conflicting intentions. As long as their volitional strengths remain high, the conditions for an optimal realization of the other intentions, namely an unequivocal commitment for this one intention, are not fulfilled.

This restriction does not apply to all conflict constellations. We have to assume that an agoraphobic person is also in a state defined by conflictual intentions. Her desire to move around freely stands against her fear of an uncontrollable catastrophe. The elimination of this fear through exposure therapy dissolves the conflict. The realization of one intention leads to the deactivation of the other. We have seen that apparently this works in three out of four agoraphobics, but what happens to the fourth? Maybe in that fourth person, we have a more complex, less obvious, conflict constellation and not just the obvious conflict between the desire to be able to move around freely again and the fear of an uncontrollable catastrophe. With respect to this conflict constellation, the same approach which is effective with other phobics, might have still other, more complex implications. If the existence of these other intentions—of course, I am referring here to normally unconscious intentions—is not taken into regard, then the path is not free for the realization of the intention "I wish to be able to move around freely again."

Therapy researcher: Among these possibilities naturally the latter is in line with the psychodynamic interpretation of phobias. Such a complex, non-obvious conflict constellation is assumed for all phobias. The apparent efficacy of successful exposure therapies, according to all research studies, is not always so easily accepted for what it is: essentially a manifestation of long-term improvement or elimination of the agoraphobic symptoms. The prediction of symptom substitution has not been confirmed. In the meantime, there are so many careful clinical descriptions indicating that the effects achieved by exposure therapies are long lasting that holding on to the concept of symptom substitution under these circumstances would represent a complete denial of these clinical experiences. This of course also calls into question all those psychoanalytic assumptions on which the prediction of symptom substitution was based.

This is not to say that unconscious conflict constellations do not play any role in agoraphobias. Perhaps they play a crucial role in the twenty-five percent who do not respond to exposure therapy. Maybe they even play a role in a larger segment of agoraphobics, but then we would have to give a reasonable account of the effects exposure therapy has on such an unconscious conflict constellation, and why it causes positive changes in some patients and not in others. We also still have to explain how a markedly non-realization-oriented approach, such as client centered therapy, can achieve almost equally strong symptomatic changes as realization-oriented behavior therapy. Earlier you speculated that it might be that such therapies, which are directed towards better understanding, focus on the weighing and choosing process responsible for intention formation. This would mean that these therapies would ultimately be effective because they achieve a change in intentions. I would like to follow this assumption now and try to explain why this could in fact be so.

1.15   The Process Aspect of Motivational Clarification

The proven effect of client-centered therapy for the treatment of phobias is especially well suited for demonstrating that the process of weighing and choosing prior to intention formation in the Rubicon model is a good starting point for bringing about therapeutic changes.

I wish to illustrate this with some of the essential features of the client-centered and other related humanistic approaches. As a rule, the therapist lets the patient decide what should be talked about in therapy. This assures that the issues addressed in the session are important to the patient. At some point the patient will probably begin to discuss his most urgent "current concerns" (Klinger, 1977). The therapist will, on the one hand, show his interest in a way that makes the patient feel accepted and appreciated in his concerns. On the other hand, the therapist will also add a more directing component to his response which guides the patient's attention in a certain direction. The therapist always focuses on how the patient experiences what he reports, how he evaluates it, which emotions come up while talking about it and what kinds of thoughts are going through his mind. Unlike with actions, where his attention is focused on the environment or external events, he reflects on the experiencing, appraisal, feeling, deciding and acting of the patient's self. His goal is to enhance the "processing depth" in the explication process by "offers for deeper processing" (Sachse, 1992). The patient's emotional participation is an important criterion for the depth of processing and this increases the more the patient's important goals, values, and convictions are affected (Lazarus, 1991; Greenberg, Rice & Elliott, 1993; Sachse, 1992). Emotional participation thus is great when the patient reflects on crucial goal intentions. At its higher levels, the depth of processing is defined by its reference to important "affective schemata." Goal intentions can be viewed as an essential component of such affective schemata. Table 1.1 illustrates the eight stages of depth of processing, with which the treatment method was operationalized in the studies by Sachse (1992).

Table 1.1:
The eight stages of the "depth of processing scale" according to Sachse (1992, pp. 221—225).
The description of the scale was taken from Sachse in a shortened version.

Stage 1: No recognizable processing of relevant issues

Client is not concerned with working on issues that might be relevant for him, for his problems and for resolving his problems, respectively; rather, he is addressing general knowledge (issues from his semantic memory so to speak). This is why on this level no central questions can be identified that would be aimed towards working through a problem.

Stage 2: Intellectualization

On this level, the client is focused on relevant personal issues, on aspects of his problems; hence he does not focus on general knowledge but on personally relevant issues. This is why he is closer to explication than in stage one. The way he is dealing with these issues is that he is busy searching for personal theories which might deliver explanations for his problems, while they are not really relative to his feelings.

The main question the client is concerned with is: How can I explain X? Which theories can I apply for explaining X? These questions are being processed without the client paying any attention to his emotions, this means affects and affective processing are not involved in answering these questions. This also manifests itself in the fact that a client working on this level may appear unemotional, sometimes not even concerned.

Stage 3: Report

Client reports about a problem by describing situations in which it comes up, including other persons taking part in that problem etc. He may also describe his own problematic behaviors or emotions. Basically these are descriptions of problem aspects. This is presumably where explication begins: First the problem has to be described before one can then become aware of which questions evolve from it, or which aspects of the problem still remain unclear. Deriving of questions with the goal to clarify motives and affective schemata requires first a realization of what the issue is. The client is working on the central question: What actually happened? What constitutes the actual problem?

Stage 4: Evaluation

Now the client may develop evaluations for certain issues he brought up, thereby activating affective schemata, motives, values etc. (without which he could not arrive at any evaluations). By doing so, he exceeds the mere objective reporting of the events; this processing stage is, in a way, deeper than the stage of "report" because it includes affective processing. The client does not yet consider that the assessment is based on his part in the situation due to his role, but he considers it as the attribute of an object: "X is stupid;" "Situation Y is disgusting," etc. So here the client is focusing on the central question: What is the value/non-value of an issue?

Stage 5: Personal appraisal

On this level the client gives personal appraisals that he recognizes to be his own ("I find Y stupid" etc.). This is while still concentrating very strongly on the evaluative aspects of his assessments (i.e. on the value or non-value of X).

The client pursues the central question: How do I evaluate this issue?

When concerned with his personal evaluation, the client has presumably activated affective schemata or motives which are the basis for these affective judgments. Nonetheless, his attention is still largely focused on external aspects: When asking: "How do I evaluate X?," the evaluation-triggering situation X still remains the center of his focus as well.

He has still not turned his attention inwards to his affective schemata, i.e. to their effects, so that he can represent them. Therefore, a processing level in which the triggering event still remains in the foreground is not yet a good starting point for the formation of a representational picture.

Stage 6: Personal meaning

At this point the client is concerned with the affective emotional consequences of his affective processing: with his emotions, with his moods and the so-called "felt senses" which certain situations, objects, etc. have elicited in him due to the affective processing. The client is examining the central question: Which feelings, moods or "felt senses" does the issue cause in me? Exploring emotions, affects or felt senses is significant for a representation of schemata and motives, as only activated schemata can be represented. To be able to judge if a client is working on emotions that have emerged at that very moment (which would indicate that the respective schemata are activated) or if he reports on past emotions (meaning that the respective schemata are not activated) it sometimes does not suffice to pay attention to the content of a statement, but one has to actually *hear* it. The nature or quality of the client's voice allows us to draw some conclusions as to whether or not an emotion is present .

Stage 7: Explication of relevant meaning-structures/formation of representations

On this level the client attends to the affective schemata and motives relevant for the respective emotion and is working towards their representation, their becoming conscious, etc. This level thus refers to the essential process aspect of the explication: to the formation of representations. The client is exploring the central question: What makes me feel this way regarding this issue?

Stage 8: Integration

Integration refers to processes which emerge after (or already during) the formation of a representation: The client recognizes the interrelatedness among the meaning of this schema and other things he knows about himself; he may realize that he processes situation X in the same fashion as situations Y and Z; that his way of processing has already played a role in the past, or the like. He may acquire an awareness that the assumptions underlying this processing can no longer be held on to. He is, therefore, examining the central question: Do I find in me any links between the newly represented meaning or other meaningful aspects? Or to which changes do the new representations lead?

Sachse has found a strong link between the so-defined depth of processing of the explication process and therapeutic success in client-centered therapies. The achievement of a high processing depth on the side of the patient does not happen by itself but is largely dependent on the therapist's behavior. A deepening of the depth of processing can be facilitated by appropriate statements from the therapist that stimulate the patient to work more deeply, but superficial statements can also prevent this. The therapeutic outcome benefits most when the therapist relates to the core of what the patient wanted to express and when he simultaneously stimulates the patient with his answer to explore this more deeply, and if the patient is sensitive to the therapeutic offers, by reacting to it with a deepening of his processing.

A positive therapeutic outcome in client-centered therapy can therefore be achieved if the patient reflects extensively on the inner context of his most important intentions which determine his present life situation; not in an intellectual-rational fashion, but rather in a way where he identifies with his intentions. This is apparent in that he experiences the appropriate feelings belonging to those intentions. At the highest levels of this experiencing process (Gendlin, 1961), self exploration process (Tausch & Tausch, 1971) or explication process (Sachse, 1992), the intense feelings which accompany the motivational clarification process are expected to gradually turn into a growing clarity and confidence.

The highest stages of this process are described by Greenberg, Rice & Elliott (1993):
"7. Although still experientially involved, (client) is able to stand back and examine own mode of functioning in the context of own needs, wants, fears, values, shoulds, and   personal qualities.
8. Broadens the exploration and reexamines own mode of functioning in other situations.

Resolution: New awareness and understanding of important aspects of own mode of functioning in a way that restructures the issue. There is a new awareness of what he/she wants to change, and the sense of having the power to make the changes" (p. 147).

This last paragraph describing the final goal of the clarification process fits well with the Rubicon model. The patient is supposed to develop an awareness of the intentions he had so far. They are to be placed into a new perspective and the patient is supposed to develop a new awareness of what he wants to and can change from this new perspective. This brings us back to volitions and the concept of volitional strength, and there we are again, on the right bank of the Rubicon.

Greenberg, Rice and Elliott (1993) summarize therapeutic procedures aiming at such a clarification process under the heading of "process-experiential-approach"—in this they consider themselves to be the successors of Rogers and Perls—and emphasize that it is the process and its qualities that are important rather than establishing certain answers that the therapist already knows. Here they see an essential difference from the psychodynamic approach, which requires that the patient reaches specific insights. This is why in the psychodynamic approach the content of interpretations is ascribed such an important role. They are supposed to help the patient arrive at the necessary insights.

By now the "process-experiential-approach" has been clearly further developed beyond classical client-centered and Gestalt therapy as far as the technique is concerned. Greenberg, Rice and Elliott detail various techniques which all aim at enhancing the clarification process. For example, the "two chair dialogue" is recommended to illuminate all sides of a motivational conflict. This technique has the patient switching chairs representing the different conflict components and bringing them into a clarifying dialogue with each other. The effects of individual techniques such as these has been empirically investigated (Greenberg, 1986). The books by Greenberg, Rice and Elliott (1993) and by Sachse (1996) provide an excellent overview of the possibilities developed within this approach to directly enhance motivational processing.

These advanced developments of the classical humanistic approaches are conceptually based largely on the same fundamentals as many of the newer cognitive-behavioral approaches (Goldfried and Robins, 1983; Safran & Segal, 1990). They all see psychotherapy as a change of schemata which, although somewhat differently specified,   essentially refer to the same. The scientific studies and the authors they refer to are also largely congruent. In light of this common foundation, the differences in the therapeutic consequences drawn from these foundations are somewhat surprising. These consequences seem to have more to do with the approach the authors originally come from than with the scientific foundation they refer to today. Without this explanation it is difficult to understand that one group of authors still settles down on the left bank of the Rubicon and the others only on the right side. The schema-theoretical foundation should actually facilitate or at least suggest that the same therapist, often even within the same therapy, crosses the Rubicon time and again in order to support his patients where their problem situation requires it the most. As early as 1986, Grawe presented a schema-theoretical conception, largely congruent with the above mentioned authors, with the explicit goal to fill the gap—in our terminology the Rubicon—which until then had separated the worlds of clarification-oriented and mastery-oriented therapies. Since we intend to explore the possibilities of a psychologically founded psychotherapy, we will have to return to the schema-theoretical approach at a later point (sections 2.28-2.32). Many results produced by psychology in the meantime are concentrated in the schema-construct (Läderach & Verdun, 1995).

However, I do not wish to interrupt my chain of thought and would rather go more deeply into the content aspect of the above described motivational clarification process. The process-experiential-approach by Greenberg, Rice and Elliott (1993) is explicitly not a disorder-specific approach as were Roger's client-centered approach and Perls' Gestalt therapy. Although in today's client-centered therapy there are developments in the direction of a disorder-specific differentiation (Teusch & Finke, 1993, 1995), it is empirically proven that a motivational clarification process can achieve distinct improvements in symptoms and well-being even without a disorder-specific format (Grawe, 1976; Grawe, Donati & Bernauer, 1994; Greenberg, Elliott & Lietaer, 1994). This makes sense as the procedure is not directed towards the disorder-specific symptomatology. This is a significant distinguishing feature in contrast to cognitive-behavioral therapies such as exposure therapy. So far I know of no studies proving that motivational processing achieves better outcomes when it is specifically geared towards the patient's symptomatology. The above mentioned approaches would still have to demonstrate that.

What would actually be more plausible is tailoring the clarification process towards what should be directly changed by it, such as the special characteristics of the patient's functioning that prevent the formation of clear intentions with respect to the patient's most important needs. Exactly such specification can be found in the work of Greenberg, Rice and Elliott (1993). They describe six different techniques to help the patient when the exploration of clear emotional meanings—in the language of the authors, that is the goal of the process-experiential-approach—is being obstructed by specific problems. Examples for this are the technique of "experiential focusing" for the problem of "unclear felt sense" or the technique of "empty chair work" for dealing with "unfinished business."

Much more widespread in psychotherapy is an emphasis on the content of the motivational conflict components. This is the everyday life for the psychodynamic therapies, the second big camp that has erected their tents on the left bank of the Rubicon. You mentioned earlier that the examination of wishes and fears and the conflicts between them is largely the domain of the psychodynamic approaches. I interrupted you at this point in order to talk first about the process aspect of the processes left of the Rubicon. I think it is now time to yield the floor to you.

Therapist: Throughout this discussion you have addressed many issues I also wanted to talk about, even if from a different perspective of course. For instance, in describing the motivational clarification process I would have put a stronger emphasis on psychodynamic aspects, after all motivational clarification takes place particularly in psychodynamic therapies. Their concepts even more explicitly suggest a clarification of the motives underlying the patient's behavior and experience. Even in long-term psychoanalysis this is generally formulated as the explicit goal. However, the shorter the planned duration of therapy the more this goal is limited to those parts of motivational functioning that appear to be specifically relevant for the patient's problems, up to the point of "focal therapy," in which the therapist focuses only on working on a central conflict. I have so internalized this thinking in terms of conflicts so much that I automatically apply it in my therapeutic practice.

Although on the one hand confusing, it might also have been useful for me to be so clearly shown that evidently a clarification of motivational conflicts is also possible without making any pre-assumptions about the content of the conflicts. I never saw this so clearly, although I do apply many of the above mentioned procedures. However, I always have some preconceived ideas about the nature of the conflicts of my patients in the back of my head, which do not emerge just in the sessions, but which I have already carried into therapy.

After what you said about motivational clarification it might seem as though all these pre-existing assumptions about conflict dynamics, which stem in part from psychoanalytic theory and in part from the wealth of therapeutic experience accumulated over decades, are essentially unnecessary excess baggage. If this were actually the case then the psychoanalytic approach would lose its foundation because its most important tools, the work on transference, resistance analysis, and the method of interpretation, all presume the therapist's clear understanding of the patient's conflict dynamics. So I ask myself whether so many therapists could have been collectively wrong for so long. It is difficult for me to believe that especially since in my own work I develop an understanding in which the conflict dynamic just about always plays a functional role in each case. I do not want to exclude the possibility right from the outset that so many therapists, including myself, could have been collectively wrong, but in light of the far-reaching consequences I by no means want to draw premature conclusions on this topic.

I feel somewhat flooded by the many facts and concepts we have discussed so far and at this point I would like to take stock and look back on how far we have come in our explanation of the mechanisms of psychotherapy. I think, this might lead to a better assessment of where any still unanswered questions lie, and whether there might still be a need for explicit considerations and conceptions of motivational conflicts within an overall concept of psychotherapy.

Therapy researcher: I find an intermediate stock taking to be an excellent idea.

Psychologist: Me too, I am interested to know where you think our discussion has taken us a step further with respect to your initial questions. You are probably in the best position to judge whether our understanding of the mechanisms of psychotherapy developed so far is useful for the therapeutic practice.

Part 3: Working Mechanisms of Psychotherapy

1.16 The Working Mechanism of Intention Realization

Therapist: So at this point I will attempt to take stock of our discussion as far as I see it. Both new and surprising for me was just how far one can get when viewing therapeutic problems under **expectancy-value-aspects**. The **concept of expectancy** was known to me as part of the social learning theories, especially the concept of self-efficacy expectation by Bandura (1977 a, 1982), but I always felt that it was locking an appropriate acknowledgment of the motivational component. However, this deficit can be remedied with the concept of intention realization via goal setting, plan development and action control and evaluating the action results with respect to the retroactive effect they have on intentions. It appears to me that the therapist's simultaneous observation of **realizability** and **desirability** for the analysis and modification of behavior is a very practicable and useful rule of thumb in practice.

The distinction between post-intentional **realization orientation** and pre-intentional **reality orientation** is also very useful and it will help me to orient myself in the future towards what the issues are or should be in therapy. The concept of **intention realization** seems largely congruent with Grawe's working mechanism of **mastery**, but it has more far-reaching implications because it can be used not only in relation to problems, but for other applications as well. Behavior therapies appear to me by and large as realization-oriented. They assist the patient in realizing particular intentions. After having taken a closer look at the Rubicon model, I find that I actually like the term "**intention realizing procedure**" better than "mastery-oriented procedure." At any rate, it is obvious to me that realization-oriented support is one of the most important tasks for therapists and "**intention realization**" one of the most crucial working mechanisms of psychotherapy.

Our discussion has made it more or less clear what this mechanism comprises in terms of therapeutic possibilities. For one thing, there are different possibilities which may influence the patient's **expectations**. The concept of **response expectation** for involuntary behavior was less familiar to me than that of **self-efficacy expectation** for voluntary behavior. That also explains why I was less clear than I am now about the significance of the **self-fulfilling function of expectations** for the explanation of psychological disorders in the negative sense, and for the explanation of improvements in the positive sense. Now I am much more aware that a therapist must principally take into consideration which implications this has or might have on the patient's expectations in everything he does, because these expectations in turn may have a very real positive or negative influence on everything else in the course of therapy.

I am also more aware that the **changes in expectations** have to be regarded both as a **general** and **disorder-specific working mechanism**. With anxieties, this disorder-specific significance is without question quite obvious. But it appears to me that response expectancy in depression may have quite a similar disorder-specific function as in phobias (Kirsch, 1990), and this possibly also holds for more psychological disorders. I definitely underestimated the significance of the **induction of expectations for improvements** as a **general therapeutic working mechanism**. I was surprised just how many phenomena can be explained by this and I think it would be great if this knowledge and the consciousness evolving from it, along with the necessary know-how, could be imparted to all therapists.

At the same time, the Rubicon model makes one realize that the realization of intentions requires more than just the installation and modification of expectations. Willing also requires **capability** and the existence of **possibilities**. Those unaccustomed to approaching problems in an **action-oriented** fashion will likely lack many of the capabilities that Kuhl defined as important properties of effective **volition processes**. A problem solving-oriented procedure, therefore, not only serves the achievement of a certain goal, but it can also be viewed as a sort of training of volitional and other action-relevant skills, which may generally benefit the realization of the patient's intentions in the future. In addition, a new consciousness will develop in the patient in that over the course of these processes, his attention is directed towards new aspects of his experience and behavior.

Therapeutic procedures geared towards intention realization can without doubt have impacts which go far beyond improving the patient's capacity for coping with a certain problem, this being one of the reasons why far-reaching changes have often been demonstrated for such procedures even in areas apart from the problems for which the patient is seeking therapy. "**Intention realization**"—I will use this term from here on alternately with the term "mastery" introduced by Grawe—appears to me as an unusually powerful working mechanism of psychotherapy. Concurrently, this term refers also to one of the most crucial, but also one of the most complex therapeutic tasks. The realization of this working mechanism requires first a differentiated general know-how with respect to the establishment of expectations, the enhancement of volitional processes and the formation of necessary sub-capacities, and second, an even more multifaceted disorder-specific knowledge and know-how. Learning all this knowledge and training in all these skills alone can make up a large portion of a therapist's training.

I like that in the Rubicon model the concept of volitional strength is conceived of as the product of **realizability** and **desirability**. Internalizing this link should actually make one forever immune to a one-sided realization-oriented, or a one-sided motivation-oriented procedure. I also liked how you demonstrated that therapeutic work on one side of the Rubicon also has effects on the other side. The decrease in fears over the course of a realization-oriented procedure, for instance, in the course of a successful exposure therapy, leads to a changed constellation of motives on the left bank of the Rubicon which creates new choices, thereby allowing more space for strengthening other intentions or forming new ones. This explains why in the course of such therapies there are often far-reaching changes in experience and behavior beyond a pure decrease in symptomatology.

1.17 The Working Mechanism of Intention Modification

Inversely, it has also become more clear to me why a purely clarification-oriented therapy, such as client-centered therapy, may lead to similarly far-reaching symptomatic and behavioral changes as behavior therapies. If, regardless of the many possibilities in his life situation, an individual is very dissatisfied or overly controlled by an objectively unjustified fear such as agoraphobia, one can say—in the language of the Rubicon model—that he has not developed intentions with sufficiently high volitional strength for the fulfillment of his actual wishes. According to the Rubicon model this situation is preceded by a process of choosing from among a variety of wishes and fears. Because the process of choice has led to an outcome which allows no optimal realization of wishes, it makes sense to repeat this process, so to speak, in order to obtain an awareness of the various decisions, assumptions and motives which led to the choice to reflect them in terms of how sound they are and to revise some of the decisions possibly unconsciously made at an earlier point. It has to be either the process itself or the premises that went into it, i.e. the patient's wishes, fears, assumptions, etc., or all of these jointly, which have to be responsible for the patient not arriving at a clear—in terms of the patient's wishes—"biased" intention formation. In clarification-oriented therapy, such as client-centered therapy, or the process-experiential-approach, therapists focus on both possibilities and work on these. The patient's attention is always directed back towards the process of choice itself and the premises going into it (emotions, wishes, fears, convictions, etc.). That way these are repeatedly weighed and checked out from all possible angles and perhaps revised, and the choice process itself almost always takes place in a different way and much more consciously than the one underlying the previous intentions.

So, first something procedural gets changed, namely in the process of weighing and choosing. This not only leads to a change of balance for the currently treated constellation of motives, but the patient may additionally acquire new procedural capabilities he will be able to apply in a different situation at a later point. The acquisition of new procedural action-oriented capabilities as part of the intention realization I talked about earlier, which is supported by the therapist with suitable advice and interventions, is analogous to this.

Furthermore, different choices and decisions due to the changed process are likely to emerge, resulting in a new pattern of intentions and volitional strengths.

In my opinion, given all that, one can only be in agreement with Grawe's conclusion that there has to be a second working mechanism which achieves its effects in a fundamentally different way in addition to the principle of mastery. He termed this working mechanism "**motivational clarification**." This definition focuses on the process. In the context of our discussion we could also define this working mechanism as "**intention modification**" in contrast to intention realization. This definition entails more than just motivational clarification because intention modification can also be produced by means other than motivational clarification (sections 1.23, 3.8, 3.10, 3.13), but it does include the latter. This working mechanism has its own functional laws and requires its own know-how distinguishing itself markedly from that necessary for intention realization. Let us put off the question of what sort of know-how is optimally required for that, and which role the knowledge of motivational conflict dynamics plays for now. What is certain, however, is that a therapist should be able to lead the patient through a **motivational clarification** process and to assist him with suitable interventions, such as those described by Sachse (1992, 1996) or by Greenberg, Rice and Elliott (1993) so that this clarification **process** happens differently than the process of choice previously underlying the intentions.

For many patients the result of such a clarification process—a new constellation of intentions—will suffice so that from then on they will have the capability to independently realize their intentions. Just as persons not in need of therapy, they form concrete plans in the service of their changed intentions and transform these into appropriate actions. The realization of their intentions makes them more satisfied and improves their feeling of well-being, etc. Even in an agoraphobic patient, bythrough the development of appropriate volitional strengths for such intentions as: "I want to be able to move around freely again, I wish to be independent, I would like to be in control of myself," the firm resolution can grow to expose herself to the feared situation and to face her own fear. From there, the subsequent process does not differ much from the one in exposure therapy and can therefore also lead to similar effects on the symptomatology. Outside of therapies it probably happens very often that people face their own fear, thereby preventing themselves from developing a phobic disorder.

We have now explained why clarification-oriented therapies may eventually produce changes quite similar to those we find in realization-oriented therapies, and vice versa why realization-oriented therapies may cause far-reaching changes in intentions and insights similar to those in clarification-oriented therapies. I find it very satisfying that we are able to explain these findings without having to allege with some common-factor-approach or with the problematic assumption that these therapies ultimately do the same thing under a different name or different disguise. Our discussion has really convinced me that all these effects really can be brought about in quite different ways.

Therapy researcher: I would like to emphatically underline this last point again. I have already come up with some evidence for these findings, but I can add even more to it. Earlier you assumed that following successful clarification work even patients that are treated with just a clarification-oriented approach can eventually accomplish intention realization and problem solving. This assumption is indeed correct and there is direct evidence for that.

In a study by Grawe (1996) three different therapy conditions were compared, an explicitly clarification-oriented procedure ("heuristic psychotherapy"), a more mastery-oriented procedure ("interactional behavior therapy"), and a therapy condition combining both mastery and clarification-oriented procedures ("general psychotherapy"). All three therapy conditions were based on a plan- or schema-theoretical foundation, respectively. The patients in each therapy condition were presented with a therapy session report at the end of every therapy session in which they were asked to assess whether or not they had significant clarification or mastery experiences during the session. Figure 1.4 illustrates one of the central results of the study.

The figure shows the course of the assessments for those items of the therapy session report referring to "positive mastery experiences." The columns represent the first, second and third therapy phase of each therapy (the duration of the therapies varied within and between the treatment conditions).

As expected, patients undergoing realization-oriented therapy reported more positive mastery experiences than did those undergoing clarification-oriented therapy. This was especially true in the first two-thirds of therapy. After a sufficiently long therapy duration—the clarification-oriented therapies lasted on average 49 sessions, notably longer than the other therapeutic conditions—an increasing amount of intention realization was indeed accomplished in clarification-oriented therapies as well. This is exactly what we could expect according to the previous analysis. If therapy limits itself to clarification-oriented interventions, it can take awhile before the appropriate conditions are established for realizing those intentions that have become more clear through therapy.

However, the most persuasive confirmation of what we had so far theorized is contained in the findings for the third therapy condition. In this type of therapy the therapists were specially trained in and concentrated on using a combination of clarification- and mastery-oriented interventions individually tailored to the patient's problems and the state of the therapy. This represents an approximation of what Grawe has termed "general psychotherapy" (Grawe, 1995). Although the therapists in this condition on average were less experienced, this treatment condition was clearly assessed by the patients as the most successful in all aspects of the therapy process (for comprehensive details, see Grawe, 1996). The patients undergoing this therapy clearly made the most positive mastery experiences overall. According to our previous ideas this may be explained by the fact that the therapists using this approach were the ones who most consequently matched their procedure with their patients' needs, instead of proceeding with mastery- or clarification-oriented methods regardless of the conditions on the side of the patient.

Therapist: I think the Rubicon model helps us to understand the relation between Grawe's two working mechanisms of clarification and mastery more clearly. For me they no longer stand unconnected next to each other, but refer to two phases in the development of actions, that is to say, two phases of **one** process. Mastery/realization requires clarification and clarification without realization does not lead to wish fulfillment. I feel this is a true gain in knowledge, especially since I can now relate additional concepts, such as expectations, desirability, intentions, and many more to this process on a more finely tuned basis.

Psychologist: You have repeatedly referred to Grawe's four working mechanisms. However, in our taking stock we have only acknowledged two of those so far. What's happening with the other two working mechanisms? Can they also be integrated into our view?

1.18   The Working Mechanism of Process Activation

Therapist: **Problem actuation** has good possibilities. All the approaches discussed so far place maximal value on the patient's **immediate experience**. In exposure therapy, the patient is required to expose himself to his fear; he must put himself into the situation; he himself has to reach the decisions and live up to them in his own actions. The patient goes through a change in that he acts differently, even if these actions oftentimes do not manifest themselves until outside the realm of therapy.

The immediate experience is equally important for the clarification process. Attention is focused on whatever is going on in the patient at the time, not on external events, but on what the patient is perceiving, thinking, feeling, and what he is eager to do or avoid. When there is too much talking going on without arriving at the "felt senses," the therapist may resort to measures such as the empty chair or split chair technique in order to enhance the immediate experience of what is talked about. When merely talking, it is important to promote emotional participation, making reference to the patient's own values and intentions. Attention is also directed to the processing itself, to the individual "modes of processing" (Sachse, 1996), that is how the patient deals with the issues he experiences.

In psychodynamic therapies the immediate experiencing plays a very crucial double-role in transference work and resistance analysis. The therapist concurrently uses and enhances what is happening at the very moment by addressing and interpreting it.

Underlying all these procedures is the assumption that only what is happening processually can be changed: the fear of fear, the impulse to avoid certain behaviors, the inclination to look away in uncomfortable situations, the concern about what the other person (the therapist, for instance) might do; all these problem behaviors and experiences can only be modified while evolving in a certain situation, because change happens when different experiences and behaviors are taking place in these situations instead. Change manifests itself in the current experience and behavior. Talking about experiencing and behavior without either of these processes actually going on can be useful for preparing the ground for change, but the change itself materializes in the moment of the actual experiencing.

This assumption is substantiated by many research findings. In process-outcome-studies different aspects of processual activation have time and again turned out to be crucial for the therapeutic outcome (Orlinsky, Grawe & Parks, 1994), and in experimental outcome research all those procedures which explicitly promote the immediate experiencing in the treatment of the problems did particularly well (Grawe, Donati & Bernauer, 1994).

With the designation "**problem actuation**," Grawe places special emphasis upon the therapist's task as well as on the fact that what therapy is all about, is largely the modification of problems. One might as well call this modification principle **the principle of immediate experience** or **process activation**, thereby focusing more on what is happening in the patient as well as making allowances for the fact that processual activation is equally important for the modification of non-problematic behaviors.

Processual activation is not an end in of itself. It has positive therapeutic significance only in conjunction with the realization or modification of intentions. Consequently, this principle of change has a different logical function than the two working mechanisms previously discussed. These have their own innate value. Processual activation is an important property of effective therapeutic changes and has an important functional significance for them, but its function for the actual therapeutic goal is one that is less direct. It has a mediating function for the realization and clarification processes. Clarification and realization processes joined with processual actuation are what Alexander (1950; Alexander & French, 1946) termed "**corrective emotional experience**." Along the lines we are following, one could say that therapeutic changes are largely based on corrective emotional experiences, or even that they consist of those. Alexander's working mechanism of corrective emotional experience is even more an abstraction of what is happening in therapy than Grawe's. It comprises three of Grawe's four working mechanisms. This theoretical construct fits nicely with the mechanisms of psychotherapy delineated by us, but without a conceptual elaboration on a more experiential level a working mechanism formulated at such a high level of abstraction may be not defined concretely enough to be helpful for therapeutic practice.

It is remarkable that all important therapeutic approaches agree that the processual activation of the problems to be modified has great significance for therapeutic success in light of the, otherwise large, differences between the various therapeutic approaches. Processual activation of experience and behavior represents a rich and promising technology with many possibilities which is what makes it a very challenging therapeutic task as well and all these possibilities can only be utilized by transcending the limitations of the single therapeutic approaches. Based on this processual activation has a

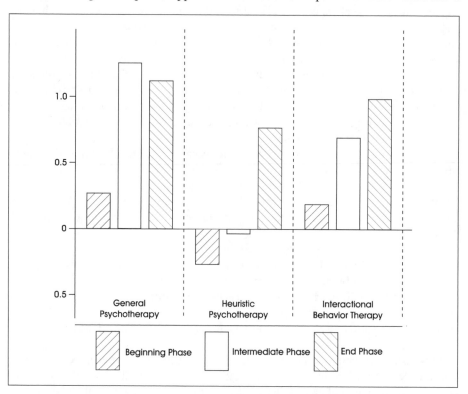

Figure 1.4:
Positive mastery experiences in the course of therapy for three different types of therapy (General Psychotherapy, Heuristic Psychotherapy, Interactional Behavior Therapy). The columns are based on the patients' self-assessments in a therapy session report filled out directly following each therapy session. This report contains, among other items, four items related to the patients' positive mastery experiences. These four items were averaged. The values on the ordinate (y axis) show the extent of affirmation and negation (positive and negative values) of positive mastery experiences. For each type of therapy, the assessments over four therapy sessions from each phase were averaged.
The figure is based on the numbers reported in Grawe (1996, p.66).

good chance to be recognized by all as a general therapeutic working mechanism. This concept surely seems to deserve an established place in a psychologically founded psychotherapy.

Psychologist: It appears this way to me as well. I still have something to say about this concept. The emphasis on "processual" only makes sense if one sets it off from something else, such as "content related." Such a differentiation for instance would be relevant for the question of conscious or unconscious processes or for the differentiation between nonverbal and digital communication (Watzlawick, Beavin & Jackson, 1969). I suppose I should postpone these references for when we get into these topics in more detail later. Given our plan, it is quite obvious to me that this will be necessary.

1.19 The Working Mechanism of Resource Activation

Therapy researcher: I am also afraid that would lead us too far afield right now. Seeing as how we have already looked at three of Grawe's four working mechanisms, I think we should now also turn to the fourth, that of resource activation. True, I already mentioned this particular working mechanism earlier in conjunction with expectancy induction, however, that was before you introduced the Rubicon model to us which has greatly influenced the ensuing course of our discussion. Considering all these newly forthcoming aspects, the working mechanism of resource activation presents itself as follows:

Targeted resource activation requires adopting a resource perspective. It is almost commonplace to say that one can regard everything from a positive and a negative side, from a **resource perspective** and from a **problem perspective**. For psychotherapy this statement though is not necessarily for granted, because there, traditionally, almost everything is regarded from a problem perspective. To understand a patient's problems, assuming a problem perspective is natural, necessary and appropriate. By believing, however, that the **modification** of problems can also be conceived from this same perspective, is to be on the wrong track. For achieving changes, too much of a problem perspective has the effect of lead weights on your legs. Where should the strength and the means for change come from if not from what the patient already brings with him, from the intentions and possibilities he or his life situation already contains? Wanting to bring about change from a problem perspective, is proceeding from a fundamental misconception, namely that it is the therapist who changes the patient. In reality, however, during a successful therapy, it is the patient who accomplishes the changes through interaction with a supportive therapist who is giving the patient the impulses to do so. An important requirement for positive therapy outcome is that the patient feels self-responsible for changing, this is supported by a large number of empirical findings (Orlinsky, Grawe & Parks, 1994; Schulte, 1996).

If one looks at the patient's situation from a problem perspective, identifies and analyzes what it is that he cannot do, he is not ready to do, what he fears, what he avoids, what he has not accomplished, which possibilities he has not developed, what is not going well in his life, which constraints he is under, and what he is dissatisfied with; then what is supposed to be the motor powering the vehicle of his change? Seen from this perspective, it is exactly the present experience and behavior which contribute to sustaining his problems. How should this very behavior lead to his improvement? This appears illogical. When the patient first has to change this behavior, before any improvements can take place, who is to effect this change, the therapist? How should the therapist manage to achieve that the patient no longer behaves so problematically? Where should he or she start? Should the therapist maybe simply instruct the patient to no longer behave this way, but differently? Certainly, he has heard all this before.

Even if the therapist, with such simple instructions, could bring the patient to change his behavior, what would be the reason? At the minimum, we would have to assume that the patient is willing to accept and follow the therapist's advice and instructions. Consequently, there has to be something outside of what we saw from a problem perspective in the patient that is important for change, something that is not problematic, but something that can be seen as helpful for change, as a resource.

In every person's life there is more than just one particular aspect, such as the willingness to follow advice, which can be seen as a positive resource. It is merely a question of how you view it. Looking at a person's life situation, and a patient's as well, we can focus our attention on the individual's positive sides and potentials, what he has already achieved, what works well for him, what strengths he may have, what interests motivate him, what he likes and likes to do, which other persons are committed to him, what amiable sides he has, which experiences he can refer to, and what he has gone through etc. Many of these resources can simultaneously represent potential resources for the process of change.

The therapist may pay attention to these resources during his conversations and his dealings with the patient, and by addressing them give the patient the chance to present himself from this side so that these resources can be brought into play for therapeutic purposes. This will have the effect that the patient does not see himself reduced to his problematic sides, but views himself also as perceived and reflected in his positive sides. Through this, he will feel himself upgraded as he may realize some of his identity goals in therapy. This may counteract his lack of courage and his demoralization. He feels better without having done anything for his change and sees himself understood by the therapist in a way that does not leave him with a weakened self-esteem. Both of these factors improve conditions for the ensuing course of therapy. Together with the induction of expectation for improvements, this form of explicit reference to and processual activation of positive resources is well suited to trigger and enhance a positive feedback process such as I described earlier in my attempt to explain the mechanism of expectancy induction.

The patient's resources, however, can still be activated and utilized for therapeutic purposes in an even more specific fashion. They can be ascribed either to the desirability or realizability component of the action phase model by Heckhausen.

Extant intentions of the patient may be used to enhance desirability of all those behaviors required for certain therapeutic steps. The therapist must constantly be aware of the fact that these steps can be accomplished with the desired volitional strength only if they represent the realization of the patient's own intention, that is to say if they emerge as a result of existing and sufficiently strong intentions. One cannot conclude by the simple fact that a patient has enrolled in therapy, that she supplies sufficiently strong intentions for all that is required of someone in order to achieve a desirable therapeutic goal. Very often a link between such new steps and pre-existing intentions must be worked out in therapy first. When it is not obvious for a patient just for which intentions she should accomplish, a step regarded as necessary by the therapist, the step will most likely not be accomplished. This is why an activation of intentions crucial to accomplishing certain steps is quite an important task for the therapist. At any rate, their existence cannot just be presumed, the therapist must try to activate, strengthen and promote them.

The desirability of behaviors beneficial to therapy can also be enhanced by the weakening of competing intentions. Earlier you gave an example for that in the concept of the formation of a complementary relationship. The complementary relationship deactivates intentions that would otherwise impede therapy, and attempts to address and promote those intentions advantageous for therapy. A patient's wishes to do something for the therapist, in order not to look bad in front of him, also count as intentions that can be used as resources. Even contrary intentions can be regarded as resources for the initiation of changes, such as the wish, for example, to prove to the therapist that he is not right. Through paradoxical instructions, such intentions can be utilized to bring about the opposite of what the therapist prescribes or predicts for the patient.

Other resources can be attributed to the realizability component. Included therein are first the capabilities and habits of the patients. The therapeutic procedure should be designed so that the patient gets to utilize his capabilities and habitual behaviors. Additional resources would then be, for instance, therapy-conformed expectations of the patient, possibilities offered by the patient's life situation and chances for support by close significant others etc. A therapist who appears credible and competent will also be able to increase for his patient the perceived realizability of those steps that are crucial in reaching the therapeutic goal. To make the therapeutic relationship a resource for the patient is one of the most noble tasks facing the therapist. A good therapeutic relationship affects the motivational component and the realizability component for therapy-oriented behavior in general and, by the same token, represents one of the most crucial forms of mobilization of the patient's existing resources.

Resource activation can happen in a way that is related to the **content** or to **the process**. Content-related means that the motivational or potential resources are directly addressed. This increases not only the patient's self-esteem but in addition this has the general positive effects I mentioned earlier. Yet even more important is the processual resource activation, i.e. the possibility that the patient in therapy can behave according to his positive intentions and abilities and can use these to approach his problems.

The problem perspective determines what is to be changed, the resource perspective determines how it is to be changed. A therapist reflecting on what should be changed about the patient is taking the problem perspective. If, however, he is reflecting on the way in which he, together with the patient, should approach the problems, then he should make this predominantly dependent on the resources the patient brought with him into therapy. This is when the resource perspective has more to offer. "**Problem perspective for the content aspect of therapy** (what should be changed?), **resource perspective for the process aspect** (how can it best be changed?)," this is how one could summarize these thoughts into a compact rule of thumb.

With the resource perspective being so important for the **how** of the change, one may wonder how so little attention has been given to this perspective in psychotherapy so far. I know of a large number of different methods of problem analysis, but not of a single method of resource analysis, the appropriate training is just not to be found within most therapy training programs. Why is such a crucial perspective for therapy planning and for therapeutic success neglected? In my opinion, it is due to the fact that in a predominantly method-oriented psychotherapy the question of how changes are to be brought about is in fact already predetermined by a method. Where there is already an answer, no question need be posed. I suppose that for a long time, therapists have not posed the question of patients' resources in a systematic fashion because, depending on the answers to this question, they logically would have had to adjust their procedures. This would have required giving up a predetermined procedure. This is where I see the empirically well substantiated significance resource activation has for therapeutic outcome offering a strong argument for an indication-oriented general psychotherapy. The how of the change has to be determined by the conditions on the side of the patient and not by the therapist's presumptions and preferences.

1.20   Working Mechanisms Instead of Therapeutic Methods

Therapist: Have I understood you correctly in that the question of indication has to be predominantly viewed and answered from a resource perspective? This would mean not the problems, but rather the resources the patient brings along for the process of change should determine how the therapist proceeds?

Therapy researcher: No, this would be like throwing the baby out with the bath water. Of course, the type of problem is important for the type of treatment. This is a logical conclusion from our previous thoughts. For instance, via problem analysis one has to determine, whether we are dealing with a realization problem or a motivational problem, or both. A motivational problem is present when intentionwise, the conditions are not given for the therapy to be directed towards the realization of a clear intention. In such a case, the therapeutic procedure would by all means have to have a distinct emphasis on intention-change. As we previously pointed out, the question of clarification or realization is seldom a question of either/or, but in therapy often both would be appropriate. If after careful consideration it is decided that the therapy should have a emphasis on realization, then the kind of problem or disorder plays a crucial role for the ensuing indication. As a result of the disorder-specific research performed over the last two decades, a more or less comprehensive experiential knowledge about the individual dynamics of the specific disorder exists for almost all psychological disorders (Fiedler, 1997; Margraf, 1996; Reinecker, 1994 a). A therapist should have knowledge of these empirically based findings and make use of them for diagnosis, therapy planning and implementation (Schulte 1996). The therapist should know what to be especially aware of in regard to a specific disorder, and which procedures are well established for it. This was quite clearly demonstrated by the example of agoraphobia. At any rate, this disorder-specific knowledge should be integrated into diagnosis and treatment planning. This does not mean that the exact treatment procedure is established beforehand. What is meant so that the treatment will also have a disorder-specific component. Additional considerations with respect to the resource perspective are important: Given these resources, how can the therapeutic goals delineated as important from the problem perspective, best be brought about in the patient?

So, actually considerations from both the problem perspective and the resource perspective are used for diagnosis and treatment planning. I specifically emphasized the resource aspect because so far therapy planning has tended to be one-sided, relying solely on problem analysis (Bartling et al., 1992; Tuschen, 1996; Hollen, 1996; Bohus, 1996), while resource analysis is neglected. This is already expressed by the term "problem analysis." Therapy planning (Schulte, 1996), however, requires a problem **and** a resource analysis.

All our contemplation leads to the fact that one cannot conceive indication solely as the selection of "the" right therapy method. Instead it has to be conceived of as an initial, and still temporary step towards composing an optimal treatment for a specific patient, followed successively by many more composing steps over the course of therapy planning. According to this view, therapy is not played according to a score, but is rather a continuous improvisation (Caspar & Grawe, 1992, 1996).

Therapist: This agrees well with my own opinion and with what I actually do in my daily practice. I almost feel like a musician in our conversation, like one who has long improvised, but for whom some crucial improvisational principles have just now become clear. Many of these principles I have been applying in a de facto sort of fashion, much the way someone is able to speak a language without being conscious of its grammatical rules. Perhaps a clearer knowledge of these principles will help me to better improvise in the future, but with this analogy one question emerge: Might it not be necessary to learn how to play according to the score so that we can better improvise later?

Therapy researcher: If by that you mean a therapist must first learn how to be methodically oriented in therapy in order to later proceed more freely, my answer would be no. Acquiring therapy skills and methods from manuals may quite possibly be a way to learn the therapeutic craft. It can give an inexperienced therapist some security. But focusing on the manual should not keep the therapist from paying attention to forming a therapeutic relationship, to activating resources and to considering problem aspects other than those considered in the manual. A manual-guided procedure should make up only a part of the entire therapy. The therapist should also remain open to the other perspectives relevant for therapy.

My opinion is, one can also learn therapy by becoming immediately somewhat familiar with the wider terrain and all of its paths. From the very beginning, one can acquire the principles and learn the different possibilities for their implementation, rather than methods. With the help of therapists serving as models, one can learn to implement these principles very well. By being given the opportunity to observe positive therapist models and view how they implement the same working mechanisms in many different ways, one learns to see the invariant features in the multitude of concrete procedures These are therapeutic rules that can, depending on the conditions, be implemented flexibly and with wide variety.

Both role playing and conducting a therapeutic method according to a therapy manual can be used to train such variations. At the beginning of their careers therapists can already learn to conceptualize their patient's situation under the perspectives detailed here and to design an appropriate treatment plan which considers all the working mechanisms we have discussed (Grawe et al., 1996). Of course, realizing these working mechanisms must first become routine and years may pass before one would be in the situation of exhausting the full range of possibilities. Yet in my view, given the appropriate training, doing therapy on the basis of a clear knowledge of the working mechanism of effective therapy is better for the patient than a manual-guided and method-oriented therapy, because the latter is always at risk of not really accounting for all of the patient's crucial characteristics and the full complexity of his problems (Grawe, 1997 b). But to date there is still an absence of training programs in which one learns from the beginning to work towards a patient-oriented general psychotherapy.

Therapist: This brings us to questions of therapeutic training. On the one hand, this is good, as it signals that we have come quite a ways in understanding the mechanisms of psychotherapy. On the other hand, I find this a bit too fast, as we have at least postponed one aspect many therapists find important, namely the question of whether psychotherapy can indeed work without a detailed concept for motivational conflicts and their role in psychological functioning and in the therapeutic process. I think it is about time to finally address this question.

Part 4: Psychotherapy From the Conflict Perspective

1.21 The Therapeutic Relevance of Motivational Conflicts

This time I would like to start by myself. Thus far, we have essentially affirmed the significance of motivational conflicts as possible causes of problems relevant to psychotherapy. Solving such conflicts with the goal of forming clear intentions for the patient's most important wishes is the general goal of clarification-oriented therapeutic procedures.

However, we were not quite sure how important it is whether or not the therapist himself has a clear understanding of such conflicts. In speaking about the working mechanism of motivational clarification, the examples you chose were therapies not requiring an explicit understanding on the part of the therapist, such as client-centered therapy and the process-experiential-approach. At first glance, the efficacy of these clarification-oriented procedures seems to prove that an explicit conflict understanding on the part of the therapist is unnecessary. Yet I would like to call this into question.

The fact that it is possible to successfully perform therapy without an understanding of the conflict dynamics—to the left as well as to the right of the Rubicon—does not imply that all psychodynamic assumptions about specific conflict constellations and conflict dynamics must be wrong. Nor does it imply that based on these assumptions one would not be able to bring about changes in the motivation landscape left of the Rubicon, i.e. changes that may be different and may go beyond the processes discussed by us. If we were to take what we have thus far delineated on the mechanisms of psychotherapy too far, one might arrive at the conclusion that the whole psychodynamic psychotherapy approach may be superfluous. I think we cannot leave it at that and this point must be explicitly discussed.

Therapy researcher: I agree. After all, the relative majority of psychotherapists remains psychodynamically oriented and that is reason enough to engage in an in-depth discussion of the most important assumptions of this approach.

The emphasis of the psychodynamic approach lies in motivational clarification using transference work, dream analysis, resistance analysis and interpretation as its most important tools. The process of clarification, with regard to the processual level, is distinctly different from the one which evidently leads to positive therapeutic effects in client-centered therapy and in the process-experiential-approach.

We had ascribed the effect of client-centered therapy to a very specific kind of clarification process and emphasized the processual aspect of that particular method. The therapist focuses his attention on the **process** and not on the content.

The psychodynamic therapist focuses his attention on the process in a different way, but also on the meaning of the content. Even what happens processually, such as transference reactions or resistance behavior, is interpreted with respect to the content. The

content of the insights worked on is what is important and not just the simple fact that clear intentions were accomplished. The insights should be "right." They should adequately address what has unconsciously happened in the patient so far. The criterion for the correctness of the insights is in each case the therapist's level of knowledge with respect to his patient's conflict dynamics. The insights should place the patient in a position to be able to more consciously control his truly existing impulses, anxieties, and defense mechanisms in the future.

This ambition differs from that held by humanistic clarification-oriented therapists. Psychodynamic therapy requires that, **prior to** the patient, the therapist comes to a clear understanding of the patient's conflict dynamics so that he may assist him in reaching the correct insights at the appropriate points in the therapeutic process. A therapist thinks in terms of the content and processes the information attained by therapy from content-related aspects. For psychodynamic therapy, therefore, an individual case understanding is indispensable, and the core of each case conception is the understanding of the conflict dynamics assumed to be underlying the patient's problems.

As long as they stick strictly to psychodynamic principles, psychodynamic therapists are bad behavior therapists and bad client-centered therapists alike, because they refrain from doing, or at least do to a lesser extent and less professionally, that which leads to a positive therapeutic outcome in these therapies according to our discussions so far. Instead they do something else and whatever that is, it also seems able to bring about therapeutic changes (Sloane et al., 1975; Grawe, Donati & Bernauer, 1994). They direct the therapeutic process from content-related aspects with the goal that the patient gains clearity about certain motives.

According to these considerations, one should assume the therapeutic effects resulting from psychodynamic and client-centered therapies to be qualitatively different from each other, although both are clarification-oriented therapies. Actual evidence for this can be found (Biermann-Ratjen & Eckert, 1985; Stuhr, 1997).

Even more important for our thoughts however are indications that content-related clarification work can also lead to significant therapeutic changes, in contrast to clarification work in client-centered psychotherapy and the process-experiential-approach.

This question was thoroughly researched for the 42 psychoanalytic therapies included in the "Menninger study" (Wallerstein, 1986, 1989), the most in-depth study of psychoanalytic long-term therapies so far. According to assessments by psychoanalytic experts, no significant insights with respect to the most important unconscious conflicts took place at all in 25% of these therapies. That means the direct treatment goal was not reached, and also, there were no other significant therapeutic changes registered in these cases. In another 25% of the therapies significant insights were reached, and the expected positive improvements were brought about as a result. These 50% confirm the significance that correct insights have for therapeutic changes. In 5% of the therapies significant insights were achieved but this did not amount to any significant improvements. These therapies indicate that bringing about correct insights is not always a sufficient condition for a good therapeutic outcome. In 45% of the therapies positive changes were recorded, seemingly unrelated to the achievement of insights. Rather, the authors ascribed theses changes to the influence of "supportive factors." These 45% indicate that the achievement of insights even in psychoanalytic therapies which are solely focused on that is not the only working mechanism. In light of our previous reflections on therapeutic working mechanisms, such a result cannot come as a surprise to us. These working mechanisms even come into play when not intentionally implemented by the therapist. Their positive influence, however, could be much greater if they were implemented systematically and in a competent fashion. Most likely this study imparts a realistic picture of the therapeutic significance of appropriate insights related to contents. They are one possible way to bring about therapeutic changes, but they are by no means the only nor most important, not even in therapies entirely focused on bringing about such insights. In other psychodynamic therapies as well, besides psychoanalytic long-term therapies, the actual changes are to a large extent attributable to working mechanisms other than those associated with achieving appropriate insights with respect to the most crucial conflicts.

There is more empirical evidence substantiating the significance of content-oriented clarification work in psychotherapies. Interpretations, the most important intervention available as part of content-oriented clarification work, whenever researched, have mostly proven to be beneficial for a positive outcome in therapy (Orlinsky, Grawe & Parks, 1994). This finding is quite well supported as it is based on twenty-four significant correlations found between interpretations and therapeutic outcome in various statistical group investigations.

Studies which directly address questions of the precision or correctness of interpretations of content are even more appropriate for our question about the importance a content-related understanding of the patient's psychodynamics has for therapeutic intervention. The first empirical study on this was done by Silberschatz, Fretter and Curtis (1986). With one of the methods for conflict measurement presently available, the plan formulation approach, the most important conflict components of three patients studied in a single case analysis were defined with remarkably high agreement among the assessors. Based on videotapes of the therapy sessions, the individual interpretations of the therapists, who at the time of therapy were unaware of these conflict formulations which had not been established until afterwards, were then assessed as to how well they agreed with the plan and conflict formulations developed by an independent team of experts. It turned out that "accurate" interpretations led to a deepening of the therapy process, non-accurate interpretations, however, did not. The deepening of the therapy process was measured with the experiencing scale by Gendlin (1961).

This pioneering study was followed by two more investigating a similar research question with a different method of conflict measurement using a larger sample of psychoanalytic therapies. Using the "Core Conflict Relationship Theme (CCRT)" method by Luborsky (1977), Crits-Cristoph, Cooper and Luborsky (1988), elaborated psychodynamic case conceptions for 43 patients, who on average had undergone a psychodynamic treatment of 53 sessions. Then independent experts evaluated for each therapy how far the intea:rpretations by therapists in two relatively early therapy sessions agreed with this case conception. The quality of the agreement correlated significantly with the therapeutic outcome.

In a follow-up study, using a similar methodology, Crits-Cristoph, Barber and Kurcias (1993) found that the agreement of therapeutic interpretations with an independently developed case conception via CCRT in an early phase of therapy correlated significantly with the quality of the therapeutic relationship in the late phases of these therapies. The "accuracy" of the interpretations thus has a favorable effect on the therapeutic relationship as well as on the quality of the ensuing therapeutic work and the result-ant outcome.

For transference interpretations the quality, not the quantity, was found to correlate significantly with the therapeutic outcome (Crits-Cristoph, 1997). However, though statistically significant the correlations are not very high. They indicate a moderate significance of the content accuracy of transference interpretations.

Thus, there are empirical findings which could be interpreted as an argument in favor of the usefulness of clarification work which is well supported contentwise, based on an appropriate case conception. Yet, definitive answers to the question of the mean-ing of content accuracy of insights and interpretations cannot be expected until there are experimental studies in which exactly this aspect can to be varied in a controlled way.

1.22   On the Relevance of Corrective Emotional Experiences Regarding Unconscious Conflicts

An appropriate understanding of the patient's conflict dynamics might even have a therapeutic relevance beyond that of the actual content-related clarification work. The previously mentioned study by Silberschatz, Fretter and Curtis (1986) on the quality of interpretations is based on the "plan-formulation-approach" (Weiss, Sampson & The Mount Zion Psychotherapy Research Group, 1986) developed by Weiss and Sampson with their colleagues at the Mt. Zion Hospital in San Francisco. This concept assumes that on the one hand, the patient comes into therapy with positive goals that serve his self-realization. On the other hand, there are fears, "pathogenic beliefs," that inhibit the achievement of the goals. In Sampson and Weiss' concept these pathogenic beliefs are frequently associated with feelings of guilt. They state that in the therapeutic relation-ship the patient will develop the desire to be accepted by the therapist according to his goals and will therefore "test" the therapist in order to see whether she can be trusted in this respect. This means that he will behave according to his fears in order to see how the therapist will react. If the therapist passes the test, responding not according to the patient's fears, but his wishes, then step by step (test by test) the fears will become debilitated, and along with that an increasingly trustful therapeutic relationship would develop (Silberschatz, 1986).

As in the study on the quality of interpretations, this assumption was empirically investigated using individual case studies (Silberschatz et al., 1988). For the patients, several "plans" i.e. conflicts with their single components were formulated. The tests expected to evolve in therapy, and how the therapist would ideally have to react in order to pass the test, were derived from this. Videotaped therapy sessions were rated as to how well the therapist, who knew nothing about this during therapy, responded to the patient's tests. As assumed, it was found that following a passed test, a deepening of the therapy process occurred, which was interpreted by the authors as an indication of the debilitation of the patient's fears.

This debilitation of fears which is taking place below the patient's consciousness level can be viewed as "**corrective emotional experience**" in accordance with Alexander

(Alexander & French 1946). The effective therapeutic action takes place on the processual level without ever being addressed as an explicit theme. True, the goal is for the patient to gain insight into his plans and conflicts, but long before that occurs the patient already behaves according to his fears and tests the therapist. Already at this early point, the therapist must be prepared for such tests by developing an appropriate understanding of the patient's most important conflicts right at the beginning of therapy.

Even if an explicit insight for a conflict is not achieved in the course of therapy, this conflict, through a debilitation of the relevant fears below the consciousness level, can also be changed in such a way that it will come to a formation of clear cut intentions in the sense of the patient's positive goals, possibly leading to far-reaching modifications in behavior. Only if the therapist has an explicit understanding of the patient's dynamics, is she able to utilize such possibilities in a consciously calculated way.

One can easily imagine that such a clear understanding of conflicts is not only helpful for tailoring the therapeutic relationship, but also for other important therapeutic decisions: Which therapy setting is best suited for a processual activation of the most important conflicts? Considering the conflicts, which meaning to the patient do the therapeutic goals and the methods that I as the therapist have in mind for this patient imply? For instance, if I consider the patient for group therapy, which impact will the members participating in this group possibly have for this patient, considering his conflicts? Is that therapeutically disadvantageous, or can I make targeted use of that? etc.

For a therapist who does not care about the conflicts of his patient all these questions do not even come to mind. Such a therapist consequently refrains from the large palette of therapeutic possibilities, risking that the therapy fails, or takes a sub-optimal course, because the therapeutic actions have meanings for the patient, which remain unconscious, not only to him but to the therapist as well.

Looking at the Rubicon model again, we now find ourselves located on the utmost left side of the left bank, where wishes and fears are evolving and passing, prior to the process of weighing and choosing, which for Heckhausen was what the left bank was all about. Heckhausen was certain that beyond this left side there must indeed be important processes taking place, but his Rubicon model with its systematic questions stops at this point. The therapeutic relevance of motivational conflicts, however, goes beyond the process of weighing and clarifying. The knowledge of a patient's conflicts can help a therapist to guide the content-related clarification work in a particular direction. We remain amidst the process of clarification with this. Yet, it may also assist the therapist in making therapeutic decisions having a direct—that is, not via a clarification process—impact on the patient's wishes and fears. With this, the initial variables for the clarification process would be changed, leading to consequences for the intention strengths and ultimately the action resulting from that.

This supports what I mentioned once earlier (section 1.17) namely the conceptualization of a working mechanism "intention change" that can be realized in various ways, by motivational clarification, by activation and deactivation of intentions (section 1.12), and by corrective emotional experiences.

Knowledge of the patient's most important conflicts is therefore not only useful for clarification-oriented therapists, but for all therapists in fact, even for those preferring to work on the right side of the Rubicon, such as the cognitive-behavioral therapists, because what happens on the utmost left side of the Rubicon landscape has an impact on all that takes place in therapy. When everything goes well and ends up well in therapy without the therapist having given any thought to the patient's conflict dynamics, the therapist can consider himself lucky in that obviously no serious motivational conflicts impeded the patient's intentions required for a successful therapeutic outcome. This seems to happen often, but not often enough to justify the general neglect of this area.

Psychologist: May I just take up that point? For a while now there has been a question on the tip of my tongue that I finally must mention. So far you have been talking about cognitive-behavioral therapies. I had the impression you emphasized more the aspects of behavior therapy than of cognitive approaches when referring to their therapeutic procedures, but what about the cognitive therapies in the narrower sense, I mean therapies along the line of Ellis (1962) or Beck (1967)? Do the "irrational beliefs" denoted by Ellis really represent something so different from the "pathogenic beliefs" from the Mt. Zion group? Do cognitive therapists not also work de facto on the goal of debilitating their patients' fears? And doesn't this actually settle them on the left bank of the Rubicon as well, similar to the psychodynamic therapists?

1.23 On the Mechanisms of Cognitive Therapies Under the Conflict Perspective

Therapy researcher: With this question you are addressing an issue which represents perhaps the secret of the outstanding effectiveness of the cognitive therapies. Cognitive therapies have been particularly well researched empirically and proven effective. This is true for the explicitly mastery-oriented therapies, such as cognitive mastery training and problem solving training which in their emphasis on cognitions differ from other forms of behavior therapy, but otherwise agree in procedure with other behavior therapy principles. This also holds true for therapies by Beck and Ellis (for the research status concerning the four kinds of cognitive-behavioral therapies mentioned see Grawe, Donati & Bernauer, 1994, pp. 402—466). Your questions are more directed to the latter two forms of therapy, which are not easy to directly locate in the Rubicon landscape. This does not mean that their mechanisms can be less well explained. If one differentiates between mastery-oriented and clarification-oriented therapies, the cognitive therapies are pretty clearly attributed to the mastery-oriented therapies. However, when differentiating between therapies aimed at intention realization versus intention modification, it becomes clear that the therapies according to Ellis and Beck not only proceed with the goal of intention realization, but that they are also specifically aimed at modifying the initial variables for the process of intention formation in that they make an attempt to debilitate the patient's fears.

In principle, the type of procedure is very similar to the problem solving approach of behavior therapy. A problem is identified in a structured fashion. In the case of cognitive therapies these are implicit assumptions underlying behavior and emotions, "irrational ideas" (Ellis), "dysfunctional beliefs" (Beck), "automated thoughts"

(Meichenbaum, 1977), which interpret events, trigger emotions, and control behavior. A goal is defined, the achievement of which will alleviate the respective problem. Those are alternative, "more rational," "more functional" thoughts that support the behavior in the sense of positive intentions. And steps towards achieving these goals are implemented. The implicit assumptions are subjected to empirical and rational scrutiny, both in the form of a dialogue, for instance in the sense of a "Socratic Dialogue," as well as in the form of tests on the level of direct experience and behavior (processual activation), in that the patient exposes himself to a situation in which his fears are actuated. The patient is given very specific instructions before being "sent into" these situations which increase the likelihood that he will make corrective experiences. That is to say, experiences which do not confirm his previous expectations. It is first and foremost these real experiences which no longer have the character of purely cognitive rational events, but are accompanied by strong emotions. The patient should especially learn—Ellis expressed this by the term "rational-emotive therapy"—how strongly his emotions depend on his implicit assumptions. So, the goal in cognitive therapies is to shake up the validity of certain implicit assumptions the patient has. Now, if instead of assumptions, we say "expectations," and instead of invalidation of those assumptions leading to problematic emotions, we speak of "corrective emotional experiences," then we are actually moving again on the familiar grounds of our previous reflections on other forms of therapy.

As far as expectations are concerned, all the various kinds of expectations that we mentioned before are explicitly addressed:

- **Outcome-expectations** with respect to what will happen if the patient does specific things. Will significant others, for instance, turn away from the patient on a long-term basis if he sometimes says no to them, puts demands on them, or articulates anger?
- **Self-efficacy expectations:** Is a challenge facing the patient really unbearable or impossible to master, or is it just a difficult situation and may be aversive, which has been mastered by him before in the past and could be mastered again, especially with reasonable preparations?
- **Reaction expectations:** Can the patient really not take it if some people turn away from him if he articulates his real feelings? Will he really feel completely alone, unloved, and worthless?

A cognitive therapist does not only argue with the patient about how rational these expectations/fears are—she lets the patient test these expectations in reality. She works towards directing the patient into making real corrective emotional experiences. She prepares the patient for these reality tests by working on acquiring and practicing alternative positive cognitions in therapy and additionally teaching the individual improved skills that appear to be crucial for the successful mastery of the respective situation.

Cognitive therapies can hardly be viewed as clarification-oriented. Working on problematic cognitions happens via systematic instruction and practice and under the therapist's direct guidance. That usually takes only a short time. The emphasis of the therapy lies on changing cognitions by rational and empirical questioning and practicing of more positive cognitions in real situations. But the cognitions we are talking about, predominantly have the character of fears, or are closely related to those. Earlier though, we settled fears way over on the left side of the Rubicon model. Along with wishes, they belong to those variables entering into the choice or clarification process, eventually leading to intentions of a certain strength. In the case of agoraphobia, we already addressed fears and the conflict between the wish to move around freely and the contrasting fear that something terrible might happen once one realizes that wish. This is an obvious conflict which is either already conscious in the patient or is quickly accepted by the patient as such. The fears worked on in cognitive therapies have a less obvious character. It is not due to problematic cognitions that patients come into therapy, but due to symptoms, such as depression, social fears, etc. The context or association to certain cognitions is created by the therapist. These oftentimes have the character of implicit assumptions and thus are not clearly conscious for the patient. In the procedures developed by Beck and Ellis, only those implicit assumptions/fears can be treated which the patient rather quickly can agree to when the therapist shows him that his behavior is controlled by these cognitions. Fears further away from consciousness would require a longer clarification-oriented therapy phase in order to become cognitively represented in the patient in such a way that the cognitive therapy approach, with its aim towards modification of such fears, could be applied.

Ultimately, cognitive therapy is also about modifying conflictual intentions. The patient's "irrational" fears inhibit wishes the therapist assesses to be appropriate, and which she wants to promote by working on and developing supporting cognitions. The existence of these positive intentions however is so taken for granted that in cognitive problem formulations one usually does not speak in terms of conflicts but only in terms of problematic assumptions representing only one side of the conflict.

We can thus say that behavior therapy, cognitive therapy, and psychodynamic therapies likewise are about changing conflictual intentions. The difference lies in the consciousness level of these intentions. Psychodynamic therapies seek to change conflictual intentions that still remain very far from consciousness, behavior therapies are aimed at those that are obvious, and cognitive therapies at those that lie in between.

1.24 On the Integrative Potential of the Cognitive Therapy Approach

What I just spoke about is true only for the cognitive therapies according to Beck and Ellis, which are both very structured and designed to be therapies of short duration. There are also cognitive therapy approaches that closely approximate those of psychodynamic therapies with respect to the consciousness level of the conflicts to be modified. Young's (1994) Cognitive Therapy for Personality Disorders focuses on the modification of maladaptive schemata acquired early in life, which control the patient's world view to such an extent that he is unable to question them, taking them instead as a given. In this cognitive therapy approach there is also an approximation to psychodynamic therapies in that the therapeutic relationship is ascribed an important function for the processual activation of the patient's problem-relevant schemata.

The cognitive therapy concept by Safran and Segal (1990) gives even stronger weight to interpersonal aspects and the therapeutic relationship. Their theoretical concept and their therapeutic procedure is directed predominantly towards a modification of interpersonal schemata. Here as well, the processual activation of the problematic schemata in the therapeutic relationship plays a functional role in the identification and change of these relational schemata.

Therapy approaches like Young's, as well as that by Safran and Segal, labeling themselves cognitive, are, as far as the understanding of mental disorders is concerned, closer to therapy concepts developed on a psychodynamic background such as those by Strupp and Binder (1984) and Luborsky (1984). They are nearly as close to these conceptions as to the concepts of Beck and Ellis. The crucial role attributed to conflictual relationship patterns is the connecting tie. The theoretical proximity to the approach by Mardi Horowitz (1988 a) is even closer. Horowitz makes an explicit attempt to link psychodynamics and cognitive psychology. Apparent similarities exist also to the interpersonal schema conception by Leonard Horowitz (1994), which also originated from psychoanalytic concepts. In both of these latter approaches disturbed "person schemas" are attributed a central role for the understanding and changing of psychological disorders.

With respect to the understanding of mental disorders and where to start with initiating therapeutic changes, the schema construct is able to bridge the theoretical gap between otherwise clearly different therapeutic approaches. However, differences in the therapeutic consequences drawn from this theoretical link remain. I already mentioned that the approaches by Greenberg, Rice and Elliott (1993) and Sachse (1992, 1996), which I cited when delineating the motivational clarification process, also call upon a schema-theoretical foundation largely overlapping with that of the aforementioned authors. The authors, however, draw different therapeutic consequences from these foundations in each case. Each of the authors adheres to the therapeutic consequences that are predetermined by his original therapeutic approach. Today we have a cognitive-behavioral consequence arising from the schema-theoretical approach (Goldfried & Robins, 1983; Safran & Segal, 1990; Young, 1994), a humanistic consequence (Greenberg, Rice & Elliott, 1993; Sachse, 1996), and a psychodynamic consequence (M. Horowitz, 1988 a; L. Horowitz, 1994). Wachtel (1997, 1980) in addition uses a schema theoretical approach in order to tie together psychoanalysis and behavior therapy.

The therapeutic approaches listed, all of which refer to a central construct of cognitive psychology, clearly indicate the different views in psychotherapy coming closer together and demonstrate the importance theoretical concepts developed in the realm of empirically oriented psychology have for that. However, they also simultaneously indicate that this alone is insufficient to budge the ingrained views found in the area of psychotherapy. Additional insight must come in that each of these therapeutic consequences is only one of the possible consequences that can be drawn from this theoretical foundation. Obviously a largely similar theoretical foundation allows several different ways for generating changes and these do not exclude, but supplement each other. Their usage beyond the limits of the traditional theoretical approaches is not just possible but is expressly called for by the totality of findings in psychotherapy research.

Without an understanding of the mechanisms of the various forms of therapy from a unifying theoretical perspective, no optimal utilization of the already overall existing therapy potential will be forthcoming. Obviously just understanding psychological functioning and the development of psychological disorders on the same theoretical foundation does not suffice. An understanding of the various possible mechanisms of psychotherapy is also required. One does not necessarily suggest the other.

It would be quite satisfying for me if we could link our understanding of the mechanisms of psychotherapy to an understanding of psychological functioning and of the emergence and perseverance of psychological disorders. I think we should attempt that in a later phase of our conversation because that is what I actually imagine a scientifically founded psychotherapy should be.

I sort of drifted away from the cognitive therapies to a more general discussion about the possibilities of a non-school-oriented psychotherapy. It is no coincidence that this happened to me while dealing with the cognitive therapies, since these appear to have the largest integrative potential from among all the therapeutic approaches. The cognitive therapy approach has been close to behavior therapy since its inception. But we have also seen that it is possible to establish a greater approximation to psychodynamic therapy approaches than, for instance, between behavior therapies and psychodynamic therapies. One example for this is the cognitive-analytic therapy by Ryle (1990). There is, however, also a tie to newer humanistic approaches via the schema construct which appears to have potential for further development.

It seems to me that a theoretical and practical integration of the various therapeutic possibilities on a cognitive-psychological basis is presently best achieved by an approach introduced by the Italian psychologists Guidano and Liotti (Guidano & Liotti, 1983, 1985; Guidano, 1988). This approach integrates behavior therapy and psychodynamic principles and procedures without adopting their theoretical constructs.

Earlier I made an attempt to demonstrate that in fact all the major therapeutic approaches discussed here deal with intentional conflicts by attempting to solve them in the direction of a more unequivocal intention, but that these conflicts are related to very different levels of consciousness. The approach by Guidano and Liotti is especially well suited for illustrating this using an example of a psychological disorder without interrupting the train of thought. It stands to reason to chose agoraphobia once again, which already served us as an example.

1.25   On the Relevance of Motivational Conflicts for Mental Disorders—Agoraphobia as an Example

The numerous successes attributed to the cognitive-behavioral treatment of agoraphobia mark the upper margin of the effectiveness achieved by today's psychotherapy. Among many other patient groups success rates lie distinctly below 75%. It is quite possible that a large portion of those patients who have not achieved a positive therapeutic outcome, undergoing various therapeutic methods, could be better helped if therapists more regularly focused on the Rubicon landscape in its entirety, from its outermost left to its right border, and utilized all the therapeutic possibilities available. In my eyes, this would be a true realization of a general psychotherapy. Guidano and Liotti's approach comes closer to this goal than most of the other approaches mentioned.

One cannot take offense at behavior therapists for being proud of their successes with agoraphobics, and that they use this as an argument. Ironically perhaps, the especially good success rates for agoraphobia have to be ascribed to the fact that behavior therapists performing exposure therapies with agoraphobics, unconsciously and unintentionally, attain something which had been advertised by therapeutic approaches which are actually quite different. I am referring to the positive influence on unconscious motivational conflicts.

The hidden insinuation naturally calls for some explanation which I would like to simultaneously use for explaining the relevance of motivational conflicts for the understanding and treatment of psychological disorders more concretely, utilizing a specific psychological disorder as an example.

In the following, I stick to a view of agoraphobia advanced by Guidano and Liotti (1983, 1985; Liotti, 1988, 1991).

Table 1.2 contains a listing of the most important agoraphobic symptoms according to Guidano and Liotti (1985, p. 126). This listing and all following data on the characteristics particular to agoraphobics are based on studies from a sample of 115 agoraphobics analyzed and treated by Guidano and Liotti.

When we look at situations agoraphobics avoid, two psychological categories stick out: They avoid "being alone" and "crowded places." For most agoraphobics this is relatively close to their consciousness. One can either immediately, or after a few therapy sessions, have an exchange with them about this.

When asking agoraphobics about the reasons for their avoidance behavior, we see that largely the fear of a terrible malady plays an important role: that something might be wrong with their heart, that alone, without anyone around, they might suffer a heart attack, that they might act crazy or go insane in public, "panic" in front of everybody, and the like. These fears usually do not hold up for very long, once the person is confronted with diagnostic findings and rational arguments.

Looking at the content of their thoughts and fears (see point three in Table 1.2), still another important and common essence to their fears emerges: "To lose control."

According to Guidano and Liotti, proceeding from theses three contents of fear: "being alone," "being confined" and "losing control", easily gained from the symptomatology, one reaches an understanding of the conflict dynamics underlying the agoraphobic symptomatology.

In conjunction with his attachment theory, Bowlby developed the hypothesis that the foundations for the development of agoraphobic symptoms as an adult are laid in childhood, specifying four pathogenic familial interaction patterns which may prepare a child for the development of agoraphobia later in life under specific interpersonal conditions (Bowlby, 1973, chapter 19). Guidano and Liotti followed the lines of these assumptions with an analysis on the life histories of their 115 agoraphobic patients. Repeatedly they detected two reemerging patterns:

Parents of children later developing agoraphobia had severely limited the autonomous discovery and scope of movement of their child outside of the family environment. Anything outside of the family environment was portrayed to the child as a somewhat dangerous place, which the child cannot cope with, and from which he or she had to be protected. Through this the child is bound to perceive him/herself, compared to other children, as less capable of dealing independently with an unfamiliar environment, as weaker and in need of protection, and the child develops a self image in accordance with this.

A second, often observed similarity to be found in the relationship history of agoraphobics is the direct or indirect threat to be alone or left alone. This can happen in very different ways: direct as a disciplinary threat, or indirect in a setting where parents fight with each other, or through emotional loss of an important care taking person due to physical absence, disease or psychological disorder.

We can assume both patterns to be associated with strong emotions. The need to discover the environment is among those innate motives, not only of humans, but also of other living beings. If this innate motive is severely limited, most likely strong negative emotions such as anger will result. Yet the context of the limitation inhibits the experience of anger, as the limitation is happening in the context of a necessary protection from danger, out of love for the child. The limitation has thus a highly ambivalent emotional context. It is equally negative and positive.

With loneliness it is similar. On the one hand, loneliness is positive: It opens up the possibility for autonomous activity, for unlimited discovery of possibilities offered by the environment. On the other hand, loneliness means being without protection in a potentially dangerous environment, to have to be self-reliant, which causes fear, because one was told that one cannot cope alone with the environment, and that one is dependent on protection. Loneliness as well has an ambivalent emotional meaning.

The logical implications of the experiences made by the child are in of themselves contradictory. This impedes a conscious reflection and representation. Through the ambivalent internalization from interaction patterns ambivalent emotional schemata develop that are not available as conscious contents, but that nevertheless have a strong impact on the experience and behavior. Interpersonal interactions are perceived with these non-conscious meanings. The child develops ever more refined strategies in order to control his environment with respect to these meanings. He exerts influence on his interaction partners in order to compensate this weakness, controlling the dangers in his environment through avoidance and precautions. Control over the external conditions becomes the tool enabling him to act in this world of contradictory meanings. Therefore, the greatest fear of the agoraphobic is to no longer be in control.

In stable conditions, he can find a somewhat functional balance in his most important interpersonal relationships through the gradually automated control strategies. However, this balance is jeopardized with every important change in the emotionally important environment. The control strategies become overchallenged, leading to anxiety attacks which the agoraphobic reacts to by again exerting control over the environment through avoidance. Guidano and Liotti have just about always found important changes in the most significant relationships prior to their patients' first anxiety attacks, when looking at their histories. In the relevant literature such changes are oftentimes described. Guidano and Liotti (1983, chapter 10) present a list of changes that can jeopardize the relationship balance and that become potential triggers for agoraphobic symptoms.

Why does exposure therapy work so well with agoraphobics, although most behavior therapists pay no attention to the described conflicts? One reason might be that agoraphobics, aside from the treatment of their fear, simultaneously make an important corrective relational experience with respect to the two previously described conflicts. They are explicitly instructed by their therapist to autonomously discover their environment and are expressly supported in this. The emotional protection and support they receive explicitly helps patients to become more autonomous. It is the opposite of restrictions. The therapist does everything so the patient feels he is able to cope with his environment on his own and that he no longer feels needy and weaker than others.

Consequently, in exposure therapy the patient makes exactly the opposite relational experiences from the ones made as a child. These new relational experiences no longer contain any ambivalence. They are unequivocal. They support the patient in his capability to be alone, autonomous, exploratory, outward reaching, and strong. They are clearly oriented towards intention realization, not towards weighing or clarifying. They are not neutral and definitely not restricting. These new relational experiences do not leave the patient alone, nor do they make him feel that he, unlike other people, would be dependent on constant protection.

Here something happens that is very similar to the corrective experiences the patient, according to the psychoanalytic concept by Sampson and Weiss, may go through when "testing" the therapist in line with his fears, and the latter passing the test. It is very likely that in the course of behavior therapy many agoraphobic patients make corrective emotional experiences at this level of unconscious conflicts, leading these conflicts to a progressive solution in the absence of any clarification process, without these conflicts having been explicitly addressed.

These new relational experiences open result in a long-term change of intentions. While deliberately implementing the working mechanism of intention realization with disorder-specific interventions, the behavior therapist has simultaneously realized the working mechanism of intention modification.

I assume that exposure therapy for agoraphobias is no exception in this respect. Instead, it is far more likely that in most therapies, the therapeutic actions have multiple meanings: meanings which the participants are consciously oriented towards, and meanings that are not conscious, but have a real effect on the patient's mental processes and exert either a positive or negative influence on the therapeutic outcome. Included in these meanings that do not become conscious are those resulting from unconscious motivational conflicts. These may well counteract the conscious actions in that they manifest themselves, for example, as "resistance" and may even cause the therapy to fail. The therapeutic procedure consciously and purposefully performed, however, may also have a very positive meaning for such unconscious conflicts, and contribute to a positive therapeutic outcome. The treatment of agoraphobia with behavior therapy might be such a case, which actually would even better explain why these therapies achieve such overall positive and long-term success.

Naturally, the symptom-oriented treatment will not dissolve the conflict in a positive fashion in all circumstances where the conflictual motivations contribute to the perpetuation of the symptomatology. Whenever the case, it would be important for the therapist to support the patient with appropriate clarification-oriented and intention modifying measures. For this, an understanding of the conflicts and their effects on the perception, feeling, thinking and acting of the patient is needed. Based on this understanding, the therapist might be able to help the patient, step by step to work on an understanding about of the motivations determining his experience and behavior so that he is able to consciously change certain parts of his life based on a clear consciousness, and additionally to expose himself to new corrective experiences even outside of therapy.

Table 1.2 :

The most important agoraphobic symptoms according to Guidano and Liotti (1985, p. 126).

1. Avoidance behavior	Leaving home, particularly alone
	Being alone in the house
	Crowded public places (movie houses, theaters, department stores, etc.)
	Public transportation (buses, subway, etc.)
	Traffic jams
	Long trips, air travel
	Sittings in barber's or beautician's chair
	Elevators, cable cars, and other closed-in, narrow places
2. Anxiety attacks	Subjective state of acute fear or panic
	Rapid heart, palpitation, precordial discomfort
	Nausea, vomiting, abdominal cramps, diarrhea, desire to urinate
	Dyspnea, feeling of choking or suffocation, hyperventilation
	Restlessness, tremulousness, muscle tension, weakness of limbs
	Paresthesia, numbness, dizziness, feelings of extreme weakness or fainting
	Perspiration, cold hands
3. Thought contents	Fantasies (particularly when the patient is forced into the avoided situations) of:
	• falling
	• losing consciousness
	• being unable to move, paralyzed
	• losing orientation in space
	• giving a pitiful display of himself or herself to bystanders
	• criticism, scorn, or indifference from onlookers toward the patient's suffering
	• going insane
	• dying
	Seeking of physical explanations for the distressing mental state
	Dependency problems
	Pessimistic views
4. Other possible disturbances	Difficulty in falling asleep
	Orgasmic dysfunction
	Theatrical or hysterical attitudes
	Depersonalization

All this could be done far more efficiently if steps towards intention realization were included rather than limiting therapy to clarification-oriented procedures. The reality content of the corrective experiences would be increased, resulting in a more efficient realization of the working mechanism of the intention modification. Therefore it is those therapists who until now have predominantly worked with intention realizing procedures who should especially benefit the most from a content-related understanding of their patients' motivational conflicts.

Guidano and Liotti treat the symptoms in agoraphobics using mastery-oriented interventions that have proven to be the most effective. At the same time, however, they attempt to motivate the patients to work on a better understanding of their motivational conflicts which serve as a breeding ground for their symptoms, and offer active clarification-oriented assistance for this if the patients are open to such an extended therapeutic goal. Such therapies typically last significantly longer than pure exposure treatments but lead to more comprehensive therapeutic successes, according to Guidano and Liotti. There are no conclusive experimental comparative treatment studies thus far available to substantiate this statement. It would be interesting to discover if with such a systematic combination of clarification-oriented work with respect to unconscious motivational conflicts and mastery-oriented treatment of the symptoms integrated by a coherent case conception one could achieve a better therapeutic outcome than with each of these procedures alone. After all we have discussed, this would make sense.

Psychologist: I think we have to be careful not to arrive at a premature conclusion. The assumptions by Guidano and Liotti seem plausible. I would like to remind you, however, that in the past there have also been views which describe agoraphobic symptoms as very often having a specific function in the partner relationship and which are thereby sustained. Yet whenever tested, this assumption could not be confirmed (Schulte, 1996). In some cases such an instrumental function may exist, but today it is not believed to be a specific characteristic of the agoraphobic disorder.

Even if conflicts, such as the ones described by Guidano and Liotti, might have originally been underlying the development of agoraphobic symptoms, that does not mean at the same time that they also have a current function in perpetuating the condition. Again, it might be the case, but would have to be verified in each individual case.

Therapy researcher: I agree with you that one has to carefully distinguish between causal and maintaining conditions with respect to psychological disorders. Yet the positive outcomes of clarification-oriented procedures in the case of agoraphobias (Grawe, 1976; Teusch, 1995) could be an indication that motivational constellations do contribute quite often to a perpetuation of agoraphobic symptoms.

Therapist: You just said that one must specifically verify whether motivational conflicts have a perpetuating function for the symptomatology. Although this makes sense to me, I ask myself what does it entail? By now we put the greatest value on the reliable diagnosis of psychological disorders with the DSM or ICD. If we wish to include motivational conflicts in our diagnosis, then one should actually be able to assess them in a somewhat reliable fashion. Are there reliable methods available for that?

1.26 Conflict Dynamics as a Task of Empirical Research

Therapy researcher: This still remains a problem even today, although numerous efforts are under way which attempt to solve this problem. It has become increasingly inappropriate to leave dealing with conflicts to particular schools of therapy. Conflicts are so important for mental health that they concern all therapies. Intra-psychic conflicts are a considerable source of stress and play a functional role in the development of many mental as well as other health problems (Emmons & King, 1988; Emmons, King & Sheldon, 1993; Lauterbach, 1990; McClelland, 1989). If that is the case, a psychotherapy oriented towards empirical research findings should pay explicit attention to intra-psychic conflicts. So far only those therapists settled on the left side of the Rubicon are doing that. The proven effectiveness clarification-oriented therapies or therapies specifically working with conflicts have for mental health, underlines the significance of motivational conflicts for psychotherapy. Clarification-oriented therapies achieve their effects by influencing psychodynamics. In addition, my previous explanations suggested that not only clarification-oriented therapies in the actual sense can exert a positive influence on motivational conflicts, but that any therapy is likely to do that, even without the participants being conscious of this.

In proportion to the relevance that motivational conflicts likely have for psychotherapy, empirical research on this is, by comparison, rather rudimentary. Conflict-specific research as intense as that which already exists in disorder-specific research is first required before we can give an empirically founded account which states that specific knowledge of the dynamics of intra-psychic conflicts is required in order to therapeutically influence these in an optimal way. I intended to demonstrate how something like that could look with the example of agoraphobia. While Guidano and Liotti have recruited all existing empirical knowledge for their conception, for now it represents only a set of plausible assumptions for which there is some preliminary evidence, but which still needs explicit verification via appropriate methods.

The example of agoraphobia in particular shows us that it really is time to base assumptions about the functional role of motivational conflicts for both psychological disorders and for psychotherapy on an empirically sound foundation. Psychoanalytic assumptions regarding this are sort of like a foray through the "supermarket" of human motives: For Fenichel (1945) and Katan (1951) agoraphobia is based on a deferred sexual temptation; according to Deutsch (1929), it is based on suppressed hostile impulses towards the mother; Weiss (1964) sees causally a regression to a developmental stage with strong unresolved desires for dependency, and Ovesey (1962) locates the core of agoraphobia in a dependence/independence conflict. Of course, we cannot continue like that, because who or what should decide who among these scientists is right or wrong?

There is only one way and that is to bring these assumptions into a form in which they can be empirically tested, and then actually testing them. This, however, is a long way off. Disorder-specific research is a good example with a similar starting point and similar processes that needed to be passed through. Development and progress in disorder-specific research were closely connected with progress in diagnostics and measurement methods. It was only the development of reliable diagnostic systems like the DSM or ICD which created the grounds allowing us to be more assured about referring to the same when talking about certain fears, depressions, etc. Only since the time that we have agreement with respect to special instruments for measuring changes in these symptoms, such as the Beck-depression scale, can we be somewhat sure we are referring to the same thing when determining a disorder has been treated with more or less success.

However, today we still do not have as fully developed instruments for specifying conflicts and for measuring their changes. A consequence of this is that we are lacking an important requirement for an appropriate operationalization of assumptions regarding conflict dynamics and their empirical investigation. The accounts given in the psychodynamic literature on this are, thus far, lacking the level of precision required for true progress in scientific knowledge. Usage of the same psychodynamic terms leaves the impression among those who use them that they are referring to the same issues.

Yet, there is absolutely no guarantee that they are really talking about the same thing. Unless these terms are precisely operationalized and the issues referred to are specified by measurements, this remains unnoticed. Anybody who has ever participated in a "rater training" and has learned how to rate complex psychological constructs such as empathy, positive regard, dominance, hostility, etc. knows exactly what I am talking about. In the beginning one might think it is obvious what is meant by the terms but if one has to assess the actual therapeutic interactions with respect to these features, it turns out that the raters assess the same processes in quite different fashions. This is as true of experts who have already used these terms for many as it is of less experienced raters. In the course of such a rater training when one experiences how the same term may be applied to totally different processes and vice-versa how differently the same process can be conceptually conceived and defined, one can be shocked about the degree of misunderstanding that must have previously taken place between people who tried to communicate via these terms. Almost more frightening than that, however, is the lack of consciousness one had for the fact that through all this time one had communicated on the basis of a "pseudo-understanding." Against such a background how are we to arrive at inter-subjectively valid statements on the dynamics of mental functioning?

I already pointed out that there is currently a change for the positive with respect to this. On the part of psychodynamically oriented therapy researchers (for instance Luborsky & Crits-Christoph, 1990; Perry, 1991; Silberschatz et al., 1988) methods have been developed in the past years for a more precise and reliable measurement of the most important conflict components: wishes, fears and defense mechanisms. In Germany an association of psychodynamically oriented therapists and researchers has attempted to develop a method called "Operationalized Psychodynamic Diagnostics" (OPD Working Group, 2001). Their goal is the construction of a similarly composed instrument for conflict diagnostics as those already existing for the diagnosis of psychological disorders, the DSM and the ICD. Such an instrument could be utilized for both research and clinical purposes. This would create a basis for the regular inclusion of conflict dynamics in therapy studies, for the formation of homogenized patient groups according to their conflict constellations and for research on therapeutic interventions specifically tailored to them etc. For now, all this remains incompletely realized but a development in that direction can easily be seen, and at the end of this development we might well have a psychotherapy that has reached a higher level overall than is the case today. Once reliable instruments exist and are employed, an actual process of scientific understanding can start. Many of the presently operationalized concepts will be seen as no longer tenable and rather unfruitful. They will be revised and replaced by others which again will be tested, etc. At any rate, eventually we will know more about the actual functional significance of conflicts for psychotherapy than we do today. And this will surely not take another hundred years to arrive at as did coming to an appropriate attempt of their operationalization since the first formulation of psychodynamic concepts on conflicts.

In academic psychology as well, methods for the quantification of conflicts were developed independently from psychodynamic assumptions (Emmons & King, 1988; Lauterbach, 1990, 1996; McReynolds, 1990; Grosse Holtforth & Grawe, 1997). The state of development of these methods begins to approach a stage at which they can also be employed for the measurement of conflict changes in the realm of psychotherapies (Lauterbach, 1996).

At the moment, this research has been concerned mostly with the development of methods and, to a lesser degree, with research on substantial questions. However, we can assume that content-related questions will soon move into the foreground. It will take some time until enough investigations will have been performed allowing us to base statements concerning conflict dynamics on solid empirical findings. Which of the assumptions made thus far about conflict dynamics will be confirmed, and which will have to be abandoned, remains an unanswered question for now. Extrapolating from other areas of psychotherapy, we must realistically assume that a great number of the psychodynamic assumptions that are regarded as valid today will have to be abandoned. Just think of the original assumptions about the working mechanisms of behavior therapy, such as the example of systematic desensitization previously mentioned. After forty years of empirical research, almost nothing of the original assumptions made by the founder (Wolpe, 1958) of this method can still be maintained.

Imagine twenty or thirty years down the line, with intensive empirical research being conducted all that time, both on the function of conflicts in mental processes and on the specification of therapeutically-relevant conflict constellations, as well as on how to effectively influence them in therapy, how likely is it that all this knowledge would be irrelevant for the planning and implementation of psychotherapies? I mean it is foreseeable that overall the quality of psychotherapeutic work will significantly increase as soon as therapists begin to base their work on well backed-up knowledge about therapeutically-relevant conflict constellations and how to effectively influence them.

I can hardly imagine that the portion of therapists who today still pay no explicit attention to intra-psychic conflict dynamics would stick to their current attitudes. The majority of cognitive behavior therapists clearly pay such little attention to their patients' conflict dynamics today because empirically founded, well described concepts are lacking. I find their lack of trust in the tenability of today's psychodynamic assumptions justifiable. The number of highly different assumptions alone is enough to make one skeptical. What is the criterion for deciding which of these assumptions should more likely be believed and which not? Which rational criterion exists for the question of whether to follow Freud, Jung, Adler, Horney, Klein, Hartmann, or Sullivan, etc.? I can only agree with anyone who thinks science should be something other than a question of the right taste. Those who find that constructs such as penis envy or castration fears do not do anything for them can still get something out of an empirically-based conception of conflictual constellations of motives and their functional role for psychotherapy.

Psychologist: I endorse both parts of what you are saying. For empirical-scientific psychologists many of the psychodynamic constructs and assumptions are unacceptable with regard to method and content. It is the extent to which all the knowledge on human mental functioning acquired by empirical psychological research is ignored that is provocative in terms of content, and the inaccuracy previously addressed for method. Unfortunately that has created a great deal of bias in psychology against everything that somehow has to do with psychodynamics. Yet a psychology without concepts on motivational conflicts cannot be a complete psychology. It excludes something without which the human being could not be understood. My understanding is that conflicts are part of the innermost nature of the human being. They definitely not only have importance for psychotherapy but for an understanding of the human being in and of himself. Conflicts do not only have a negative meaning such as we put forth in our previous discussion, but they are also absolutely indispensable for the development of a mature adult individual. I also find myself in a conflict situation right now, namely the conflict between my desire to say a great deal more about this and my concern about that leading us too far afield from what we wish to clarify at this moment. I will solve this conflict in a way demanded of me and all others a thousand times in life, that is via inhibition and putting off my spontaneous impulse in favor of later satisfaction more appropriate to the situation. I would like to ask for your agreement here that we will pick up this topic of conflicts again at a later point, when we are not so explicitly focused on the explanation of therapeutic changes.

What interests me now is how you assess the status of our discussion regarding the questions you posed in the beginning. Which of your questions have we answered satisfactorily and which not? And what new questions have possibly arisen in the meantime?

Therapist: Before I return to my initial questions, I would definitely like to bring up another question that has evolved more and more through the course of our conversation: What is the role of relationships in therapy? So far we have hardly talked about relationships. It is pretty clear though that psychotherapy is almost entirely about relationships. Can one truly understand how psychotherapy works without attaching a much more important role to relationships, more than we have done thus far?

And since we are already talking about relationships: Could we also go a little more in-depth into the mechanisms of interpersonal therapies? We have now talked about almost all major therapeutic approaches, about the cognitive-behavioral therapies, humanistic therapies, the psychodynamic therapies, even briefly touching on hypnotherapy. Among the major therapy approaches there is one still missing: the interpersonal therapies. By now, I have acquired a better understanding about the mechanisms of the therapies discussed. Something I found particularly satisfying was that their mechanisms could be explained from a uniform perspective. I am now all the more curious about whether the mechanisms of interpersonal therapies could be conceived from this same perspective.

Part 5: Psychotherapy From the Relationship Perspective

1.27 The Significance of Interpersonal Relationships for Psychotherapy

Therapy researcher: I do not feel the significance of relationships in psychotherapy has not been touched upon, but maybe I have not made this as explicit as desired. The relationship aspect is included in many issues I spoke about. That goes for the therapeutic relationship as well as for the interpersonal breeding ground for mental disorders. Perhaps together we can try to relate our previous considerations to the therapeutic relationship. The significance of interpersonal relationships for the emergence of psychological disorders is such a comprehensive topic that

I would suggest going deeper into that at a later stage in our discussions. In the realm of explaining the mechanisms of psychotherapy it would go beyond the scope of our discussion. In fact, I have not yet really attempted to explain the mechanism of interpersonal therapies. There is good reason for that. To do that I need the entire Rubicon landscape, from its left all the way to its right border. Only after our discussion about the significance of unconscious motivational conflicts are we sufficiently prepared to include the processes at the very left border of the Rubicon landscape in our explanations. But now we should be ready to use the concepts already discussed to also explain the mechanisms of interpersonal therapies. I think we should get into the therapeutic relationship next. Afterwards I will make an attempt to explain the mechanisms of interpersonal therapies with the concepts thus far developed.

Therapist: Let me attempt to apply what we have delineated thus far about the therapeutic relationship. It is actually a good test for me of how well I am able to apply the concepts developed in our discussion, to my own practice.

There is an initial and very important differentiation between what happens **processually** in the therapeutic relationship versus what is talked about regarding the **content** which seems important to me. We already emphasized the significance of processual activation for changes. Whatever is actually happening in the therapeutic relationship in the moment is processually activated by definition and is therefore highly relevant under the change aspect of change.

1.28 The Therapeutic Relationship From the Aspect of Process Activation

In normal conversations the participants' attention is largely focused on the conversational contents. In conversations during therapy, the therapist must concentrate predominantly on what is happening processually, because it is there, on the processual level, that the processes relevant for changes occur. The contents of conversation are therapeutically relevant in so far as they represent and initiate what is happening processually, or direct it in a specific direction. Consequently, they become part of the therapeutically relevant process.

Naturally the contents of the conversations can also address problem-relevant processual events outside of therapy and can help to bring about changes and to give those a certain direction. Wherever no close relationship exists between what is talked about in therapy and what is actually happening either in or outside therapy sessions, the contents are therapeutically insignificant. Conversations about psychological processes or problems that remain mere contents and are not transformed into processual events produce no changes.

The dyadic situation in the thearpy session offers the therapist an excellent opportunity to observe what is occurring processually in the patient. This diagnostic source bubbles up even more profusely, the more complex and relevant the situations the patients finds himself confronted with in therapy are for his problems. The therapist himself is part of this situational offer and in as much also part of the diagnostic repertoire. Whatever the therapist experiences in his relationship with the patient, yields important clues for how the patient relates to other people. However, the individual therapy situation represents diagnostically the least informative situation among all conceivable therapeutic settings, especially if it remains strictly limited to the therapist's office. Seeking out real situations for therapeutic purposes outside the therapist's office offers extended diagnostic possibilities. Yet more opportunities for observing what is processually activated in the patient, and intervening in the activity by interrupting or guiding, are offered if partners or family members such as father, mother or siblings are included in the therapy. This is particularly the case when dealing with interpersonal problems. Although occuring in therapy, such processes, however, are generally not viewed as belonging to the therapeutic relationship.

The distinction as to what belongs to the therapeutic relationship or not becomes even more clouded in group therapy. The group therapeutic setting is created specifically to establish or facilitate a situation in which processual activation of relationship problems can occur. But those are not relationships which belong to the patient's environment without therapy. Consequently, the manifold relationships in group therapy can be considered equivalent with the dyadic relationship in individual therapy, and therefore fall into what we generally call a therapeutic relationship. The group situation is, by comparison, considerably more complex than individual therapy, because the dyadic relationship between therapist and patient in group therapy is embedded in a complex processual relational situation.

So as not to overload my forthcoming ideas about the therapeutic relationship, I will for now stay with the simple relational situation of dyadic individual therapy. I am dragging my feet on this, as it often bothers me that in the psychotherapeutic literature the setting of individual therapy is, in a way, treated as "the" natural setting for psychotherapy, leaving group therapy, couples therapy and family therapy to appear more as exceptions or deviations from the rule. Taking as the criterion the opportunities for the realization of the working mechanisms mentioned in our discussion, it should, in fact, be the other way around because such opportunities appear to be greater in all these other settings than in that of individual therapy. It appears to me that the dominance of individual therapy in psychotherapy is largely based on the fact that it can be established much more easily and is more congruent with the patient's expectations. Our knowledge about the mechanisms of psychotherapy only rarely justifies individual therapy clearly as the setting of first choice because the potential for therapeutic effects is greater in other settings.

This is especially true from the perspective of process activation. Whenever interpersonal problems are concerned, processual activation is actually a reason for creating an enriched interpersonal environment compared to the setting of individual therapy. Yet the opportunities for processual activation are, of course, not the only aspects requiring consideration in the choice of the therapeutic setting. There may be other reasons for a therapist to work with a patient alone, or at least partially alone.

Looking at the therapeutic relationship in individual therapy, processual activation requires the therapist to always maintain an awareness of whatever occurs processually between him and the patient in the very moment. He should never let his attention be completely absorbed by the patient's story but concurrently always, or at least periodically, keep an eye on what is activated processually in the patient while telling his story, and on what is actually happening processually between him and the patient.

It seems to me that next, the distinction between **resource perspective** and **problem perspective** is important.

1.29 The Therapeutic Relationship From the Problem Perspective

Whatever occurs processually in the therapeutic relationship can always be diagnostically examined with respect to whether a problem of the patient manifests itself in it and what kind of problem this is. What the patient says can also be viewed from the **processual problem aspect**. Watzlawick, Beavin and Jackson (1969) called this the "pragmatic communication aspect." The patient may, but must not necessarily have an awareness for such problems manifesting themselves on this pragmatic level of communication.

The problem can first be a manifestation of a motivational conflict actuated by the therapeutic relationship. Such motivational conflicts have usually evolved from familial relationship patterns. You explained this earlier using the example of agoraphobia. These conflicts may later manifest themselves in similar relationship patterns with different significant others, in this case the therapist. This is known in psychoanalysis as transference. The relationship tests according to the concept of Weiss, Sampson and the Mt. Zion Psychotherapy Research Group addressed earlier by you (section 1.22), could be viewed as a special form of transference. Of course, a therapist is not a neutral individual in a relationship. Whether he or she is suited for a processual activation or transference of the specific conflictual relationship patterns of a patient largely depends on his/her own personality and individual relationship behavior. Even if a patient tends to carry certain motivational conflicts repeatedly into new relationships, the specific therapist he sees might be completely unsuitable for such "transference." The therapeutic relationship is, therefore, not a guaranteed and by no means a solely sufficient diagnostic instrument for identifying conflictual relationship patterns.

But even when problematic interaction patterns emerge in the therapeutic relationship, the reasons do not necessarily always lie in the patient's disposition for transference he or she has brought into the session. One other reason might be that the patient elicits problematic transference tendencies in the therapist. I find the term "counter-transference" commonly used for this phenomenon to be a rather unfortunate one. The term suggests that counter-transference is always a response to the patient's transference. However, it could just as well be the therapist who actively carries very specific relationship patterns into therapy and then elicits, as a reaction in his patient, a "counter-transference." It seems to me much more appropriate to assume that both interaction partners will be likely to behave in the therapeutic relationship according to their habitual relationship patterns. With some luck, these relationship patterns are less conflictual and more consciously controlled by professional guidelines on the part of the therapist. However, this does not have to be so. If a therapist is blind to his own transference tendencies, he will search for the reasons behind resultant problems in the patient, and will project his difficulties onto the patient. Naturally, problems can also emerge in the therapeutic relationship, when both sides carry conflictual relationship patterns into it.

According to all this, the therapeutic relationship can be viewed as a diagnostic instrument for identifying unconscious motivational conflicts on the part of the patient. Yet it is neither a reliable nor an objective instrument. The instrument can "fail to indicate" conflicts that really exist as well as give a "false indication" although the conflicts seen by the therapist are not on the side of the patient. The therapeutic relationship alone is, therefore, not a reliable instrument for the identification of motivational conflicts. The danger of non-indication decreases, the richer and more relevant the relationships offered in therapy are for the patient's conflicts. That is one reason which speaks for an expanded interpersonal setting. The danger of false indication can best be counteracted by appropriate self-experience on the therapist's part and/or by adequate supervision.

In patients with severe motivational conflicts it is very likely that their conflicts will manifest themselves in the therapeutic relationship, because the more significance the conflicts have for the patient, the more he will perceive his relationships in light of meanings resulting from that, and then behave in therapy accordingly. This processual activation of an important problem is, as we have discussed, a good basis for its therapeutic change.

There are two possibilities for influencing such problems therapeutically. One is on the processual level. The therapist can structure the relationship in such a way that the patient will make corrective experiences with respect to his fears that are part of the conflict. This can happen either intentionally or unintentionally. Earlier you gave examples for both. The therapist can act intentionally so that he passes the relationship tests the patient confronts him with or he can unintentionally achieve such a corrective effect by behaving complementary to the patient's wishes while he implements a procedure with a totally different rationale. Your explanation earlier of how something like that could happen in behavior therapy with agoraphobia was very convincing. For exerting deliberate influence on conflicts such as those manifesting themselves in the therapeutic relationship, the therapist must have a clear understanding of these conflicts and be well prepared for when and how they might come up. The therapist having a good perceptual sensitivity for what is happening processually on the relationship level and a good ability for conscious control of his own relationship behavior in accordance with his professional psychological knowledge is the basis for using these therapeutic possibilities. The therapist should be able to sensitively perceive his spontaneous feelings and action tendencies towards the patient yet he should not give them free reign, but respond to the patient according to the well reflected psychological and professional insights made rather than his or her own spontaneous reactions.

Another possibility for exerting therapeutic influence on such motivational conflicts manifesting themselves in the therapeutic relationship, is to make what is processually happening the content of discussion. This is in order to make conscious what was thus far unconscious and, therefore, happening without the possibility of conscious control. The therapist can thereby address what the patient is doing or experiencing in the moment and encourage the patient to reflect on the underlying reasons. By turning process into content one can make the previously unconscious conscious.

Therapy researcher: I would like to interrupt you just briefly. Two relevant research findings come immediately to mind just now.

"Turning process into content" as you express it seems to be a very potent form of therapeutic intervention. In a comprehensive meta-analysis by Orlinsky, Grawe and Parks (1994) on all process-outcome connections being found so far in empirical research, "experiential confrontation" turned out to be one of the most efficient therapeutic interventions of all. This entails the therapist confronting the patient with his own experience and behavior that is taking place in the very moment, thereby directing attention towards what is momentarily processually activated and turning this into content. There are a lot of reasons why this is the most efficient way to create a new awareness in the patient for what he experiences and how he behaves. However, one has to concede that these results did not just refer to the patient's relationship behavior towards the therapist, but to all experiencing and behavior momentarily happening. This may also refer to intra-psychic processes, for instance; that is to say to emotional control processes, implicit evaluations, etc.

One could be tempted to conclude that transference interpretations might be a particularly useful tool for achieving meaningful insights into central conflicts and should, therefore, be used by the therapist whenever the opportunity arises. Yet empirical findings on transference interpretation as a therapeutic tool indicate that it should be used only with discretion and restraint. According to the majority of empirical studies, the frequency of transference interpretations per therapy session correlates negatively with the therapeutic outcome (Henry et al., 1994). On the other hand, in cases where the transference interpretation is congruent with a carefully worked out case understanding, it correlates positively with the therapeutic outcome (Crits-Cristoph, 1997). I mentioned this previously in another context (section 1.21).

Piper et al. (1991) as well as Henry et al. (1994) report on results demonstrating that transference interpretations are not indicated as tools for improving a problematic therapeutic relationship. In fact that they could even have a negative impact. In many cases patients responded to transference interpretations with increased defensive behavior, and defensive patient behavior is highly and consistently linked to a negative therapeutic outcome (Orlinsky, Grawe & Parks, 1994). Henry, Schacht, and Strupp (1986, 1990) have investigated psychodynamic therapies utilizing the "Structural Analysis of Social Behavior (SASB)." SASB is a method for the micro-analysis of interpersonal behavior. Through the glasses of this method, the transference interpretations oftentimes turned out to have an ambiguous interpersonal meaning. On the one hand, they were meant to be a friendly teaching while they simultaneously contained a latent devaluating criticism. The critical component is, of course, not intended, and the therapist usually has no awareness of it. This is seen by Wile (1984) as an unwanted effect of certain aspects of psychoanalytical theory.

"Certain interpretations commonly made in psychoanalysis and psychodynamic therapy are accusatory. Therapists appear to make them, not because they are hostile or insensitive, but because of the dictates of their theory. Clients are seen as gratifying infantile impulses, being defensive, having developmental defects, and resisting the therapy. Therapists who conceptualize people in these ways may have a hard time making interpretations that do not communicate at least some element of this pejorative view" (Wile, 1984, p. 353).

Clearly, according to that, "turning process into content" might not be ideal. It may also imply increased therapeutic risk. The risk lies predominantly in that the patient might feel accused and react defensively, which may produce a negative impact on those characteristics known to constitute a good therapeutic relationship. A therapist wanting to address her patient's problematic relationship behavior which is processually activated, needs to place utmost value on doing this in a fashion and in a context that allows the patient to experience the intervention as a positive assistance. Especially in such moments the therapist should very actively be referring to the patient's resources and letting the patient feel that she wants to support him to become more like how he wants to be. As soon as the therapist detects any defensiveness as a response to her interventions, she should back off and abstain from addressing these problems as part of the therapeutic relationship. There is still the possibility of utilizing the knowledge of the patient's conflicts in the way previously described by responding to the patient's behavior on the processual level and thereby debilitating his fears. It is also possible to address the same conflict in reference to other relationships outside of therapy for which there are normally sufficient opportunities. The widespread belief in the utility of transference interpretations is, among other things, based on the assumption that it would decrease the patient's problematic relationship behavior. This has proved to be an illusion. Already in 1979, Luborsky et al. reported on empirical evidence showing that rather the opposite is fime, something that has in the meantime been confirmed in a study by Joyce (1992).

Therapist: When compared with what I learned during my analytical training, these results are somewhat surprising. Although they actually do make sense. What consequences can we draw from that? It seems clear from these results that processually, the therapeutic relationship may be very helpful in diagnosing a patient's unconscious motivational conflicts. However, addressing the therapeutic relationship as a problem should only happen in a rather restrained fashion and with the priority of giving explicit attention to its resource function. A good therapeutic relationship is an essential requirement for a positive therapeutic outcome. Content-related transference work is, however, only one of many tools for influencing motivational conflicts. It can always be replaced by another tool. So as far as the therapeutic relationship is concerned, the resource aspect has absolute priority over the problem aspect.

So far we have discussed the therapeutic relationship from the problem aspect, focusing only on the diagnostic-therapeutic function with respect to motivational problems. Yet **realization problems** of a patient may also manifest themselves in a therapeutic relationship. It may turn out that the patient behaves, in many respects, in such inept ways that he may not get a chance to realize his wishes in relationships. Disturbing peculiarities in his communication and interaction behavior may become noticeable. Generally, psychotherapy is a suitable place for receiving realistic feedback one might not otherwise get in real situations or at least not in such a way that one can accept it and productively make use of it. Yet such feedback with respect to how (little) well, or how (un)skillfully one does something, inherently contains, of course, the potential for being hurt. Feedback should therefore only be given in a highly active resource-oriented context, when the therapist is really sure that the therapeutic relationship will not suffer from it. For this procedure as well, there are possibly constructive alternatives such as creating a group therapeutic setting or including real interaction partners. The resource function of the therapeutic relationship should always be given priority.

1.30 The Therapeutic Relationship From the Resource Perspective

This brings us to the most important aspect arising from our discussion on the therapeutic relationship. In the first place the therapeutic relationship must be seen from the **resource perspective**. It must become a positive resource for the patient to the greatest extent possible, and for the therapeutic outcome this is a make or break situation. Schulte (1996) offers a compact summary of the characteristics marking a good therapeutic relationship according to the current status of empirical research:

The therapist should impress the patient as a professional and competent expert. Both requirements can also be derived from the significance we previously ascribed to the induction of positive expectations for improvements in therapy. An induction of positive expectations requires that the therapist, as a person, makes a credible and trustworthy impression to the patient.

The patient should feel appreciated by her therapist and feel that the therapist is on his side. The patient should feel himself understood and supported by the therapist in his innermost concerns. He should have the feeling that he and his therapist share the same goals, that the therapy serves his own goals, that he is not dominated and controlled in therapy but is in charge of himself.

With these requirements met, therapy represents a significant additional positive resource in the patient's life. A therapist who succeeds in creating such a relationship with the patient has in this sense successfully realized the principle of resource activation.

In order to activate the resource of a good therapeutic relationship, the therapist has to utilize his own professional and personal resources to activate the resources the patient brings along. Previously (section 1.19) you detailed the multitude of patient characteristics viewed as potential patient resources which can be used in therapy. I do not need to repeat them here.

Resources can be categorized in terms of **desirability** and **realizability**:
- What refers to already existing **wishes**, **intentions**, and **goals** of the patient?
- What refers to the patient's positive **abilities**? That means everything that can somehow help promote the realization of the patient's intentions.

Whatever relates to both of these aspects serves to strengthen the patient's self esteem, if coming up in therapy in one way or the other.

Resource activation means not only expressly tending to and utilizing the motivational tendencies and abilities the patient shows **spontaneously** in therapy, but it means also **stimulating latent tendencies** and **possibilities** both for their own purposes and in order to activate them for therapeutic purposes. The patient's life situation at the beginning of therapy is oftentimes marked by the fact that possibilities actually existing are not used or no longer used anymore. Here therapy can give an impulse for expanding or re-expanding the life space actually in use.

Resource activation can also be viewed from a **process** and a **content-related** aspect. **Processually** and with regard to the therapeutic relationship, resource activation means the patient receives explicit opportunities from the therapist to relate to the therapeutic situation and the therapist in accordance with his existing motivational tendencies and strengths. Resource activation means that such occasions are explicitly made available to the patient. Regarding the **content**, resource activation means that within the therapeutic relationship the patient is given the opportunity to verbally present himself with his positive sides and is actively, and without his own doing, reflected in these sides by the therapist. Not only the problems are discussed, but also the goals and values appreciated by the patient and the strengths he has. The criterion should be that by addressing these issues the patient feels upgraded in his self.

From what I have attempted to summarize here, I see much more clearly what you meant when you said that earlier we actually talked a lot about the therapeutic relationship before explicitly making it a topic. Actually, almost everything we previously said about resource activation also contained statements about the therapeutic relationship, as resource activation happens to a large part in, through, and for the therapeutic relationship, apart from the fact that a good therapeutic relationship can be viewed as the result of a successful resource activation and itself represents an important resource for the patient. In fact, we also discussed the significance of interpersonal relationships for psychotherapy from the problem aspect more in detail than I was aware of when I wondered why we had not looked more into the importance of relationships. All the statements on unconscious motivational conflicts were actually also statements about internalized relationship patterns repeating themselves in the patient's current relationships. This suddenly became clear to me when you discussed the "Core Conflictual Relationship Theme (CCRT)" method as a method of conflict measurement. These conflict definitions are indeed derived from the descriptions of interpersonal interactions. That means these conflicts act like internal representations of relationship patterns manifesting themselves again in real relationship patterns.

1.31   On the Interpersonal Nature of Human Mental Life

From the perspective of this method, psychodynamic formulations have an interpersonal content at their core. Two of the three psychodynamic components, wishes, fears and defense mechanisms, are directly related to other people. According to that, intra-psychic conflicts could be seen, in a way, as frozen relationship patterns experienced throughout the life history. They may be reformulated again into interpersonal processes and become therapeutically relevant in the present only so far as they have a negative impact on the patient's current relationship patterns. Until now, I was never so clear on this interpersonal nature of intra-psychic conflicts. Intra-psychic conflicts, even those that are unconscious should, in fact, principally manifest themselves in observable, processual patterns and should, due to this, avail themselves to being operationalized. From this angle however, it is difficult to understand why behavior therapists and empirical psychology have remained so far apart from psychodynamics. Unconscious conflicts are, in fact, nothing other than contents of the implicit memory, influencing current experience and behavior, as do many other contents of the implicit memory as well.

Psychologist: This is a rather refreshing view of what is to be understood by unconscious conflicts, and perhaps this view is not even so far off. Yet I do feel an obligation to maybe protect my colleagues and perhaps also the behavior therapists. All this is far away from the psychodynamics originally taught to us by psychoanalysis. In Freud's conception of unconscious conflicts, unconscious fantasies played a very important role. They are seen not simply as traces of real, experienced relationship patterns. Wish fantasies, particularly sexual wish fantasies and feelings of fear and guilt elicited by them play an important role and they may have little to do with real relational processes. Had empirical psychology accepted Freud's speculative ideas as scientific theories, it could have closed up shop. Also, the idea of wanting to base a developmental psychology on a retrospective analysis of adult's fantasies and memories, instead of the observation and analysis of children's actual experience and behavior has, in my view, accrued justifiable opposition. After all, there were certainly enough children available for observation and research, something which has definitely taken place in the meantime.

Empirical research on infants and small children has arrived at quite a different picture of the mental life of children than that depicted by Freud, even if the research was performed by scientists with a psychoanalytic background (Stern, 1992). Early relational experiences in children do indeed have a great influence on their ensuing relational history and also play a functional role for the development of psychological disorders, as the research on attachment subsequent to Bowlby's pioneering studies has demonstrated (Schmidt & Strauss, 1996; Strauss & Schmidt, 1997). In light of this, many basic psychodynamic assumptions have been empirically confirmed in the meantime. But at the same time a number of Freud's substantial assumptions about development had to be relinquished. This is especially true for his theory on sexuality. However, this has not changed the fact that these concepts are as widely circulated as ever.

It is completely consistent with the self conception of empirical psychology, at that time and today, to distance itself from the speculative nature of Freud's theory formation as well as from his abstention from any empirical testing of his theories. But it is regrettable that due to this empirical psychology neglected to conduct its own kind of research on the significance of early childhood experiences for later life, of unconscious processes and unconscious motivational conflicts. Neglecting certain issues on methodical grounds has always been a weakness of empirical psychology. Psychodynamic research of the kind you mentioned earlier is, however, completely acceptable to an empirical psychologist, and would have never provoked resistance such as that which empirical psychology developed towards psychoanalysis.

In the meantime, the concepts and methods of psychodynamic research have moved closer to those of empirical psychology, and empirical psychology has found an interest in questions that for a long time were the focus of predominantly psychodynamic researchers. This refers to unconscious processes, defense mechanisms, conflicts, the self, and many more. A comprehensive overview on this can be found in a publication by Barron, Eagle and Wolitzky (1992). An especially important area where themes overlap is interpersonal relationships. I believe today there can be no more doubt that interpersonal relationships and their traces in the human memory are the most important breeding ground for psychological disorders. This important knowledge remains for now still covered up by the tremendous success of disorder-specific approaches in clinical psychology and psychotherapy. Disorder-specific research has contributed so much to the understanding of the disorder-specific dynamics of the various psychological disorders that some seem to believe we have already arrived at a sufficient understanding of psychological disorders and their optimal treatment (see for example Fiedler, 1997). Earlier you presented a number of empirical findings from psychotherapy research questioning whether a purely disorder-specific approach could be the basis for an optimal treatment of psychological disorders. I find this to be unlikely due to yet other reasons. I would very much like to delve deeply into that, but I must refrain from doing so. We should postpone that until later, I think.

Yet I would like to at least point out that our mental life is so much of an interpersonal nature that it is highly unlikely for any therapeutic approach to turn out as optimal that does not attribute great significance to the interpersonal dimension and does not elaborate on it in an appropriate way. Therefore, I like that we have made a plan to also reflect on the mechanisms of interpersonal therapies. What I do know is that they are far from implementing what I just demanded, but their emphasis on the interpersonal relationships is reason enough to give them in-depth discussion. That is surely good preparation for our upcoming considerations. I myself, however, am not an expert on these therapeutic approaches. If we wish to attempt to view their mechanisms from the perspective of the ideas developed thus far, then one of you should take over.

1.32 On the Working Mechanisms of Interpersonal Therapies

Therapy researcher: It is not so simple to take a position on the working mechanisms of interpersonal therapies, because there is no "the" interpersonal therapy approach. In a broad sense, this term becomes an empty one. In one form or another, an important role is accorded interpersonal relationships within almost all therapeutic approaches. Just about all approaches also utilize the setting of group therapy to bring about changes in interpersonal behavior. An interpersonal setting which exceeds the dyadic setting of individual therapy alone does not quite justify talking about a separate therapeutic approach, although therapy in a group setting does indeed have its special characteristics and similarities that go beyond the borders between the various schools of therapy (Yalom, 1974; Grawe, 1980 a).

I think it would make more sense, therefore, to conceive as interpersonal therapies in the narrower sense only those attempting to achieve changes in already existing important relationships, and not those seeking to produce changes in the patient's general relationship behavior. These are mostly partner and/or family relationships and the therapies aiming to change them are mainly, but not exclusively, conducted in the couples or family therapy setting.

One reason for performing therapies in couples or family settings could be the aspect of resource activation. In an extended interpersonal setting, more and different resources can be activated than in individual therapy. The love a couple has for each other can represent a powerful resource for working on goals difficult to achieve. The willingness of parents to give everything for their children can motivate them to change their behavior if they see that this is necessary for the well-being of their child.

From the aspect of process activation there are two rationales which speak in favor of a couples or family therapy setting. Such therapies are obviously indicated whenever the treatment goal is to improve the partner or family relationship(s). They can be based on very different theoretical assumptions about the origins of these disorders. For instance, there are psychoanalytic and behavior therapeutic partner therapies with different assumptions and accordingly different procedures. A second rationale for couples and family therapies is found in the assumption that specific aspects of the couple and family relationships have a functional role for certain disorders such as anorexia, psychosomatic disorders, depression, or schizophrenia. It is assumed that the couple or family relationships require change in order for the symptomatology to change. Therapy is directed towards an improvement of the real relationships in order to positively influence the symptomatology.

It was originally assumed that special features of the family interaction are the cause of the disorders. This communication theory conception of mental disorders was first formulated by Ruesch and Bateson (1951) and found its first application to a specific mental disorder in the double bind theory of schizophrenia by Bateson et al. (1956). This conception was later followed by many more such as the conception of the development of anorexia out of specific familial relationship patterns (Minuchin, Rosman & Baker, 1978). These communication-oriented or systems-oriented views of mental disorders with their conclusions for treatment advocated by Minuchin (1974), Selvini-Palazzoli et al. (1977), Haley (1963, 1976), Watzlawick, Beavin and Jackson (1969) can be conceived of as a separate therapeutic approach. This approach sees itself in opposition to psychoanalysis and this is certainly true with regard to its practical conclusions.

Though it does share an essential common feature with the psychoanalytic approach: Both assume that not the symptoms themselves, but the underlying causes have to be treated. In psychodynamic therapies these are the traces of past relationship patterns in the form of unconscious conflicts, in systems therapies these are present relationship patterns assumed to be the causes for mental disorders, and the treatment then focuses on the assumed causes.

Today, the original view that familial relationship patterns are the causes for mental disorders is no longer shared in its unidirectional form by most systems-oriented therapists. It has been replaced by an interactional perspective. Reciprocal influences between the familial interaction and the disorders are assumed. But the conclusion that familial relationship patterns are an effective starting point for changing mental disorders has remained.

Since we would like to explain the mechanisms of the actual therapeutic procedure and not debate the correctness or incorrectness of assumptions made by different schools of therapy, it is, therefore, not important to us **why** treatment concentrates on current relationship patterns but the fact **that it does**. The actual focus on working with present relationships with real significant others, is something all the approaches just mentioned share with other couples and family therapies which have a different theoretical concept. Thus, we should clarify the mechanisms of those therapies that actually direct their procedures towards the modification of currently important relationships. We can refrain from the theoretical rationale for that.

What effects do interpersonal therapies in this narrower sense bring about and how can we explain these effects? I am going to spare us the information on what kind of interpersonal therapy can be viewed as how effective. For that there are detailed overviews (see Grawe, Donati & Bernauer, 1994, pp. 514—578). What we want, in fact, is to arrive at a better understanding of how therapeutic changes come about, and we can therefore limit ourselves to those procedures for which there is enough evidence that they effectively bring about changes.

1.33 On the Mechanisms of Couples Therapy

The effectiveness of behavioral couples therapy can be viewed as well supported. Usually the procedure tends to focus on instructing and supporting the couple by active interventions in order to improve their communication and problem solving. Looking at this procedure from the perspective of the Rubicon model, we see that it has to be located, much like individual behavior therapy, on the right bank. The couple having the mutual intention to come along better is a precondition, and the procedure is directed at assisting the couple in realizing this intention. The procedure contains the same elements as other behavior therapeutic procedures aimed at both the development and promotion of concrete action plans as well as specification of the where, when and how.

An important element of the communication training, which is almost always part of the procedure, is learning how to listen to each other and to show more of an interest. The partners learn not only better communication skills, but applying these regularly in their relationship will lead to better reciprocal understanding and feelings of being understood. The motives and emotions of the other and perhaps also one's own behavior in the relationship become more transparent, similar to the motivational clarification process that takes place in the realm of individual therapies which we talked about earlier. This may lead to a change in intentions in both partners and to a long-term change in the relationship behavior.

The findings of two studies investigating explicitly clarification-oriented couples therapies suggest that better understanding of one's own motives and those of the other in a partner relationship, is the most effective way to improve a relationship on a long-term basis. In general there are only a few studies on humanistic and psychodynamic couples therapies, not very convincing methodically, but these two studies have a distinctly good methodical quality and can be viewed as specifically informative.

In a study by Johnson and Greenberg (1985 a, b), a couples therapy labeled as experiential therapy—the therapy focused on the partners' emotions and experiences in their marital interaction employing gestalt therapeutic and client-centered procedures—was compared with behavioral problem solving training. Speaking in the terminology previously developed by us, we are talking about a comparison between an explicitly clarification-oriented procedure and an exclusively realization-oriented procedure. Both therapies turned out to be highly effective when compared with a control group, but by the end of the treatment the clarification-oriented therapy proved to be still significantly superior. Eight weeks later, some of these differences had evaporated, but scales for the cohesion and satisfaction with the marriage demonstrated there was still a difference in favor of the clarification-oriented therapy. So far this is the only study in which another procedure, when compared with behavioral couples therapy, proved to be superior by the time therapy was completed. One reason for that might be that the behavioral couples therapy investigated did not include communication training which is normally a standard element of behavioral couples therapy. It could be that the above mentioned positive effects of improved listening and responding were missing, and in that sense, the failure to arrive at a better understanding of oneself and the partner in the couple relationship might be responsible for this result that does not fit into the long list of studies favoring behavior couples therapy.

Another study yields evidence that understanding oneself and the other with respect to each other's experience and behavior in the relationship seems to be the best guarantee for long-term improvement of the relationship. The well designed study by Snyder and Wills (1989) compared an "insight-oriented marital therapy" with comprehensive behavioral couples therapy. In the behavior therapy the procedure was, as usual, directed towards better problem solving and better communication with one another. In the insight-oriented therapy, we could even say: clarification-oriented therapy, the therapist worked towards each partner developing more understanding for the other of how, due to his or her original upbringing and life history, he or she had become the person being partly so difficult for his or her partner. The goal was for both partners to develop a better understanding of why they would feel and behave towards one another in the way they did. We could call this motivational clarification on the relationship level.

Both therapies achieved positive effects in a multitude of successful cases, but by the end of therapy, and even after another six months, the positive changes achieved through realization-oriented therapy were still a bit higher than those of the clarification-oriented. These results are pretty much in line with a large number of similar results from previous studies on behavioral couples therapy in comparison with other procedures. However this study differed from the others in that four years later a careful follow-up was conducted which yielded a highly surprising result: four years after treatment termination 39 percent of the couples treated with realization-oriented therapy were divorced, while only 3 percent of those undergoing clarification-oriented therapy were (Snyder, Wills & Grady-Fletcher, 1991). Understanding each other better seems to be more significant for a good relationship in the long run than having the skills to communicate well and to solve problems with one another. The clarification of one's own motives and those of the other person in the relationship can obviously lead to changed intentions, and thereby to a lasting changed experience and behavior in the relationship, similar to what we have discussed earlier for individual clarification-oriented therapy. The conjointly acquired knowledge and understanding of how problems in the relationship arise due to the two life histories, evidently helps move the partners closer together, rather than separating themselves from each other. If the need to fence oneself off from the other becomes too great, then the—in their own right—valuable communication and problem solving skills acquired in a realization-oriented couples therapy are no longer of sufficient help to find each other and to pursue mutual intentions. If, in spite of good communication and problem solving skills, the partners decide to separate then the problem apparently does not lie on the level of abilities, but on the level of motivation. They have lost the basis for pursuing mutual intentions. Therapy must then concentrate on developing mutual intentions, and clarification-oriented couples therapy is obviously better suited for this.

Again we are faced with the same phenomenon we already know from dealing with individual clarification and realization-oriented therapy. It is that either one or the other takes place, and that the obvious "one as well as the other" of clarification and mastery/realization is impeded by the underlying theoretical concepts. It will be interesting to see what the outcome will be for both couples and individual therapy once clarification and realization procedures are combined.

What are the specific advantages of therapy in a couples setting? For problems in the relationship, the advantages are obvious: Therapy in a couples setting offers the opportunity for ideal **process activation** of those problems that need to be changed. Through the presence of both participants, these problems are either already processually activated or can be easily activated by the therapist. The processual activation is also not limited to the therapy sessions themselves but takes place continuously in the couple's everyday life. The therapy session is the place where "**process becomes content**" as previously stated. The "experiential confrontation" which has proven to be so effective for bringing about changes in individual therapy takes place continuously in couples therapy, and that is in both clarification-oriented and realization-oriented therapies. **Meta-communication** about what is taking place in the relationship is one of the major issues in couples therapy. In individual therapy meta-communicative comments comprise a much smaller portion of the overall issues discussed. Previously we came to the conclusion that one has to be very careful in making a certain kind of meta-communicative comment in individual therapy, in particular transference interpretations, so as not to jeopardize the foundations of the therapy. The interpersonal setting offers an ideal opportunity for reflecting on interpersonal processes activated in the moment. With this, new structures of awareness for their interaction can evolve in both partners that again can be the basis for controlling future relationship behavior more consciously in the direction of certain intentions. The emotional participation of both partners is usually high, because what is happening is highly relevant for their own intentions.

Process research has proved this to be very positive for the expected therapeutic outcome (Orlinsky, Grawe & Parks 1994).

This great advantage of couples therapy, the processual activation of problems to be changed, may, on the other hand, also lead to specific difficulties. Continuous activation of the problems can actually hinder or just as well thwart their being constructively worked on in therapy. This may lead to a situation analogous to that which sometimes confronts us in individual therapy when the patient's relationship problems manifest themselves so much in the therapeutic relationship that it becomes impossible to create a sufficiently good working relationship in order to mutually pursue certain therapeutic goals.

As we have seen before, in individual therapy one would attempt to counteract this difficulty by resource activation, that is, give the patient the chance to also show himself also from his positive sides. Additionally, one might try to deactivate the intentions that determine the problematic behavior by behaving complementary towards the patient's most important relational schemata in order to weaken the fears most likely underlying his problematic interpersonal behavior.

The rationale of resource activation can be easily adopted for couples therapy. Each of the partners, and the couple together, is given the opportunity to show themselves from their positive sides, in order to develop an awareness of the advantages of their relationship. Through appropriate interventions the therapist can promote situations in which the beautiful sides of the relationship can be increasingly experienced together. This can happen for instance by assigning "homework" to a couple overchallenged by child care and other tasks, to take one evening per week for themselves in order to do something nice, while simultaneously imposing a ban not allowing them to talk about their problems during this evening. Thus, one tries to awaken and encourage intentions different from those leading to the problems.

The possibilities for forming a complementary relationship and for weakening the fears on the process level by appropriate therapist behavior are limited in a couples setting, as the other partner can sabotage these. The therapist must always keep an eye out for the impact that her relationship behavior towards one of the partners may have on the other. In this case the therapist has to look for other possibilities to deactivate the problematic intentions endangering the therapeutic work. Through individual sessions with one or both partners, he can attempt to create an appropriate basis for joint work in the couples setting, since in the dyadic setting he has again all the previously mentioned possibilities of the individual therapy setting. Hence individual and couples settings can be combined in order to "dose" processual activation and be able to utilize the advantages of both settings. There is also the possibility to abstain completely from trying to treat the relationship problems in a couples setting for the time being, because the continuous problem actuation would in itself be too much of a problem, and instead approach the behavior of the individual partner in the relationship much the same way as other relationship problems in individual therapy. We would then—similar to our thoughts on unconscious motivational conflicts on the individual level—be moving around on the utmost left edge of the couple therapeutic Rubicon landscape by attempting to change the initial variables entering into the motivational clarification process on the couples level.

We can, therefore, nicely explain the mechanisms of successful couples therapy using the same working mechanisms previously detailed, and the Rubicon metaphor can also be similarly applied to couples therapy as well as to individual therapy. Changes can be created in two ways, namely by a **clarification process** helping a couple to better understand each other, thereby contributing to the development of changed intentions, and by interventions promoting a better **realization of extant intentions**.

The great advantage of couples therapy lies in the **processual activation** of the problems to be changed. This working mechanism can, as far as problems in the partnership are concerned, be optimally realized in couples therapy.

Yet it has been empirically shown that other problems as well, such as depressions, phobias and psychosomatic disorders, can be successfully improved by couples therapy. How can the change of such non-interpersonal problems through interpersonal therapy be explained?

One possible explanation would be that a functional connection between certain relationship patterns and certain psychological disorders does in fact exist, as assumed by those advocating an interpersonal approach (see above). If the relationship patterns change, which—as we have just seen—is very well possible through couples therapy, the disorders change as well. How exactly this happens, and how one is to imagine the way changed relationship patterns have an effect on individual psychological functioning to make symptoms vanish, the above mentioned representatives of interpersonal therapies leave in the dark.

In my eyes this is a weakness of interpersonal therapy approaches. They make statements on the psychological functioning of the individual, for example, about anorexia, schizophrenia etc., without having an elaborated conception of the principles of individual psychological functioning and without reference to the existing relevant scientific knowledge on that. The corresponding publications are lacking references to relevant psychological studies. Only among those family therapists with an originally psychoanalytic background, such as Bowen (1972, 1976, 1978), does one find a more marked reference to individual psychology concepts, but then only to those belonging to psychoanalysis.

I have never understood why advocates of interpersonal therapy approaches do not make reference to relevant findings of either social psychology or clinical psychology, although that would stand to reason. I, personally, feel it makes no sense to seek to explain changes in individual mental functioning without considering the relevant status of research on that.

So far no empirical confirmation exists for assumptions some representatives of the interpersonal approach have made on specific connections between certain familial relationship patterns and specific psychological disorders. There are also no studies proving that specific changes in the relationship patterns would lead to specific changes in the symptoms. In this specific formulation, many interpersonal assumptions thus far lack empirical evidence. If subjected to proper methodical scrutiny, many of these assumptions would probably suffer a fate similar to that of Wolpe's original conception of the mechanisms of systematic desensitization (Wolpe, 1958).

There could, however, be a softer, less specific formulation for the assumption of a functional relation between changes in real interpersonal relationships and the improvement of psychopathological symptoms, one possibly having a better chance for empirical confirmation. A bad relationship can be viewed as a considerable source of stress. Stress takes its toll on the physical and mental health (Brown & Harris, 1978;

Dohrenwend & Dohrenwend, 1974; Totman, 1979). If the relationship improves in the course of couples therapy, that means an accompanying decrease in stress and with it a weakening of the breeding ground for psychopathological symptoms. However, assuming that a stress reduction through an improved relationship would always be a sufficient condition for the improvement of specific symptoms would be an incommensurate account for the specific dynamics of the single psychological disorders. But the basis for an improvement would be enhanced if the stress level in the relationship were reduced. Under these improved conditions the working mechanisms to which we have previously ascribed the effects of psychotherapy may become effective, such as changes in expectations and motivations, for example. The progress made in the relationship by couples therapy can then lead to changes going way beyond the partner relationship, that is to improvements in symptoms and well-being.

It is very likely that the **induction of positive expectations for improvements** in interpersonal therapies plays a role similar to that in other therapies. In family therapy studies indications have been found that family therapy has a better effect when the identified patient and the family thought a family therapy to be appropriate (Grawe, Donati & Bernauer, 1994). With all the participants convinced the treatment rationale is appropriate, and with the therapist proceeding from this rationale consistently and thereby making a competent impression, the chances are good that a positive feedback process is set in motion which can bring about positive improvements in all participants. As a matter of fact, in the practice of family therapies, improvements appear to not only take place in the identified patient but oftentimes also in other family members (Berger Bertschinger, 1994). One might imagine that this positive feedback process is found to be even stronger in an interpersonal system, because observation of positive impacts on one family member may lead to an increased belief in the benefits of the therapy among other family members, and thereby may improve the conditions for further positive effects.

I already mentioned the significance of resource activation for improving the relationship in couples therapy. The setting of couples therapy itself can additionally be viewed as a resource of a special kind which may increase the efficacy of therapy beyond that of individual therapy. In a study by Hafner et al. (1983), an eclectic individual therapy was compared with a "spouse aided therapy," that is a therapy in which the patient's partner is included as an additional resource, in order to improve the efficacy of the treatment. The study examined patients of a psychiatric hospital with relatively severe mental disorders such as depressions, agoraphobia, personality disorders, alcohol addiction, schizophrenia, and many more. Treatment took place in an outpatient setting and lasted ten sessions for both therapy groups. In both treatment conditions it was left up to the therapists to apply the interventions they thought appropriate. Psychodynamic, cognitive and behavioral techniques were used.

Both therapies achieved comparable improvements in the patient's main symptomatology but those therapies including the partner as a resource also lead to a decrease in other neurotic symptoms, to significant improvements in marital satisfaction and to more intense sexual relations. These additional effects had a long-term positive effect on mental health. Three months after the therapy, the mental disorders of those patients whose partners had participated were more improved than those patients treated alone.

This opportunity to activate patients' existing interpersonal resources is rarely realized in psychotherapy and the study by Hafner et al., shows that existing possibilities to improve the outcome are also not realized, although this would certainly be possible in many cases. The partner need not necessarily always be included in every therapy session for the entire therapy duration. A therapy could take place alternately or for shorter periods in the individual or the couples setting in order to activate the resource function of a relationship for therapeutic purposes.

Overall, sufficient indications exist today that the partner relationship of an individual can greatly influence his or her mental health. Therefore therapists have every reason why they should pay explicit attention to this important real relationship in their patients' lives. This applies to both the problem and the resource aspects. It does not necessarily follow from this that the partner has to be directly included in therapy, or that there must always be regular couples therapy. Between pure individual therapy without explicit reference to the most important real relationships in the patient's life and pure couples therapy, there is a wide spectrum of possibilities for making use of a patient's relationships for therapeutic purposes. Important aspects to consider are whether the partner relationship can be utilized for the processual activation of the patient's major problems and/or as a resource for supporting the therapeutic goals.

1.34   On the Mechanisms of Family Therapy

What I just said about the therapeutic significance of partner relationships goes just as well for relationships to other family members, that is in particular to parents, siblings and children.

If an improvement of family relationships is the direct therapeutic goal, then the family therapy setting is well suited for bringing about improvements. Family therapies almost always brought about improvements in family relationships whenever empirically investigated (Grawe, Donati & Bernauer, 1994). This finding can be very well explained with the concepts so far discussed.

A family therapy setting is particularly well suited to processually activate problems on the level of family relationships. This opens up good possibilities for influencing the problems. In terms of the utility and the risks of a processual activation of relationship problems between family members, the same considerations apply that I have previously elaborated for the couples setting.

In family therapy too, we have different procedures with different aims. These correspond in part to the emphases of those therapeutic approaches already discussed. They can simply be transferred to the other setting. Behavioral family therapy has, for example, a problem solving oriented or intention realization oriented emphasis. Similar to couples therapy, the point is to assist the family in better communicating and solving problems with each other.

This is also true for systems-oriented family therapies, but not so exclusively. They also aim at changing the family members' intentions. The basis for that is a system-oriented problem definition. Often this is worked out not just by one therapist, but with other therapists observing the family interaction through a one-way mirror, who then, together with the acting therapist, elaborate an understanding of the family-specific problem constellation. Specific therapeutic interventions are derived from this problem formulation using the existing dynamics within the family to bring about new familial interactions. A significant time lag is often left between therapy sessions so that these interventions may unfold their effects in the family's everyday life. Through the interventions bound up forces are supposed to be untied, so to speak, which will then unfold their own dynamics. Changed family interactions mean—and depend on the fact—that individual family members behave differently than before as a result of either a change of intentions achieved by the therapeutic interventions or due to a better realization of previously extant intentions.

The effects of changed family interaction on the family members' individual experience and behavior can be well explained by the expectancy-value-theories already mentioned by us several times. I wish to illustrate this with two examples. The point of departure for family therapy could be, let's say, that an essentially adult son might have difficulties becoming independent from his original family and due to this, his interpersonal relationships do not develop appropriately to his age. He becomes depressed and has severe self-esteem problems. His parents are very concerned about him. The setting of family therapy could reveal that the son's problems with leaving home have to do with his feeling responsible for his mother and not wanting to abandon her. Between the mother and father intimate partner exchange has been lacking for quite some time, and as for emotional exchange, the son has become a sort of partner-substitute for the mother. Without having had a clear awareness of this so far, he believes he would bring disaster upon his mother, endangering all that holds the family together, were he to pursue his own goals. From his mother's side the problem actually looks like this: She is very concerned about her son and therefore takes so much care of him. She in fact does not feel emotionally dependent on her son. If in the course of therapy the mother develops an awareness that, by her concern, she has inadvertently contributed to her son's problems, perhaps then she will trust herself to behave more independently from her son, will do more things on her own, find less time for her son, and possibly intensify her relationship with her husband again, and so on. The son might initially be irritated and also annoyed that his mother lavishes less care on him. He has to learn how to do without the caring tenderness to which he has become so accustomed. By the same token though, his mother's changed behavior opens up new personal freedom for him, it changes the world of meanings he has so far lived in. He sees that his mother gets along fine without him, that he can leave her be, and that she can go her own way. He starts to spend more time outside his parent's house. His more independent behavior in turn reassures his mother. She feels even freer to look after her own affairs. The therapy has decreased the **desirability** to be so overly caring about the other in both the son and the mother, and to worry over what might happen if one was less concerned about the other. This is why the striving for autonomy on both sides gain in intention strength and can exert more influence on behavior.

A family therapy can also exert influence on the individual experience and behavior of the family members through the **expectancy component**. Let's take the example of a family having an adolescent child with a behavioral disorder. The family is under severe stress. The parents argue constantly about how to deal with their difficult child and eventually contact a family therapist. If by means of interventions the therapist successfully manages that the father and mother argue less, can communicate better and can cooperate in the service of shared intentions, then this can have a considerable impact on their growing child's behavior via changed expectations (in particular, expectations with respect to the results of his behavior and to the contingencies in the interpersonal environment). Where for instance the child has so far received different answers when attempting to test personal freedom, one parent allowing, the other prohibiting, the child might now receive from both parents clear coherent messages agreed upon by both partners. A secure space for development with clear boundaries is established for the child, without him or her being drawn into parental conflicts and coalitions with one parent. The child will know in the future what to expect, and this will manifest itself in clear intentions. The parents have a less difficult child to deal with, will not slide into constant conflicts through coalitions between child and one parent, and thereby gain some freedom for more positive interactions with one another. Setting clear limits has an effect predominantly on the child's realizability expectations. This will change the child's behavior and this, in turn, has an impact on parental wishes and fears and, by having an impact on the desirability component, changes their intentions and behavior. Naturally, the changed behavior on the side of one parent has positive repercussions for the partner and for other family members and through this could lead to further changes.

Due to these multiple positive feedback possibilities in family systems, it is not surprising that family therapists have taken great interest in self-organization and chaos theories. It is not exactly a butterfly flapping his wings that could elicit a "family storm," but relatively small changes in family interaction in fact, according to this way of think- ing, can activate a latent potential for change through positive feedback processes and furthermore possibly lead to far reaching changes. It therefore makes sense that family therapists tend to spread out the single therapy sessions over time allowing the effects of these processes to unfold between sessions.

It is likely then, that in addition to the working mechanisms just now mentioned, a considerable portion of the effectiveness of family therapies can be attributed to the principle of resource activation. This important general working mechanism of psy- chotherapy has been explicitly emphasized in family therapy more strongly than in all other therapeutic approaches. In Karpel's book *Family Resources-The Hidden Partner in Family Therapy* (1986), this working mechanism has been elaborated in a very dif- ferentiated way for family therapy.

Process activation, intention modification, motivational clarification, intention realization, expectation modification and resource activation—the concepts with which we explained the efficacy of all therapeutic procedures discussed so far—can thus also by used for family therapy to explain how therapeutic interventions influence family members in their individual experience and behavior. In his work, of course, a family therapist must account for factors exceeding those which concern the individual, much like a group therapist. Groups, families and couples function according to their own principles that need to be paid attention to by anybody wishing to utilize and change the interactions in such a super-individual system for therapeutic purposes. However, I do not want to go any further into this, as it was not our original question. My intention was to demonstrate how interventions on the higher systems level take an effect on the individual's experience and behavior and can thereby bring about therapeutic changes on the individual level.

When asking if and how psychological disorders can be effectively treated by family therapy, it is the effects at the individual level that interest us. Given these considerations, it seems possible that by changing family interactions we can achieve positive effects on the individual experience and behavior and, thereby, essentially also on psychological disorders. Yet this will only take place in those cases where there is actually a functional relation between specific familial interaction patterns and the psychological disorders that need to be treated. Otherwise it could be expected that in a family therapy with a member suffering from a disorder, the family interaction and perhaps the individual well-being of some of the participants may change towards the positive, however the psychological disorder largely remains because no specific influence is exerted on it.

The current state of research offers no clear cut answer to this question. Positive effects of systems-oriented family therapy on a family member's psychological disorder are not as well backed up as the positive effects on family interaction (Grawe, Donati & Bernauer, 1994, p. 574). Besides, in comparative studies individual therapy treatments aimed at symptom reduction proved to be at least equally effective, if not more. The central assumption of family therapy: "improvements in the family interaction lead to improvements of the psychological disorder in the identified patient" so far has only the status of an assumption. Convincing and sufficiently replicated empirical confirmations of this assumption are still pending. Surprisingly, this central assumption of systems-oriented family therapy has, for the most part, not been adequately investigated. In line with our previous considerations, it should not even be surprising if it turns out that this assumption in its general form is empirically untenable. Several times before I already addressed the fact that each psychological disorder has its own dynamics and regardless of what goal the therapy might have, the disorder specific dynamics must always be broken up by disorder specific interventions that have been empirically proven. These disorder-specific dynamics have not been sufficiently acknowledged in the existing systems therapy concepts of mental disorders, and because of that are also not sufficiently accounted for in family therapy treatments.

So far there is also a lack of empirical evidence for the assumption that specific familial interaction patterns lead to specific psychological disorders, that is to say that there exists for instance "the" anorexia family or "the" psychosomatic family (Minuchin, Rosman & Baker, 1978). My opinion is that such specific assumptions are as unlikely to be empirically confirmed as was Alexander's assumption (1950) that specific unconscious conflicts would lead to specific psychosomatic disorders. The actual connections are most likely more unspecific. Conflicts are in fact a breeding ground for psychological disorders (Emmons, King & Sheldon, 1993) as well as certain familial interaction patterns, such as coalitions in the family, in fact are quite frequently associated with mental disorders (Fürbringer-Lienhard, 1992). Although to which mental disorders a particular unconscious conflict or coalition formation in the family leads to, and whether they do at all, most likely depends on many other influences.

Based on what we have discussed, it cannot be expected that insight into an unconscious conflict will lead to a decrease in symptomatology in every case, even if originally developed due to this conflict. This oftentimes requires specific interventions for supporting intention realization which specifically take into account the peculiar dynamics of the specific disorder. It seems equally unlikely that the alleviation of a coalition formation through family therapy will lead to the improvement of the psychological disorder which may have developed on the basis of this familial interaction pattern. But improving family relationships should help create a better basis for the continuing long-term improvement of such symptomatology by disorder-specific interventions.

Based on the current status of the research and all the considerations we have so far made about the mechanisms of psychotherapy, I find it unlikely that the specific assumptions on the working mechanisms of systemic family therapy will be empirically confirmed. These assumptions do not refer to the empirically-based knowledge we have today on what brings about changes in psychotherapy. In this respect, however, family therapy is in the same situation as most other therapy approaches.

Therapist: Your last comment encouraged me to say something that was frequently running through my head during our discussion of family therapy. I am quite surprised how many common features the systemic approach shares with the psychodynamic approach although systemic therapists vehemently separate themselves from the intra-psychic view of psychodynamics.

Both approaches originate from the assumption that it is not the symptomatology itself that should be treated, but its underlying causes. Although this unidirectional view in systemic therapy has in the meantime been largely superseded by an interactional conception, the assumption of a current functional relation between symptomatology and interaction patterns, or unconscious conflicts, respectively, remains. Both approaches place a value on a well elaborated problem formulation specifying these functional relations. This becomes especially clear when comparing psychodynamic focal therapy approaches with the approach by Selvini-Palazzoli et al. (1977). Both develop the problem formulation independently of the patient, assuming that in the beginning of a therapy it cannot be communicated to the patient and derive far-reaching therapeutic consequences for influencing the underlying problem constellation from that. The difference lies in what the therapy aims at. One aims at unconscious conflicts, the others at current relationship patterns. You already mentioned that unconscious conflicts relate, ultimately, to relationship patterns or develop from those. In this case, however, we are dealing with previous family relationship patterns of early childhood, whereas systemic therapists try to establish a link between the patient's current relationship patterns towards significant others and the disorder. Viewed this way, the two therapeutic approaches have more in common than one might suspect at first glance, more in fact than with other approaches that first seem to be less different.

It actually makes sense explicitly investigating the question of whether and how conflictual family interaction patterns, like those of interest to systemic therapists, manifest themselves in today's small children of these families in the form of unconscious intra-psychic conflicts leading to psychological problems later in adulthood. This would be a link between psychodynamic and systemic assumptions.

Psychologist: Studies similar to that are already underway, not exactly in the form that you sketched, but empirical investigations looking at the impacts of early attachment experiences in young children—one might also speak of familial interaction patterns—on the development of psychological disorders later in life. Earlier you referred to Bowlby's assumptions about the underlying basis for the development of agoraphobia. These studies however were performed not by systemic therapists, but by developmental psychologists. They appear to be highly relevant for psychotherapy, and I think we should return to them later on round. Anyway, this is an area in which psychological research has come up with very useful concepts and findings for psychotherapy, which I think are thus far not sufficiently acknowledged by psychotherapists.

Now, it is very tempting to switch right over to the many interesting questions we have postponed time and again in our conversation. What I mean are questions relating more to basic psychological functioning than to what takes place in therapy, and more to the conception of psychological disorders, than to the mechanisms of psychotherapy. I think we have gotten quite far with our attempts to explain the mechanism of psychotherapy. We have now given thought to all the major therapeutic schools with respect to their mechanisms. As a fundamental scientist who is not that familiar with the practice of therapy and psychotherapy research, I have learned a lot. This will help me to be a more competent conversational partner in second dialog when I will have to contribute more to our discussion. Before we switch to a new topic we should maybe take a look back at our discussion and distill the most important results from that. Although I have listened more than contributed myself, perhaps I should try to summarize what, in my view, appear to be the most essential realizations I have drawn from our discussions.

Part 6: Summary and Conclusions

1.35 The Multiple Meanings of What Happens in Therapy and Their Consequences

The longer our conversation, the more it becomes obvious to me that whatever takes place in psychotherapy can be viewed from many different perspectives at any given moment, and acquire quite a different meaning depending on that perspective. None of these perspectives and their resultant meanings can be considered "the" right one from the beginning. Obviously what happens in psychotherapy is so complex that it is not so easy to exhaust the number of possible fruitful perspectives. From these different perspectives, certain patterns of mental activity emerge on the side of the patient that suggest certain patterns of therapeutic action. Every perspective opens up a new world of meanings in which the patient's psychological functioning and therapeutic actions can be related to one another.

When a therapist chooses a perspective on a patient in terms of the DSM or ICD, he opens up a world of meanings leading to disorder patterns in the sense of psychopathological syndromes. This world of meaning suggests disorder-specific patterns of therapeutic action.

For the same patient, at the same time, a different perspective could just as well be taken which focuses on his interpersonal behavior. This perspective was first consequently focused on by Sullivan (1953) and in the meantime has been further developed methodically. Benjamin (1993) elaborated this perspective especially well. It suggests patterns of interpersonal behavior on the patient's side. The interpersonal patterns of therapeutic action suggested by this world of interpersonal meanings are very different from the disorder-specific patterns mentioned earlier.

The same patient, however, could also be viewed from a conflict dynamic perspective. Patterns consisting of wishes, fears and defense mechanisms underlying the patient's observable behavior and conscious experience are evolving from this. A therapist directing his therapeutic actions towards these, often unconscious, patterns is proceeding in a manner quite different from a therapist thinking in disorder-specific patterns.

Looking at the same patient from a problem solving perspective, we focus on yet another aspect of his mental activity. Therapeutic action then focuses on improved intention realization and action control.

We enter into yet another entirely different world of meanings in viewing the same patient from the resource perspective, because we arrive at therapeutic conclusions not suggested by any of the previously mentioned perspectives.

So what takes place in therapy is never clear cut but basically has many potential meanings, each according to the perspective one adopts. Upon adopting one of these possible perspectives, one should remain aware that one is not looking at "the" reality, but at one of many reality constructions. Among these various reality constructions or worlds of meanings there is no arbitrariness. These reality constructions are only relevant for psychotherapy if they refer to actually extant connections between therapeutic interventions and the patients experience and behaviour. Only then can changes in these patterns of experience and behavior of the patient be achieved by the therapeutic interventions. Such connections can only be investigated by empirical research. Consequently, one of the tasks of psychotherapy research is such a perspective-specific type of research. Within the respective reality construction hypotheses on significant connections have to be formulated, tested and verified, keeping in mind, however, that one is moving within only one of many possible reality constructions.

Therapy researcher: May I latch onto this here and add something? Even if one establishes significant connections within one of these therapeutic realities and can utilize these for a targeted change of the patient's respective patterns, this does not mean that the relevance of this perspective for psychotherapy has been verified. What use would it be if one were able to bring about significant changes in the world of unconscious conflicts, if these would not manifest themselves in any experiential or behavioral changes perceived as improvements by the patient or significant others? Therefore, in each case a link between the specific world of meaning of a certain perspective and a criterion outside of this reality construction must be established which is generally accepted as a relevant evaluation criterion. These criteria should be determined by society; they are not only or not even predominantly the business of psychotherapists (Grawe, 1985). Which functions psychotherapy should fulfill for the benefit of the individual and society is not to be answered from the side of a perspective-specific therapeutic construction of reality. Regardless of how well founded they are within this perspective, the therapeutic goals derived from a given perspective only receive general acceptance by their proven relevance for the fulfillment of tasks assigned to psychotherapy by society. Schulte (1993) has arrived at a view which is essentially in agreement with that, though from a different point of departure. This view proposes what it is that the success of a psychotherapy should be measured against (Schulte, 1993). Psychotherapy research and outcome measurement in therapy must always have a perspective-transcendent reference point. Otherwise, we run the risk that the given perspective turns into an absolute and represents the criterion for its own relevance. In psychotherapy all this has lead to endless discussions geared not so much towards a gain in knowledge but towards a pure defending of the existing stances.

In one of the previously listed perspectives mentioned by you, it seems that the societal tasks of psychotherapy and the perspective-specific therapeutic goals are matched. This perspective is, therefore, especially important for psychotherapy and is particularly vulnerable to be regarded as absolute. I am referring to the disorder-specific perspective. The therapeutic goals derived from this perspective need no additional empirical rationale for their relevance. Over the course of the last two decades we have seen that a more differentiated elaboration of the disorder-specific perspective has lead to an improved realization of the respective therapy goals at the same time. This has been accomplished by both improved diagnostics and by intensive disorder-specific epidemiological, etiological, and interventions research. The disorder-specific perspective is, therefore, from among all the above mentioned perspectives, the one whose relevance is most indisputable today and, by the same token, the most well elaborated. In psychotherapy's current developmental stage this lends to this perspective a strong dominance over all the other perspectives.

The disorder-specific perspective, however, has by no means always been the dominant perspective in psychotherapy. For decades it was the psychodynamic perspective which was so dominant that it has long been an obstacle to the development of the disorder-specific perspective despite its obvious relevance. The strong influence of the psychodynamic view is the main reason for why it took so long until the individual dynamics of psychological disorders were taken seriously and thoroughly researched, something which is mainly the merit of behavior therapists. They were the first to take the individual dynamics of psychological disorders really seriously, against all criticism from the psychodynamic side which disqualified this as a superficial treatment of symptoms. In the past two decades great progress has been made in the elaboration of the disorder perspective, and still more is to be expected. Even under optimal circumstances it may still take some time until this progress finds its way into the outermost corners of the psychotherapeutic service delivery system. When this eventually does occur, the quality of therapeutic services will have significantly improved compared to today. Unfortunately, conditions for this are not quite optimal right now. The disorder perspective would first have to be separated from its close tie to one particular school of therapy, namely behavior therapy. Only if it is not viewed as part of a specific therapy orientation, will disorder-specific knowledge really be implemented in a changed mental health care practice.

In our discussion earlier, we never equated the perspectives with the therapeutic approaches, but more often viewed their respective procedures through the glasses of the different perspectives outlined. By doing so we have conceptualized the various perspectives as simultaneously valid, supplementary views of the therapeutic process, preparing essentially a different relationship among these perspectives than in the past or even still today. The psychodynamic and the disorder-specific perspective, for instance, as core elements of two therapeutic approaches strongly competing with each other, have historically existed in an exclusionary relationship. Following decades dominated by the psychodynamic perspective, the disorder-specific perspective is currently so much on the advance that a disorder-specific behavior therapy is already being touted as **the** "modern psychological therapy" of the future, compared to which all others are left in its wake (Fiedler, 1997). We should almost have been prepared for this absolutization of one school of therapy, because so much speaks for the significance of this perspective, and because it has, in fact, turned out to be so fruitful.

However, the monopolizing of research findings established from within one perspective for a given school of therapy is not consistent with scientific principles. Those who consider the reception of research findings elaborated from the disorder-specific perspective a scientific obligation for others cannot remove themselves from the demand to do the same with regard to results produced from other perspectives. In addition to the disorder-specific perspective, we have so much empirical knowledge about the significance of other ones for the outcome of therapies that it would not be consistent with a fundamental empirical research attitude to ignore these perspectives, neither for explaining the mechanisms of psychotherapy nor in the planning and implementation of therapies.

Psychologist: Let me continue my summation of our thoughts so far and add to it some theoretical considerations. One disadvantage of the perspectives mentioned as examples earlier is that they are not linked theoretically. If we had a common theoretical frame they would not just simply exist next to each other, but the frame would detail in which ways they could supplement each other.

As we have seen, certain perspectives linked together by Heckhausen's action phase model, designated by us the Rubicon model, help us in productively illustrating the mechanisms of very different forms of therapy. If we canvass the Rubicon landscape from right to left, the right bank of the Rubicon is dominated by the **perspective of intention realization** with the concepts of action control as well as intentional and volitional strength resulting from the product of **desirability** and expected **realizability**. The expectation component can then further be differentiated into different expectations such as outcome expectations, self-efficacy expectations, reaction expectations, and those concerning contingencies in the environment and general expectations for improvement. Expectation concepts in the sense of personality characteristics, such as general control expectations (Rotter, 1966; Flammer, 1990), we have thus far ignored, justifiably if I may say so. Otherwise we would have had to include in our considerations other personality characteristics functioning as moderator variables between therapeutic influences and their effects.

On the left bank of the Rubicon the **perspective of intention change** dominates along with the concepts of processual and content-related motivational clarification, the activation and deactivation of intentions, the wishes, fears and conflicts between them, and corrective emotional experiences related to all those.

The Rubicon model thus implies **two superordinate perspectives**, that of **intention realization** and **intention change**, with each having many sub-perspectives. We have been able to constructively place many phenomena from the world of psychotherapy in relation to these perspectives and concepts. Linking these concepts using the Rubicon model is, according to the above mentioned aspects, a great advantage, because it effectively prevents that they exist as unconnected concepts bearing no relationship to each other, or that the perspectives exclude each other.

The perspectives derived directly from the Rubicon model do not however suffice to adequately explain the effects of therapeutic procedures actually assessed. For this, we had to include additional perspectives. One of these is **processual activation**. Important concepts result from this perspective such as the transformation from process to content, manifesting itself as the transformation from the unconscious to the conscious on the intra-psychic level, and, on the interpersonal level, as meta-communication. These concepts allow themselves to be easily brought together with those of the Rubicon model, while not being derived from this model themselves.

The other necessary extension was the **resource perspective**. While not a result of the Rubicon model, it can easily be connected to its concepts, and it is suggested by an overwhelming amount of research findings.

An additional limitation of the Rubicon model finally lies in the fact that it is an intra-psychic model. It remains limited to the individual. Yet psychotherapy by nature is entirely an interpersonal business and is essentially concerned with interpersonal issues. We therefore must supplement the *intra*-personal perspective of the Rubicon model with an **interpersonal perspective**, or else we are not able to adequately take into account either what is happening on the level of the therapeutic relationship or all other interpersonal relationships of the patient.

For our later discussion I would like to suggest that we plan to think about possibilities for integrating all these perspectives in one unifying view, that includes all those already contained in the Rubicon model as well as those we still need to conceptualize due to empirical results. It should be a view or model more far-reaching than the Rubicon model, but it should concur with the most important assumptions of the latter, so that our previous thoughts are taken into account. This actually takes me already into our next discussion round for which I have gained some clearly outlined ideas in the meantime. Are we ready for this, or does one of you still have something to add to our summary?

Therapist: I most definitely still have something to add. For me this summary is not quite finished. I would like to go back again to your thoughts on the multiple meanings of what happens in therapy from the therapist's perspective.

Each of the perspectives mentioned by you erects its own world of phenomena and meanings. Each of these worlds—that was the fundamental thought behind all we talked about—is important for the effects of psychotherapy. However, a therapist is unable to concurrently develop a consciousness for all these worlds. She has her eye focusing on the processes of either one world or the other. Perhaps she is able to focus attention simultaneously on, or to alternate quickly between two or even three worlds, but it is impossible to focus on all. Whatever is happening in each of these worlds is too complex, and an individual's capacity for simultaneous processing is too limited.

With this, it does not mean these perspectives lose their relevance for whatever is happening. What is happening always has meanings on all these levels or perspectives. So while the therapist focuses her attention on one of these worlds of meaning, attempting to bring about certain effects there, the changes that are taking place simultaneously also have meaning in the other worlds. This can be positive or negative with respect to a good therapeutic outcome.

While the therapist has her attention in the world of intention realization, for instance, attempting to improve the patient's action control, her behavior can have meanings in the interpersonal perspective colliding with the patient's unconscious conflicts. The therapist's behavior, which she may have not reflected on in terms of its interpersonal meaning, has very real impacts for the patient's world of unconscious conflicts. For example, it may strengthen certain fears. This can result in no progress whatsoever on the level of intention realization. The therapist may not find the explanation for the lack of impact her interventions have in the world of meaning on which she currently focuses. To detect the reasons for that and to adequately respond on this level would require a switch in perspective. It would also require possessing well elaborated concepts and ways to perceive, think and react in this other world of meaning. In short, it requires training.

This was only one of many possible examples illustrating that what a therapist strives for in one world of meaning may hinder therapeutic progress in one of the other worlds. This hurdle could just as easily be found in the world of the patient's real interpersonal relationships or in the world of unconscious conflicts. A clarification-oriented therapist trying to make an unconscious fear more accessible to the patient may completely forget, or neglect the world of the resource perspective, over challenging the patient with her approach, albeit being correct with her understanding of the problem on the level of unconscious conflicts. Earlier you gave us another empirically confirmed example about the damaging impact transference interpretations can have on the relationship level (section 1.29). The therapist focuses her attention on the perspective of problem actuation and, in the process, completely forgets the resource perspective.

What happens on one level can have both a negative and positive impact on the other level. Earlier we heard an example from you outlining how a behavior therapist performing exposure therapy for a patient may simultaneously achieve positive effects with respect to unconscious conflictual meanings of "being alone" and "being confined" (section 1.25). It is certainly more the rule than the exception that what happens in therapy can have simultaneous effects on different levels, which is the reason why there may be positive therapeutic effects evolving in these situations that the therapist was not aiming for. You reported earlier on the results of the Menninger study on psychoanalytic long-term therapies showing that therapists who had entirely focused their attention on motivational clarification and intention change quite frequently achieved positive therapeutic effects that we would actually ascribe to the realization of intentions according to the Rubicon model (section 1.21). Most likely, positive expectations for improvement are in most cases achieved, although the therapists are not consciously directing their attention towards this expectation perspective, but rather to a totally different aspect of their procedure.

The simultaneous effects of therapeutic events on various levels of meaning are most likely one of the main reasons that it is not so easy to anticipate the course of therapy from a given point in time. The effects actually coming up oftentimes look quite different from those anticipated by the therapist. I had reported the same thing from my own practice at the beginning (section 1.2). The therapist's attention is concentrated on one perspective and codes the therapeutic events according to these meanings, the events however simultaneously have functional meanings within one or more other perspectives and then lead to unexpected effects. Such effects can emerge although both therapist and patient have their attention focused on other aspects in the therapeutic process. An awareness of effects is not a necessary condition for real effects. I think therapists are frequently mislead by this. They attempt to come up with an explanation for what is occurring in their therapies on the level of meaning preferred by them—exactly how I reported this initially for myself (section 1.2)—however the reasons for what is actually taking effect in reality lie on one or several other levels.

I can imagine that in this way therapists are tempted again and again to form certain assumptions within their preferred perspective that then cannot stand the test of empirical reality. In retrospect, I believe that this has happened to me repeatedly. One could possibly get to the real reasons only by systematically observing and evaluating the therapeutic events from all important perspectives at the same time. I do not envy your task as a therapy researcher in having to deal with this complexity. That is a formidable research task. In light of the simultaneous consequences and influences within the many perspectives, it should not be surprising if only a relatively modest portion of the variance of therapeutic outcome within one perspective can be explained. More cannot be expected according to the thoughts discussed here. If the greatest part of the outcome variance were explainable within one perspective, then that would mean only this perspective would be relevant for the impacts of therapy. According to our ideas this would seem highly unlikely.

For the same reasons it is not surprising how difficult it is to locate truly consistent, major differences in the effects between different forms of therapy. Therapies may differ greatly in their targeted effects, but what is explicitly done on one level not only has a meaning and an effect for this particular level, but has simultaneously different meanings for other levels leading to specific effects on these other levels. According to that, the impact a certain form of therapy has comes closer to the firing of an old musket's scattering of buckshot than to the accurate firing of a precision weapon. The areas of dispersal for the effects of different therapeutic procedures strongly overlap although "aimed" at different points.

The functional relations existing within these various perspectives can be used for bringing about therapeutic effects in an optimal way only if one does this consciously and with a clear goal. Under no circumstances should our ideas be understood by therapists to mean that it does not really matter what one does as a therapist in one of the worlds of meaning, as the effects on another level would be incalculable anyway. A therapist can achieve much better effects if he is knowledgeable in many, and ideally in all, important perspectives and can apply them effectively. Only then can he determine which of the perspectives are especially important for a given patient and then, by simultaneously switching within or by quickly and flexibly moving back and forth between perspectives, interpret the meaning of what happens and influence it in order to achieve certain goals.

1.36   Indication and Case Conception in a General Psychotherapy

Unfortunately, it is not the current everyday practice of most therapists I know—with the exception of maybe those expressly claiming to be eclectic—to switch constantly between various perspectives in a flexible fashion in an effort to view the therapeutic case from as many different angles as possible. Due to their training, preferences and aversions, most therapists have a habit of approaching their patients with mostly the same perspectives in mind. Some of the perspectives we outlined are either completely blocked out or, at the very least, routinely neglected. As this is the norm in the context of a method-oriented psychotherapy the therapists normally do not feel bad about that. The perspectives from which therapies are planned and implemented are largely prede-termined independently of the individual patient. Within the perspectives, differential indication decisions are made but only within these pre-determined perspectives.

One example for that is the disorder perspective. Within the disorder perspective it has been increasingly well-detailed which therapeutic procedures are particularly suited for which disorders. When I began my career as a therapist most of these differentia-tions did not yet exist. If we are to experience even further advances in this area, as you promise, attributing those disorder patterns—for instance with patients demonstrating certain disorder patterns consistent with DSM categories—to specific therapeutic actions which are described in manuals will become ever more possible. I share your concern that these easily available, close-at-hand aids could have the effect that therapists do not develop or will lose the awareness for this is being just one perspective among many that can be considered as relevant for psychotherapy. In such a scenario their patients would not profit much from this progress. They would be treated in accordance with a marvelous, empirically valid manual, but by therapists who are blind to the many other influences impacting the therapeutic outcome of their patients on other levels of meaning.

In reality, I think one can be somewhat relaxed about this. It may only be an intermediate phase in the development of psychotherapy. If psychotherapy research continues to assess the objective effects of such disorder-specific manualized therapies, then those which neglect important perspectives would reveal a limited effectiveness.

In addition, the increased usage of manualized therapies in everyday practice will also inevitably reveal other limits of this particular therapeutic conception. In my practical experience, there are so many patients who are severely suffering but who do not fall into any DSM category with their problems, and so many others with several DSM diagnoses in combination, that the attempt to prescribe a certain disorder-oriented treatment plan produces great difficulty. I therefore believe that therapists who more or less limit their view to the disorder perspective will, in the long run, not do any better than those therapists, who have absolutized other perspectives, such as the psychodynamic, for instance, and who are eventually confronted with a limited effectiveness of their therapies. However, I also believe that behavior therapy has in the meantime developed beyond the point where limiting itself to the disorder-specific perspective poses a great risk. Only recently, one of the leading behavior therapists, Schulte (1996), presented a dual-therapy model, in which he ranks the relationship perspective equal in importance to the disorder perspective. The basis for this major developmental step forwards from classical behavior therapy was that there were so many empirical research results demonstrating, without a doubt, that whatever takes place on the relationship level has great significance for the therapeutic outcome. I believe developments like that are irreversible.

If the research situation regarding other perspectives gained significant momentum equal to that gained for the relationship perspective, then behavioral therapists like Schulte would most likely not hesitate to also draw the appropriate conceptual consequences. In detail, such consequences may look different from the ones we drew out of the current state of research, but they would represent a variation of essentially the same effort, namely to draw conceptual consequences from the results of psychotherapy research for an understanding of therapy, similar to what Schulte has already accomplished with his dual therapy model. Ultimately, this means a step in the direction of a general psychotherapy as we understand it here. We are dealing with the same endeavor: Psychotherapy must not orient itself towards ideologies, but instead towards the empirically best-founded concepts available.

Of course, we can draw different consequences from the respective state of research. I am far from assuming that the view developed in the course of our discussion represents the only sensible interpretation of the current research status. It does, however, very much agree with my practical experiences, and I can make rather good use of it in my daily work. That is actually more than I had hoped for when we began this conversation.

I would like to return one more time to the problem of how to come to an indication. The possibility exists for differential indications **within** the various perspectives. This would be the case if, for example, due to a patient's specific psychopathological symptomatology, a therapist decides which disorder-specific procedures he should treat the patient with. Our considerations, however, yield the necessity for a preliminary indication previous to that in the sense of an explicit psychological decision about which perspectives seem especially relevant for the therapy with this particular patient. Every therapist who works method-oriented has, independently of the patients, de facto already made pre-decisions about how to eventually treat the patients coming into therapy. A large portion of indication and therapy planning is thus accomplished non-patient-oriented. Because of this, a considerable portion of the existing therapeutic possibilities available for the patient in question will inevitably not be fully exhausted, or worse yet, not even considered.

In my opinion, our reflections inescapably lead to the conclusion that the decision on the priority of perspectives must be made in a **patient-oriented** way. For each case it must be determined anew which perspectives are particularly important for the patient. For that, essentially all perspectives have to be considered. This is currently not customary and happens only in exceptional circumstances. Usually, the institution or the therapist the patient ends up with will be the decisive factor determining which perspectives will be considered for him, and which not. If a patient finds himself with a therapist who performs individual therapies almost exclusively, this therapist, in comparison to an interpersonally oriented therapist, will normally pay much less attention to the question of whether for this particular patient a group, couples or family therapy setting would be best indicated considering the aspects of resource activation and process activation of the patient's most important problems. It would be the same the other way around.

A basically clarification-oriented therapist will find something in need of clarification in every patient, most likely disregarding the many possibilities of the disorder-specific mastery of problems which could also be taken into consideration for this patient. Vice versa, disorder-oriented therapists tend to reduce their case understanding largely to the elaboration of the disorder-specific dynamics, taking into account other factors, such as intra-psychic conflicts and interpersonal relationship patterns, only if their disorder-specific procedures are unsuccessful. The list of such examples is endless.

If we conceive the indication to be a scientifically-based decision about which perspectives from among those previously delineated are relevant for a particular patient's therapy, and which to a lesser degree, we have to state that in today's psychotherapeutic practice such professional decisions regarding psychological indications are just not existing at all. A large portion of the de facto decisions regarding indication result from the patient's own selections. Their decision about who to turn to with their problems is far from a scientifically sound decision of what would be the best treatment. Lack of knowledge and misinformation about the therapeutic possibilities and their actual effects, just as much as irrational preferences and aversions due to external appearances of the therapeutic approaches, lead to decisions very different from those produced by a systematic diagnostic examination which takes into regard all relevant perspectives. Still another large segment of de facto indication decision happens through the assignment of the patient to a particular therapist or institution. These assignments are frequently made by persons who, due to their lack of information or questionable convictions, take into consideration only a small portion of the therapeutic possibilities available. We must therefore assume that this way of arriving at an indication does not lead, on average, to a situation in which the patient will receive the optimal treatment. Only if we could replace the way indications are established now with scientifically-based professional decisions that take into account all perspectives, could we expect a marked improvement in psychotherapeutic practice.

Ideally, a professional indication decision should result from a diagnostic examination that considers all relevant perspectives and that takes place prior to the actual therapy. In this diagnostic phase the therapist involved in the examination would have to take into account all relevant perspectives in his diagnostics, gathering enough information for each so that he is able to make those indication decisions, that later, after having worked out a more detailed case conception, would be difficult to revise.

We have stated clearly how important it is to induce positive expectations for improvement at the beginning of a therapy. A professionally competent, thorough diagnostic examination can only lead to the patient having the impression that he is in competent hands. The diagnostic examination in itself then, even if not actually directed towards bringing about changes, can therefore contribute considerably to the induction of positive expectations for improvement. The extent to which this will be the case depends on the extent to which the patient perceives the clinic or institution or the therapist doing the diagnostics as a positive resource. This in turn depends on how professional both the institution and the diagnostic process appear as well as on the therapist's competence and the experiences the patient makes in his relationship with her. If the patient feels understood and accepted by the therapist in his own concerns, and senses that the therapist is engaged in these concerns, then this creates, in combination with an impression of competence, a very good basis for the emergence of positive expectations for improvement. The only thing still missing is the offering of a credible treatment rationale. Fulfilling this third criterion of the four, which are, according to Frank (section 1.4) necessary for the induction of positive expectations for improvement, must be the psychological goal of the diagnostic process, whereas attaining the fourth criterion, the competent realization of this treatment rationale, would then be the task of the actual therapy.

The task of the diagnostic investigation would be to get the patient on the right track, both mentally, that is to say with respect to his expectations and, realistically, that is to say with respect to the therapy he actually receives. A well-considered decision on what the best therapeutic setting would be is especially important in the diagnostic phase. This requires adopting the interpersonal perspective. Which of the possible therapeutic settings: individual, couples, family or group therapy, is best suited to processually activate the patient's problems in need of change? Under the resource perspective, which of these settings offers the best chances? Perhaps a combination of settings will be the best solution regarding the considerations arising from both perspectives.

Is a specific disorder so relevant for this patient that a disorder-specific approach should be given high priority? What would then be required from the patient? How are the demands this therapy puts on the patient to be evaluated from the resource perspective? How likely is it that the patient will be receptive and able to meet these requirements? From both the problem and relationship perspective, how are the demands this therapy puts on the patient to be evaluated? In performing the disorder-specific procedure, does the therapist run the risk of getting into difficulty with the patient either on the unconscious conflict level or the relationship level?

Are there wishes or fears or even unconscious conflicts on the patient's part that might be relevant for what sort of person would be the optimal therapist for the patient, for instance concerning gender, age or interaction style? Once again this would have to be evaluated from the angle of both the processual activation of problems and the resource perspective.

In terms of goals, should the therapy be concentrating on intention realization/problem solving or on intention change/clarification, or both? Again, this also has to be considered from both the resource and problem perspective. Which problems should the therapy focus on? What demands does this put upon the patient? Is the patient ready and able to participate in a therapeutic procedure set on this goal?

For the therapist eventually taking on the therapy, are there important hints as to how to design both the therapeutic procedure and the relationship that would enable him to both utilize extant resources, and to avoid a therapeutically detrimental processual activation of problems?

Once all this has been considered by the person doing the diagnostic examination, it is obvious that in most cases she will not simply suggest a manualized treatment, although a disorder-specific treatment may represent an important part of the suggested therapy. From among the therapists and institutions known to her, she will select those that she believes will offer the optimal therapy, closest to the criteria resulting from the diagnostic examination. The therapist who has done the diagnostic examination can summarize the most important points of her suggestion on less than a page and submit this to the therapist doing the actual therapy. Ideally, she will also arrange for the first contact between patient and therapist.

Previous to that she would conclude the diagnostic process by explaining her suggestion to the patient and preparing him, as much as possible, for what to expect and what he himself should contribute to the therapy. The goal of that discussion is the induction of realistic positive expectations for improvement.

A patient having gone through such a diagnostic process prior to beginning a psychotherapy will, on the one hand, actually have better chances for a good outcome than someone ending up in therapy by self-selection or by an uninformed assignment. The reason is that he is more likely to receive a therapy that fits his problems, possibilities and conditions. On the other hand, positive effects can already be expected due to the diagnostic examination itself on the basis of the induction of positive expectations for improvement. At any rate, the therapist eventually conducting the therapy will, compared to a therapist knowing nothing about his patient, not only have a valuable head start in terms of her knowledge, but also in terms of the trust she receives from her patient, since the therapist doing the diagnostics has imparted to the patient that this particular therapist and this particular therapy are ideal for him.

I believe that a psychotherapy service delivery system with such a pre-therapy process would, on average, achieve significantly better therapeutic outcomes than is presently the case. On top of that, such a service delivery system would also be cost-saving because the enormous expenses accumulated so far because of mistaken indications and less than optimal treatments (Meyer et al., 1991) could be considerably reduced. At any rate, the costs resulting from such a pre-therapy diagnostic process would be negligible in comparison to the savings.

I am aware of my having just painted a portrait of psychotherapeutic utopia. Not only do we not have a sufficient number of therapists who are capable of performing such "multi-perspective" diagnostic examinations, there are also not enough therapists for eventually performing the indicated therapies. After all, the latter too would have to be able to think and act in all these perspectives. In their case conception they would have to further detail all those perspectives relevant for the planned treatment rationale, because in order to ??? the patient, they need, of course, a more detailed and concrete case understanding than the diagnosing therapist was able to develop in the course of the relatively short diagnostic process. This, however, could be done in the course of therapy and would already be a part of it.

For case conceptions, questions quite similar to those I just listed for deriving the indication would have to be posed and answered. Yet the information gathering and processing would have to be considerably more concrete and differentiated than is necessary in the pre-therapy diagnostic context, and above all, the information must be brought together into a coherent picture. The therapist should have an understanding about how the patient's mental processes are functionally connected to each other, since the therapist's interventions concentrate on exactly these processes, thereby contributing to their functioning differently in the future as opposed to the way they did before. So the therapist should elaborate a clear understanding of her patient's mental functioning, derive an understanding of the patient's problems from that and use her understanding for intervening in his ongoing mental processes. The working mechanisms we have outlined before can serve as a general guideline, but must be brought from the abstract level on which they are formulated, down to the level of "behavior-in-situations," where the actual therapeutic process takes place. Every concrete realization of a working mechanism is an intervention in what is going on in the moment. For a concrete application of the working mechanisms the therapist should, therefore, have a clear understanding of what is going on, not just between the patient and her or other participants in the therapy, but also for what is going on intrapsychologically in the patient. It is the function of case conceptions to enable such an understanding.

We have no concepts for this task so far. The concepts we discussed do not allow us to develop a good understanding of how the patient lives his or her life and how his or her problems evolve from this. These concepts help us to understand how changes are achieved by psychotherapy. What we have focused on was the therapy itself and the process of change. The priority was not yet to understand what is going on in the patient. So far we have come up with an understanding of the mechanisms of psychotherapy that really does not account for what is mentally going on in the patient. While I am already quite satisfied with what we have so far accomplished, ideally I would still like to gain an even deeper insight into how it is that therapeutic events can lead to long-term changes in the patient's mental functioning. For this we would need concepts about the patient's mental processes. That is, we need a psychology specifically suited to the purposes of psychotherapy. This psychology should agree as much as possible with our previously developed concepts. While mentioning this, I naturally turn to you, our psychologist and basic researcher. Do you believe we are capable of jointly formulating concepts of a psychology that is specifically adapted to the requirements and purposes of psychotherapy, similar to what we did previously for the explanation of therapeutic changes?

Psychologist: I do not feel one hundred percent competent to do this, but if I did not even think it was worth trying I would not be sitting here. Up to this point, I have not been able to contribute all that much to the results we arrived at through our discussion. Our colleague from psychotherapy research actually accomplished the lion's share, which had to do with the nature of the topic in our first round. I am, however, prepared to be more actively involved in our next discussion. You may rightly expect this from me as the issue is to develop a psychology especially suited for therapeutic purposes. Quite frankly, the wording frightens me a bit. But I believe it is all too clear to the three of us that psychology has a different meaning here than when we usually talk about academic psychology. What we aim for is a much more modest endeavor: What exactly can psychology contribute to a therapist's goal of attaining an understanding about what is psychologically going on in his/her patient? What kind of concepts can psychology provide for that? How can the mechanisms of psychotherapy, as they have been outlined by us so far, be psychologically understood? I would like to take on the challenge of explaining all that, because that is why I am here. For right now, however, I think we all deserve a break.

Therapy researcher: We have certainly earned that. I am extremely curious about our next discussion, but for now, I too must gain some distance on what we talked about in our first round. The break will do us all good, and then we can approach our next topic with renewed vigor.

Second Dialogue

Towards a Psychological Understanding of How Psychotherapy Works

Or:

Foundations of Psychological Therapy

Part 1: Mental Processes From a Systems Perspective

2.1 Experience, Behavior and Unconscious Processes in Psychology and Psychotherapy

Therapist: Reflecting on our first conversation, I am actually still wondering about how easy it was to explain the effects of the various therapeutic techniques from a uniform perspective. In the light of this I ask myself even more, how is it possible that the various therapeutic approaches are so difficult to integrate? The fact that therapeutic changes can be induced by different therapeutic approaches is quite clear. Equally obvious is the conclusion that the therapeutic process can be viewed from various perspectives, that from these different perspectives a variety of possibilities arise for intervention, and that these different possibilities can, at least in part, complement rather than exclude one another.

Nonetheless, why do so many therapists get caught up in their original perspective and take so few chances to utilize any of the possibilities outside of their own perspective? There must actually be a significant reason inhibiting the adoption of another perspective. Not even an approximation at the level of theoretical foundations seems to suffice in getting past the obstacles. You had mentioned in our first conversation that by now humanistically-oriented authors (Greenberg, Rice & Elliott, 1993; Sachse, 1996), psychodynamically-oriented (M. J. Horowitz, 1988 a, b, 1991; L. M. Horowitz, 1994) and cognitive-behaviorally-oriented authors (Goldfried & Robins, 1983; Safran & Segal, 1990; Young, 1994) all refer to a schema-theoretical foundation. Yet despite the overlap in the theoretical foundations, the therapeutic techniques derived from these foundations vary significantly. They mostly agree with the conventional procedures of the particular approaches. Some still direct their attention and interventions predominantly to what the patient is experiencing, others focus on what the patient is actually doing, and yet others are aimed at revealing those unconscious processes thought to be underlying both. It is almost as though in retrospect a different, "more modern" theoretical formulation was developed for an essentially unchanged approach.

These various approaches seem not only to imply differences in terms of localizing the causes of psychological problems but also fundamentally different ideas about what constitutes a person's happiness or unhappiness. We might as well speak of different images of man. Could it be that it is, indeed, this level of fundamental beliefs that determines to which therapeutic approach or even kind of psychology a therapist feels drawn? I doubt that most therapists base such fundamental premises or beliefs on explicit reflections or consciously balanced decisions. For many, there is probably more involved on a personal level than just a professional view they apply in the context of their daily work. The decisions about these implicit assumptions are made on a more fundamental level and in a different fashion than via explicit scientific theories. It is the same level of fundamental beliefs on which "religious wars" in philosophy and philosophy of science are being fought. And while the battle ground for these wars is the level of rational reasoning, it seems that the nature of these arguments is almost always a post hoc attempt to rationalize pre-existing beliefs that are not based in rational thoughts or decisions. They are more akin to belated rationalizations of implicit assumptions previously acquired in a different fashion.

In retrospect, it now becomes clear to me that my leaning towards specific therapeutic approaches originally evolved out of such implicit premises and out of an intuitive/emotional decision rather than out of a consciously weighed choice. What I learned in my first years of therapy training was, for the longest time, a welcome yet actually post hoc rationalization of my intuitively-based pre-decisions.

On this level of fundamental beliefs, those who feel drawn to a phenomenological-experiential perspective, can find in Rogers (1951), Perls et al. (1979) and their successors a detailed account for what they are already convinced of. Those leaning towards depth psychology will find in Freud, Jung and others, what they are intuitively seeking, while the theories by Mowrer (1960), Bandura (1977a), Beck (1976) and other empiricists can serve the sober-minded as scientific justifications for their "so-being."

I am not a philosopher of science, but I can hardly imagine that such unreflected premises, which may indicate as much an inclusion of a specific perspective as an exclusion of another, can be the basis for science in the true sense. Science ought to be—or am I maybe too naive?—built on rationally founded explicit premises. Perhaps it is due to these more intuitive premises that many therapists find it difficult to take note of the complete state of knowledge and development in psychotherapy. As a psychologist concerned with basic research, what is your opinion on that? Do you agree? Is my assumption only true for psychotherapy, or do you find this to be the same for psychology?

Psychologist: If I were able to answer right now that this is only true for psychotherapy, I could, indeed, be proud of psychology. You brought up a cross that psychology has had to bear for a long time. If psychology had not carried this load from its beginnings, the discipline would have gotten much further ahead. In psychology as well, just like in psychotherapy, far-reaching pre-decisions about what kind of conclusions one could generally arrive at were made through ultimately irrational exclusions. For instance, someone who assumes that the subject of research in psychology is limited to observable behaviors, will scarcely be able to give a differentiated account of the inner world of experience. He will also not be able to develop a theory of consciousness. For that reason he will also not place any value on the transformation of unconscious into conscious processes as an effective mechanism when applying his concepts to psychotherapy. I would like to give you an example of how long the impacts of this chain of exclusions can last.

Recently, the German news magazine "Der Spiegel" published an issue entitled "Who is 'the self'? New findings in the research on consciousness" (Vol. 16/1996). For a moment I was so naive as to assume that this would be the long-awaited report on the latest findings in psychology, being pleased that finally somebody would present a more positive image of what today's psychology has to offer. Wrong! The contribution was solely about neurobiologists' and philosophers' work and did not waste much time on questions that I as a psychologist am "desperately" interested in. Not so much as one word about psychological research, as though the "self" and the consciousness did not exist at all as subjects of the psychological striving for knowledge. Out of fairness I have to admit that this was not the journalist's fault but merely a reflection of the fact that psychology has only recently reverted to concerning itself again with the question of consciousness as its own research topic. It makes every person who lacks fair knowledge of psychology really wonder: How can it be that a science, after a century of development, is unable to give any sort of reasonable account of what constitutes the core of the human psyche?

Psychology however, suffers not only from the heritage of behaviorism. Restricting one's access to mental processes and to psychological disorders by reducing it to the conscious experience, as was the case with introspective and phenomenological psychology, means excluding all mentally relevant processes not directly reflected in experience. Included therein, for example, are pre-attentive processes of perception and memory which—while occurring below the level of our conscious perceptive ability—influence both our experience and behavior. The processes of non-verbal regulation in relationships which cannot consciously be perceived by us in real time due to our limited capacity for conscious information processing, but do become visible on film in slow motion, serve as another good example. Neither phenomenological nor behaviorist psychology can adequately account for such processes, yet a large section of the so-called cognitive psychology has been concerned with these processes over the last three decades. Perceptual psychology, psychology of memory and emotion are mainly focused on examining all those processes underlying our conscious perceptions, memories and emotions. These processes that are usually inferred from the results of psychological research experiments are largely unrepresented in our conscious experience yet can be considered preconditions for it (Miller, 1962; Neisser, 1974; Mandler, 1975; Nisbett & Wilson, 1977). **As a rule** they are unconscious. Today, it is indisputable that such unconscious processes do exist and that they have a significant impact on our conscious experience and behavior (Shevrin & Dickman, 1980; Marcel, 1983 a, 1983 b; Perrig, Wippich & Perrig-Chiello 1993).

In addition, there are other types of unconscious processes, namely those that were once conscious, but are now running automatically (Schneider & Shiffrin, 1977; Shiffrin & Schneider, 1977). These processes have the capability of entering consciousness but are normally unconscious.

Additionally, an increasing number of authors assume that aside from those processes marked by the qualities of our conscious experience, all sorts of other simultaneously occurring processes must exist which never enter our consciousness but nonetheless have a significant impact on our behavior and mental state. The advantage of this massively parallel information-processing is that it allows much more information to be processed than could be accomplished by conscious information processing which has a rather limited capacity. In return, these processes lack the possibility of being subject to both sharp perception and logical thinking, to language, and to the conscious, deliberate control of action. There are conflicting views on whether these processes are fundamentally different from the conscious processes as well as whether or how they become subject to conscious experience. Most of the authors assume that—unlike the pre-attentive processes which cannot enter consciousness—much of the simultaneously occurring kind of information processing can basically become conscious if it happens to fall into the privileged status of conscious attention. But what this is dependent on and how this is precisely happening, turns out more and more to be a very complex question.

Finally, there are those processes which are completely unconscious, because their entering consciousness is avoided. It is these kinds of unconscious processes that Freud had in mind when he developed his concept of the unconscious. Psychodynamic psychology, parallel to but largely separate from behaviorist and phenomenological psychology, has been dealing with these processes for almost a century. Freud's concept of repression implies that these processes would be conscious had they not been repressed. By now, there is extensive empirical evidence for Freud's basically correct assumption that there is something like a motivated repression. Yet, conceived of from a broader view, the question of how such processes become conscious presents itself as different and more complex than Freud had imagined. The process of becoming conscious does not mean a reversal of repression, since consciousness can by no means be conceived of as the normal condition of mental activity. With the current state of research today, we are faced with the opposite problem. The majority of mental processes remain unconscious. Why and when do some processes become conscious? What actually are the specific functions of the consciousness within the entirety of mental activity?

"Six decades ago our psychoanalytically-oriented predecessors wrestled with the problem of formulating a credible account of the unconscious. Paradoxically, perhaps, having gathered such convincing evidence for the existence of extensive and elaborate nonconscious information-processing in more recent years, contemporary psychologists are now faced with the opposite problem of adequately accounting for the nature and purpose of consciousness itself. How do certain aspects of processing result in conscious experience, and why ?" (Williams et al., pp. 156—157).

How are the various, by nature different, unconscious processes related to behavior and conscious experience? What are their implications for the understanding of psychological disorders? For therapeutic purposes, can one have a direct impact on these processes without taking the long way via the consciousness? What ways are there for one to recognize such unconscious processes in oneself or others? Can I consciously exercise influence on my own unconscious processes? How can a therapist assist a patient in gaining conscious control over unconscious processes?

These questions may force themselves on any therapist inclined to base his or her actions on the state of knowledge of contemporary psychology. They are obviously of great relevance for psychotherapy, although so far only two therapeutic approaches have openly faced these kinds of questions, namely the psychodynamic and the cognitive approach.

The psychodynamic approach, however, has only accounted for one section of unconscious processes, namely those actively avoided by consciousness. Ironically, this fact results in a gross underestimation of the overall significance of the unconscious for mental processes. With a broader view on the significance of the unconscious for all mental processes, it remains to be examined which psychodynamic assumptions regarding mental processes will last and which will have to be dismissed or modified.

The cognitive approach in therapy was founded before most of the research findings on nonconscious processes, commonly known in cognitive psychology as "cognitive processes" or "information processing," were even presented. Accordingly, the principles of treatment originally developed by Ellis (1962) and Beck (1967) cannot be regarded as a consequence of the cognitive psychology research results obtained in the meantime. But cognitive therapy has made the most pronounced efforts towards matching its concepts and methods with the latest research findings.

In my view, however, even cognitive therapy as it presents itself today cannot claim to offer a psychotherapy that is well-grounded in today's empirical psychology and its current state of research. So far, not too many of the perspectives discussed in our first conversation have been acknowledged within the field. But cognitive therapy has definitely gotten closest to this state of research.

I find the term "cognitive" both in cognitive therapy and cognitive psychology misleading and unnecessarily restrictive. In the past, the term might have been historically useful as a contrast to behaviorism. It suggests though that psychology would, entirely or predominantly, be concerned with cognitions rather than with emotion, motivation, behavior, and interactions between individuals as well, which is truly not the case. Empirical psychology focuses on all aspects of mental activity. A newly added aspect after the "cognitive turn" has been the shift of attention in psychology towards the inner processes underlying observable behavior and subjective experience, and towards the study of them. These processes always have something to do with neural activity, but so do emotions and cognitions. Many of these processes happen without consciousness, but it would be inappropriate to emphasize this very property as the nature of the subject matter, since conscious processes also belong to the range of subjects in psychology. Defining a psychology which accounts for all these considerations as **"Science of experience and behavior and their underlying processes"** seems more appropriate to me.

Strictly speaking, academic psychology has only lived up to this definition in the past thirty years. Previous to that, it had excluded at least one of the subjects from the definition. I could imagine that these exclusions which were made for decades bear at least some of the blame for the development and persistence of the present system of schools of therapy, because the most influential ones were all founded prior to this new, more enlightened kind of psychology. One cannot only blame ideologically obsessed therapists who, against all rational argument, ignore concepts and possibilities developed outside of their own approach for preventing the development of a truly scientific kind of psychotherapy. In fact, the irrational exclusions and boundaries between the different schools of therapy had their counterpart, and partially even their roots, in academic psychology.

In order to explore the possibilities of a psychologically based psychotherapy and to examine whether psychology is able to deliver a sound foundation, we will have to look out for concepts within psychology that are as free as possible from the above mentioned exclusions. For what we have in mind, all those concepts are fruitful that establish a link between behavior, experience and their underlying processes that are neither observable nor subject to being experienced. Let me come to the point: We will not be able to locate any psychological approach or theory that would integrate in a unifying framework all processes underlying experience and behavior, but we can be sure to find very interesting research areas which we can try to combine and work into a sufficiently consistent model for thinking suitable for our purpose.

Therapy researcher: It is exactly at this point that I have this big question that I could not answer by myself. Where in the world would one start searching? In light of the fact that the literature in psychology has grown enormously, the desire to stay abreast of the most important journals could make one despair already.

Psychologist: As we got down to explaining the various therapeutic methods, I was inclined to say the same. Without your guidance through this jungle of psychotherapy research results so confusing for outsiders, the rest of us would have been lost. I believe it is my turn now to take over as the guide. After all, I would not have joined in this discussion without bringing some of my own specific ideas of how to approach the subject.

Therapist: Following my comments at the beginning of this conversation, I especially cannot wait to find out about how one can connect the various manifestations of mental activity that you distinguished and have them relate to each other. Wouldn't it make sense first to work out a foundation which we could use to deal with all the individual questions that need to be answered at a later point?

2.2 A Systems Conception of the Interaction between Behavior, Experience and Unconscious Processes

Psychologist: I would suggest the exact same thing. As a starting point for further consideration, I would like to introduce to you a model which establishes a relationship between experience and behavior in such a fashion that might give us a few ideas for some of the issues to be dealt with. It is a model by William Powers (1973), which I have chosen, because it explains very well the change of perspective that contemporary psychology implemented on a broad scale. The way the title of Powers' book is phrased, reflects this change of perspective: *Behavior: The Control of Perception.* Behavior as a way of controlling perception? Given that psychology at the time was still oriented towards the stimulus-response paradigm, this was a thought "against the grain." Behavior was conceived of as a function of preceding and subsequent conditions, mostly of external stimulus conditions, and following the "cognitive turn," increasingly of internal conditions as well, such as thoughts, emotions, etc. The perception of stimuli was taken for granted. All of a sudden, perception shifted to the center of attention and became the actual basis for our subjective experience. The ultimate goal was to generate certain perceptions, and behavior was the tool by which to achieve it. This view sheds a new light on the typical psychological experiment.

Viewed from this perspective, even the rat in a Skinner box appears to be a rather rationally acting creature. It is hungry and it makes sense that it wants to satisfy its hunger. Under the given circumstances, it does exactly what is required in order to satisfy its needs. It presses the lever in order to get the food. From a rat's perspective— if it were the rat controlling its perceptions through its behavior—the situation, essentially viewed by the experimenter as successful conditioning, looks quite differently. I was once very amused by a caricature capturing this change of perspective rather well: Two rats are sitting in a Skinner box, when one rat says to the other: "Look at this, I have full control over this guy. Each time I press the lever, he throws a food pellet through the opening!"

Confronted with such a plausible change of perspective, one is inclined to ask why others had not come up with this before. Why was it exactly Powers who was able to adopt a new perspective on mental functioning? The answer lies partly in Powers' unusual academic career. Powers actually came to psychology in an unusual way. Previously, he had worked for years as a physicist, astronomer and systems engineer, and had published numerous scientific papers and developed patented technical devices for astronomical purposes, before eventually taking an interest in psychology. As a psychologist he continued to strive towards developing a concrete model of mental functioning, a model which meticulously details down to the neural roots how processes in the human organism actually function.

With this, Powers anticipated a development that can be considered one of today's leading research trends: The cooperation between neurobiologists and cognitive psychologists in an interdisciplinary cognitive science (Roth & Prinz, 1996) with the overall goal of giving an account of man's cognitive performance down to its neural roots. The neural foundations add a fourth class of variables to the examination of behavior, experience and their underlying non-conscious mental processes in cognitive psychology. In light of the complexity, there is again a tendency among some cognitive psychologists to exclude subjective experience from being a research subject. Eimer (1996 a) expressly demands this as a requirement for constructive cooperation between neurobiology and psychology: "To sum up, the brain-consciousness-problem" does not exist, not for cognitive psychology nor for neurobiology focused on the foundations of mental processes, because in cognitive psychology—unlike in everyday psychology— the experiential aspect of mental processes is systematically excluded. By precluding the conscious experience, cognitive psychology can generate descriptions of cognitive performances and processes, the foundations of which neurobiology is able to examine in the brain" (Eimer, 1996 a, p. 433). This methodologically-founded exclusion reminds one all too well of the explanations with which behaviorism excluded experience as a research subject. Such attitudes have led to the kind of problem I addressed earlier as illustrated by the Spiegel article on the self and consciousness. The problem is that psychology is not even consulted when it comes to matters that clearly are genuinely psychological questions.

Excluding experience is exactly the opposite of what Powers had in mind. In fact, it was precisely these exclusions made by behaviorism that he intended to get away from. The pivotal question Powers was concerned with was that of the "material" comprising the contents of our experience. Luckily not all cognitive psychologists and not even all neurobiologists share Eimer's view. From both sides, the psychological and the neurobiological, there are by now a variety of highly interesting discourses on the problem of consciousness. I will go deeper into that later in our conversation. Eimer's quote however indicates that the exclusions criticized by me do not just stem from psychology's dim and distant past, but that there are, indeed, periodical tendencies towards such exclusions.

By making the relationship between experience and behavior a core issue in his model, Powers was intent on getting away from some of these exclusions in psychology. His initial question was: In what ways do organisms relate to their environment, and how is it that one can even have a perception of the environment? His answer: In terms of what we receive, we are in contact with our environment exclusively through the receptors of our sense organs, in terms of what impact we have, through our muscle movements. The impact our environment has on our receptors leads to stimulations which only vary in intensity. Our individual receptors can perceive and pass on nothing other than the **intensity** with which they are stimulated.

Intensity of stimulation is thus the only **neural signal** which the individual receptors can pass on via the nerve pathways to the other parts of the nervous system. Several intensity signals from various receptors are then sent to cell groups specialized in this task, in which these multiple first order signals will be integrated into a new second order signal. The output of this **integrator** is a new quality neural signal. Intensity signals of various receptors are converted into **sensations** by the first integrator. These could be any sensation, from that of color or tone to the taste of lemonade caused by the integration of intensity signals of sweet and sour receptors.

The taste of lemonade has now become a perceptive quality which would not exist without the transformation of the first order signals, the intensity signals, in the organism. The taste of lemonade does not exist without an organism experiencing the sensation, even if there were, chemically seen, the exact kinds of molecules gathered in a glass. Our phenomenal reality does not exist "outside" in the environment, but it is created by the organism through a multi-level transformation process.

In the next transformation step a new perceptive quality from second order neural signals, i.e. from sensations, is created, namely that of **configurations**. Configurations abstract invariant relations between sensations. A configuration could be the perception of a chair, for instance. The configuration remains invariant even if the chair is being looked at from different angles. A certain chord played by different instruments in different octaves can be considered a configuration as well. Here again, for the transformation of second order neural signals into those of third order, very specific types of nerve cells are responsible without which a transformation of such kind could never occur.

A configuration is a holistic pattern. If somebody showed me an image displaying only fragments of a chair, the above described transformation process would nonetheless create the perception "chair." What we learn from this is that we carry certain perceptive expectations into the environment, testing whether the actual stimuli correspond with the expectations. These perceptive expectations are performances achieved by our memory. Gestalt psychology in particular has studied the creation of holistic configurations (Gestalten) from fragmentary stimulus patterns in-depth.

In a further step of transformation third order neural signals are being converted into a new perceptive quality, that of **changes**. Transitions from one configuration to the next generate fourth order neuronal signals perceived by us as **movement**. Such changes in configurations are experienced by us, for instance, while driving a car.

Therapy researcher: May I interrupt here with a question? You mentioned that neural signals undergo qualitative transformations. Does Powers really assume that the emergence of these different perceptual qualities can be linked to specific neuronal structures or patterns? And if so, is this mere speculation or are we talking about documented facts?

Psychologist: Powers did indeed offer some neurophysiological support for his model, but only up to the fourth level. The model, however, is comprised of a total of nine levels. He assumed that neurophysiological evidence would emerge eventually for the higher levels as well, but—unfortunately—no such data were available at the time he was writing his book. He could have simply refrained from offering any neurophysiological support, focusing instead on a purely psychological model; however, doing so would have conflicted with his original purpose. Powers regarded his model as an accurate description of reality, including even neural processes. He viewed his first four levels as a model of actual neural processes, not just as fictitious constructs within hypothetical models.

Great progress has been made in the brain sciences since the publication of Powers' book. Therefore, to answer your question based on what Powers wrote back then would mean providing outdated information. It makes more sense to summarize instead what current neurobiological research has to say about the neural foundations of the processes Powers described. However, that would require somewhat lengthier discourse (see section 2.8). For now, allow me to continue with a basic description of Powers' model; I haven't even gotten to the parts I consider the most relevant for our purposes. I am sure many opportunities for more focused discussions will arise as we go along— that is one reason why I have decided to begin with this model. First, let's get an overview of the model in its entirety, and then we will focus on specific components or related questions.

I had arrived at the fourth level—that of changes. Through the next transformation, structured **sequences** are generated. This means that changes must occur within a certain order. A good example of this principle would be a melody. Even though every tone in the melody can be exchanged, the melody itself remains the same. The constant underlying this perceptual quality is temporal order.

Here you can see again how our perceptions are profoundly influenced by our expectations. When we know a melody well, we expect at a specific point in the melody to hear specific tones, and we are surprised if suddenly we hear something else, or we are left hanging in suspense when a tone is missing. Indeed, when we listen to someone practicing an instrument, this sense of anticipation—this waiting for the fulfillment of our perceptual expectancies—can be quite torturous!

The next level concerns the perception of **relationships** between two or more perceived events. These can be causal relationships—such as one billiard ball striking another—temporal relationships, probabilistic relationships, and so forth. Regarding the storage of relationship perceptions in memory, we would have to assign relationships established via classical conditioning (associations) to this level of regulatory activity. Once associations between stimuli have been formed through temporal contingency, the presentation of one stimulus will trigger the expectation of the other. The perception of these kinds of relationships is indispensable to our sense of orientation in the world.

On the seventh level, termed the program level by Powers, the signals from the levels we described earlier are integrated into **action programs**. Programs are structured sequences of actions and events directed towards a common goal. Their essential features are conditional branches—points in the stream of action demanding a check or a decision. The principles of logic and reason prevail on this level. This is the level of consciously controlled action upon which self-awareness or consciousness typically resides. Programs can have complex structures and may in themselves be hierarchically interlocked. Figure 2.1 schematically depicts the hierarchical-sequential structure of action organization on the program level. Figure 2.2 shows a routine course of action—the purchase of a necktie—deconstructed as a sequence of actions and decisions on the program level. I have adopted this example from Becker (1995).

Given their internal logic, the processes transpiring on the program level can be depicted conveniently via flowcharts. Certain functional characteristics define this level as unique and separate from others. One should not take the term "level" too literally, though, given that events on the program level can in turn be broken down into hierarchically organized components. Programs consist of hierarchy levels that are mutually interlocked. They do not always have a distinct pyramid-shape as suggested in Figure 2.1. There are no predetermined, fixed hierarchy levels. Rather, structures change depending on the type of action and its context. Depictions such as Figures 2.1 and 2.2 are intended to show functional relationships among processes rather than fixed structures.

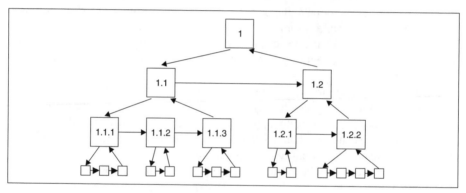

Figure 2.1:
Schematic Representation of hierarchical-sequential action organization according to Volpert (1983). Action 1 consists of the sequence of both action parts 1.1 and 1.2. These, in turn, consist of the sequence of action parts 1.1.1, 1.1.2 etc., which again can be broken up into sequences of action parts.

On the program level, many links become evident between Powers' theory and other psychological concepts. For instance, Miller, Galanter, and Pribram's (1960) TOTE-unit, which practically ended stimulus-response-psychology, belongs to this conceptual level. Similar concepts include Schank and Abelson's (1977) "scripts," Hacker's (1986) CCF-unit (comparison-change-feedback unit), Volpert's (1983) hierarchical-sequential action organization, Ford's (1987) "Behavior Episode Schemata," and other schema-theoretical and action-theoretical approaches. This list demonstrates that the program level places us squarely in the midst of information processing psychology and the psychology of action, which continue to be major influences in contemporary psychology.

Learning that occurs on the program level transcends simple conditioning through temporal contingency. More complex logical and meaningful relations are formed here, and such changes involving meaningful relationship patterns are at the core of what is meant by the term, "higher learning."

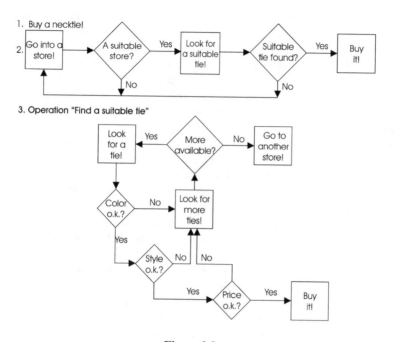

Figure 2.2:
Example for describing the flow of everyday actions on the program level
by connecting hierarchical and sequential TOTE-unities.
The figure is taken from Becker (1995, p.74).

This higher learning, however, includes and builds upon simpler forms of learning—that is exactly the point Powers was trying to convey. According to the logic of the model, we may also assume that higher level processes impact lower level ones. Learning on the program level, for example, should influence simple conditioning processes. There is indeed evidence for just that. I shall return to this point later on (section 2.16). The transition from the relationship level to the program level marks, so to speak, the transition from behaviorist stimulus-response psychology to information processing psychology and to the psychology of action.

I would not have introduced this model though if it ended with the program level. In fact, it is only here that the model becomes interesting for the field of psychotherapy. Beyond the program level, Powers assumes the existence of two additional levels. The next higher level is termed that of **principles**, and above that, at the highest regulatory level, the **system level**. Given that the transition from the sixth to the seventh level marked the move from stimulus-response psychology to the psychology of action, we have good reason to be curious how the inclusion of an eighth and ninth level in turn transcends the psychology of action. Let's keep our suspense in place for a moment, though, while I address the aspect of Powers' control theory emphasized in the title of his book (i.e., perception).

On each level of the hierarchically organized system, incoming neural signals corresponding to particular perceptual qualities are linked via feedback loops to specific kinds of behaviors. These behaviors serve to align the perceived signal with a specified reference value, provided that a discrepancy between the signal and the reference value has been detected. Such a feedback-loop is depicted schematically in Figure 2.3.

Behavior, then, does not function to create certain objective conditions or end products, but instead is aimed towards achieving and maintaining subjective perceptions of very specific qualities. Even if behaviors create these perceptions via their effects on the environment, the distinction is not an exercise in splitting hairs. Indeed, the implications of this distinction for our understanding of mental functioning are profound.

On each level, the incoming neural signal—generated itself via level-specific transformations of low-level receptor intensity signals—is compared against a reference value, which, in turn, is provided top down from the next higher level. If a comparison yields an **incongruence** between the incoming ("is") signal and the reference ("should") value, certain level-specific behaviors are activated. Based on biologic predisposition or prior experience, certain behaviors are deemed effective at reducing the sensed discrepancies; these behaviors are then selected and executed. Each higher level provides desired perceptions or perceptual expectancies for the lower levels, and the behavioral output aims to create the conditions for a match for these expectations. Thus, both behavior and perception are oriented towards attaining certain desired perceptions. Ultimately, perceptual expectancies are determined by the highest system level. In terms of output, behavior **potentials** are activated that in the past have proven effective at reducing perceived discrepancies. The actual behavior in each specific situation must of course be adjusted, depending on the varying unique circumstances in a given setting. Without such fine-tuning, behaviors would have little chance of leading to the desired perceptual outcome. Figure 2.4 depicts the hierarchical interlocking or layering of feedback loops among the different levels.

On the one hand, then, lower levels function as the prerequisite foundation for higher regulatory levels. Phylogenetically speaking, each higher regulatory level with its new perceptual quality and corresponding behavioral potentials constitutes an **emergence** of lower level processes. By emergence, I mean that through interactions of processes on one level, an entirely new quality of perception and behavioral potential—a new regulatory level—is created. This principle of lower level processes serving as the precondition for higher levels applies throughout the nervous system. Lesions or degenerative processes that interfere with normal development of lower level perceptions are linked with profound disturbances on higher regulatory levels. For instance, some neurons exist that are specialized on the recognition of faces (configurations) (Roth, 1995, pp. 158—161). In his book, *The Man Who Mistook His Wife for a Hat*, Oliver Sacks described the rather tragic consequences associated with malfunction in these cells. Let's revisit this issue later, when we learn more about the neurobiological underpinnings of Powers' regulatory levels.

On the one hand, then, lower level processes are essential for intact higher-order functioning. On the other hand, though, higher regulatory levels influence lower levels in the hierarchy. Higher levels determine lower level perceptual expectancies or setpoints, and they activate specific behavior potentials. This "top down" principle posits that lower regulatory levels submit to the order imposed by higher order reference values. In synergetics, the somewhat graphic term "**enslavement**" illustrates this principle. Similarly, higher regulatory levels correspond to the synergetic "order patterns"

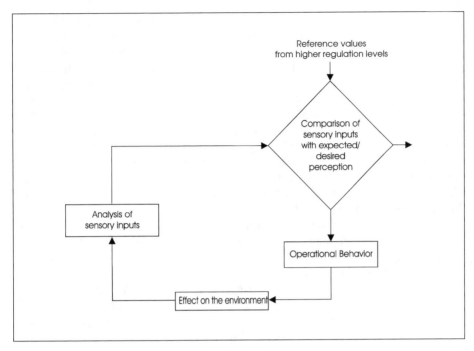

Figure 2.3:
Feedback circuit (loop) for the modulation of incongruence signals as the core element of Powers' control theory (1973).

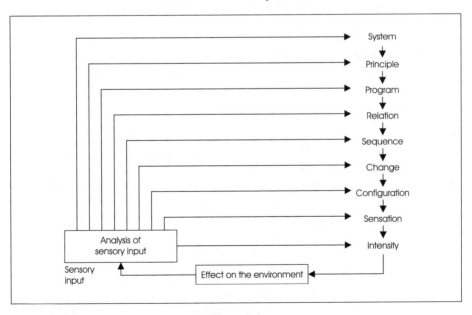

Figure 2.4:
Hierarchically interlocked feedback loops with the nine regulation levels by Powers.

or "attractors." Later on, when we will examine the pathogenesis of mental disorders and the process of change in psychotherapy from a dynamic systems perspective, you'll see how the concepts of emergence and enslavement will again play a critical role then (section 2.44). Let me just mention here that these ideas can also be applied to less "dynamical" systems like that of Powers. As far as I can see, the common feature here is the principle of hierarchical organization, which has been widely recognized as an essential component of complex systems. Powers' model, which he termed "control theory," is in itself a sophisticated elaboration of this principle within the field of psychology. Carver and Scheier (1981) adopted the main principles of control theory and developed them further, to the point that, today, control theory is no longer linked inextricably with Powers' name and idiosyncratic ideas. Through Carver and Scheier's adaptation, one might say that control theory has become a "de-powered" but nevertheless very influential theory of mental functioning.

I interrupted my discussions of the different regulatory levels when we were talking about the program level, but I had also mentioned that the whole model only starts to get interesting for psychotherapy once we arrive at the top two levels. Let's take a closer look at these highest levels of regulation.

Much of everyday life occurs on the **program** level. Most of the time, we are busy pursuing goals that we are aware of, we make decisions about alternative paths to get there, we take action accordingly, we check to see if our intentions pan out as planned, we revise our goals and plans over time, and so on. With our discussion of Heckhausen's action model—which took up much of our first conversation—we have already been exposed to one sophisticated model of mental processes on the program level. These issues also have obvious relevance for psychotherapy—therapists are vitally concerned with their clients' everyday actions, their decisions to pursue certain goals, and their conscious efforts towards attaining these goals.

Therapy researcher: In fact, the very process of doing psychotherapy can be described and analyzed from a program level perspective. For example, Thommen, Ammann, and von Cranach (1988) used the method of "video confrontation" to compare in-session activities of three therapists from different schools. As hypothesized, therapists' "social representations" differed in this study, depending on therapists' theoretical orientations. In other words, therapists from different schools pursued different goals and strategies. Vogel (1983) also demonstrated that behavior therapists working with agoraphobic patients tended to be more effective to the degree they pursued therapeutic goals with greater consistency. Research has also shown, however, that therapists do not always base their actions on the principles of logic and reason (Caspar, 1995). According to Caspar's analyses of information processing among experienced and inexperienced therapists, many decisions in initial therapy sessions are based on intuition. Of course, that does not mean these decisions are necessarily wrong.

Psychologist: Intuition happens outside of conscious information processing. It would make sense, then, to suspect that intuitive decision making takes place on a regulatory level different from Powers' program level. Intuitive reasoning cannot be depicted easily via flowcharts because—by definition—it does not follow the neat, rational patterns of logic. The limits we encounter when we presume that therapists rely on rational reasoning demonstrate exactly this point, that there must be other principles guiding the regulation of complex behavior—principles beyond the logical or rational control of action. The field of psychology has only recently begun to recognize the existence of these qualitative differences in regulatory modes and to investigate the relations among these levels (Kirkpatrick & Epstein, 1992; Epstein, Lipson, Holstein & Huh, 1992; Denes-Raj & Epstein, 1994; Epstein, 1994; Prinz, 1996). Later we will return to these non-conscious, non-rational principles of information processing and action control as well as their links to conscious activity. Indeed, without a thorough understanding of these issues, we have little chance of ever fully understanding mental disorders, which—almost by definition—do not follow the laws of logic and reason.

Before reviewing the literature on non-conscious regulatory processes, though, I wish to say a few words about the highest levels of regulation within control theory. Some interesting implications for psychotherapy arise from the interconnections among the program level and the two highest regulatory levels and some research evidence to support these interesting ideas exists, but we will get to those later. Perhaps I can spark your curiosity about the research results by first describing what takes place beyond the program level.

2.3 The Interplay of Conscious and Unconscious Processes on the Higher Levels of Psychological Activity

When we ask a person what he or she is doing at a given moment, the response we receive will most likely describe behavior on the program level. However, this would not be the only reasonable way to respond, not even if we restricted ourselves to a single activity. According to Powers' model we could expect nine different correct responses—one corresponding to each regulatory level. Figure 2.5 uses an example adopted from Carver and Scheier (1981) to illustrate the regulatory levels of the model.

In this example, visitors have just dropped in by surprise and their host, wanting to offer them something to drink, is preparing to make some coffee. When asked about his current activity, the host might respond on the lowest regulatory level: "I'm flexing the muscles of my hand with just the right intensity to pick up the measuring spoon." On the program level, he might respond: "I'm making coffee for my guests." On the highest level his answer might be: "I'm becoming self-actualized"—perhaps with the additional explanation, "...by being friendly and hospitable towards people I care about."

The responses, "I'm being friendly towards others" (principle level) or "I'm becoming self-actualized" (system level) might tend to evoke some laughter if used in real life. Nonetheless, they might reflect reality. To illustrate with another example, let's consider what might happen if we saw someone sitting at a café, reading a newspaper by himself, and we asked him what he was doing. We would be surprised to hear a response such as: "I'm protecting my self-esteem." This response would correspond to the system level, and it might in fact be accurate. Indeed, the newspaper reader might suffer from a lack of friends or a spouse, and he might be embarrassed by being alone in public—in a setting, moreover, where most customers are accompanied by others.

To create the impression (to others as well as to himself) that his solitary status reflects a conscious choice rather than unwanted isolation, he might focus all the more intently on the act of reading his newspaper.

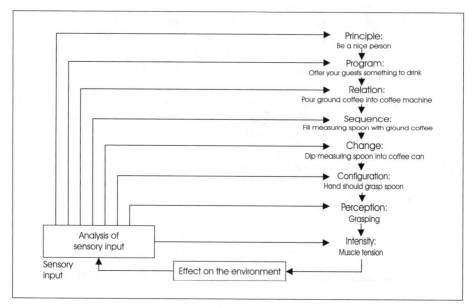

Figure 2.5:
Example of a control theory view of a routine activity,
which can be interpreted differently on each regulatory level.
The figure is taken from Becker (1995, p. 79).

These examples may suffice to show why Powers assumes the existence of levels beyond the program level, where conscious awareness usually resides and social interactions are normally described. These higher order levels supply the reference value for the program level, guiding and directing our conscious activities. Often, these higher order goals prevail across numerous situations or even life domains, for instance, take the higher order goals from our examples: "Be friendly towards others," and, "Protect your self-esteem." These intentions determine perceptions and behaviors of our fictitious characters, not only in specific situations, but they influence perceptions and actions across many life domains.

Given the enormous importance of these highest regulatory levels for our understanding of mental illness, I will return to this topic at a later point (see section 2.36). To ensure that our knowledge base is sufficiently broad to allow for an understanding of the psychotherapeutic process, I shall now describe some of the more basic features of mental functioning. Based on what we have said so far, let's formulate a preliminary summary:

Any single action in a given situation carries multiple meanings for the individual. Actions are influenced by conscious intentions in each situation, but they simultaneously function to satisfy higher order goals. These higher level intentions may or may not be consciously accessible. Our newspaper reader, for example, may have some conscious awareness that his actions serve to protect his self-esteem, even though his present focus may be more concretely on the act of reading. On the other hand, he may have little or no awareness of this deeper function, even though he might easily accept and consciously recognize this point in the context of therapeutic conversation. A third possibility is that he is light-years removed from such deeper insights, that he might protest furiously when confronted with well-meaning therapeutic interpretations in this regard. Indeed, his conscious experiencing of the situation may be restricted entirely to the program level. He may feel but a vague sense of discomfort; to an observer, it might appear that he seems tense. His constant monitoring of his surroundings might suggest an unusual level of vigilance for someone who is just casually reading the newspaper. He himself might attribute his own discomfort to the noise level, to the slow service, or perhaps to other, similar factors.

Of these three individuals, whom would you prefer to see as your patient in therapy? Which types of problems or concerns would arise from their different perceptual perspectives, their modes of consciousness? The first client, arriving for the first session with a clear sense that his social isolation compromises his self-esteem, may be a satisfying case for you as a therapist, especially if you prefer a realization-oriented or problem-solving approach to dealing with patient concerns. You might use realization-oriented therapeutic techniques to improve the client's social network or work on his cognitions in relevant situations.

The second might also be quite satisfying to work with given his readiness and ability for genuine insight. Even a relatively brief, clarification-oriented course of supportive therapy might elucidate the situation for him and suggest ways to approach the problem—perhaps alone or with the help of the therapist.

Our third newspaper reader would be unlikely to show up for psychotherapy to begin with. Certainly, he would not describe low self-esteem as his main concern. Let's assume him to already be in therapy with you because of other symptoms—psychosomatic ones, perhaps. Helping this client would pose a far more difficult challenge. It might be relatively easy for you as the therapist to conclude that much of the client's behavior serves to protect his fragile self-esteem. But it would be hard, if not impossible, to discuss this fact in session—even innocuous questions or hints in this direction might evoke his outrage in protection of his self-esteem. It would be difficult to help this patient given that one's conceptualization of the problem cannot transcend the program level—the only level where discussion is tolerated.

I will not proceed any further with my therapeutic considerations for the time being. Both of you have far more expertise in that arena. What I wanted to show with these examples is that, as we move beyond the program level, we are really moving along the banks of the Rubicon (recalling our model from the first dialogue). The landscape to the right of the Rubicon belongs primarily to the program level. Problem definitions on this level require "intention-realizing" kinds of therapeutic interventions. To really help our third client, however, we would likely need "intention-altering" or clarification-oriented interventions. Certainly, such measures would be needed once you would want to address the self-esteem issue in therapy, or once you would be forced to discuss it, given that the client's problems might not change otherwise.

Then in the process of case conceptualization if a therapist notices that problematic client experiences or behaviors seem largely determined by upper level goals outside of current awareness, it would make sense to include interventions aimed at clarifying or altering intentions.

Therapist: I am beginning to grasp the meaning of these two regulatory levels. Powers' terminology seems unfortunate, though. It seems obvious to me that he is talking about conscious or unconscious motivations or intentions. These are the kinds of motivations that do not come to mind easily when you ask someone about the reasons behind their current behavior. Depending on their level of initial insight, though, clients may learn over the course of therapy to recognize and discuss these underlying motivations—presuming, of course, that a trusting relationship has already been established between client and therapist. We might also encounter types of motivations for which the client has absolutely no awareness. These would be akin to the unconscious motivations targeted in depth psychology. Ironically, these "deep" motivations are at the highest level in Powers' hierarchy, suggesting that we ought to speak of "height-" rather than "depth psychology." It seems people generally lack awareness of motivational goals or reference values that reside on the highest levels of regulation.

In the field of psychotherapy quite a number of similar terms and concepts have been proposed over the years for these kinds of motivational reference values. All of these are thought to influence behavior and experience broadly, similar to what we find in Powers' model. For example, the principle level in Powers' hierarchy might subsume constructs such as Adler's (1920) "Leitmotive" (leading motives), Berne's (1967) life scripts, Ellis' (1962) and Beck's (1967) irrational beliefs, the Mount Zion group's (Sampson & Weiss, 1986, see section 1.22) pathogenic beliefs, and Young's (1994) early maladaptive schemas.

Grawe and Caspar's (1984) "plan concept" was developed *a priori* on the basis of a similar hierarchical model. From its inception, this model included a method for the identification of motivational influences beyond the program level. This method, initially termed "vertical behavior analysis" (Grawe & Dziewas, 1978; Grawe, 1980 b), was based originally on Miller, Galanter, and Pribram's (1960) hierarchical model of behavior. The ideas were further revised and elaborated over the years and are now known as "plan analysis" (Grawe & Caspar, 1984; Caspar, 1989, 1994, 1996). Working with this method, therapists start by identifying and articulating the plan guiding clients' current, observable behavior. Then, therapists systematically inquire regarding which higher order intentions are being served by the lower-order plans. Eventually, one arrives at a level of abstraction Powers' might term the system level.

Viewed from a systems perspective one disadvantage that might easily be overlooked otherwise becomes blatantly obvious: That these conceptualizations are geared exclusively towards problematic types of intentions or motivations. A therapist using these models to guide case conceptualization would be led to focus primarily on the problematic aspects of functioning, potentially neglecting equally important positive client **resources**. The method of plan analysis as well as Grawe's more recent method of schema analysis aim to avoid this kind of imbalance. In schema analysis, therapists are specifically encouraged to identify positive motivational schemas as well as negative emotional or avoidance schemas (Grawe, 1986; Grawe, Grawe-Gerber, Heiniger,

Ambühl, & Caspar, 1996). Thus, therapists switch perspectives: When working on intentional or motivational schemas, they view clients from a **resource perspective**; when working on negative emotional schemas, they assume a **problem perspective**. This method yields a more balanced picture of higher-order reference values, which—according to systems perspectives—determine human perception and behavior.

It has also occurred to me that Gollwitzer's (1987) identity goals or higher-order goal orientations—which we discussed in the context of the Rubicon model—also conceptually belong to Powers' principle level. This parallel demonstrates once again the basic compatibility between the Rubicon model and the view of mental functioning suggested by Powers' model.

2.4 On the Simultaneity of Conscious and Unconscious Processes and Their Significance for Understanding Mental Processes

Therapy researcher: I have a question on Powers' model similar to that which I had earlier about the Rubicon model (see section 1.12). What do you think Powers might say about the possibility that processes controlled by different control hierarchies occur simultaneously? Figure 2.5 seems to suggest there is always one hierarchy at a time being activated. I explained earlier why I would find this assumption questionable.

Psychologist: You are right, Figure 2.5 may create that impression. I am not sure what Powers himself might have said about this issue. He never elaborated on the question of simultaneity, not in his original description of control theory (Powers, 1973) nor in the later two volumes of his other writings (Powers, 1989, 1992). I have my own thoughts on this topic, which I wanted to share with you anyway. These ideas are quite central to my understanding of mental processes, as you will later find out.

Let's stick with the example shown in Figure 2.5 for a moment. As we observe the hostess preparing coffee for her guests, we might notice a lot more detail than what is suggested in Figure 2.5. For example, the hostess has a certain body posture, which may appear open or closed. Her movements may flow naturally or they may seem stiff. Her facial expression may seem bland or animated. She may avoid or seek eye-contact. Her voice may seem determined or hesitant. What she says may seem friendly and open or hostile and guarded. She may initiate conversation or restrict her responses to the bare minimum. She may offer large, generous portions or small, stingy ones. Her mood may seem happy or subdued. Her language may be intimate or more formal. Perhaps her muscles are sore, and she may or may not try to hide this. She is dressed a certain way; has a specific hairstyle; her hands may or may not be manicured. All of this takes place in a specific setting. Her taste in furniture may be exquisite or rather garish. Her home may appear tidy or messy. Music may or may not be playing in the background; this music may seem sophisticated but boring, or shallow but entertaining. Her coffee might be served in her best china or in her everyday mugs, the list could be continued ad nauseam.

All of this is happening simultaneously and can be observed at the same time. Preparing and offering coffee may be at the forefront of our hostess's current conscious awareness, but only a small portion of all the simultaneously transpiring processes is represented in consciousness at any one time. Conscious awareness focuses on but a small facet of all the ongoing processes, of incoming perceptions, of actual behavior and even of the emotions accompanying the stream of current activity. The majority of what is happening transpires outside conscious awareness. Nevertheless, we have to assume that even these unconscious aspects of perception and behavior are governed by feedback-loops, as shown in the coffee-making example of Figure 2.5. Without such governance, it would be impossible for these unconscious processes to transpire in a coordination fashion. It then follows that even these unconscious processes are oriented towards goal attainment. These goals can be traced from observable behavior all the way to the level of principles or higher-order intentions.

These regulatory processes are oriented towards the attainment of certain perceptual goals; specifically, towards the attainment of several goals simultaneously. Therefore, human experience and behavior are always determined by multiple intentions.

Of these intentions, only a few are represented in consciousness at any one time, and only a few are consciously pursued by consciously controlled action. Nevertheless, unconscious behavior may sometimes be more critical than conscious behavior in terms of leading to the attainment of higher-order goal. In our example of serving coffee, for instance, some of the unconscious nonverbal behavior may have been more important than her conscious acts in terms of attaining the goal at the principles-level of "be friendly towards others."

At any one time, then, there are always multiple control processes transpiring in simultaneous and parallel fashion. When analyzing mental processes from this kind of a systems perspective, we are thus led to modify existing, earlier models. For instance, Volpert's (1983) principle of hierarchical-sequential organization would have to be supplemented by a model that emphasizes more explicitly the **simultaneous-parallel organization of mental activity**. If we assume the existence of additional regulatory levels beyond the program level, it seems to me that—inevitably—we also have to assume the existence of some sort of simultaneous-parallel organization of mental functioning. Indeed, the logic of a control systems perspective mandates such an assumption. But there is also good empirical evidence for this, and more elaborate models exist that tell us about these processes transpiring parallel to conscious awareness (Shallice, 1972, 1978; Mandler, 1975; Shevrin & Dickman, 1980; Marcel, 1983 a, 1983 b; Yates, 1985; Epstein, 1994). I shall return to this point later on (section 2.12) because a thorough understanding of these processes is really necessary if we are to fully comprehend human functioning in its natural context. This is exactly the kind of complex understanding psychotherapists need if they ever want to really help people in the context of their lives.

In experimental psychology, researchers typically focus on a single aspect of mental functioning at a time. This aspect might be selected because of its theoretical importance. The researcher will typically aim to study this key variable in isolation and measure it with the greatest possible precision. By isolating the variable of interest in this way, however, a very obvious fact is being ignored: That mental processes are generally embedded in the context of many other processes, which transpire simultaneously. The principles governing such simultaneous activity have become a focus of research only within recent years. Nevertheless, there is good evidence today for the existence of such a parallel organization of conscious and unconscious processes. In fact, we are now beginning to understand the conceptual implications of this kind of parallel mental processing. I mentioned earlier some of the authors who contributed in this domain. The implications of this work are quite crucial for our discussions here, so I will devote more attention to this later on (see section 2.33). Some of the key terms for these topics in contemporary psychological literature include parallel information processing, connectionism, neural networks, self-regulation, chaos theory, synergistics, and dynamical systems theory. For now, let's focus again on the components of mental functioning. We shall return later to these relatively new perspectives and their implications for mental functioning and the process of therapy.

2.5   On the Functional Role of Conscious Mental Processing

Our discussion here has specific implications for one particular component of mental functioning—**the function of consciousness**. Therefore, I would like to make a few more preliminary remarks on this topic before we move on. If it is true that at any given time only a few conscious processes, but a great many unconscious processes are transpiring simultaneously, then the question presents itself: Why should it be that only a few particular processes are taking place at a conscious level? According to the perspective we are taking here, conscious awareness is a special kind of process quality of mental functioning. Conscious awareness marks a small portion of the processes transpiring at any one time. What factors are influencing which of these processes are being targeted by conscious awareness?

When directed by a startle response, our attention will focus automatically on specific events or processes. Yet we can also direct attention deliberately towards distinct segments within the range of the perceivable. In Figure 2.5, imagine that several additional control hierarchies extend to the left and to the right. Our attention resembles a spotlight that highlights more or less well-defined sections of these simultaneous-parallel processes. This spotlight of attention lifts the illuminated sections into the light of conscious awareness (Jung, 1978). The light may fade gradually at its edges; there may be a fuzzy boundary between light and darkness, between consciousness and the unconscious. Consciousness is not an all-or-nothing matter. The brightly illuminated areas correspond to the quality of waking consciousness, whereas darker areas correspond to decreasing levels of consciousness and to unconscious processes.

The spotlight can be adjusted upwards and downwards and from left to right. If shifted sideways, new goals move into the light of conscious awareness, replacing those that were previously pursued. Thus, goals are transformed into consciously pursued intentions that thereby have the benefits of conscious action control and perception bestowed upon them. If the spotlight of attention is adjusted downwards, conscious awareness focuses on the details of momentary activity. For instance, obstacles in the stream of action are now being perceived more consciously, and coping becomes more deliberate, whereas previously such obstacles might have been avoided "automatically." With the shifting of our "attention spotlight" towards lower regulatory levels the quality of the controlled action can actually be improved. A good example of this principle would be an actor rehearsing certain passages over-and-over until he achieves the desired expression.

Finally, our "consciousness spotlight" can be shifted upwards, from its usual focus at program level up to the level of higher-order intentions. This corresponds to the self-reflective question of why we do what we do. Vallacher and Wegner (1985, 1987) have come up with the term "action identification" for the internal representation of action hierarchies. Actions can be identified on different levels. We already encountered different possibilities for identifying the same action earlier with the example of the hostess preparing coffee and the solitary newspaper reader at the café.

According to research conducted by Vallacher and Wegner, action identification on an abstract level can be advantageous in some contexts and for some purposes. For other types of action, however, identification on a very concrete level is more advantageous. Vallacher and Wegner argued that action identification is selected for particular contexts according to its differential success.

Most of the time actions are identified on the program level. Nevertheless, one can typically answer immediately when asked for the reasons behind an action that was just identified on the program level. People have an idea—a concept—of these higher-order intentions and are able to call them into consciousness. They can do so despite the fact that attention does not reside primarily on this higher level but rather on the lower level of concrete goal pursuit.

It could also be, however, that these higher-level intentions have never been clearly formed. That is one reason why the abstract meaning of one's action may not be represented in "conceptual memory" (Perrig, Wippich & Perrig-Chiello, 1993) and is not intentionally accessible to conscious awareness. When higher-order concepts have not been formed, meanings for lower-order actions are indeed "unthinkable." In such cases, it would be impossible to identify any higher-order intention. New meanings might eventually emerge though through the taxing process of extended self-focused attention and reflection. First a new level has to be formed for the internal representation of one's action. After such an identification has taken place, new possibilities arise for the conscious control of perceptions and behaviors with respect to that new intention. This process will then increase the chances for effectively attaining these higher-order intentions.

My reflections here have focused on intentions designed to **create** or produce certain kinds of perceptions. We might call these kinds of intentions **approach intentions**. Approach intentions are relevant for psychotherapy as viewed from a resource perspective. From a problem perspective, however, the kinds of intentions designed to **avoid** certain perceptions are more relevant. Behaviors serving these intentions have an avoidance rather than a constructive function, therefore, we might label the overarching intentions **avoidance intentions**. In the same way that light-emitting stars are easier to detect than black holes (which are, in fact, stars with such great mass that they "swallow" all light), it is easier to identify approach intentions rather than avoidance intentions in the process of self-reflection. We cannot observe avoidance goals directly, but—like black holes—we can infer their existence from their effects.

The perceptions we seek to avoid cannot be experienced on a conscious level almost by definition. Just like our behavior, our attention is governed by overarching goals. Indeed, conscious attention is embedded in the process of intentional control. That is why higher-order avoidance goals ensure that attention is not focused on that which is to be avoided or on the process of avoidance itself. Consciousness results from the act of being conscious of something, but when conscious attention is consistently steered away, we suffer from a lack of consciousness for these control processes. Avoidance interpretations, then, cannot be thought, and without accurate avoidance identification of our actions we lack the very foundation which might make conscious control of avoidance behavior possible.

Not all avoidance goals are necessarily at an unconscious level. We can very well be aware that we avoid certain situations. Perhaps we can even pinpoint precisely what it is that makes these situations so uncomfortable that we avoid them. This can only happen, however, to the degree that our awareness of the avoidance process—our action identification—is itself consistent with reference values provided from higher-order regulatory levels.

We can call this highest regulatory level the ego or the self of the individual. In doing so we arrive at the following formulation: On the highest regulatory level, mental functioning is oriented towards producing certain perceptions of the self. Given our discussion just now, we might add that regulation on this level also includes the avoidance of perceptions that are incongruent with self-related reference values. One of the most important reference values related to the self is the mandate for some minimal amount of agreement or consistency among intentions. Intentions that conflict sharply with one another generate a strong discrepancy or incongruity signal on the highest regulatory level (see more detail in section 2.41).

According to this line of reasoning, conscious attention is also employed in the service of this primary self-goal—to avoid conscious awareness of conflict. Having awareness of such self-protective avoidance would in itself include awareness of the avoided content. Therefore, conscious awareness of avoidance is fundamentally incompatible with mental functioning. This incompatibility makes it difficult—without outside intervention—to gain awareness of one's own high-level avoidance tendencies. Again, the avoidance is so pervasive that it includes awareness of the avoidance. A therapist or any other outside agent who attempts to direct attention towards such avoidance is working in diametric opposition to the patient's control processes. Such attempts will increase the perceived discrepancy between actual perceptions and desired reference values at the highest-level comparator.

Given that mental functioning is geared towards discrepancy reduction, we would expect that the discrepancy-enlarging effect of emerging conscious awareness will trigger renewed avoidance, including the avoidance of emerging awareness. This process resembles Freud's concept of resistance. Let's say that this avoidance is unsuccessful in terms of reducing the perceived discrepancy. In fact, let's assume that additional therapeutic interventions are introduced, increasing the pressure towards conscious awareness. At this point, we would expect strong emotions to accompany the whole process. As we shall see later (section 2.18) these comparison processes always correspond in quality and intensity to certain kinds of emotions. In any case, with strong pressure towards gaining conscious awareness of the avoidance, two possible consequences arise at this point:

One of these possibilities is constructive. It entails alleviation of the discrepancy between the actual and the desired value through a fundamental shift or adjustment in the self. This is what Rogers (1951) was aiming for with his process of self-explora- tion. If successful, such changes at the highest regulatory level will trigger adjustments in reference values across all subordinate levels. In the best case scenario, then, a fun- damental restructuring of the self can result from the redirection of self-reflective at- tention onto processes that were incompatible with the old self. Such self-restructuring should be accompanied by pervasive changes in experience and behavior. This is how change is conceptualized in Greenberg, Rice, and Elliott's (1993) process-experiential approach, which you introduced in our first dialogue. Traditional psychoanalysis also strives towards the same outcome, albeit via a different set of therapeutic techniques.

Although we have not yet covered all aspects of mental functioning, we are begin- ning to see parallels between our control-systems formulations and concepts advanced by different schools of therapy. For instance, we can see how the psychodynamic ideas of "alleviating repression" and "resistance" fit in here. According to our systems per- spective, resistance, repression, and other forms of intentional avoidance result simply from the functional characteristics of mental activity. If one adopts a self-organization perspective, as I will suggest we do later on, these phenomena can be explained without resorting to mental entities such as the ego, id, or the unconscious. The parallels we see here between our views and other perspectives, such as the psychodynamic approach, should not obscure the fact that major differences exist elsewhere. Our systems per- spective suggests methods for attaining therapeutic change that are entirely different from those which flow from Freud's ideas. I hope to return to this point in our third round of discussion.

There are also other, more destructive ways of eliminating the unbearable self-dis- crepancies generated by emerging conscious awareness. One such possibility is total systems collapse, which may be expressed in a form resembling schizophrenia. Epstein (1979) views schizophrenia as a breakdown of the system, caused by the unbearable perception of discrepancies at the highest system level. Another destructive method for alleviating such unbearable systems-level discrepancies would be suicide. In the Menninger study (Wallerstein, 1986, 1989) mentioned by you earlier 6 of the 42 patients committed suicide over the course of long-term, intensive psychoanalytic treatment. Conceivably, these frequent suicides are last-ditch efforts to protect the self from the mounting pressure associated with emerging conscious awareness of unacceptable or conflictual intentions.

The speculations I advanced here regarding the functional role of consciousness as viewed from Powers' control systems perspective should still be viewed as preliminary. I will have more to say on this topic at a later point, but then from an entirely different perspective, which may shift our image of consciousness once again. At that point, I shall also integrate current literature on this topic to a greater degree. I just wanted to show here that adopting a systems perspective—with the additional assumption of simultaneous-parallel organization of mental activity—leads to rather interesting questions about the process of psychotherapy. Once we assume that mental activity is patterned in a simultaneous-parallel fashion then the additional assumption of a regulatory level beyond the program level becomes a logical necessity. Clearly, there has to be some sort of monitoring mechanisms ensuring that a minimum amount of compatibility or consistency is maintained. If different intentions are completely discordant the whole system could be brought to a standstill. Most importantly, incompatible intentions cannot be pursued simultaneously. Therefore, one of the reference values passed down from the systems level to subordinate levels concerns the maintenance of a certain unity, compatibility, or consistency among the lower-order processes (see section 2.41).

Conflicts threaten this unity. Lasting, serious conflicts among different intentions and the control processes they regulate result in incongruence signals on the highest system level. When these are strong incongruence signals, it would also be appropriate to speak of alarm signals. Depending on the strength and persistence of these signals, corresponding negative emotions are triggered. Like the other processes involved in such conflict, these emotions may not be experienced at a conscious level. Nevertheless, even if they lack the quality of conscious experience, the impact they have on the individual's state is real. These emotions can lead to psychosomatic symptoms or become the breeding ground for other mental disorders.

Powers never applied his control theory to the domain of mental illness, not even in his later writings (Powers, 1989, 1992). As far as I know, Pitman (1987) launched the only direct attempt to apply control theory to the explanation of mental disorders. Pitman conceptualized obsessive-compulsive disorders as resulting from incongruence signals at high regulatory levels. These discrepancies, according to Pitman, cannot be eliminated by any behavior in the individual's repertoire. He also regarded conflicts as predominant reasons for the persistence of these incongruence signals. Like Powers, Pitman expected that neuroanatomic correlates would one day emerge for his control systems theory of obsessive-compulsive disorder. Pitman's work is an example of how control systems theory can be applied to mental illness. So far, however, it is the only work of this kind, suggesting that control theory may not have obvious clinical relevance. In my view, this is due to the neglecting of emotions in control theory. Mental disorders are also emotional disorders; so much so, in fact, that only a theory that assigns a central role to the emotions can do them justice. Later we will have to devote more time in our discussion to the emotions, and then we shall address this deficit of control theory.

Based on Powers' own writings, we would have to conclude that control theory does not really lend itself to answering questions about psychotherapy. This relates to the fact that Powers' theory is least elaborated at the top three regulatory levels, even though they—and the relations among them—are among the most relevant for psychotherapy. Powers wanted to formulate a very basic theory about the functioning of living organisms. Later in his career he also conceptualized the functioning of social systems from a control theory perspective (Powers, 1992). His epistemological goal was of greatest importance for him—how is it that an organism arrives at its knowledge of the world and how does this contribute to our understanding of the organism's behavior? This is where control theory shows some overlap with constructivist concepts; notably, with Maturana and Varela's (1980) concept of autopoiesis, as Powers himself recognized (Powers, 1992).

Powers' 1973 book also contains a section on the potential of psychotherapeutic change from a control theory perspective. He argues that, in principle, it is impossible to change a person in the direction of externally imposed criteria. This is indeed consistent with his control theoretical view. Every externally based change attempt will lead to certain perceptions, which will then be compared against internal reference values. Thus, each change attempt is evaluated ultimately against the highest-level reference values, the patient's self or sense of individual identity. Individual behavior, then, is determined by these reference values rather than by external influences. This leads to the conclusion, for instance, that operant reinforcement cannot lead people to do things they do not want to do. According to Powers, true change is possible only through internal reorganization of the system itself. Change is possible only via modification of intrinsic reference values, and this cannot occur in opposition to the individual's goals. Therefore, psychotherapy should aim not merely for the alleviation of symptoms ("incongruence signals"), but rather should help people find their own reference values, their own sense of identity.

Unfortunately, Powers owes us an elaborate answer as to how such change might actually occur. From a control theoretical view, the entire system functions to maintain currently existing reference values. The system's dynamic is truly cybernetic; that is, it is governed by recursive feedback-loops that support homeostasis. However, the pathogenesis of mental disorders involves progressive developmental processes, which cybernetic control alone cannot explain. New reference values emerge, but how do they actually come about? How does Powers' reorganization actually unfold over time? As long as we lack a good conceptual understanding of these issues, we remain unable to comprehend the change processes in psychotherapy. Furthermore, we will not be able to understand the mechanisms underlying the effectiveness of psychotherapy, which we had set as a goal for this second round of our discussion.

For this reason I think that later it will be necessary for us to switch to a **"dynamic" systems view**. This way of thinking about systems specifically tries to account for progressive forms of change, for the emergence of qualitatively new phenomena (see section 2.44 and the following pages).

But I am jumping too far ahead. Before we dynamically revise our perspective here, let me first tie up a few loose ends. I have made few references so far to empirical work because I did not want to interrupt my train of thought. However, I also do not want to create the impression that the view I presented here is merely one among many. The main tenets of our systems view fit very nicely with empirical findings. Solid evidence that has emerged in theoretical psychology and in neurobiology confirms and extends our systems conceptualization. Indeed, psychological science has a lot to contribute here, and I think it is time to hear what some of these scientists have to say.

2.6   Linking the Systems Conception with the Rubicon Model

Therapy researcher: Please allow me to add a word or two here. I can now picture how one could link the three highest levels of Powers' model with our considerations from the first dialogue. Remember, we had to extend the Rubicon model beyond its left edge in order to account for wishes, fears, and conflicts. In my imagination I just rotated the Rubicon model (see Figure 1.3, section 1.11) by 90° so that the right Rubicon bank is at the bottom, and the left bank on the top. Then, I projected it onto Powers' control hierarchies. The Rubicon now becomes the transitional point between the program and the principles level. The world of wishes and fears, originally located left and now up above the Rubicon, then corresponds to the principles level. On the program level, wishes and fears that exist only in the individual's subjective world are "translated" into spatial-temporal reality, the place where real action takes place. This can occur with or without consciousness.

If an intention is consciously pursued, we might say that its status is privileged—it is in a privileged state of "intention realization." This does not mean, however, that other concurrently activated intentions are not being realized. They may influence behavior by other modes of action control. Intentions that are pursued over the course of an entire life, for example, do not require the privileged status of conscious control, especially when they are being pursued in familiar environments. Newer intentions or old intentions that are pursued in unfamiliar environments do require conscious control. Conscious, deliberate control is also needed to protect newer intentions against the intrusion of older ones. Realizing newer intentions always involves behavior change. Planned behavior change therefore always requires the privileged status of conscious action control.

These ideas take us back to familiar territory such as Kuhl's concept of action control from our first dialogue. Our discussion just now makes it more clear that Heckhausen's action phase model—from the choice phase to the phase of action realization—is concerned with only consciously regulated mental processes. However, many other processes are transpiring simultaneously outside of conscious awareness. Once we assume the existence of such simultaneous-parallel processes, we might further suspect that these processes can sometimes conflict with each other or hinder one another. Our conversation has convinced me, then, that unconscious conflicts are better viewed from a systems perspective, with its features of hierarchic-sequential organization and simultaneous-parallel processes. Heckhausen's action phase model, in contrast, does not seem such a natural fit for modeling unconscious conflicts.

From a systems perspective, it is also clear why conflicts among intentions at the highest regulatory level can have such deleterious effects. On all regulatory levels, discrepancy signals mediate subsequent experience and behavior. On the systems level, what is being monitored is the discrepancy from a desired degree of compatibility or consistency among lower-order processes. After all, one essential trait of a system is its holistic nature. Therefore, it makes sense that a minimum of consistency must be maintained in order for the system to function. Conflicts are the opposite of consistency. They jeopardize and interfere with the overall functioning of the system.

This also elucidates the connection between conflicts and mental illness. The permanent emotional disturbance that characterizes most mental disorders can be viewed simply as a correlate of permanent incongruence signals on the highest system level. These discrepancy signals alert the organism to the presence of conflicts. These high-level signals also provide reference values for lower regulatory levels. The goals passed down from the systems level may lead on lower levels to avoidance of certain perceptions, or to behaviors that seem to run counter to the person's own wishes and interests. Such seemingly counterintuitive actions become understandable when viewed as resulting from alarm signals on the highest level—the level that is beyond consciously acknowledged intentions.

What you said earlier about conscious awareness also helps me to understand the effects of conflicts among intentions. You mentioned that conscious attention can be shifted or redirected in order to reduce incongruence signals on the highest level. Conscious experiencing is governed by the laws of logic. When two logically incompatible intentions are present and both are pressing for realization, conflict is inevitable. Naturally, the resulting dissonance will be even more unbearable to the degree that these intentions become conscious. It makes sense, then, that redirection of conscious attention would be used by the self-level to reduce discrepancy signals on the highest regulatory level.

Thus, the strategic deployment of conscious attention can be used to regulate tension caused by conflicts in the system. One possibility is to direct all or some conscious attention away from the conflicting processes. Unless some life change alters their contingencies, the conflicts will continue to exist below the surface. To the degree that they transpire outside of conscious awareness, the tension associated with these conflicts will be diminished. Therapists frequently encounter this situation at the beginning of treatment. Conflicts among higher-order intentions might have been present for quite some time and are now interfering with the patient's mental or physical health. Since conscious attention is being steered away from these conflicts, however, the patient cannot use his conscious or volitional resources to improve his situation. The goal of therapy should then be to help the patient gain some conscious awareness, which would allow him to use his conscious, volitional capacities to resolve the conflict. Perceiving the conflict on a conscious level would enable the patient to come up with a deliberate plan, which might then reduce the tension created by the conflict.

Unfortunately, as you mentioned earlier, the amount of tension would initially increase as the patient gains conscious awareness of the conflict. Enduring and overcoming this tension would require "willpower" (see section 1.10). This brings us back once again to the Rubicon model's concept of volitional strength. I can see here that combining these perspectives can yield therapeutic insights that neither model alone would produce.

I am wondering where this volitional strength, which is required for the perception and resolution of conflicts, might come from. In general, volitional strength is a product of desirability and realization expectation. Given that the primary goal is that the patient develops conflict awareness, the initial focus should be on directing his conscious attention towards the conflicts and underlying intentions. How is it that patients can come to view the enduring of such tension and the giving up of their usual avoidance as something desirable? How is it that sufficient volitional strength can be generated, so that patients develop a willingness to face their conflicts? The immediate consequences of facing conflict are highly undesirable. How can patients be motivated to solve conflicts for which they lack awareness? In terms of the "realization expectation" component, things do not look much better. Why should patients suddenly expect to be able to endure conflict-tension, when they have not been able to do so in the past? For what reason should patients develop self-efficacy expectations that would enable them to overcome conflicts that they have not even perceived so far?

One cannot assume that the volitional strength for such "facing and enduring" is generated by the goals involved in the conflicts themselves. Instead, volitional strength must be generated from a different goal. At least three goals must be activated, then, in order to overcome conflicts: The two goals in conflict with one another, and a third goal to create the volitional strength for the facing and enduring of conflicts. As you can see here again, doing justice to the complexity of phenomena in psychotherapy requires assumptions of parallel information processing and parallel behavioral control.

Based on these considerations, we can conclude that one of the most important tasks for therapists involves the activation and promotion of such "third" motivating goals. Particularly when targeting conflicts, therapists ought to activate patients' resources and use the therapeutic relationship to facilitate the development of such goals. The less successful a therapist is with these strategies, the more "resistance" against facing the conflict can be expected. The objective must not be to work on the resistance against facing the conflict, but to support the volitional strength needed for facing the conflict.

The view developed so far is in some ways congruent with the psychodynamic perspective. Both assume that conflicts and the avoidance of conscious awareness play an important role in mental disorders. Our view differs, however, in that resource activation is viewed as a crucial component of treatment targeting conflict resolution. This emphasis leads to therapeutic consequences that differ from the psychodynamic approach.

Facilitating conscious awareness for previously unconscious conflicts also entails work on the right bank of the Rubicon. Just as the therapist who wants to perform exposure therapy with an agoraphobic patient must enhance volitional strength for his patient to be able to expose himself to the feared situation, the therapist wanting to help a patient gain consciousness for a previously unconscious conflict needs to enhance the volitional strength for directing conscious attention towards areas the patient has avoided in the past. In both cases volitional strength cannot simply be presumed to exist. It seems to me that in clarification-oriented therapies this therapeutic task has not yet received the attention it deserves, mostly because its underlying concepts do not suggest the importance of this issue.

Therapist: I found these practical conclusions, which actually go far beyond those in our first conversation, quite interesting. Actually, I would like to continue with such practical conclusions, but I still feel ill-prepared for that. I am not quite sure whether I have understood the concept of mental functioning well enough in order to think independently about it. Some aspects of it, such as emotions, have still not been addressed explicitly. Though not my true preference, I would like to suggest that we refrain—at least for the time being—from too many therapeutic conclusions.

The thoughts about the simultaneity of conscious and unconscious processes and ideas related to the role of consciousness for psychological functioning have been the most interesting for me so far. If I understood you correctly, the thoughts are not really based on Powers but more on your own ideas and reflections on other authors' work. Why did you go into so much detail about Powers' model? I suppose there is a reason for that, but at the moment I do not see it.

Psychologist: You are right. It is time I explain a little more. The two core messages arising from Powers' systems model are what made me choose this model as a starting point. These core messages are:

1. What we perceive is largely determined by what we ourselves bring to the environment.

2. Mental activity is oriented towards the generation of perceptions that are consistent with specific goals.

The far-ranging implications of these two messages become clear when we recognize that perceptions are the foundations of all experience. Cognitions other than perceptions—memories, mental imagery, and thoughts—all require pre-existing perceptions. Thus, one of the implications of Powers' model is that cognitions are generally the result of an active, goal-oriented construction process. Cognitions have a function that serves certain goals. We experience our perceptions and memories as a mirror of current or past reality. According to Powers' model, however, they represent **a subjective reality generated in the service of specific goals**.

Therapist: I am just beginning to recognize the broad implications for psychotherapy of such a control theoretical view. If what we perceive, what we remember, and what we think about is not a reproduction of what is and what was, but instead constitutes a function of certain mental reference values, then the issues treated in psychotherapy also have to be viewed from this perspective. It seems to me, then, that everything a patient tells us ought to be examined from three perspectives:

1. What the patient says is partially a description of what really happened in the past and present—a depiction of reality.
2. What the patient says also serves to influence me as a therapist, so that progress towards his goals is facilitated. My reactions are elicited to provide perceptions that are consistent with the patient's goals.
3. Even if it did not influence me, the patient's narrative still has an approaching or avoiding function in the service of his goals. Even if the patient did not express his thoughts, this third function would still exist. Whatever the patient perceives, remembers, thinks—especially what the patient thinks about himself—is in part always a story in the service of his goals. This reminds me of a book by Erich Fromm entitled *Jenseits der Illusionen* (*Beyond Illusions*, Fromm, 1981). In this book, Fromm argues that one of the essential tasks of psychotherapy is to free people from illusions about themselves. According to our control theoretical view, this in itself would be an illusory goal. At best, damaging illusions could be replaced by less harmful ones, or by ones that facilitate well-being.

Psychologist: One could certainly see it that way. Calling people's thoughts about themselves an inherent illusion, though, might lead to misunderstandings, given that the term "illusion" usually carries negative connotations. However, if one assumes that mental activity exists to serve certain goals, then there is no way one could ignore that people's consciousness of themselves also serves certain goals. This leads us again to wonder which functions consciousness actually has. Yet, we are still not sufficiently prepared to address this question. I think we should comment now on the two core messages derived from Powers' model, given their far-reaching implications. It seems important to examine thoroughly what we can learn from these two messages. What does empirical research have to say about that?

Part 2: Foundations of Experience and Behavior

2.7   Perception as an Active Construction Process

According to Powers, we live in a self-created world. Although it is true that a world with physical and chemical patterns exists independently of our existence, this is not the world of our experience. We live in a world created for us by our signal-processing systems, a world that is made up of physical and chemical effects on our sense organs. There is no other world for us.

One can estimate the complexity required for the transformation of basic sensations into meaningful perceptions by calculating the ratio between the number of nerve cells of a particular sense organ and the number of nerve cells involved in the processing of these raw signals. Each inner ear has approximately 3,000 inner hair cells that generate primary auditory information. We can contrast the total of 6,000 hair cells (2 x 3,000) with about 100 billion central neurons available for the processing of auditory information. Approximately a million retinal ganglia cells exist per eye, but the number of nerve cells involved in the process of seeing is estimated to be about 200 billion (Roth, 1995, p. 111). Thus, before we actually read a letter, understand a word, or recognize a melody, our brain has converted rather simple input information into meaningful perception through an astonishingly complex transformation process. Later we will see that memory plays a crucial role in this process.

Powers' assumption that even the simplest perceptions, such as color, result from the interplay of several different intensity signals is confirmed by brain research. Our retina has three types of cones responding to different wavelengths that strongly overlap with one another: One type of cone is most sensitive in the short-wavelength blue-violet range, a second in the medium-wavelength green range, and a third in the long-wavelength yellow-red range. The three types of receptors are stimulated to different degrees by light of a certain wavelength. All three types of receptors, not just the one most sensitive for this particular light, respond to a light of certain wavelength. The emerging signal, the perception of color, results from the relative activity of all three color receptors. In this way we are able to distinguish more than one million shades of color (Campenhausen, 1981).

Powers' formulation that every hierarchy level has a signal of its own quality could give rise to misunderstandings. Physical and chemical events in the environment are translated into the language of the brain via sense organs. The mode of expression for this language is the changing activation of nerve cells, stimulated by chemical and electrical signals such as membrane and action potentials, neurotransmitters and neuropeptides. But these signals are themselves neutral in meaning. Meaning is produced by the simultaneous stimulation or inhibition of certain nerve cells. In this context Roth (1995) speaks of "ensemble coding." Hence, it is neither the electrical or chemical signals themselves, nor the neuronal code of a certain individual nerve cell which represents the perceptual quality, but basically the interplay of an entire cell group or assembly that may be distributed across different brain areas. Apart from that, perceptual quality depends on the area where the stimulation is processed. Should the visual cortex be stimulated, one sees; the auditory cortex, one hears. This happens regardless of whether the stimulation really emanates from the eye or the ear. Stimulating certain brain areas with electrodes can trigger color and movement sensations (Creutzfeldt, 1983).

This means that one has to differentiate between signals and meanings. Meaning is not located in a single cell, nor in a certain electrical signal, but results from a spatially distributed arousal or activation pattern. Of course, the question arises as to what mediates the "wiring" of this spatially distributed activity to a certain perceptual content, especially since each single nerve cell participates in the representation of different singular features, and the arousal pattern corresponding to a certain perceptual content does not necessarily need to be represented by the activities of exactly the same nerve cells. Today, many neurobiologists agree that synchronous stimulation plays a crucial role (Reitboeck, 1983; Eckhorn & Schanze, 1991). Eckhorn and his associates have shown, for instance, that there are "coherent oscillations" in the visual cortex of cats when certain visual stimuli are presented (Eckhorn et al., 1990).

The principle of distributed arousal patterns makes the emergence of perceptions less susceptible to dysfunction, which would be more likely if perceptions were dependent on the functioning of individual nerve cells. Once a certain arousal pattern is "wired together" through frequent repetition (learning), it is much more easily activated in the future. In his concept of "cell assemblies," Hebb developed quite some time ago a concrete idea of how mental representations can be mapped onto neural networks (Hebb 1949, 1958). The plasticity of synapses whose transference potential or "weight" is altered with every activation or every learning procedure plays a crucial role in this process. Hebb's ideas were expanded upon by Hayek (1952) and von der Malsburg (1981). Von der Malsburg was able to prove that the formation of cell assemblies not only serves the permanent storage of information (learning), but that the modifications of synaptic efficiency postulated by Hebb can happen very fast, namely within 100-200 ms, so that the formation of cell assemblies can also be the basis of very rapidly occurring perceptual processes (see also Flohr, 1996).

According to Hebb, the connections between nerve cells are reinforced through each synchronous activation in which synaptic weights are changing. This creates an etching or wiring. Every synchronous activation of nerve cells leads to their being even more easily stimulated in the future. This resembles a positive feedback loop. Edelman (1987) refers to this wiring as "reentrant mapping." This is how neuronal groups emerge. Neuronal groups, in Edelman's terms, or Hebb's cell assemblies are what underlies neuronal arousal patterns. With the advancing facilitation of neuronal connections (synaptic transference potentials) an arousal pattern can be activated with increasing ease. Activating one part of the specific cell assembly leads to the activation of the entire cell assembly through positive feedback. The activation can happen "bottom-up" through stimuli acting on nerve cells that are part of the cell assembly. However, this activation can also happen "top-down," in that, for example, intentions activate deeply ingrained arousal patterns. Through repeated facilitation of the connections in spatially distributed neuronal networks, a certain tendency for perception and action emerges. The distributed organization of cell assemblies and the large number of participating cells, along with the huge amount of synaptic connections among them—all of which can be individually varied under the influence of specific situational conditions—make stability and flexibility simultaneously possible. The arousal pattern as a whole is very stable due to the positive feedback mechanism; however, segments of it can also be varied depending on the situation.

An easily activated arousal pattern that is bound together by, among other things, synchronicity, can be labeled as memory. Objects stored in memory are much more rapidly recognized, even if the full stimulus information is not available. Once objects are stored in memory, the stimulus information also no longer requires conscious attention for recognition. Instead, the perceptual content is available automatically, without major effort. The easily activated arousal patterns are tested like hypotheses, using the data of incoming stimulus information. Perception is "constructed" based on the arousal patterns available in memory, but the actual environmental conditions also exert an influence on the final emerging perception. Hebb's cell assemblies, Edelman's neuronal groups, i.e. ingrained neuronal arousal potentials, would be what Piaget (1976), Bartlett (1932) or Neisser (1974, 1976) referred to as schema. The process of constructing perception from environmental conditions (as communicated by the senses) would resemble Piaget's concept of assimilation. The more easily we actively construct perceptions on the basis of our memory, the more immediate the object of perception appears as something already existing in the environment, which flows into us through our sense organs. This paradox runs through our mental life at all levels. The more we bring our higher-level intentions into the environment, the more we tend to view them as inherent components of the environment.

Through the example of perception we recognize easily the mismatch between our natural conscious experiencing and the insights gained from psychological and neurobiological science. From a neurobiological angle, Roth (1995) arrives at a clearly constructivist view of perception, and based on this, of all psychological functioning.

"While our sense organs do not detect much of what is happening in the external world, our perceptual world, conversely, in terms of its contents, contains much of what has no recognizable correspondence in the external world. Included therein are those evidently simple perceptual contents such as colors, or spatial viewing (objects in our environment do not have color; our environment is not perspective-constructed, i.e. distant objects are not small). Especially included, however, are all categories and notions with which we (unconsciously or consciously) structure the world, everything meaningful in our perception (the events in our environment are in of themselves without any meaning), attention, consciousness, self-identity, mental imagery, thinking and language. We apply these highly complex constructs to the world, but they are not adopted from it" (Roth, 1995, p. 232).

This process of constructing perceptions occurs without conscious awareness. Indeed, according to Roth's view, the activity of all well-coordinated neuronal networks takes place without consciousness. According to his view, consciousness comes into play when new neuronal links are established. This is particularly true when we are confronted with new problems. I regard this definition of consciousness as overly restrictive, but the view that especially the activity of the most well-coordinated neural activation patterns is not coupled with consciousness agrees nicely with my previous considerations on the significance of unconscious processes.

From what we just said, it becomes clear that memory has a decisive function for understanding the foundations of our experience and behavior. "**Memory is the glue that holds together the unity of perception.**" This is true for all those perceptual contents that are not already inherently wired by the construction of the sense organs or by phylogenetically acquired mechanisms (this is also a form of memory of course), but whose coherence has to be acquired in early childhood or adulthood. We grasp the world through actions, through the co-occurrence and logic of the events we encounter, and these perceptions stream into our memory as "experience" (including phylogenetic experience). **Memory is therefore our most important 'sense organ'** (Roth 1995, p. 242). In light of its central importance for psychological functioning, we need to discuss memory in greater depth (see sections 2.10-20). Before doing so, however, I should add a few thoughts regarding my understanding of perception.

The idea that perception is an active process of construction has been explicitly propounded by Neisser (1974) and substantiated by a great deal of research findings from experimental psychology. According to Neisser, we have to distinguish at least two levels of information processing in perception: A pre-attentive processing of stimulus effects and a phase of focal attention which eventually generates the consciously perceived content in the sense of a "figural synthesis." Pre-attentive means that parallel information processing takes place at a very high capacity. The majority of stimuli processed at this stage does not reach consciousness and is also not available later as memory content. Nevertheless, it is used in the control of behavior. If we take a walk and engage in a conversation at the same time, our attention is normally focused on the conversation as well as on small fractions of the overall visual information. Obviously, we also pay attention to unevenness in the landscape, cars coming by, pedestrians, and we register them in our motor behavior. Otherwise, our walk would quickly come to an end. We can say there is a certain pre-attentive processing and behavioral control that is determined by our respective goals, but these processes are not necessarily coupled with the quality of conscious attention.

On this level we process far more information than is processed consciously. The focal attention can be directed towards any fraction of this pre-attentively registered information. This leads to actual conscious perceptions. Yet the field of focal attention is considerably more confined than that of pre-attentive perception. Consistent with our goals, attention is directed towards specific, meaningful segments of what is observable. As described previously, the perceptual tendencies are the basis which are especially easily activated for these meaningful segments.

Let me give you a good example for this: someone calling our name. For example, if we are involved in a lively conversation at a party, we perceive the jumble of voices around us only very vaguely as background noise. We do not understand what people talk about unless we direct our conscious attention to it. However, we recognize immediately if from somewhere in this garble of noise, someone calls our name. This allows us to conclude that we pay ample attention to that mélange of voices, but in a different mode than that connected with conscious perceptual quality. This has also been experimentally investigated (for more detail see section 2.15). When a story that we are asked to repeat is clearly presented into one of our ears, while the other ear—to which we are not paying attention—receives some other content, then we may follow the story with our full, conscious attention. Later we will be able to repeat the information we heard. We are unable to give any information about whatever was presented to our other ear. Yet as soon as our name pops up in what is said, we immediately turn our attention to the previously ignored ear. So we hear very well what is talked about, but what was said does not lead to conscious perceptions (Moray, 1959). We respond to our own name even "in our sleep." Oswald, Taylor and Treisman (1960) were able to demonstrate that while asleep, test subjects specifically responded, upon hearing their name called, with both an altered EEG-pattern and arbitrary movements. Thus, during our sleep a processing of stimuli takes place at the pre-attentive level.

According to Neisser, conscious perceptions are the product of a "figural synthesis." In a process of hypothesis formation and testing, a figure is produced against a perceptual background. Our pre-existing perceptual tendencies exert two sorts of influence on what we eventually perceive consciously: first, on what is pre-attentively selected from the initial information, i.e. that towards which our focal attention is actually turned; second, on what is constructed as the perceptual content, during the process of figural synthesis, on the basis of existing expectations, perceptual tendencies, hypotheses or schemata on the one hand, and the pre-attentively selected information on the other. What becomes conscious to us is the result of this construction process, not the construction process itself.

Neisser's image of perception as a two-level process is generally valid for perceptions. Treismann (1986) later specified this idea for the visual perception of objects and put it much more stringently in a theory of object perception.

According to that theory, initial elementary features of objects such as color, orientation of lines, contrast, brightness, closure, curvature and movement are obtained through a very rapidly occurring processing. How this happens, has by now, to some extent at least, been neurobiologically clarified. I will return to this in a moment.

In a second processing step visual-spatial attention acquires a crucial function. In order for the elementary features of the objects to be combined, attention has to be directed to the respective locations that lie within view. Eye movement plays a functional role in this respect. Intensive neurobiological research is presently going on, which is investigating which processes in the brain underlie visual-spatial attention (Eimer, 1996 b).

Neisser's ideas on the mechanism of perception, derived from findings in experimental psychology, have essentially been confirmed and refined by further experimental psychology research. Many of the assumed processes can, in the meantime, even be described neurobiologically, all the way to the level of individual neurons. The neurobiological foundations of perception give us psychologists many important clues as to how we should conceptualize the foundations of our experience and our behavior. Therefore, I find it useful to take you on a little excursion into neurobiology and give you an idea of what has been confirmed so far about the neuronal foundations of perception.

2.8   The Neural Basis of Perception

Earlier I mentioned that underlying our perceptions are spatially distributed activation patterns in which many cells are involved. This does not mean that the individual cell activity is nonspecific. Each cell, in fact, makes its own special contribution to the emerging percept. Different cells do respond to different kinds of environmental characteristics. The discovery of a great number of highly specialized nerve cells goes back to the pioneering works by Hubel and Wiesel (1959, 1962, 1968), for which the two neurophysiologists received the Nobel prize for medicine in 1981. One experiment by Hubel and Wiesel (1962) entailed offering different stimulus patterns to cats whose eyes— via stupor and fixation—were constantly staring at a particular monitor. With the aid of microelectrodes the scientists recorded the response patterns of over three hundred different nerve cells from different areas of the visual cortex. This enabled them to discern how the individual cells responded to different stimulus patterns. The measurements demonstrated that the individual nerve cells are equipped with clearly distinguishable "receptive fields" of varying complexity, similar to the retina's ganglion cells. Depending on how the fields' center and periphery are arranged, the nerve cells respond to varying stimulus characteristics. One cell "response type" for instance, reacts to edges with a certain orientation (angle) in the visual field, another to edges with a different angle, still another to bars, or another one to movements in a certain direction, and so on. Each nerve cell is, to a certain extent, a "detector" for one very specific characteristic of the object presented. Thus there are detectors for edges, for movement, etc. The left side of Figure 2.6 shows schematically the receptive field of a simple cortical cell with an excitatory center and an inhibitory periphery, the right side depicts the response behavior of the cell after being presented with three bars at varying angles.

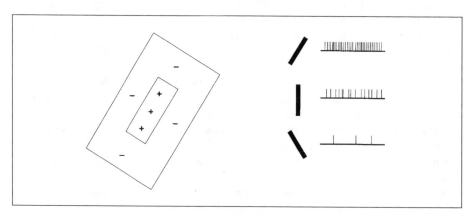

Figure 2.6
Schematic representation of the functional organization of simple cortical cells.
Left: The receptive field of such a cell consisting of an excitatory-center (+) and an inhibitory periphery (-).
Right: The black bars represent perceptive stimuli having an effect on the cell.
The cell response behavior depends on the stimulus orientation in its receptive field.
In this case, the bar angled right leads to the strongest cell activation.
Figure taken from Eimer (1996 b, p.289).

Most cells have a simple receptive field and were therefore termed "simple cells" by Hubel and Wiesel. Others reveal a more complex response pattern ("complex cells") and still others even more complex response patterns ("hypercomplex cells"). These different cell types were found more frequently in certain regions of the brain.

From their research results, Hubel and Wiesel arrived at a hierarchical model describing the interplay of these different cell types which bears a strong resemblance to the lower levels of Power's model (see Figure 2.7).

According to that model, the properties of a simple cell are formed by integration of concentric retinal ganglion cells, the properties of complex cells by integration of simple cells, the properties of hypercomplex cells by the integration of complex cells, and at the pinnacle of this hierarchy finally, "gnostic cells" were assumed that respond specifically to complex objects such as hands or faces. Konorski (1967) developed a model

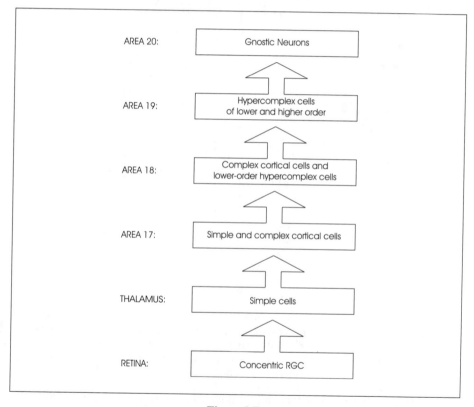

Figure 2.7:
Hierarchical model of visual information processing according to Hubel and Wiesel. The complexity and specificity of the visual cells increases from the periphery (retina) to the highest visual centers in the cortex. While retinal ganglion cells (RGC) with concentric receptive fields tend to respond to the simplest visual characteristics, "gnostic neurons" in the lower temporal lobe of the cortex respond to complex shapes (e.g. faces or hands). The response properties of higher-order cells are formed through the integration of the response properties of lower-order cells.
Figure taken from Roth (1995, p.141).

in which there are specific representational cells for complex objects. These "gnostic cells" specialized in recognizing a very specific complex object would be located at the peak of a functional hierarchy of cells whose response characteristics would become increasingly more complex through integration and being wired together. Such gnostic cells were jokingly referred to as "grandmother cells," firing at precisely the moment when one's grandmother steps into the field of vision.

With respect to faces, Konorski's concept of gnostic neurons has received confirmation in the meantime. Independent of one another, several research teams have found

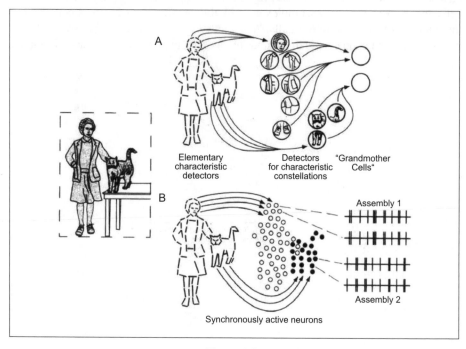

Figure 2.8:
Two different models for solving the problem of connection:
(A) Integration through anatomic convergence. This model assumes that at the lower processing levels elementary object characteristics, such as the orientation of contours, are detected first. At the higher processing levels, cells with increasingly more specific response properties are then created through progressive convergence of the wiring. At the peak of the hierarchy, neurons (the so-called "Grandmother cells") are located, serving as specific detectors for entire objects, in this case for the woman and her cat.
(B) Connecting of object characteristics through neural synchronization. The time-coding model assumes that objects in the visual cortex are represented through assemblies of synchronously firing neurons. In the example shown here, the woman and her cat would each be neurally represented through such an assembly (marked by open and filled-in symbols).
These assemblies consist of neurons that detect elementary object characteristics. The association of the characteristics is illustrated by the temporal correlation between the neurons of an assembly (right). According to the time-coding hypothesis, all those neurons belonging to the same cell assembly each fire synchronously. Between both assemblies there is, however, no permanent temporal relationship.
Figure taken from Engel (1996, p.202).

"face-specific" neurons in the brains of monkeys (Perrett et al., 1984; Rolls, 1984; Young & Yamane, 1993). In monkeys, these neurons generally respond to faces regardless of whether they are monkey or human faces. The response is rather insensitive to changes in size, color, lighting conditions, shape and location of the face; they demonstrate a "face-invariance" (Perrett, Mistlin & Chitty, 1987). Some neurons also respond preferably to specific facial features, such as the eyes or the mouth, or facial expressions. About 10 percent of the "face-neurons" even respond preferentially towards individual faces. Due to measurement problems no individual face-neurons have been traced in humans so far, although face-specific cortical regions have been demonstrated (Grüsser, Naumann & Seeck, 1990).

Hubel and Wiesel's hierarchical model depicted in Figure 2.7 comes very close to the lower hierarchy levels in Powers' model. We see then that Powers' idea of modeling the special features of psychological functioning down to the level of neural processes was not pure fantasy. At the time of its initial publication in 1973, this model actually fit rather well with the concepts of theoretical neurobiology then prevalent. Not until a few years later did doubt increasingly begin to appear about whether or not this hierarchy model was tenable in its original version (Stone & Dreher, 1979; Stone, Dreher & Leventhal, 1979). These doubts were based on increasing evidence suggesting that distributive-parallel information processing was taking place in the brain as well.

Hubel himself developed increasingly into a proponent of such a parallel and distributed organization of neural processes (Livingstone & Hubel, 1988). Even the perception of faces, despite the existence of face-neurons, is ascribed to "ensemble coding" rather than to individual "detector cells" (Young & Yamane, 1993). Yet only relatively few face-neurons are needed for the unequivocal recognition of a face. The participation of several cells enables the formation of invariances and an increased precision in recognition through averaging. Apart from that, it would be very risky for the organism to entrust such an important function to a single cell. A temporal integration mechanism is assumed to underlie the wiring of the distributed stimulus patterns. Neurons distributed in the cortex are joined to assemblies through the synchronization of their firing. Earlier we already encountered the concept of cell assemblies by Hebb as a basis for perceptive and memory units.

In a graphical comparison, Figure 2.8 illustrates the two possibilities of how perceptive units originate. The upper part illustrates the original hierarchical model by Hubel and Wiesel, the lower, the alternative possibility of connection through a time-coding mechanism.

It is my feeling that it makes no sense to present you at this point with the evidence that neurobiological research offers which speaks for a parallel-distributive information processing in the brain. A very precise knowledge of the brain is necessary to fully understand the evidence. Comments on that (among other things) can be found in writings by Roth (1995, pp. 143—161), who, together with many other neurobiologists, believes that the permeation of distributive-parallel and hierarchical-convergent processing throughout the brain is the norm. According to Roth, the possibilities illustrated in Figure 2.8 for solving the connection problem are not in opposition, but actually supplement each other. Further illustration of that may be Figure 2.9, taken from Roth, which depicts how many individual properties have to be simultaneously processed for the perceptual unit "chair" to emerge.

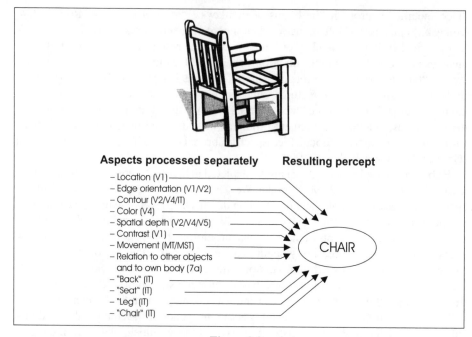

Figure 2.9:
Integration of perception using the example of a chair.
On the left, the different cortical areas are listed which are involved in the processing of the visual details, for example, in the identification of the object parts, respectively, and finally in the identification of the entire object as chair. The individual regions of the brain need not be detailed here in depth, because it is the principle which is important here and not the specific example.
Figure taken from Roth (1995, p. 234).

Roth comments on that: "There is no neuron or neural group which can represent an object, such as a chair, in all its details **and** in its different meanings. Perceiving a concrete object requires the **simultaneous** activity of many cell assemblies, each coding only very limited aspects, be it detailed aspects or categorical aspects, and these cell assemblies are widely distributed throughout the brain. There is no single center anywhere, in which all this information comes together."

This very obviously contradicts our subjective feeling. We do **not** perceive the shape of a chair separated from its color, the color separated from the distribution of its intensity, and—if we move it—separated from its movement. And we definitely do not perceive the meaning "chair" separated from the other aspects. Rather, the components of the act of perception create a unit of perception and consciousness.

But how is the subjectively felt **perceptual unit** formed within the brain? This question is identical with that concerning the constitution of objects and scenes overall. The rules according to which this happens cannot originate from the nerve cells or synapses themselves, since neurons and synapses do not know anything; what they do is neutral with respect to the meaning of their activity.

The rules of perception which constitute meaning are a result of the cognitive system's **prior experience**. Included in this prior experience is, of course, first of all the brain's basic organization, as it has emerged thanks to phylogenesis, thus the fact that our brain is a typical vertebrate, mammal, and primate brain. Also included therein is that normally the sense organs **systematically** connect with certain brain areas in a similar way in all members of a species and that, in turn, these brain areas connect with each other, in an equally systematic fashion. All this happens partially independently from specific experiences, yet not in a way that is exactly prescribed by specific genes. Instead certain genetic framework conditions exist during the brain's individual development under which the brain's structural order and, therefore, the system of creating primary meanings, grows in a self-organized **epigenetic** fashion...

What is perceived in adolescence and adulthood occurs within the frame of this, partially genetically conferred, and partially early ontogenetically acquired fundamental equipment. This fundamental equipment largely determines the perceptive and pre-cognitive phase of perception, for instance the way in which brightness, contrast, color, and movement are processed in the visual system, and how spatial and depth perception develop. The majority of these unconscious and automated processes can no longer be modified through individual experience later in life" (Roth, 1995, pp. 233—237).

I believe we can conclude our excursion into neurobiology at this point. What I wanted to demonstrate should be sufficiently clear now: What we are **able** to perceive and experience is basically determined by the nature of our nervous system. Therefore, what we perceive and experience is essentially influenced by what we carry into the environment with our nature. Yet we do not have an awareness for the extent to which this nature determines our perceptions, but live with the feeling that what we perceive is determined by our environment.

2.9   No Perception Without Expectation

From a perspective of evolutionary biology we can generalize this subject matter even further: Our entire organism can, in a sense, be conceived of as a sort of scientific theory about the world. The nature of our body, its organs, our nervous system is, so to speak, an expectation or a hypothesis about the environment, which receives an answer through selection. The organism in its entirety can be viewed as an implicit theory about the world. Metabolism is a sub-theory of the chemical nature of what kind of nutrition is appropriate, the same way our body structure and motor activity is a sub-theory of the basic physical laws we are subjected to, and the nervous system of the kind of information both necessary and useful for our well-being in this world. In the history of evolution, millions and millions of theories have preceded today's implicit world theory of the human organism. Time and again theories were abandoned through selection, and on the basis of the existing theory new hypotheses (mutations) were established, whose tenability and utility were in turn subjected to the test of selection.

The fact that so many kinds of organisms exist simultaneously indicates to us that there is not just one true theory of the world, but many possible ones. The bat with its radar-like orientation system, and living creatures with a sense for magnetic field variations or gravity, are also successfully tested hypotheses of the environment. They live in a reality different from our own, about whose subjective quality of experience we could not communicate even if we shared a common language. Our organism represents a theory of the world which by no means comprises the entire world, yet which is not falsified by it, at least not at this point in time.

The explicit knowledge of the world which we arrive at based on this organism—or based on this implicit theory—may go far beyond the range of this implicit theory, in that we gain knowledge of parts of the world, such as the existence of magnetic fields, but we can never claim to be capable of conceiving the world in all its possibilities. As far as the human organism is concerned, our explicit scientific theories are far behind those implicit theories implemented in this organism, because we are still far from having a complete understanding of how the brain operates.

The implicit knowledge of our organism then goes far beyond the knowledge we acquire based upon it. Popper sees this similarly: "Although there is actually no procedure for comparing both kinds of knowledge (this is generally true for the genetics vs. environment debate), I intuitively lean towards the assumption that the huge quantity of information we acquire via our senses in the course of life is rather small in comparison to the quantity of our genetic background with its potentialities. At any rate, there are two great sources for our information: that which is genetically inherited, and that which we acquire throughout our lives. Furthermore, all knowledge, whether inherited or acquired, represents historically a modification of our previous knowledge; and all acquired knowledge can be traced back step by step to modifications of inherited or acquired knowledge. The value of acquired information is almost entirely based on our innate ability to utilize it in conjunction with our unconscious, inherited knowledge, perhaps even to put it to use for the purpose of correcting that very knowledge. Of course, the majority of acquired information received through our senses is unconscious as well" (Popper & Eccles, 1982, p. 158).

In speaking of knowledge, we refer to it here in a very broad sense. For instance, it also includes needs and the related value system, the emotions. Our needs are also expectations towards the environment serving the organism's maintenance and reproduction. Implicit knowledge refers to more than our normal notion of knowledge related to cognitive knowledge.

The entire mechanism of our nervous system can be viewed as an expectation towards the environment, as a set of assumptions about how the world is structured, what is to be expected from it and what can be achieved in it. The brain's special capability consists of transferring this principle of confronting and testing of expectations, so well tried in phylogenesis, to the ontogenetic development and current psychological functioning. We constantly transform our biographical experiences into expectations that we in turn carry into the environment. Some of these expectations will be confirmed. We might also say, they will be reinforced by the environment. Through differential reinforcement certain expectations are selected which then leads to their being even more preferentially carried into the environment.

At the neural level, expectations correspond to the neural activation tendencies we talked about earlier. They are organized in cell assemblies or neural groups. In his theory of the selection of neural groups Edelman (1987, 1989, 1995) also talks about "differential reinforcement" as a principle of selection. Those neural connections resulting from "reentrant mapping" that efficiently reduce a momentarily existing need tension, and that thus have been biologically proven successful, become differentially reinforced. According to Edelman the wiring of neural groups occurs according to their function for standard biological values. This may be the fulfillment of a basic need, but—as I will outline later—it may also be the reduction of an inconsistency in psychological functioning.

On the psychological level the neural activation patterns correspond to structural patterns of psychological functioning which evolve from differential reinforcement. The reinforcement consists of reducing a presently extant inconsistency. Inconsistency reduction ties structural patterns together. I will go further into this at a later point.

So neural activation tendencies organized in cell assemblies or neural groups underlie the structural patterns of mental activity. We have referred to these activation tendencies as expectations towards or hypotheses about the environment. The more well ingrained and better connected the activation tendencies are through differential reinforcement, the more they develop from a mere assumption into a rather well confirmed component of an individual theory of reality. This way the entire theory is gradually put together by biographically repeatedly confirmed "postulates," which become the foundation of the individual's interaction with his/her environment. In contrast to the neural basis of psychological functioning which I spoke of earlier in this section, these biographically acquired postulates are not "hardware expectations" but "software expectations," that is to say, they may be reprogrammed. The most commonly used term in psychology for these biographically acquired software-expectations is "schema" (Läderach & Verdun, 1995). According to psychological perception research, schemata underlie our perceptions as expectations we have towards the environment (Neisser, 1974, 1976). Yet according to cognitive psychology, they underlie not only our perceptions, but more or less directly almost all aspects of mental activity as well. Authors like Piaget (1976) and Neisser view them as a fundamental organizational unit of mental activity. A hierarchical organization is assumed for schemata as well. Far less common is the assumption of a distributive-parallel organization, but if we conceive schemata in the sense of Hebb's cell assemblies, as I suggested earlier, then the conception is, at the same time, associated with the notion of a spatially distributed and temporally simultaneous-parallel organization.

If we imagine schemata as hierarchically organized, similar to the feedback loops of Powers' control levels, we eventually need to design, at the top of the hierarchy, some-thing like a superordinated self-schema which largely determines the individual's mental activity. Since schemata are to be conceived of as the individual's implicit expecta-tions towards or about the world, the expectations summed up in the highest-order schema, the self-schema, in a way would have to be conceived of as the individual's implicit theory of reality. It is exactly in this sense that Epstein (1993 b) conceives the self, viewing it as a "reality theory." The schemata equal "postulates" which are carried into the environment. This designation of the self may seem awkward at first, but within the context of what I previously said it actually becomes fairly clear what is meant by this. Epstein's conceptions of the self and the personality theory associated with it fit smoothly into the view developed by me so far. Following through on that, I will later begin with Epstein's theory as a foundation for a more in-depth explication of Powers' thoughts on the highest regulation levels of mental activity, designated by him as the principal and system level.

Therapist: Of course, this interests me tremendously, because I think the ideas about these highest regulation levels really have to be more tangibly detailed and refined, before they can be useful for psychotherapy. I do not want to keep you from giving us a more in-depth presentation, but all this time now a particular question has been gnawing at me, and I just have to get it out. This question concerns all levels of regulation that are part of mental activity. The question is, how can the control processes that you outlined for us change? After all we talked about, we now have more of an idea about how perceptions form and how they are functionally connected to behavior and goals. As yet, we do not have an idea as to how perceptions, goals and behavior can **change**. We now know that perception has to be conceived of as an active process of construction, in which we carry certain expectations or perceptive tendencies into the environment. Consequently, changes in experience and behavior must then stem from the fact that the expectations carried into interactions with the environment change. Since according to control theory, mental activity is focused on creating perceptions consistent with certain goals, it would mean at the same time that changes at a certain level in the hierarchy are only possible if the higher-order goals change.

Expectations and goals are, however, also the main components of expectancy-value theories, which we attempted to use in explaining the mechanisms of psychotherapy in the first dialogue. We proceeded pragmatically, simply deriving from the findings of therapy research how expectations and intentions could be efficiently changed. Here the question evolves once again, and as I see it, in a more fundamental way: According to the image of psychological functioning depicted by you, how are long-term changes in mental functioning at all possible? How can we conceive of changes or "learning" in line with these notions?

Psychologist: Fortunately, I am well prepared for this question since you were bound to ask it sooner or later, seeing that the questions you brought up at the beginning of our first conversation remain insufficiently answered so far, and certainly concern the conception of change.

But I must warn you in advance that my answer to your question will not necessarily be short and concise. Your question concerns an area of psychology which is both one of its oldest and most current research fields. In the more than one hundred years since Ebbinghaus's (1885) first depiction of findings from the psychology of memory, a lot has been brought together that is highly relevant for the understanding of mental functioning and for the therapeutic processes of change as well. Delving into this field also means that we must stay with it for a while, as otherwise we would not be able to reap the full harvest psychology of memory offers for our project. So before I delve deeper into the psychology of memory, I would like to be sure that you really wish to venture so far into the fundamentals. After all, it is very unusual for psychotherapists to concern themselves in detail with the psychology of memory. In most instances, according to my experience, psychotherapists prefer issues that can be immediately applied in practice.

Therapist: I have understood through our conversation so far that it is absolutely necessary for us to study memory thoroughly. If memory represents the sum of all expectations, and if, according to our first conversation, psychotherapy essentially means changing expectations, then how shall we ever be able to understand processes of change in therapies without arriving at a clear picture of the individual features of what we seek to change? So, as far as I am concerned, however long our excursion into the psychology of memory will be, I am all for it and promise to soldier on.

Therapy researcher: Same here, we will do what must be done.

Psychologist: Okay, then let us get right down to it. Several times now, we have already come to the conclusion that the most important foundation of our experience and behavior is memory. In a very broad sense this statement is nearly banal, namely if we conceive of our organism's entire genetic nature as a species-specific memory, as I have done earlier. The genetic hardware, of course, cannot be changed in the realm of psychotherapy; rather, it represents the set limitations for the therapeutic process of change. Only the biographically acquired software, which we, in a more narrow sense, call memory, can be changed via psychological tools. If we imagine how much an individual up to adulthood has absorbed into memory, then we cannot but have very modest expectations with respect to how much of that is changeable in the course of a psychotherapy that comprises perhaps forty therapy sessions. Bearing this in mind, it makes immediate sense for us to view whatever the patient brings in with his memory as a resource and to make appropriate usage of it.

Whatever seems problematic to us and in need of change from the problem perspective, definitely represents only a small portion of the overall existing contents of memory. According to our ideas from the first dialogue, it is certain expectations and certain values/intentions that must be changed in order to change the patient's problematic experience and behavior. These expectations and values are part of his memory and are embedded within. I believe it is very useful to keep in mind that what ultimately has to be changed represents only a small fraction of a much more comprehensive whole. If, with his/her therapeutic procedure, the therapist does not account for the whole, i.e. the other particular features represented in the patient's memory, but focuses solely on the problem to be changed, then it should not come as a surprise that the retaining function of the memory proves to be much stronger than the absorbing function. Given these fundamental considerations from the psychology of memory, everything you said in our first dialogue about the importance of resource activation makes perfect sense to me.

At any rate, from our present perspective we can say: If we are interested in exerting a permanent influence on the patient's experience and behavior, it means that part of his/her memory must be changed. For this, it would be useful to know how the memory operates. I will try to give you an overview, specifically detailing those particular points which appear most relevant for psychotherapy.

2.10 Memory as the Sum of All Expectations and Activation Tendencies

All we have said thus far allows us to conceive of the contents of memory as tendencies towards very specific activation patterns in a tremendously vast neural network, which provides for a practically unlimited number of various activation patterns. The number of nerve cells in the human brain is estimated at approximately one hundred billion. The nerve cells' function is to receive, process and conduct electrical and chemical signals. A single neuron alone is already considered a complex processing system. Via chemical or electrical synapses it connects with up to ten thousand other neurons, by which it may either be activated or which it may activate. The connection between two nerve cells is established, on average, via ten synapses, and not via just one. There are excitatory and inhibitory synapses, whose influences also depend upon at which end of the dendrite they begin. The ratio of excitatory to inhibitory synapses is especially important for the activation processing and integrative performance of the single nerve cell. Depending on the number, starting point, and numerical ratio of excitatory to inhibitory synapses, very different conditions of activation may be created. Furthermore, there is a spatial and temporal summation of synaptic activity. An action potential in a single nerve cell can usually only be triggered if the activating post-synaptic potentials accumulate across several synapses. So, from another single nerve cell, a neuron can only be activated if there is a connection to it via a sufficient number of synapses. Usually, however, the summation results from several pre-instated neurons synchronously exerting an activating influence of the same kind on the neuron (Birbaumer & Schmidt, 1996; Roth, 1995).

Given the complexity that already exists at the level of a single nerve cell, the amount of connections it can have with other nerve cells (even those further away), the overwhelmingly large number of nerve cells that exist, and the fact that a single nerve cell's function is also dependent on where it is located in the brain, we can imagine quite clearly that all our mental processes and contents, as well as the contents of memory, are based on specific neural activation patterns. The number and variability of the possible activation patterns are practically unlimited. A single word can be represented by a certain activation pattern, much the same way as can the pursuit of a complex intention. It makes immediate sense that there has to be something like a principle of hierarchical organization, in which higher-order and more comprehensive activation patterns are based on more specific and circumscribed ones, simultaneously embedding them into a higher-order pattern. Apart from that, it is clear from the outset that many activation patterns have to be simultaneously actuated, in order to explain how we, for instance, simultaneously coordinate our body posture and movements, imagine something, talk about it and observe other people's reactions to that. Temporal synchronicity is the most common feature of our neural activity. With mental processes, such as perceptions, images, memories, thoughts, and emotions, being so closely attached to neural processes, as frequently demonstrated, we have to assume, for mental and neural processes alike, a temporal parallelism with which many processes run parallel to or in conjunction with one another.

So the individual content of memory is, in fact, represented by a specific neural activation pattern, for which, due to previous ingraining, there exists an increased tendency in the form of synaptic transmission weights, as Hebb imagined it in his concept of cell assemblies. When we remember something, an earlier neural activation state under the influence of current context conditions is "reinstated." The contents of memory exist not in the form of fixed, invariant structures, but they are, in each case, (re)constructed anew on the basis of existing synaptic transmission weights under the influence of current contextual conditions, i.e. synchronously activated other activation patterns (perceptions, images, moods). So remembering as well should be conceived of as an active construction process (Bartlett, 1932; Neisser, 1974). Remembering is not a true reflection of what was, but remembering is a product of what was previously perceived and the influence of the present situation in which memorizing occurs (Loftus & Loftus, 1980; Loftus & Marburger, 1983).

Therapist: You talk about this all so casually. However, is this finding not of great practical relevance? Should this not be taken into consideration when, for instance, assessing testimony before a court of law, more so than is presently the case? If remembering indeed cannot be simply conceived of as something that really happened, then this would also have a significant impact on psychotherapy. What a patient tells us about his or her biography might then have to be viewed as a tri-fold transformation of the actual original events:

- Initially, it would be transformed through the subjective interpretation of the events at the time, which need not necessarily be congruent with what was "objectively" happening;
- It would be further influenced by the function which the current self-report would fulfill in terms of the patient's impression management in front of the therapist;
- and the third transformation would be through the influence of the current context on his/her memory.

If memories such as perceptions have to be brought into congruence with certain reference values, in the way control theory postulates, would the patient's currently actuated goals not also have to be considered as influencing the recall context? It would indeed then be expected that the patient preferably "constructs" such memories matching his currently actuated goals. Additionally, the recall context then naturally also includes what the patient believes the psychotherapist might like to hear from him. Here I am thinking about hermeneutically oriented therapists (Lorenzer, 1970, 1974), who pursue the ambitious goal in therapy of reconstructing, together with the patient, the patient's actual life history. Does this not inevitably lead to the construction of a new story? One that is largely influenced by today's motivations as well as by the therapist's and patient's attributions alike, a story that consequently is always a reinterpretation of what "really" happened?

Psychologist: These conclusions are surely justified. I think, however, that this is true not only for memories but also for cognitions in general. Memories are a special form of cognition and, in my opinion, cognitions basically have multiple functions for mental processes. They are in part a reflection of what is and was. Simultaneously, they are interpretations in the sense of current intentions, and they control behavior in the sense of these intentions. Later I want to go even deeper into that. But I am not nearly finished with what I wanted to say about memory.

2.11   Differentiating Various Forms of Memory

Conscious recollection and retaining/keeping in mind are those memory processes that are reflected in our subjective experience. The processes of retaining which underlie our mental processes and their changes have to be considerably more complex than what is reflected in our conscious experience. The vast majority of memory processes are introspectively inaccessible. They can only be inferred. To a large extent memory processes are unconscious processes. It is, therefore, not surprising that the most comprehensive account on the topic "unconscious information processing" presented in recent times came from memory psychologists (Perrig, Wippich & Perrig-Chiello, 1993).

From among our memory processes, we can consciously access only those labeled by memory psychologists as short-term memory or working memory. An initial, very obvious criterion for differentiating various forms of memory is the length of time over which we are able to retain information. In their multiple storage model, Atkinson and Shiffrin (1968) distinguish between three consecutively acting memory systems: a **sensory memory**, in which sensory information received from one of the sense organs is retained for a few hundred milliseconds; a **short-term memory** of limited capacity; and a **long-term memory** of very large capacity. Figure 2.10 represents a schematic view of Atkinson's and Shiffrin's multiple storage model.

The information entering via the sense organs is received by the sensory memory, but then quickly decays unless it becomes subject of our attention. The sensory memory, therefore, belongs to the pre-attentive processes we spoke about in our last section.

Information we devote attention to is received by the short-term memory. It is then superseded by other contents unless it is maintained by being actively called to mind. Only information received by short-term memory can be transferred to long-term memory. The probability of that happening increases with the length of time information is maintained in the short-term memory.

Therapy researcher: May I interrupt here? Is it really true that only that which once had the status of conscious attention can basically become part of long-term memory? If that were the case, it would be highly relevant for psychotherapy. After all, the structures and contents of our consciousness are surely part of our long-term memory. Would we not have to conclude from this that basically only what has once been the subject of our attention can be subject to consciousness? Would that in turn not also imply that consciousness is something that must essentially be created through a process of conscious attention? What consequences would this have for the psychodynamic unconscious? Would we not have to assume that all contents of our unconscious, in terms of biography, were at one time part of conscious experience, before being banned from consciousness? Negating this, we could never count on establishing consciousness by reversing repression. The appropriate contents would not be at all accessible in the long-term memory, rather, they would have to be newly created. In that case, the term repression would be misleading. What has never been part of consciousness, cannot be banned from it.

Psychologist: Following upon all we have said, your argument makes sense. Yet I will be able to answer your questions much better after we have made some more distinctions between the different forms of memory processes. Let us put off the question of the unconscious for now. I wish to make just one more point before continuing: The model of Atkinson and Shiffrin and the conclusions you have drawn from it are only valid for one part of the long-term memory, namely for the explicit or conceptual memory. There is, however, another form of memory, the implicit memory, which is particularly important for the question of unconscious behavior control.

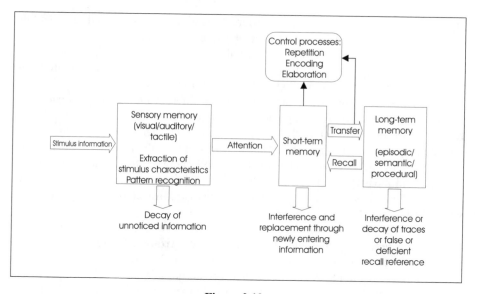

Figure 2.10:
Schematic representation of the multiple storage model by Atkinson and Shiffrin (1968).
Figure adapted from Goschke (1996 a, p.372).

According to today's research status, the multiple storage model by Atkinson and Shiffrin needs to be supplemented or at least modified by a further differentiation of various forms of both long-term and short-term memory, because there are more and more facts emerging which do not agree with the original conception of the short-term memory. These facts concern the short-term memory's capacity. According to Miller's (1956) renowned essay "The Magical Number Seven, Plus Minus Two," the capacity of our working memory consists of seven information units or "chunks." Later studies have repeatedly confirmed this capacity. The capacity in most humans tends to be more below than above that number. Yet there are also findings contradictory to these capacity limits. Test persons have been shown to be capable of solving rather complex brain teasers, even while the assumed capacity of their short-term memory was fully challenged, for example by making them loudly repeat eight numbers. So their conscious processing capacity considerably exceeded that of the short-term memory.

Results such as these brought Baddeley (1990) to assume a **working memory** consisting of three sub-systems instead of one undifferentiated short-term memory: a phonological short-term memory for retaining language information; a visual-spatial component for retaining visual imagery; and a modality-unspecific central executive. By now, much empirical evidence exists for the first two forms of working memory designed specifically for various sense modes. The phonological memory is mostly important for the understanding and production of language. Yet there is hardly any substantial evidence about how the central executive operates. It could be that we have here one of those homunculi, which appear in psychology every time something has not yet been completely understood.

For our considerations in the context of psychotherapy, these differentiations of short-term memory are only of indirect relevance in that they demonstrate to us the importance of distinguishing the memory's different functions. Scientific findings about the functioning of long-term memory are, however, directly relevant.

Looking at long-term memory, one must also distinguish between different forms of memory or memory processes. Figure 2.11 illustrates the taxonomy of different forms of the long-term memory according to the current research status.

We can infer from Figure 2.11 that at least eleven different forms of long-term memory are distinguished today. At this point, it may be useful for us to recall that all these forms of memory were inferred from observations and measurements with subjects intentionally exposed to different influences. Influencing the memory influences the basis for later experience and behavior. The process between the influence and its observable and measurable effects must be inferred. So whenever I speak of memory processes, I am always referring to **inferred processes**. Instead of memory processes, we could also speak of **learning processes**.

The simplest form of learning is **non-associative** learning, such as the change in responses to repeatedly presented stimuli. With **sensitization** the response becomes stronger, with **habituation** it becomes weaker. This very basic form of learning we can already observe in simple organisms such as ocean snails (Kandel & Hawkins, 1992). Most likely though, it also plays a crucial role in explaining the emergence of fears (Eysenck, 1987) and the mechanisms of some therapeutic procedures, but only as part of a more complex learning process. In our first conversation, for example, you showed that it is plausible for a change in expectations to take place both through exposure treatment and through systematic desensitization. This could be ascribed to associative learning. But the basis for the change in expectations might also be that the anxiety response, either through a repeated presentation of the anxiety stimulus or by remaining in the fear-triggering situation, becomes habituated. The short-term decrease in the anxiety response in the situation then leads to a permanent change in expectations through associative learning.

We speak of **associative** memory on the basis of whether connections between different stimuli or between stimuli and responses are newly formed or modified due to experiences. Stimuli and responses correspond to certain neural activation patterns. So

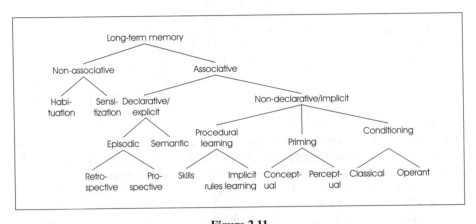

Figure 2.11
Taxonomy of different forms of long-term memory according to Goschke (1996 a, p. 367)

associative learning means that new connections between different neural activation patterns are formed and existing connections are modified. At the neural level, this takes place through the modification of the synaptic transmission weights (see above).

The most important distinction in the associative memory is the one between the **explicit or conceptual** and the **implicit** memory. This distinction is of such fundamental importance for the understanding of psychological functioning and mental disorders that we should explore it in some more detail.

The **explicit** memory refers to those parts of the memory processes associated with the subjective experience of remembering. According to Tulving (1972), two sub-systems can be distinguished, an episodic and a semantic memory.

The **semantic** memory holds factual knowledge about the world, about the meanings of words, etc. These contents are not categorized in space and time. Often we do not know any more when and where we acquired these contents of semantic memory.

The **episodic** memory refers to events in their spatial-temporal context. A portion of it is also known by the name **autobiographical memory**. It can be further distinguished into retrospective and prospective memory. The **retrospective** episodic memory refers to past events, while the **prospective** memory refers to the retention of plans and intentions.

Contents of the **implicit** memory are not associated with conscious recollections; however, they significantly influence our experience and behavior. They are particularly important for the understanding of unconscious processes and for the question of parallel-simultaneous behavioral organization. In Figure 2.11 three different forms of implicit learning are differentiated, namely **conditioning**, **procedural learning** and **priming**, whereby each form of learning is in turn subdivided twice.

2.12   Implicit and Explicit Memory

The distinction between **implicit** and **explicit** memory is essentially equivalent to the distinction between a **perceptual** and a **conceptual** memory as outlined by Perrig et al. (1993). The perceptual memory is the phylogenetically older one. It facilitates a simpler form of learning without the participation of consciousness. "Particular to perceptual memory is the processing and retention of episodic information running automatically with the ability to control behavior without consciousness influencing these processes at all. The properties of automatic motor movement control can also be attributed to this memory. The conceptual memory is a memory constructed and mediated through our consciousness, storing the meaning of episodic experience associated with our experience. The retention of meaningful experience comprises the contents of our consciousness, it is, however, not identical with consciousness" (Perrig et al., 1993, p. 43).

According to Perrig et al., the two memory systems are associated with two fundamentally different ways of psychological functioning: associated with the perceptual (implicit) memory is an "associative response function," associated with the conceptual (explicit) memory is a "constructive interpretive function." In order to avoid a mix-up with the distinction previously made between non-associative and associative memory, we might also speak of an automatic or unconscious response function. Or we might simply distinguish between a **response function** and an **interpretive function**.

Perrig et al. summarize the distinction and the relationship between response function and interpretive function in the following core statements:

– "Human behavior is controlled via the associative response function using perceptual representations without the participation of consciousness.

– Following a perception, only contents having passed assessment by the interpretive function may become subject of conscious recollection.

– A conscious decision based on a clear recall experience is always and exclusively the result of reactivated conceptual representations and its utilization by mental operations of the interpretive function.

– A familiar process within the response function correlates with a feeling of familiarity within the interpretive function.

– The fundamental principle of response-interpretive-covariation [the interaction of unconscious and conscious processes, K.G.] and the linkage of perceptual and conceptual memory traces is not only the foundation of decisions but of higher learning and knowledge formation overall " (pp. 51—53).

Figure 2.12 provides a graphical illustration of the relationship between the two forms of memory, conscious experience—denoted by the term consciousness in the figure—and behavior, as assumed by Perrig et al. in their model of conscious and unconscious behavioral control.

The "model of conscious and unconscious behavioral control" illustrated in this figure is a good example that today's psychology has surmounted the exclusions I mentioned earlier at the beginning of this dialogue. The model explicitly places expe-

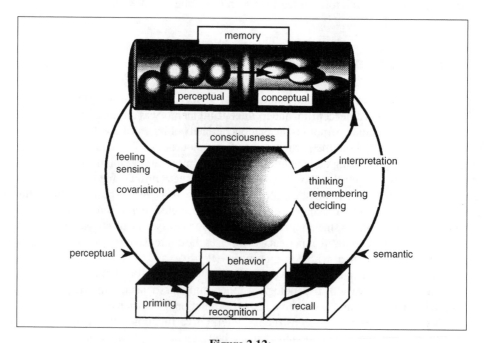

Figure 2.12:
Framework model of conscious and unconscious behavioral control according to Perrig et al. (1993, p. 42).

rience, behavior and inferred unconscious processes in relation to one another. It also makes some very specific statements, as indicated by the one-way arrow on top indicating that the contents of conceptual memory may be activated by perceptual memory, but that the contents of perceptual memory may not be activated via the contents of conceptual long-term memory. I will go into that in more depth in a moment.

2.13 Differences in Accessing Explicit and Implicit Memory and Their Relevance for Psychotherapy

The different ways of accessing explicit and implicit memory appear to be particularly important for psychotherapy. Basically, the contents of explicit memory can be recalled through intentional decisions. Conceptual memory is not modality-specific. It is the **meanings** that are stored without regard to the sense modality by which they entered. A subject learned through reading is, for example, also recognized in hearing.

A predominant feature of conceptual memory is that nearly every aspect of a subject or event once entered can lead to the recollection of the entire content. This **content-addressed recall** is based on the similarity or the association between the recall references (perceptions, images, thoughts) and the information is stored in the form of neural activation patterns which can be reactivated. The activation of only parts of such an activation pattern stored in the memory can lead to the activation of the entire pattern. What occurs is the completion of a pattern based on partial information until a holistic gestalt is reached, such as we know from gestalt psychology research on perception (Tschacher, 1997). We are able to recognize a person by his/her walk or voice. The recall happens extremely **fast**, and usually with ease. A word is barely off the lips and the associated meanings usually come effortlessly to mind. In addition to that, the recall is relatively **robust** with respect to vague information. We will also recognize a blurred face or an indistinctly spoken sentence.

Also, the recall from conceptual memory is highly **context-sensitive**. Depending on the context of meaning in which the recall occurs, different pieces of information are integrated into a current representation (Goschke & Koppelberg, 1991). Part of the recall context is also the person's inner mindset: What comes to mind as memories is also dependent upon the motivational and emotional state at the moment of recall. Preferably all those contents are recalled which, at the time they were stored, were associated with a similar motivational and emotional state. "This context sensitivity is in line with the previously mentioned view by Bartlett which maintains that the contents of memory are not fixed, invariant structures, but that we have to conceive of recall as a (re)constructive process, in which an earlier condition is more or less re-instated under the influence of manifold current context conditions" (Goschke, 1996 a, p. 380).

The current contents of consciousness are the point of departure for steering towards other contents of the conceptual memory via semantic or episodic connections. We can speak of a "top-down activation" of meaningful contents of memory. On the other hand, most of us know from our own painful experience in exams or similar situations that the intentional access to existing contents of memory in and of themselves is not always so easy, and we are not even talking here about the avoidance of uncomfortable issues.

What determines whether one remembers something well or not so well has been intensely studied in the psychology of memory. Much of this research is more relevant to preparing for exams than to psychotherapy, but it still also opens some interesting perspectives for psychotherapy. The research on this was stimulated by a pioneering article by Craik and Lockhart (1972). They came up with the thesis that achieving recall largely depends on the depth of processing that occurs during learning, and much evidence for their idea exists. A text is better retained if it was well understood when read, i.e., if it has been related to extant contents of memory. Yet if one is later asked what font the text was printed in, one might not be able to remember this, regardless of how well the semantic content was memorized. A person who already paid explicit attention to such surface characteristics while learning might perhaps recall the font better than the content. In the course of the empirical research on the correlation between learning conditions and recall achievement, Craik and Lockhart's thesis had to be modified, however.

Today in psychology of memory the prevailing view is that the more congruent the processes of information processing are during encoding and recalling, the better the recall performance (Goschke, 1996 b). These processes, as I mentioned earlier, are strongly influenced by the context in which recall takes place. From a clinical view-point, it is especially the motivational and emotional context that is relevant. The influence that current motivations have on the recall is, of course, highly relevant, and the clinical relevance of the fact that memories depend on the current mood is directly evident. Contents retained in an uplifted mood, or which are otherwise associated with a good mood, are much more easily recalled in a good mood; conversely, the same is true for depressed moods. This phenomenon is referred to as state-dependent learning (Goschke, 1996 b). I believe this to be a phenomenon which ought to be acknowledged by psychotherapists in their work.

Therapist: If my understanding of this association is correct, I believe that something like this is already done in psychotherapy in many cases. In psychodrama or in family reconstruction techniques for instance, through recreating concrete and not just verbal conditions as they existed during the learning of emotionally significant experiences, we attempt to activate as many detailed and vivid memories as possible. This means, we try to processually activate emotionally significant contents of memory through conditions similar to those present at the time of learning. To put it in the terminology you previously introduced with respect to the underlying neural processes: By activating parts of formerly ingrained neural activation tendencies through creating concrete and, as much as possible, similar situations we hope to (re)activate associated activation patterns, which are difficult to reactivate today by actual perceptions such as the emotions and thoughts experienced by the patient in the original learning situation. We do that because we assume that these activation patterns exert an influence on the patient's experience and behavior still today without being subject to conscious control. With such techniques of processual activation then, we try to achieve that those processes, which unconsciously exerted an influence on the psychological functioning before, can now be consciously experienced. Reactivating and consciously experiencing these processes allows new mental contents to form which will help these processes to become potentially accessible to deliberate control. Thus they will fall under the control of present conscious intentions.

Psychologist: With this you have already anticipated in part what I wanted to say about accessibility to the contents of the **implicit** or **perceptual memories**. Perceptual representations, that means those for which conscious contents were never created, can only be activated "bottom-up," not "top-down," and can thus not be intentionally activated. "The perceptual representation can only be reactivated by presenting the same stimulus again, through so-called data-driven (bottom-up) processing. Processes of conscious awareness have no access to this database. Introspectively and without repeated external stimulation, it is, therefore, not possible to make these data accessible in a so-called concept-driven (top-down) processing. On this database, no strategic decisions (deliberate control processes, K.G.) are possible. The structure or form of these memory contents are solely the results of automated processes. They are lasting and—with appropriate data-driven reactivation—behaviorally effective even after a long time. These memory traces are tied to the sensory nature of the respective sensory system in which the stimulus-response coupling has taken place and are therefore modality-specific" (Perrig et al., 1993, p. 46).

All contents of the implicit memory and, as a result, the foundations of a large fraction of unconscious processes can thus only be activated and reactivated **processually**, and not by making them the subject of discussion. This seems to be of utmost relevance for psychotherapy. The reactivation requires the creation of a stimulus situation as similar as possible to that in which these mental contents were originally acquired. We do not gain access to these processes through talking. The path from perceptual to conceptual memory is a one-way street, as the horizontal arrow at the top of Figure 2.12 should demonstrate. If contents of the perceptual memory have been processually reactivated bottom-up, conceptual contents can be formed, but the reverse is not possible. Contents of the implicit memory cannot be recalled directly, not intentionally nor by making them the subject of discussion, as can contents of the conceptual memory. For psychotherapy this means: Access to the contents and processes stored in the implicit memory is only possible by first processually activating them bottom-up through appropriate situations. Then they can become the object of conscious awareness and, via the short-term memory, part of the conceptual long-term memory. Only after this transformation can these processes be included in conscious planning and action control.

2.14 Therapeutic Change of Activated Memory Content

Therapy researcher: Doesn't this place a considerable restriction on the potential for producing change by a purely verbal therapy? Addressing unconscious processes, without having them previously processually activated, should then have no effect whatsoever on these processes. Consequently, it would only make sense to bring up processes while they are processually activated, as the therapeutic technique of confrontation would. This technique would serve to create awareness for something that had been happening unconsciously thus far. This might also explain why "experiential confrontation" has proven to be such a potent form of intervention, as I reported in our first dialogue. If these contents of the implicit memory, however, have not already been otherwise processually activated in one way or another, through the actual relationship between therapist and patient for instance, one has to go beyond the therapeutic conversation. In such a case, the therapist has to process-activate these contents or processes by role playing, experience-enhancing therapeutic techniques, or through seeking out or creating real situations in order to successfully change these memory contents.

Following your explanation, it is perfectly clear that neural activation patterns must be activated in order to be changed. Nerve cells can only create connections to other nerve cells if they are activated. Learning or changes in experience and behavior come into being via the formation of new neural connections. The change mechanism of process-activation, which in our first conversation we derived from findings of therapy research, almost inevitably results from the basic research considerations on the neural foundations of experience and behavior you presented to us. These relationships make immediate sense to me, but it is entirely new to me to see psychotherapeutic problems from a psychology of memory perspective. It is very reaffirming for me to learn that we can reach such similar conclusions proceeding from such different scientific foundations: The processes underlying our experience and behavior can only be changed if they are activated. Changes in experience and behavior require process-activation.

This is why we must activate those processes underlying fears and depressions of patients suffering from anxiety or depression, and that means the respective cognitions, avoidance responses, physiological reactions, etc., in order to exert an influence towards change. A somewhat paradoxical conclusion arises from this: The therapist has to activate what he wants to eliminate in order to change it. This would be an alternative formulation of the change mechanism of problem actuation (Grawe, 1995) derived from the psychology of memory.

On the other hand, considerations drawn from the psychology of memory also indicate that no change can be expected from processual activation alone. If you leave somebody alone in a depressed state, the individual will mainly retrieve contents from his or her memory matching that mood, which will only reinforce the depressed state. Thus simultaneously with the processual activation of the processes to be changed, neural activation patterns have to be reactivated which have the ability to exert a positive influence on the problematic activation patterns. The counterbalance to the problematic activation patterns has to already exist as a possibility in the form of neural activation patterns that can be activated relatively easily, and from which a positive influence can be expected. We can view these positive well-ingrained neural activation patterns as a person's positive resources. Seen from a psychology of memory perspective, the successful activation of such resources is a necessary condition for positive change in psychotherapy.

If only the problematic activation patterns are activated in a patient when confronting him with new perceptual contents incompatible with these activation patterns, i.e. with his expectations, it would, according to control theory, lead to an incongruence signal with respect to the standards (goals) controlling the problematic activation pattern, and therefore, to a negative emotional response. This in turn might lead to an avoidance of the perceptual contents triggering this emotional response if there were no other neural activation patterns simultaneously activated, directing the attention towards these perceptions. Turning towards the emotionally stressing perceptions has to be a perception consistent with the goals of one or more concurrently activated control hierarchies. A new neural activation pattern, which adequately reflects the real environment, can be established only if conscious attention is directed to those perceptions that do not correspond with the problem-relevant expectations. This was designated by Piaget as accommodation. Resource activation in the sense of activating positively evaluated neural activation patterns is a necessary precondition for constructive accommodation processes.

According to the psychology of memory, the synchronous realization of resource activation, problem activation and confrontation with new perceptions, which do not correspond with the expectations to be changed, creates the ideal condition for bringing about positive therapeutic changes. In the exposure treatment of agoraphobic disorders, for instance, these conditions seem to be realized almost ideally, and this perhaps explains why these therapies are so highly successful.

Psychologist: I am relieved that what I told you about memory seems to be of such great use to you. I was afraid that my basic research considerations might reach too far beyond what actually interests you. I believe that psychology of memory actually has much to offer in enabling us to better understand the change mechanisms elaborated in our first dialogue and how it is that they contribute to therapeutic changes. According to the concept of the mechanisms of psychotherapy just outlined by you, resource activation and processual activation would have the function of necessary conditions, whereas the actual corrective experience is created through the forced concentration on new perceptual contents which do not correspond with expectations. Through this, the tendencies towards specific neural activation patterns stored in the long-term memory are changed. Some of these activation patterns are, according to control theory, the goals (the motivational component of the activation pattern, which I will go into in more depth at a later point), the perceptual expectations, the action tendencies, and the emotional response tendencies which I will go into on their own later (sections 2.21 and 2.22).

In a broad sense all these components can be viewed as expectations: The reference values (goals) are expectations regarding which conditions should be met so that the individual's needs are fulfilled; the perceptual expectations are expectations regarding the kind of state the environment is in—for this purpose I also include our own body in the environment; the action tendencies are expectations regarding with which behaviors certain perceptions can be created. In this broad sense one might say psychotherapy consists of changing expectations. With this we can bridge the gap to many of the ideas in the first dialogue in which we, in connection with the expectancy-value theories, also assigned a crucial role to expectations. From a psychology of memory point of view, the value component of these theories would also have to be considered as part of the expectations which the individual carries into the environment. This conception has a great similarity to Epstein's personality theory (1990), which I will go into later in conjunction with the question regarding the determinants of the mental activity (section 2.27). What I just referred to as expectations, Epstein calls "postulates" which the individual carries into his interactions with the environment.

When I talk about expectations in a psychology of memory sense, I am referring mostly to implicit expectations, which the individual is not necessarily able to comment on when asked. When we measure expectations in psychology, such as self-efficacy expectations and control expectations, via questionnaires or rating scales, we do not measure expectations in the psychology of memory sense, as referred to here. Rather, what we measure are cognitive evaluations determined by contents of the conceptual long-term memory and a current situational assessment. Perhaps it makes more sense to refer to the expectations meant in conjunction with psychology of memory as **tendencies** towards specific neural activation patterns, as this will help to avoid a mix-up in terminology.

At any rate, the individual's interaction with his or her environment always takes place on the basis of such preexisting tendencies. Bartlett (1932) designated such tendencies with his term "schema" and also Piaget's (1976) understanding of a schema is largely equivalent to that meaning. Yet we just saw that one must differentiate between different forms of tendencies, namely perceptual tendencies, action tendencies, emotional tendencies and motivational tendencies. If these differences need to be accounted for the term schema would need to be differentiated and specified. The term schema plays such a crucial role in today's psychology that there is no getting away from it in our coming conversations. As you already mentioned, it is also used in psychotherapy as a theoretical foundation for quite different procedures.

What we considered about perception and memory so far has shown us that this is a very basic construct, because if we use the term schema for the tendencies towards specific neural activation patterns, then schemata would underlie all mental processes. We can expect to encounter this construct time and again in very different contexts.

The mechanism of psychotherapy you outlined earlier is certainly one of the main possibilities for bringing about changes through psychotherapy. According to the nomenclature of Perrig et al. (see above), we must view this kind of change as a "higher form of learning," in which conscious reflection, choosing and deciding, making plans and deliberate action play an important part. These are all terms which, during our first dialogue, we included in our reflections on the mechanisms of psychotherapy in the framework of the Rubicon model. According to ideas from psychology of memory, there are, however, also other ways to achieve therapeutic effects. These are not necessarily tied to conscious attention, but rather to what is called implicit learning. Figure 2.11 lists three forms of implicit learning: conditioning, procedural learning and priming. If one wanted to, even more forms of learning could be distinguished by the inclusion of imprinting (Menzel & Roth, 1996) and observational learning (Bandura, 1977 b).

Learning is always associated with perceptions which change the previous basis of perception. For implicit learning, implicit (pre-attentive) perceptions play an important role. That is why I want to tackle unconscious perception and implicit learning all at once.

2.15   Implicit Perception and Learning

Nobody remembers how they learned to walk or speak as a child. It is not stored in the conceptual memory. But the foundations for walking or speaking obviously exist in our memory. One can have a good command of a language without having explicitly received instruction in its grammar. We can gather from the linguistic behavior of a ten-year-old that she knows the language rules, yet she is incapable of explaining them. The child has implicit knowledge both underlying her perceptions (linguistic understanding) and controlling linguistic behavior. She has no concept of this and, therefore, no conscious access to these rules which she otherwise knows and has full command of.

What is true for sensory motor processes such as walking or speaking, is also true for many other areas of behavior. Some of these are of great relevance for psychotherapy, such as the learning of relationship rules, of emotional response tendencies and the rules for expressive behavior.

In studying the nonverbal relationship behavior in dyadic interactions, regular sequences which the interaction partners are unaware of can be observed. Because these regular patterns take place below our conscious perceptual level, many of them can only be detected with technical equipment such as a video camera. It is only when the sequences are artificially prolonged into slow motion with specially developed micro-analytical methods (e.g. Ekman & Friesen, 1969) that one notices that the interaction partners respond to each other according to rules (Merten, 1996). This is only possible if they have pre-attentively made and processed appropriate perceptions. During the processing, rules are applied, although the participants remain unaware of their existence.

The nonverbal regulation of interactions is accompanied by emotions which are conveyed to the interaction partner via expressive behavior. Many of these micro-reactions happen much too fast to be consciously perceived at all in real time. The interaction partner, however, responds to it so immediately and in accordance with the rule that he or she must have perceived it. Each of the two interaction partners receives and sends emotional messages which largely control the course of their interaction, while, at the same time, their consciousness is occupied with other contents. How satisfied both parties are with the interaction largely depends on what was unconsciously exchanged between them. Whether or not we like somebody, is, to a large extent, also controlled by events occurring outside of our consciousness.

Learning about relationship rules begins in the first weeks of life. An infant's motor behavior and the mother's expressive behavior are strongly interrelated. The expressive behavior is different in different cultures. The child acquires implicit memory contents via pre-language interactions with his closest interaction partners, which later affect his behavior as rules. A northern European, for instance, can feel the effects of such unconscious acculturation processes on himself when encountering another culture with different norms for the regulation of closeness and distance. Oftentimes one may feel that the others move in too close, and then want more personal space between oneself and the others, while the other party may experience exactly the opposite and make an effort in the opposite direction. There are no official norms for the "correct" distance between people. Each individual is influenced in his/her regulation of closeness and distance, the personal space, by implicit cultural and individual values which he or she attempts to abide by and whose violation leads to incongruence signals, in the sense of control theory.

Implicit memory contents determine which perceptions we attempt to create with our behaviors in relationships. These standards are embedded in a control hierarchy and are thus activated by the higher-order goals activated in the situation. We usually do a very good job with the situation-adequate regulation of closeness and distance; it happens so naturally without us having to make a conscious effort. Only if these standards are violated does it become clear that this aspect of the relationship needs regulation. This is one of many examples for the fact that, parallel to the control hierarchy or hierarchies filling our consciousness at the time, there are still other control hierarchies activated which exert an influence on our perceptions, emotions and behaviors without consciousness.

Between a mother and her infant there is something like an "emotional infection." Hatfield, Cacioppo and Rapson (1992) bestowed this term upon the "tendency towards automatically imitating movements, expressions, postures and intonation of another person, synchronizing them and, as a consequence, becoming one emotionally" (p. 154). If a mother is in a certain emotional state over and over again, the emotional infection leads to the child also having an increased tendency to be in this particular emotional state. A study by Malatesta (1990) demonstrated that among children aged seven to eight months, the frequency of expressing joy and interest correlated strongly with the extent that mother and child had exchanged joy and interest when the child was two to three months old. It is very likely that such emotional tendencies or emotional expectations can also be acquired as a content of memory, similar to perceptual or action tendencies. We can call such neural activation patterns that correspond to certain emotions emotional schemata (Leventhal, 1980, 1984; Leventhal & Scherer, 1987; Ulich, 1992). Emotional schemata would thus be ingrained tendencies towards emotions of a certain kind or, in short: towards emotional response tendencies. Malatesta (1990) and Tomkins (1991) even refer to such emotional response tendencies developed out of early mother-child interactions as "emotional life scripts."

It need not always be the same emotion as that experienced by the mother which is induced in the child. According to studies by Malatesta and Haveland (1982), mourning and anger on the mother's part led to specific differential emotional responses by their $2^{1/2}$ month old infants. Eventually, through frequent repetition of such sequences, those overly schematized emotional response tendencies may develop on the part of the child.

"Emotional infection" is not the only way to adopt other persons' emotional response tendencies. Much more common and more well known is observational learning, the internalization of responses which are observed in other people (Bandura, 1977 b). This form of learning does not just affect emotions, but all forms of behavior. Observational learning remains one of the most important forms of lifelong learning. Motions, handicraft skills, etc., are essentially much better learned by observational learning (imitation) than through verbal descriptions. Implicit and conceptual memory processes play a role in observational learning. If somebody observes another very carefully demonstrating how to perform a certain skiing movement, the event is processed via the short-term memory and is stored as a content of the episodic memory. One is able to recall this image as a visualization from memory. The acquisition of sensory motor skills, however, requires imitation and practice. The storage of such sensory motor skills happens independent of the conceptual memory. Amnesia patients who, due to a damaged hippocampus—which makes an important contribution to the processing of episodic and semantic memory contents—are no longer capable of consciously recalling new information, are still capable of learning complex sensory motor skills such as reading or "looking-glass" writing, the solving of puzzles, etc., through practice, almost as well as a person without brain damage (Kolb & Wishaw, 1996). They are unable to remember that they ever completed the task, but they improve with successive attempts.

Observational learning depends on the relationship between observer and model. The ideal condition is identification with the model. This requirement is especially well met in the relationship between children and an attachment figure. Bandura has contributed a lot to the study and propagation of this form of learning. All responses that can be conditioned can also be adopted through observational learning. This also applies specifically to emotions such as fear. We know this to be the case in monkeys. Mineka et al. (1984) had rhesus monkeys watch other rhesus monkeys who displayed fear of a snake. The monkeys that were watching immediately developed an intense and lasting fear of snakes which persisted undiminished and context-independent for three months.

Therapist: Does this mean that one could acquire a tendency towards an emotional response, such as fear or shame or avoidance reactions for specific situations without having ever experienced such a triggering situation? Is it sufficient for parents to behave as though the environment was dangerous and hostile in order for the child to begin to perceive, feel, think, and avoid in the same way, although the child has not made any bad experiences him- or herself? Can a son, for instance, adopt his father's unexpressed fear of failure? If this were the case, then we therapists would not have to necessarily always search for events in our patients' biographies that would explain a certain fear or an avoidance behavior due to the patient's own experiences. I still remember behavior therapists who repeatedly and almost desperately searched for the situation precipitating the classical conditioning of the anxiety response to the phobic stimulus. Oftentimes they were not able to find such a situation and dropped the subject. So, according to what you just said about the possibilities for the acquisition of emotional response tendencies, there might have never been such a situation. The patient could have also acquired the phobic fear through emotional infection or through identification learning. In our first conversation we also assumed the possibility that there could also be an unconscious conflict underlying the fear, which is to say that the fear might have a basis in current psychological functioning.

Family therapists assume that certain taboos, emotional rules or entire relationship patterns may be passed on from generation to generation. They could very well have been based in negative experiences from previous generations, possibly leading to irrational limitations in some descendants, which are not justified by a person's own experiences and life conditions. This could all be explained by observational learning.

In my own practice, I myself try to assess recurrent family patterns by elaborating a genogram (McGoldrick, 1990) for the patient's family of origin. In addition, whenever possible, I invite the patient's family in at least once so as to get a picture of which implicit norms and relationship rules are adhered to, or to get an idea about which standards the patient adopted from these for his own goals, perceptions, cognitions, emotions and behaviors. This almost always proves to be more productive than if I relied solely on the patient's memories.

Some relational processes in a patient's family may have become so taken for granted such that he or she is not able to point them out to a therapist as a special characteristic of the familial interaction, whereas an outside observer might realize it right away as a peculiarity of the family. With individual habits and life situations it is quite similar. It is the most ingrained habits that have become so taken for granted that one does not spontaneously talk about them even if there is no motive for hiding them. Lately, upon giving more and more thought to the principle of processual activation, I did something in my work which I had never done in earlier days: I visited my patients' homes in order to get a picture for myself of the concrete circumstances under which the things discussed, or not discussed, in therapy occur. Many times I felt the scales fall from my eyes. During these visits I sometimes acquire, without any words, so much information that I am then better able to understand the patient's life feeling. I am able to much more tangibly imagine which neural activation patterns have to be repeatedly activated, and what would have to be changed about the life situation and processes for the patient to be able to have perceptions which can exert a modifying influence on these ingrained activation patterns.

Generally it appears to me that one gains access to the patient's implicit memory content, which, you said, can strongly influence his relationship behavior, his individual standards and his emotions, mostly via observations and not via questioning. Via questioning I can only figure out what the patient is already able to access as a conscious mental content. If I wish to include implicit or unconscious determinants of the patient's behavior in therapy these determinants have to be inferred from his behavior, including what he says and how he says it.

Therapy researcher: This would, however, require that you have or can create the opportunity to activate these determinants which are obviously specific neural activation patterns or schemata. Otherwise you cannot observe their visible impacts. Thus processual activation is also important for diagnostic purposes, not just an important requirement for a successful intervention.

Psychologist: I believe you therapists and we basic researchers are sitting in the same boat: We only gain access to the foundations of experience and behavior through systematic observation, inference and testing of hypotheses. Actually, I think we have even more in common: We both need a theory telling us what we should observe and from where we may derive the hypotheses, according to the verification or falsification of which, we direct our observations.

Therapist: Considering the theory needed for my work—and I agree, I do need such a theory—I am almost starting to lose confidence. We are now engaged in our second conversation, and things are getting more complicated rather than more clear. Although I am really interested in what you are presenting, and I am able to bridge the gap to the world of my therapeutic experiences, I do not see that I am capable of considering all these factors in my practical work, however. You seem to be in high gear and nowhere near finished. So it will become even more complex if you continue that way. Do you really believe that a practicable conception for therapeutic practice will result from this?

Psychologist: I was waiting for these doubts, and I can understand them. But you probably understand that certain concepts such as the neural activation patterns, the control hierarchies, the distinction between synchronously on-going conscious and unconscious processes recur many times throughout the discussion in changing contexts. Eventually what we will need are some central constructs for a realistic picture of psychological functioning. I do not believe that the number of these central constructs will be impracticably huge. I find it important that in the end we will have understood these constructs and their role in mental functioning as clearly as possible. Therefore, it is best to proceed in an inductive fashion and, to acquire step-by-step an understanding of the constructs as they result from basic research. The better we have understood them, the better we will be able to apply them later to the questions of psychotherapy.

Therapist: I had promised not to get tired and I will stick to that. But it is helpful to me that you remain optimistic, as it tends to be contagious. So where were we? I believe you had just spoken about observational learning when I interrupted you.

Psychologist: Yes, I had suggested some examples of how one can acquire emotional response tendencies, conditioned responses and complex sensory motor action programs via observational learning. I had also emphasized the point that entire relationship patterns can be stored in the implicit memory, analogous to other complex regulation systems, such as grammar for language. The possibilities for the unconscious acquisition of entire sequences of events or complex regulation systems have also been tested and confirmed by experimental psychology.

Reber (1989) has carried out experiments on the learning of artificial grammars. His subjects were instructed to memorize a series of nonsense letter sequences in a first learning phase. In reality these sequences had been developed according to the application of a rather complex grammar. Following this learning phase the subjects were informed that the seemingly nonsense letters in reality followed rules. Then they were offered truly random and regular letter sequences in random order and asked to assess whether the series was properly formed grammatically. Although the subjects were unable to describe the rules, and many revealed that they had guessed intuitively, their choices were correct far more often than they would have been by chance. This tells us that the subjects had acquired unconscious knowledge about the rules underlying the series of letters and were not able to utilize it intentionally, but only intuitively.

These findings gave rise to a discussion in which it was posited that perhaps the subjects actually did consciously recognize partial rules and used them in their assessments (Perruchet & Pacteau, 1990). This possibility could not be completely excluded; however, it does not call into question the interpretation of the previously reported findings as evidence for the possibility of unconscious learning of rules. In fact Knowlton, Ramus and Squire (1992) actually found that amnesia patients scored every bit as high as normal control subjects in their intuitive assessment although their conscious recognition of the chains of letters was far worse.

Even more complex connections in the perceived environment can be learned without consciousness and have an effect on the behavior later. Lewicki (1986) showed photos of people to test subjects, and at the same time provided a description of the respective individual's character traits. In the photos certain distinguishing characteristics varied, such as the length of hair. Personal character traits also varied. Later the test subjects were asked to make judgments on their own about the traits of persons shown to them in photos. These assessments were, far more than could be expected by chance, congruent with the actual covariance of character traits and external characteristics in the stimulus material previously offered. However, the test persons were not aware of this covariance. Based on such findings, it can be assumed that we all have much "unconscious" knowledge which has an effect on our perceptions, assessments, emotions and behaviors, etc., without us having any awareness of this knowledge and its effects. It can thus be considered proven that unconscious determination of behavior is an everyday phenomenon.

According to the reported results, not only simple emotional response tendencies and situation-response-contingencies can be unconsciously acquired, but more complex rules can also be unconsciously learned. Unconsciously acquired contents of the implicit memory can thus, equally unconsciously, have an effect on perceptions, emotions and behaviors.

Even sensory motor action programs, once learned and automated thereafter, can have an effect on conscious behavior without there being any awareness of it. In particular a study by Van den Bergh, Vrana and Eelen (1990) demonstrates this beautifully. In this study, test subjects—some of them skilled in two-handed typing, others not—were presented with a pair of letters and asked to state which letter they preferred. Some letters contained combinations of characters that on the keyboard are to be typed with the same finger, others contained combinations that would have been typed in with different fingers. In comparison to the unskilled typists, skilled typists chose those letters containing the multiple finger combinations significantly more often. The authors interpreted this as showing that the multiple finger combinations being more comfortable for the skilled typists to type in, and therefore, they preferred these letters. None of the test subjects was able to tell what the differences were between these letters. This is to say that there are intuitive preferences without there being the least awareness for where these preferences come from. It would be hopeless to attempt to find out in a conversation why one has these preferences.

Using classical conditioning Corteen and Wood (1972) first coupled certain words to electrical shocks. Then, they presented these to the same subjects in a new test series in which the words could not consciously, but only pre-attentively, be perceived. They used the so-called dichotic listening paradigm. In this experimental paradigm stimuli are presented to one ear which demand the full attention of the subject, as the subject is given a certain task such as repeating everything which was heard. Simultaneously, other stimuli are presented to the other ear, the input of which receives no attention. The stimuli not attended to are not consciously perceived by the test subjects and cannot be remembered later. Corteen and Wood used the method of dichotic listening in their study.

The previously conditioned words were presented in the test person's unattended ear. The presentation of the words not consciously perceived led to the same physiological reactions, a short term increase of the galvanic skin response, as during the conditioning itself. This in itself is already remarkable. Even more remarkable, however, is that other words with a semantically similar meaning also triggered a similar reaction. This proves that even in pre-attentive perception, that is to say in unconscious processes, contents of the long-term memory can be accessed. Research findings such as those by Corteen and Wood suggest that anxiety reactions, once acquired in certain situations through direct conditioning or observational learning, can also be triggered by situations, thoughts, fantasies and memories that are spatially and temporally not connected with the original anxiety experience but only semantically associated with it. Also, it is not necessary that the individual be aware of stimuli triggering the anxiety.

Therapy researcher: If stimuli that are not consciously perceived may lead to physiological and emotional reactions such as fear, and if such stimuli need only be semantically associated with the situations that had originally triggered the respective reactions, then do we not have to assume that psychoanalysts with their view on the emergence of phobias are possibly right?

Psychologist: I would not adopt the entire psychoanalytic conception of the emergence of phobias based on these research results, although in our first dialogue you yourself told us about a study and conception by Guidano and Liotti (1985) who, as far as I know are not at all psychoanalytically oriented. According to them the most characteristic agoraphobic fears, namely fear of being alone, of being restricted in one's freedom of movement, and fear of losing control, are semantically put in relation to specific conflicts around these themes which could be shown to have been significant in the life history of the patients. This would be exactly such a meaningful association between a current situation and contents of the autobiographical and semantic long-term memory.

I completely agree with your view, expressed in the first dialogue, that the significance of conflicts for the emergence and treatment of mental disorders still needs to get more attention in empirical research. But, on the other hand, we can at least state that findings from the newer research on memory are at least in agreement with the conception presented by Guidano and Liotti.

What I presented to you is not just a singular isolated research finding but was meant to serve as an example for a whole branch of research. There are many more studies on dichotic listening that essentially confirm the findings of Corteen and Wood (1972) (for instance: Treisman, Squire & Green, 1974; Forster & Govier, 1978; Posner et al., 1973). The conclusion drawn from these results, that there is also an unconscious **semantic information** processing, has been questioned with the argument that it may not be impossible that the test subjects in these experiments may have, in between, periodically focused their attention on the non-attended hearing channel (Holender, 1986) so that the stimuli transferred via the non-attended ear did indeed enter the short-term memory and, via that, the conceptual long-term memory.

This argument cannot be maintained, however, in studies where the stimuli were, from the beginning, presented subconsciously, that is either so fast (tachistoscopically) or at such low intensity as to make it impossible to perceive them consciously. A great number of these studies exist with clear findings. In Dixon (1981) and Williams et al. (1988) one can find reviews of these. It can be considered proven that the pre-attentive perception of stimuli that are connected with once conditioned stimuli via semantic associations can trigger unconscious emotional responses. These processes run parallel to the current consciously pursued perceptions and action sequences.

If such pre-attentive perceptions persist, and thereby the unconsciously triggered emotions gain in strength, so that the person feels them consciously, the need to explain to him- or herself their own emotional condition will arise. Only the perceptions and contents of memory he or she can consciously access may be used for this. The conscious perception may be directed by that person to those situational aspects that really trigger the emotional responses and he or she may achieve conscious control over these processes that were previously unconscious. Yet, it may also be that the person in his or her attempts at explanation is moving within a search area limited to that which is already conscious, and that does systematically exclude the pre-attentive perceptions and implicit contents of memory. If on the basis of these explanations, the person tries to gain control over his or her emotional condition he or she will most likely fail, and the unconscious processes will continue on without conscious control. This may eventually lead to a situation in which the person seeks help from a therapist. One could imagine patients with a psychosomatic disorder, for instance, to be in such a situation.

I am well aware that this is a simplified view in that it does not really consider the "motivatedness" of all these processes. What I wanted to do here for now was to point out in principle how unconsciously ongoing perceptions and learning processes can impact the experience and behavior, which leads inevitably to the question of the relationship of these processes to those that are going on consciously at the same time. Giving due consideration to the concurrently activated motives and their influence on the conscious and unconscious processes would yield an even more complex, yet more realistic picture. My opinion is that we should make the motivational aspect a separate focus of our later conversation. We will most definitely have to deal with this subject rather thoroughly.

For now, I am content if I have convinced you that these processes which I briefly outlined may play a role as partial processes in the development of mental disorders and should therefore be considered in their treatment.

Therapist: I can only speak for myself. As far as I am concerned, you have achieved that goal, even if I can still not envisage how it concretely applies in therapy. I have to admit that I am surprised at the perspectives the psychology of memory opens up for psychotherapy. From my own studies on the psychology of memory way back, I remember only rather simple learning and retention curves. Quite a lot must have happened there in the meantime.

Psychologist: I can try to impress you even a little more as I still have not totally exhausted my material. There are in fact even more forms of implicit learning. One is **priming** (Perrig, 1990). Just looking at words or pictures without special instructions leads to their faster and more reliable recognition under difficult perceptual conditions (quick or fragmented presentation). Also, amnesia patients completing word fragments in indirect memory tests did just as well as healthy control subjects, although they did far worse in direct memory tests, for instance the free reproduction of words (Warrington & Weiskrantz, 1970; Markowitsch, 1992). Amnesia patients can also retain something but they are unable to consciously remember it. Their memory traces are coiled in such a way that their consciousness has no access to them. Such phenomena of discussion are a clear indication that there are different kinds of memory systems, and consequently also different kinds of perception, information processing and behavior control. Only a small portion of mental processes are introspectively accessible, namely only those equipped with the specific quality of consciousness.

Conscious recognition and implicit priming seem to be two processes that are largely independent of one another. Tulving, Schacter and Stark (1982) were able to confirm this also among healthy subjects. The test subjects' ability to correctly supplement fragments of previously presented words was independent of whether or not they consciously recognized these words.

Implicit learning is not second rate or peripheral learning. In some respects, implicit learning is even superior to conceptual learning. Its simultaneous processing capacity is much larger and less susceptible to disturbances. If the attention of test subjects is distracted while they are learning by giving them another parallel task or by lowering the processing depth in a different way, this has considerable negative effects on conscious recall, but not so much on priming in an indirect memory test. So priming is not susceptible to disturbances which lower the conscious attention.

On the other hand, in contrast to semantic memory, priming is very modality- and material-specific. Changes in the surface characteristics of stimuli have a strong impact on priming, but not on semantic memory performance. One can supplement familiar words heard before, if they are presented in a fragmented visual form, not any faster than new ones. There is no transfer from one sense modality to a next, while that is easy for the semantic memory.

This specificity of implicit learning also applies to sensory motor processes, likewise in procedural learning. Somebody playing the violin well is not necessarily a good trumpet player. When there is a transfer from one instrument to another, then it happens via the semantic musical understanding, not directly from one sensory motor program to another.

The contents of the conceptual memory can be recalled and are more flexibly employable for different purposes than those of the implicit memory. Implicit knowledge cannot be consciously connected with other contents of knowledge and not directly used intentionally. Implicit contents of memory thus exert an influence on our perceptions, our emotions and our behavior, but they cannot be included in more complex thought and planning processes and, therefore, not deliberately used as the contents of the conceptual memory can be.

To the extent that implicit learning plays a role in the development and maintenance of mental disorders, these circumstances hold considerable consequences for psychotherapy. The fact that people suffering from mental disorders are often unable to exert an intentional influence on the experience and behavior typical of the disorder tells us that the implicit memory plays a crucial role as a basis for these disorders. Perceptual and response tendencies which were learned unconsciously and stored in the implicit memory, especially emotional response tendencies, cannot be intentionally controlled by the individual. In order to gain control over these processes they have to be activated in a modality-specific fashion and then, in this activated state, become subject to conscious attention. So it is not that no control over these processes is possible; rather, the control cannot happen directly via deliberate control, but can only be exerted via a prior processual activation. In this state then these processes can be exposed to intentionally controlled modifying influences.

2.16 Conditioning and Its Significance for Psychotherapy

Therapist: You have indeed convinced me of the possibility of unconscious learning, and to convince me of the great significance that memory has for the understanding of both psychological functioning and the mechanisms of psychotherapy you really need not go any further. But I still have a question: For long stretches of your presentation, I kept asking myself, where exactly had we left conditioning? Several times you referred to conditioning more or less in passing, but never really brought it up in discussion as a topic on its own. Even in our first conversation on the mechanisms of psychotherapy, much to my surprise, learning, in the sense of conditioning, played no recognizable part as an explanatory construct.

Still, not long ago it was a whichspread opinion that the empirically investigated rules of learning, such as classical and operant conditioning, later supplemented by modeling (Bandura, 1977 b), should be made the real foundation of a scientifically based psychotherapy. In an abstract way, it already made sense to me then, since lasting changes of experience and behavior, such as psychotherapy seeks to accomplish, can be considered as learning. The only thing I could not comfortably get used to was the idea that the entirety of psychological functioning should ultimately be determined by conditioning. I found the image of man arising from this idea questionable, and that was probably also the reason for the resistance many therapists had towards behavior therapy.

I know that in the meantime behavior therapy has changed a great deal, but still, in the era when I had my first therapy training, it quite seriously claimed to have the ability to explain and treat all forms of mental disorders with the two forms of learning, classical and operant conditioning (Ullman & Krasner, 1969; Kanfer & Philipps, 1970). Until very recently, Mowrer's (1960) two-factor learning theory and behavioral analyses according to the S-O-R-C-K model (Kanfer & Saslow, 1969) were the main foundations of behavior therapy problem analyses in behavior therapy (Schulte, 1974). While behavior therapy in the eighties developed significantly beyond its original learning theory foundations, predominantly through the inclusion of cognitive concepts, there are some places where, to this day, student trainees in school-organized behavior therapy are still expected to deliver elaborate analyses on the basis of the S-O-R-C-K model as a basis for their approbation as behavior therapists. I assume, however, that this will soon be history. In more recent instructions for behavior therapy treatment planning, like that by Schulte (1996), the stimulus-response-conditioning analysis has no more than a subordinate part as an aid to the situational specification of the problem, while in addition to the empirically founded disorder analysis great weight is placed on a motivational and relational analysis.

Thus far I had thought the reason for this to be that the learning theories in psychology had become outmoded in the meantime and would be replaced by other foundations, above all by those of the sort from cognitive or action psychology. Really, it did not even dawn on me that this would ultimately leave the question about the rules of learning unanswered. If the behavioral learning theories do not satisfactorily explain changes in experience and behavior, then which rules actually determine all those changes? Now, delving into your outline in Figure 2.11 which you say reflects the most up-to-date memory research, these terms of classical and operant conditioning reemerge, and you have mentioned them many times, in passing, as more or less to be taken for granted. Does this mean that these learning theories I just mentioned are really not all that outmoded, or how should I understand this?

Psychologist: I believe Figure 2.11 can in part already answer your question. Conditioning is only one of many forms of learning. The attempt to explain and treat mental disorders with the theory of conditioning has only failed insofar as these forms of learning were made into absolutes. That does not mean that conditioning would not play any part in the emergence and treatment of mental disorders. The different memory processes depicted in Figure 2.11 do not occur in an isolated fashion and independently of one another. The issues discussed by the therapist and her patient are, by definition, derived from conceptual memory. Whatever the therapist says has a meaning for the patient which is largely influenced by the contents of his conceptual memory. The patient reflects upon it, makes decisions, makes plans to do something, deliberately follows up on it, etc. In behavioral theories nobody ever talked about all these processes that are based on the contents of conceptual memory, and which are the focus of today's action psychology. They were not even conceptually considered, unless one views Skinner's attempt to reduce all mental processes to conditioning as such a consideration. At any rate, these processes were not taken seriously as independent processes that would allow forms of learning other than conditioning.

The fact that the different learning processes are viewed in such an isolated fashion is partly a result of the methods by which they were studied. This mostly happens in experimental designs which try to specifically address just one of these learning processes. Other forms of learning that might be mixed in with it are to be explicitly inactivated. It is quite difficult to simultaneously address several forms of learning and to study their reciprocal effects in one and the same experimental situation (Schacter & Graf, 1986), which is why we so far know little about the interplay of different forms of learning. Yet we must assume that a complex impact, such as that exerted by psychotherapy, will always affect several forms of memory, and that the ongoing processes will influence one another.

A test person subjected to experimental conditioning has, in fact, not ceased to think, perceive, assess or feel other things, or to relate to the experimenter in the sense of his/her own relational wishes. The experimental procedure may trigger memories, arouse boredom or interest; the subject may like the experimenter, may want to please him or her, or the contrary; the individual may have gone into the experiment in a particular mood or with a particular motivation that has little to do with the experiment itself.

Where I am going with this is: Even in a limited experimental situation, there are always several contents of memory/neural activation patterns that are activated synchronously. So what occurs in an experimental situation has, at the same time, an influence on different forms and contents of memory. Even if the experimenter concentrates on only one of these forms of memory, it does not necessarily mean that the others are inactivated. Of course, for the therapeutic situation with its recurring sessions and long intervals in between, this is even more true than for an experiment which may last perhaps an hour. The effects which therapy sessions have may be due to completely different changes in memory rather than due to the learning processes the therapist intended to focus on.

In a situation where a behavior therapist hoped to "counter-condition" her patient with systematic desensitization according to Wolpe (1958)—I am talking about the past right now, because most behavior therapists no longer believe this to be true—there were in fact a whole host of information processing operations taking place, beyond the temporal contingency of anxiety stimuli and relaxation, each on the basis of a specific type and specific contents of memory. These other forms of learning have been thoroughly ignored by behavioral learning theories and their therapeutic applications. In the end, it inevitably had to lead to what finally happened: After a long series of experimental studies it became more and more clear that systematic desensitization has effects that cannot be ascribed to classical conditioning. In our first conversation we already mentioned that many of the effects brought about by this therapeutic method can be explained by the induction of positive improvement expectations. Improvement expectations result, however, from complex information processing in which many aspects of the patient's therapeutic situation are evaluated, in fact on the basis of implicit and conceptual memory contents. We also assumed then that habituation may play a role as a basis of these evaluation processes. According to Figure 2.11, however, habituation represents one of the simplest forms of learning overall. Even the effects of a still relatively simply structured therapeutic procedure such as systematic desensitization are most likely the result of an interplay of many, both "simple" and "higher" forms of learning. In other therapeutic approaches, where the procedure is less obviously aimed at a single goal, this will be much more the case.

So according to current research in both memory and learning psychology, some behavioristic interpretations of learning psychology research results and especially the practical therapeutic conclusions drawn from those, have to be dismissed. Yet this does not change anything about the empirical phenomena described as classical and operant conditioning. There is absolutely no doubt that conditioning is one of the most important forms of learning.

If by operant conditioning one understands the systematic influence of subsequent situations on preceding behavior, then this is seen already among newborns. DeCasper and Fifer (1980) allowed a newborn to suck on a proxy nipple (a dummy without food). By sucking rapidly or more slowly, the infant could hear either the mother's voice or that of a strange woman. Already at the age of three days, the infant adjusted the sucking speed so as to hear his mother's voice more often than that of the strange woman. Not only is this an unusual proof that learning via operant conditioning plays an important role, beginning as early as the first few days of a person's life, but it also provides evidence for the great significance of the mother-child relationship from the very first days of life on (for more details see section 2.39).

The same empirical facts can also be formulated in different terminology which is closer to what we have discussed so far than it is to Skinner's terminology. We can view the baby's sucking in a certain rhythm as a newly formed pattern of mental activity which is tied together by the reduction in a need tension. In the experimental procedure described, according to Edelman (1987), a new neural group is formed through reentrant mapping and is differentially reinforced through the satisfaction of an innate need so that the newly formed neural connections may be ever more easily activated. Thus the results of research on operant conditioning can also be placed in a different frame of reference which for these results has an explanatory power equal to that of the paradigm of operant conditioning. Yet it does not share the questionable assumptions of methodological behaviorism. After all, Edelman (1995) came up with a theory of human consciousness based on his theory of neural group selection. So one can place the findings on operant conditioning in a theoretical explanatory framework whose range reaches far beyond that of behaviorism.

The empirical phenomena that are interpreted as effects of classical or respondent conditioning exist without a doubt as well, and can be viewed on their own as a very important form of learning. Classical conditioning can even be found to exist at the level of a sea snail (Menzel & Roth, 1996), and it is one of the most well researched forms of learning overall (Mackintosh, 1983). Even today, there are still learning psychologists who consider classical conditioning to be the basic form of all learning. But this happens in a very differentiated fashion, and this view by no means goes hand in hand with a denial of the existence of higher forms of learning (Rescorla, 1988). An excellent review of the significance of classical conditioning for the development of phobias and other psychopathological disorders with reference to therapeutic considerations can be found in Mineka (1987).

In **conditioning** new associations between previously independent stimuli and between responses and their consequences are formed through **temporal contingency**. Keeping in mind that stimuli and responses are represented by neural activation patterns, conditioning thus involves different neural activation patterns becoming activated, synchronously or in quick succession. Through the temporal contingency, connections between the synchronously activated activation patterns are formed, so that in the future one is more likely to activate the other. This creates new, more complex activation patterns. Through this, the stimulus represented by one of the original activation patterns changes its meaning.

The individual may become aware of the results of classical conditioning in the form of "sensing or feeling" as depicted in Figure 2.12 taken from Perrig et al. (1993). The individual can, but need not have an awareness of how the experiential content evolved. Classical conditioning is possible without the participation of consciousness. The individual then quite possibly attributes the result of classical conditioning, such as the emergence of certain feelings in certain situations, to other causes.

Classical conditioning also has to be seen within the context of all the mental processes going on at a particular time. Specifically, at any time there are contents of the conceptual memory in the short-term memory which is connected to conscious awareness. If no previously conscious content for a certain implicit memory process or content was formed, it cannot be adequately represented in the consciousness. This would first require an intermediate step which would involve the formation of a conceptual memory content by directing conscious attention to these processes.

I mentioned Hebb's principle of cell assemblies more than once in other contexts. Cell assemblies are cell groups which participate in the specific neural activation patterns. It was also Hebb who proposed a basic principle of synaptic transmission which has become generally acknowledged in neurobiology in the meantime: "The principle of the Hebb synapse states that sensory activation states lead to a modification of neural networks only if the post-synaptic cell has been previously prepared for learning through other influences" (Menzel & Roth, 1996, p. 272). Pre-synaptic and post-synaptic membranes must be synchronously activated in order to produce an transmission of activation. This "preparation" of the post-synaptic cells can occur in different ways: through priming, through moods, intentions, fantasies as well as through lasting situation-independent response tendencies in the sense of traits or through genetic "preparedness" in the sense of innate learning tendencies (Seligman, 1971; Mineka, 1985). Via classical conditioning fear responses to spiders can be conditioned far more lastingly than to flowers, and aversive conditioning of smell and taste stimuli is more effective and long-lasting when conditioned through nausea than through electroshock (Goschke, 1996 a).

Learning thus depends, as we all know from our own experience, not just upon the stimuli in the environment, but also upon our readiness for these learning experiences, and this readiness is represented by preexisting neural activation tendencies. We effortlessly take into our memory all that interests us; that which bores us, we have to repeat many times before it becomes accessible as something belonging to our memory.

Hence, as part of learning or learning under natural life conditions, emotions play a very important role both with respect to openness to and avoiding of new learning experiences and also with respect to the acquisition of emotional reactions themselves. The tendencies for certain emotional reactions are also parts of the memory. Due to prior experiences one tends to be more prepared for certain emotions in certain situations than for others. For the acquisition of such emotional response tendencies classical conditioning plays a crucial part. However, it would be misleading to regard emotions principally as a result of conditioning processes.

Emotions are constant companions of our mental processes. They have an important function as a correlate of incongruence signals in the pursuit of intentions, that means— in the language of control theory—if certain standards are not adhered to. If over and over again certain intentions cannot be realized, time and again this will lead to negative emotions of a specific quality. These emotions go hand in hand with recurring perceptions. The neural activation pattern which represents the respective emotion and the one which represents the recurring perceptual contents are connected with one another through temporal contingency. This associative connection resembles that which, in the paradigm of classical conditioning, was mostly investigated with external, unconditional triggers of involuntary reactions, such as loud noises etc. For learning under natural conditions discrepancies between intentions and perceptions are much more relevant triggers for unconditioned emotional reactions.

Once such associations between recurring perceptions and specific emotions have been acquired, the emergence of the respective emotions will, in the future, lead to tendencies for perceptions similar to those repeatedly connected biographically with the emotion. And conversely, respective perceptions can, in the future, also trigger the emotion, although there may be no current incongruence which was originally connected with this emotional evaluation.

Through this learning mechanism neural activation patterns underlying specific perceptions, memories, fantasies or thoughts can thus activate other neural activation patterns which correspond to certain emotions. These may be very well ingrained (emotional) activation patterns that may be activated easily from many trigger points. Once activated, these activation patterns, representing specific emotions, themselves influence the mental processes by preparing other cell assemblies for activation through changing the synaptic transmission weights. It needs only some minor input through other perceptions, memories, fantasies, or thoughts so that these other cell assemblies are activated, which in turn retroactively activates the emotional activation pattern anew.

Such reciprocal positive feedback loops very likely play an important role in the development and persistence of mental disorders such as phobias and depression. If a response tendency is very strongly ingrained, even insignificant events suffice to trigger the respective emotional condition, and the latter has, due to the described positive feedback processes, a tendency to precipitate and reinforce itself. These emotional states then play their own determining role within the psychological functioning independently of the other intentions that are geared towards specific goals. At a later point when I discuss "emotional attractors" (section 2.50), I refer to exactly such emotional states which, in addition to the goal-oriented intentions, exert a controlling influence on the psychological functioning. Classical conditioning plays an important role in the complex process of the ingraining of such emotional attractors. The activation patterns tied together through classical conditioning (temporal contingency) must, however, always be viewed within the context of the entire psychological functioning. They do not inactivate the other determinants of mental functioning, but become an additional part in the interplay of the activated neural activation patterns underlying our experience and behavior.

An altogether analogous assessment was reached by Mineka in his clinically oriented review of the research findings on classical conditioning: "It seems that the major reasons for dissatisfaction with the conditioning models in the past have been that they have been too simplistic ... none of the anxiety disorders can generally be thought to originate from a single or even a few trials of classical fear conditioning or avoidance learning occurring in a vacuum, as has often been proposed in the past. Instead, there appear to be a multitude of experiential variables that can occur prior to, during or following a conditioning experience, that effect the amount of fear that is experienced, conditioned, and maintained over time... For example, early experience with control and mastery can reduce the level of fear that is experienced in several different fear-provoking situations... The dynamics of fear conditioning are powerfully influenced by the controllability and predictability of the US... Thus, it is with an acknowledgment of this kind of complexity that conditioning models will continue to prosper and maintain their usefulness in the future" (Mineka, 1985, p. 242).

I believe Mineka's assessment to be a differentiated answer to the question you asked before as to how learning by conditioning has to be evaluated. Classical conditioning is likely to play a significant role in the development of many mental disorders. But whether, and to what extent conditioned reactions will develop, depends so strongly on other mental processes at that time, that any attempt to base models of mental disorders solely on conditioning is doomed to fail from the outset. But hindsight is always 20/20. We can make this statement today because classical conditioning was so well investigated. Following Pavlov's great discovery, the attempt to check out the range of explanatory power of this newly discovered form of learning appears completely justified, even in retrospect.

The attempt to combine the learning of involuntary reactions by classical conditioning with avoidance learning, i.e. the change of voluntary behavior in the sense of instrumental or operant conditioning, in one single theory, as elaborated by Mowrer (1960), was also so obvious that it had to be made, since under natural conditions both forms of learning always interact. One should not stay put at this insight however, because under natural conditions the relatively simple forms of learning by conditioning always interact with higher forms of learning, and are thus embedded in more complex learning processes.

2.17　Change as Emergence of New Neural Activation Patterns

Therapy researcher: Have I understood you correctly in that you conceive of learning generally as the ingraining of new neural activation patterns, and of classical conditioning as a special case, in which out of already existing activation patterns which correspond to the unconditioned stimulus, the unconditioned reaction, and the conditioned stimulus, new activation patterns emerge due to newly ingrained connections? So classically conditioned phobias would have to be viewed as emerging out of previously separated neural processes that are now being wired together?

Psychologist: Yes, new mental processes which manifest themselves in changed experience or behavior principally evolve from already existing neural activation patterns that are related to one another in a new way. Temporal contingency is one of these possible relations. New activation patterns are built by a new temporal succession of the actuation of activation patterns which then correspond to new qualities in experience and behavior. Conditioning produces new spatial-temporal relations. But spatial-temporal contingencies are by no means the only possible relations. The specific possibilities that make humans so different from other highly developed living beings are indeed their abilities to form symbolic representations. These new cognitive abilities allow relations quite different from those offered by temporal succession. They allow "higher learning" in the sense of more highly developed forms of learning.

With higher learning I do not mean predominantly observational learning as addressed many times earlier, but learning which goes beyond the connection principle of spatial-temporal contingency. In higher learning, the contents of the conceptual memory are linked to each other by symbolic relations that transcend time and space. Retention having this independence from spatial-temporal conditions and from the specific modality of the reception of information is one of the most distinguishing characteristics of the conceptual memory. The abstraction from space, time, and modality-specific conditions allows symbolic relations by thinking/reflecting, choosing, deciding and acting. Problem solving requires placing memory contents in relation to one another through more abstract, for example, logical relations. These different kinds of relations also have to be represented by specific kinds of neural processes.

The view of mental functioning that I wish to impart to you here assumes that specific neural activation patterns underlie all characteristic features of mental processes. The tendencies towards these neural activation patterns are stored in different forms of memory. We have talked of perceptual tendencies, action tendencies, emotional response tendencies and could add recall tendencies, fantasy tendencies, thinking tendencies and motivational tendencies. Instead of tendencies we might also say schemata. According to this view, schemata are strongly ingrained tendencies towards specific neural activation patterns. They are represented neurally through the synaptic transmission weights between nerve cells, the particular neurons being tied together to form a cell assembly in the sense of Hebb. Through ingraining of new connections, several cell assemblies can be combined with one another in more complex, higher-order schemata. This corresponds to the principle of hierarchical organization.

The various kinds of relations between neural activation patterns in turn have to be represented by specific synaptic transmission weights. If mental processes exclude, or are in conflict with each other, this is represented on the neural level such that the activation of one activation pattern inhibits the other. So relations can be represented by the combination of excitatory and inhibitory processes.

The activation of one part of a cell assembly leads to the activation of the entire cell assembly due to the strong connections previously ingrained. The facile spread of activation within and between cell assemblies is what characterizes a strongly ingrained neural activation pattern. A schema is the manifestation of the past activations of neural activation patterns. In each new activation this manifestation of past activations stored in the memory is activated together with the perceptions being made by the person at the moment. These perceptions do not depend solely on the pre-ingrained activation patterns but also upon the neural input of the sense organ, and that again depends upon the current situational conditions. The actual resultant perceptions may be completely congruent with the pre-ingrained neural activation patterns, thereby reinforcing the previous connections. They may, however, also deviate more or less from the pre-ingrained activation patterns, thereby changing the previously ingrained connections.

A gradual change and expansion of activation patterns through new input would be what Piaget was referring to with **assimilation**. The schema becomes richer in variants, it becomes more differentiated, and new synaptic connections are ingrained which can be more easily activated in the future if the activation pattern is triggered. The invariant of a large multitude of experiences looks quite different from the invariant of a more limited number of experiences.

When the activation pattern corresponding to the perception produced by the current situational conditions is not, to a larger extent, congruent with the pre-ingrained activation patterns, the perception is considerably hampered. The result is an interference of the heretofore well coordinated processes. This should activate the corresponding emotions on the one hand (surprise or negative emotions), and direct the attention towards the cause of the disturbance, on the other. So the creation of new neural connections should often go hand in hand with conscious attention. Yet we saw earlier in many examples of implicit unconscious learning that this is not always the case.

If perceptions cannot be assimilated to an existing schema, new activation patterns to which such perceptions can be assimilated in the future must first be created by repeated experiences. The creation of such new activation patterns corresponds to what Piaget termed **accommodation**. When such new activation patterns form, the preexisting activation tendencies are also activated by the respective situation. Yet they are now being reorganized and embedded in a new higher-order activation pattern. As long as newly emerging activation patterns are not yet well coordinated they require conscious processing. Yet with frequent repetition the newly formed connections become better and better ingrained. They will become more and more easily activated and more easily gain influence on the psychological activity without necessarily being linked to consciousness.

The connections which had characterized the previous, strongly pre-ingrained activation patterns are not erased by a newly formed activation pattern integrating already existing cell assemblies in new contexts, but are instead overlaid by them. The process of memory storage is not completed with retention. Following the retention consolidation processes take place in the brain over a longer period. These were conceived of by Hebb (1949) as "reverberating" activity of the respective neural groups lasting over a certain period of time and eventually leading to a lasting structural change in the synaptic connections. "The formation of these structural changes requires time, whereas the memory trace remains unstable and susceptible to disturbances. While Hebb's specific assumption of reverberating circuits is controversial, there is much that speaks in favor of the more general assumption that memory storage is based on changes in the synaptic transmission tendencies, and that these changes are the result of a temporally stretched consolidation process... What speaks for such a consolidation process is, among other things, the observation that the stability of memory traces may be enhanced or impeded through various impacts ... even after the actual learning process, and the strength of the impact weakens as the period of time since the learning phase lengthens" (Goschke, 1996 a, p. 388).

Through research on brain-damaged patients, we know today that the hippocampus and adjacent brain areas play a decisive role in the consolidation of the contents of episodic memory. Individuals suffering from severe damage to these areas are unable to form new episodic memory contents, yet they can recall events from a long time ago. Even their semantic memory with the vocabulary is preserved. Consequently these old and well-ingrained memory traces cannot be stored in the hippocampus. But processes in the hippocampus played a decisive role in that these memory traces were "stored" in a long-term manner elsewhere in the brain, most likely in the cortical areas that specifically correspond to the quality of what is to be stored, i.e. linguistic contents in the language centers, visual content in the visual cortex, etc. If one perceives a certain visual or auditory content, if one recalls or imagines it, increased neural activity in the same brain areas is to be seen (Menzel & Roth, 1996). The different kinds of activation of memory traces, of perception, imagination and remembering obviously rely on the same neural groups, or at least on strongly overlapping ones.

Therapist: The fact that a stable establishment of new activation patterns takes time seems to me very significant for psychotherapy. The new activation patterns a therapist tries to establish together with his patient are initially unstable and susceptible to disturbances. Under stress, therefore, there is a chance that the former, much better ingrained activation patterns may reemerge and start to control the behavior again. The patient, for instance, begins once again to avoid those situations which he had automatically avoided for years, although he had already developed a new coping behavior for these in therapy. Under stress, the new, and not yet well ingrained activation pattern underlying the coping behavior is substituted by the old, much better ingrained ones, which remain as long-term, well consolidated contents of memory and cannot be erased but only overlaid.

In the treatment of depression, addictions, etc., these relapses occur all too often. "Regressive" behavior in instances of strong fatigue, exhaustion, etc., can also be considered activation of such old memory content. Regression occurs when the capacity to cope is overburdened. The newer activation patterns use up more coping capacity. If the capacity for coping is no longer sufficient to meet the situational requirements, the old, better ingrained activation patterns operate as what we might term an arresting cable before the behavior slips into complete disorganization. Before a complete disorganization occurs, psychological functioning reverts back to an earlier level of functioning, the reason being that these ingrained paths still exist in memory and are now no longer inhibited by the overlaid, newer activation patterns.

From this angle, regression can be regarded as disorganization of the level of functioning of psychological activity last acquired in the respective area. It is therefore also understandable that protection from the overload that has led to the disorganization of the higher levels of functioning may lead to a recovery or remission. Such a case, for example, would occure if a patient were taken out of the stress-producing field and put into inpatient hospital care, or even by protecting him or her through the role of being a sick person. Under this protection the already ingrained younger activation patterns can establish and strengthen themselves again and regain a controlling influence on the experience and behavior. After some time the patient will be his or her old self again without having learned something new in the actual sense.

If one understands psychotherapy as a change in neural activation tendencies, it also stands to reason that sudden insights alone cannot be the basis of long-term changes in experience and behavior. A new insight would be based on a new activation pattern that is occurring for the very first time and needs to be activated again and again so that it becomes an easily accessible content of consciousness: All perceptual, action and emotional response tendencies associated thus far with the relevant situation would have to be reorganized, i.e. have to be embedded in a new stable activation pattern directed by a new goal. The new activation pattern or schema would have to first assimilate many experiences until a stable new activation pattern is established. I think the psychoanalytic notion of "working through" refers to something very similar.

Therapy researcher: It appears to me though that this working through must not be limited to the verbal interaction in psychotherapy. Insights generally refer to one's own experience and behavior in real life and thus are associated with situations outside of psychotherapy. The experiences to be assimilated to the newly formed schema would have to be real experiences made by the patient with all their senses rather than just the verbal representations of experiences. In my opinion, it would be an important task for the therapist to support the patient in being able to make as many experiences as possible which he can assimilate to the newly formed schema. Otherwise one would have to be afraid that real situations might again automatically activate the old tendencies, as many of the old ingrained paths are not stored in the particular form of memory on the basis of which the insight had taken place. If the patient exposes him/herself to the real situations, implicit contents of memory associated with the schema are also activated bottom-up and can also be changed by new experiences. If only a top-down activation through verbal representations occurs, these implicit contents of memory are likely to remain unchanged.

2.18   Learning Under the Influence of Goals

Psychologist: Earlier we discussed the different kinds of relations that may exist or be created between neural activation patterns and that in more complex learning under natural conditions, in addition to the spatial/temporal relations there are also always others that play a role. An especially important and pervasive relation characterizing the connection between different mental processes emerges from the fact that psychological activity is always determined by **goals**. This means that learning as well always happens under the influence of goals.

The reason why I presented Powers' control theory to you so in-depth earlier is mainly because the **goal orientation of psychological functioning** is the core of control theory. If psychological problem constellations are approached with this conception, one can be sure never to lose sight of the goal aspect of mental processes. Reorganizing and creating new contents of memory in more complex learning always happens under the influence, and in the service of goals. Simpler forms of learning, such as conditioning, are embedded in these goal-oriented, more complex processes.

So, psychotherapy always intervenes in goal-oriented psychological functioning. If we conceive of psychotherapy in a very abstract sense, as the modifying of contents of memory, then included therein are also the individual's goals, and the relations of the goals to the processes determined by them. Because of their central functional role in psychological functioning, each intervention must take into consideration the currently activated goals.

In the context of our considerations so far, we can conceive of goals and goal criteria as neural activation patterns as well. These activation patterns have different kinds of relations to other patterns which correspond to perceptions, fantasies, action tendencies, emotional responses, memorized or recalled memory content, etc. The relations can be of temporal succession, causality, reciprocal exclusion, means-end relation, etc. Even these different kinds of relations have to be realized on the neural level by specific patterns of inhibition and activation. So there have to be certain neural activation patterns that "work on top of" other neural activation patterns. This can be imagined as certain "contents" being represented by certain neural activation patterns which become embedded in a "process" also represented by an activation pattern, corresponding to a relation. Such a "working on top of each other" is elemental to the principle of hierarchical regulation. Hierarchically lower activation patterns are being embedded into those of a higher order.

"Reflecting" consists of certain activation patterns working on top of others as well. If we assume that different kinds of cognitions are represented by certain neural activation patterns, then "meta-cognitions" also have to be represented by certain activation patterns. One activation pattern ties in other activation patterns. By this it turns into a superior process which works on top of other contents. This kind of relation corresponds to what Piaget (1976) termed "reflective abstraction." What was previously a regulating process becomes the content of a newly emergent process, whereby a new, superior level of regulation is established.

Thus complex learning is the emergence of new, more complex neural activation patterns which, after they become established, work on top of those activation patterns of whose combined activity they arose and which they tie up into a new context. Through the emergence of new, more complex activation patterns, new qualities of psychological functioning form. We can view both the emergence and the unfolding of the different levels of cognitive development, as Piaget conceptualized and researched it, and the elaboration of new reflection and regulation possibilities in the course of psychotherapy as a process of the emergence of new, more complex activation patterns out of the interactions of the previous ones. Today we do not really know anything about exactly how the different kinds of relations investigated in psychology beyond that of temporal association are realized on the neural level and how they differ on the neural level from those that correspond to simpler associations, such as those created in conditioning.

But we do know that there are more complex goal-determined forms of learning. They are the subject of the psychology of problem solving, action psychology, motivation psychology, and volition psychology. This kind of learning is seldomly explicitly addressed as learning, because it is part of processes that focus on aspects other than those of information reception and changes in memory content. Yet somebody who has understood a complicated problem by reflecting upon it and has solved it, has created for him/herself new contents of memory which can be relied on in the future. The person has learned something. This form of higher learning normally happens through active, self-determined and goal-oriented analysis of the environment and is by no means limited to rational learning. In a self-determined fashion the individual can expose himself to new experiences which are associated with strong emotions and which lead to a change of past perceptual, behavioral, and emotional response tendencies. A great deal of what is learned in psychotherapy can be ascribed to this more complex form of learning which always relates to the individual's goals. Learning is normally embedded in a motivational context and takes place within the scope of the individual's own self-determined activity.

You inquired earlier about the fate of "the" learning theories. For these more complex learning processes there are no specific learning theories in and of themselves, such as the behaviorist theories that mainly referred to learning. These learning processes are embedded in motivational, volitional and emotional processes. All studies focused on the influences of the components of expectancy-value theories can also be conceived of as studies of learning because changed expectations and changed values have a lasting effect on future behavior. The Rubicon model by Heckhausen, and Kuhl's theory of action control, both discussed by us in our first round, also focus on changes in the contents of memory and can insofar also be conceived of as learning theories. When I previously suggested viewing the processes in psychotherapy from the perspective of these theories, this was an expression of my opinion that those more complex learning processes with which we deal in psychotherapy are, to a large extent, embedded in motivational processes and must be conceptualized jointly with them.

In our first dialogue I went more in-depth into the Rubicon model and only quickly pointed out that there are quite a few more expectancy-value theories that could be used for the explanation of the mechanisms of psychotherapy. At this point, in conjunction with more complex learning, perhaps I should at least give an example here of how something like that could look like.

2.19 Learning in Psychotherapy From the Perspective of Expectancy-Value Theories

In the 1954 book *Social Learning and Clinical Psychology*, Rotter introduced his construct of the expectancy of action-outcome-contingencies: How strongly can I influence a certain consequential event by my behavior? He called the generalized expectations for being able to control wide areas of one's own life "internal control expectations," and developed the internal-external-locus of control scale (I-E-Scale) (Rotter, 1966) for the measurement of this personality disposition. Further developed versions of this are still used today for measuring control expectations.

Almost contemporaneously, in conjunction with studies on the relation between attitudes and motivation, Peak (1955) introduced the concept of instrumentality: To what extent can a certain behavior be seen as a means for achieving a certain goal? **Control expectations** and **instrumentality** are central constructs of Vroom's (1964) theory of instrumentality, one of the expectancy-value theories to be fairly well confirmed by later research (see also Heckhausen, 1980). These studies all refer to the real working world which Vroom kept in mind as he developed his theory. Apart from social learning theory, I do not know of any expectancy-value-theory developed specifically for the area of clinical psychology or psychotherapy. But as I will soon try to demonstrate, and as we have already seen in conjunction with the Rubicon model in our first conversation, such theories can be applied to psychotherapeutic problem constellations as well.

Vroom differentiates between action, the immediate action result and further consequences of action. First of all, the individual has an expectation as to what extent a

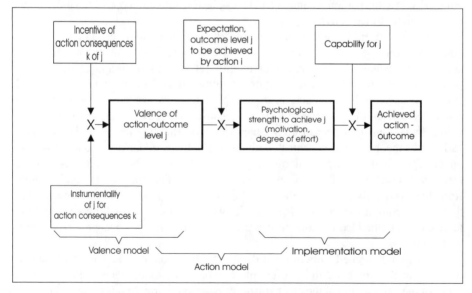

Figure 2.13:
Schematic illustration of the process model of instrumentality theory taken from Vroom (1964).

certain action will lead to a certain immediate action result. In the case of an achievement, this would be the subjective probability for success. Second, the individual has expectations about which consequences the immediate action result will lead to. Vroom refers to the degree of linkage between the immediate action result and the further consequences of the action as instrumentality.

With his theory Vroom wants to predict the immediate action result, that is to say whether, and how well one will succeed with something in a certain situation. His predictive model contains three steps (see Figure 2.13).

In the first step the product is arrived at from the instrumentality (What consequences will arise from my succeeding with this or that?) and the valence (incentive of action consequences: What does it mean to me if these consequences occur?) of the consequences of action. This yields the value that the immediate action outcome has for the respective person. If it is very important to the individual that the action consequences occur, and he or she believes that these consequences are most likely to happen if he or she only creates the basis for them, then causing the action outcome will be rated very highly by the individual. The result of the first step is, therefore, a certain valence of the action outcome. We can equate this valence with the desirability component of the Rubicon model.

In a second step this valence is multiplied by the expectation to be able to successfully bring about the action outcome with one's own behavior. This product yields the "psychological strength," the motivation, and the tendency to try to achieve the action outcome. This would correspond to the volitional strength in the Rubicon model.

In a third step, the psychological strength or the volitional strength is multiplied by the individual's ability to achieve the desired action outcome via his or her action. In case of high volitional strength and ability, we will most likely see a very good action outcome.

Let us look at the situation of an agoraphobic patient from the perspective of this theory: The patient feels very limited in her freedom to move and in her independence because she consistently avoids using public transportation such as the subway, busses, trains, and planes unless accompanied by a trusted person. She would like nothing more than to travel and finally be independent, to not be dependent on the company of others. It is her great dream to travel to far away countries and to be able to move around freely and independently. There is high incentive for her to travel.

She sees her main obstacle in her avoidance of public transportation, which she experiences as an inability to do otherwise. Were she able to use public transportation without fear it is quite obvious to her that she would venture far. So she has a high instrumentality expectation indicating that the action outcome "to use public transportation without fear" would lead to the very positively assessed action consequence "to travel far," "to be independent." This yields a very high positive valence for the action outcome "being able to use public transportation without fear."

On the other hand, she has no hope whatsoever of being able to achieve this action outcome by getting into a form of public transportation despite her fear, because time and again she has made the opposite experience. The product of the valence of the action outcome and her expectation to be able to achieve this result by her own actions is therefore low, despite the very high valence of the action outcome. This product corresponds to the volitional strength for using public transportation despite her fear, which means the volitional strength is low despite the strong desirability of the action outcome.

This is why the product from this volitional strength and the ability to use public transportation is quite low although one need not doubt her capability. She knows how to use public transportation. This third product yields the likeliness for the action outcome "to be able to be alone without fear in public transportation." The very desired action result per se therefore does not happen.

The situation described would be the ideal starting point for exposure therapy because in order to achieve the action outcome, according to Vroom's model, one would only have to install the expectation in this patient that she can achieve, with her own behavior, eventually being able to begin using public transportation without fear. As soon as she has made the experience even once that she can decrease her initial strong fear by remaining in the public transportation sufficiently long without fleeing, the respective control expectation should rise, resulting in a marked increase of her volitional strength because the increased control expectation is multiplied by a very high valence. This leads to an increase in the product of ability and volitional strength, and also to the likelihood that the desired result "to be able to use public transportation alone without fear" happens.

The difficulty is only in assisting her to make this expectation-changing exposure experience. To do so, the expectation must first be bolstered by other means—I am thinking here of the induction of positive outcome expectations and the significance of resource activation—to the point where, when multiplied by a high valence, it will lead to a sufficiently high volitional strength for putting herself through the initial exposure at all. Actually an appropriate therapeutic preparation is a very important part of exposure therapy (Fiegenbaum & Tuschen, 1996).

From Vroom's model we can, however, also derive when such a therapy most likely does not lead to the desired success. As an example let's take a new, fictive patient with an agoraphobia. One could expect a failure of the previously described procedure if the valence of the action outcome produced by the first step were already low. It results from the incentive to be able to travel alone and to be independent and the instrumentality expectation that to be able to move around freely again is very much worthwhile for the patient. Quite possibly, for this patient being able to be alone and independent might by no means be perceived positively and free of conflicts and/or she does not see that there might be any positive consequences in this for her if she is once again able to use public transportation alone. Possibly she would have to resume undesired work, carry family burdens from which she had been spared in the recent past, and so forth.

This scenario requires that we first have to create an unambiguous motivational state resulting in a high valence for "being able to use public transportation alone without fear." Motivation clarifying or intention changing interventions such as those covered by us in our first conversation would thus be indicated in order to achieve the action outcome in a patient in such an initial state.

Even if the valence were to rise as a result of such a clarification, it might not necessarily lead to a sufficient volitional strength for someone to expose him/herself to the avoided situations. In this patient as well, the control expectation to be able to achieve having no more fear in public transportation might be low. Just like the previously described patient she would have to be helped to develop a sufficiently high volitional strength with interventions designed to increase this expectation for the desired result to be likely to occur.

Quite similar considerations could apply if one would like to find out the possible causes of an actually existing undesired action outcome, i.e. a problem, in order to come up with starting points for therapeutic interventions. Vroom's model is also suited for these cases as the various components may also take on negative values. Active avoidance behavior might be especially well analyzed with this.

Vroom's theory of instrumentality gives us four possible starting points for therapeutic interventions:

- a change in the incentive or the valence of action consequences,
- a change in the instrumentality expectations for the connection between action outcome and consequences,
- a change in the control expectations for being able to cause a desired action outcome via one's own behavior or to avoid an undesired one,
- and an improvement in the patient's abilities to bring about such an action outcome.

Different therapeutic interventions are suited for each of these components. On the basis of Vroom's model one would come to therapeutic conclusions very similar to those arrived at on the basis of the Rubicon model. Since we discussed this in-depth in our first dialogue, I do not want to elaborate on this conclusion again.

What I wanted to show to you in this model was which variables definitely have to be considered, according to the expectancy-value theories, if we wish to change behavior. In the course of this conversation so far I have touched very little upon conscious deliberate behavior on the basis of contents of the explicit memory, and instead spoke quite a bit about implicit or unconscious mental processes. I did that because the processes in the implicit mode of functioning appeared to me especially important for what needs to be changed in psychotherapy. For our purposes it appeared to me very useful to undertake an explicit change in focus because normally our focus, both in everyday life, and also in psychological theory formation is more directed to verbally and symbolically coded contents.

This change in focus should by no means make you think that I do not consider deliberately controllable and conscious mental processes on the basis of the conceptual memory as especially important for psychotherapy. They are, of course, the most important foundation for the cooperation between therapist and patient. An essential part of every psychotherapy is directed towards a long-term change of deliberately controllable behavior. Such changes have to be conceived of as a complex learning process, which is the reason why we need models in psychotherapy that account for these complex learning processes that are always determined by goals. Expectancy-value models such as those by Heckhausen, Kuhl and Vroom can be viewed as approximations to these requirements.

Yet with all their advantages, these models also have shortcomings that limit their utility for psychotherapy. They largely exclude emotions. They do not consider that there are always many simultaneously ongoing processes within the individual. They focus on a certain segment of psychological functioning and pay no attention to what goes on around that, and they largely exclude all processes taking place on the basis of the implicit memory. Therefore, none of the existing expectancy-value models can be regarded as a satisfying theoretical foundation for psychotherapy solely in and of themselves.

This is why our thoughts on the mechanisms of psychotherapy from our first conversation, those based on the Rubicon model, require some supplemental ideas. We had excluded aspects of psychological functioning which play a crucial role for psychotherapy according to ideas we put forth in this second dialogue. More in-depth comprehension of the mechanisms of psychotherapy will only be gained if we combine the processes occurring on the basis of the different forms of memory, especially the implicit and the conceptual, the conscious and the unconscious mental processes, with one another into a unified perspective.

Therapist: Even if these exclusions you just mentioned did not exist, I find models like Vroom's still too complicated for direct application in therapeutic practice. Although how you applied this model to agoraphobia made sense to me, I am nevertheless unable to imagine how this or any similar model could have any practical use for me in my therapies.

Psychologist: I did not assume you could. Principally I do not think one can, or should apply the findings of basic psychological research directly to psychotherapeutic practice, not in most cases anyway. I imagine the connections between psychology and psychotherapy in such a way that one draws conclusions from psychological research for psychotherapy. These conclusions should be substantiated by research, yet tailored to the special requirements of the therapeutic practice.

When taken all together the models, theories, and research results discussed here make it pretty obvious just how illusory it would be to think one could keep everything in mind while performing therapies, not to mention trying to account for all this. For a therapeutic usage of these findings an intermediate step is required. On the basis of all this knowledge we should develop a model for the therapeutic practice that is perceived by therapists as useful and is perceived as an enrichment. The individual therapist cannot account for the connection between research and practice, it has to be supplied to him. Ideally, I imagined we might accomplish this here. We would be largely dependent on you for that though as you are the one in a position to decide what is practical and helpful in therapy.

Therapist: Of course I am more than interested, but we do not seem to be that far yet. For me quite a few topics that are highly relevant for my therapeutic practice are still missing. I only need to mention the terms emotion and motivation.

Psychologist: Yes it is time we get to that, but I would not like to leave memory and learning without at least having made the attempt to summarize what we talked about in a way that corresponds to my own ideas on mental functioning. I could imagine this view as applicable also in therapeutic practice, because it is based on a rather simple basic idea.

2.20 How to Conceive Neural Activation Patterns as the Basis of Mental Functioning

The fundamental idea is that all mental processes, from simple emotions up to complex learning processes, have specific neural activation patterns underlying them. This has already been proven for simpler forms of perception and memory. Scientific findings achieved by neurobiology and psychology can be related to one another (Roth & Prinz, 1996), but for complex processes such as the forms of higher learning discussed by us before, a direct relation between neural and mental processes remains an assumption for now. At the moment, complex processes of this kind remain only a subject of psychological study, and even that has only been so for a short time. Considerable further development in brain research is necessary before neural processes of such complexity may be approached, yet I am quite sure that this will gradually happen.

Though for the purpose of practical application in psychotherapy it is not so important to know how such processes are actually realized on the neural level. Nevertheless, I do think that it might be helpful for a psychotherapist to imagine that the processes he aims to change by psychotherapy are based on specific neural activation patterns. It does make a difference for me if I imagine such processes in my mind as a neural activation pattern, and as an interplay of ever more complex activation patterns, or if I, for instance, speak of schemata. Schema is initially only an abstract term which one may either not associate any concrete idea with, or that different people associate quite different images in their mind with when using it (Läderach & Verdun, 1995). The first is a disadvantage for thinking clearly, the latter a disadvantage for communication with one another.

Yet a neural activation pattern has a materially basis, not one based only on fantasies, as quite a bit is known about the nature and function of the nerve cells, their connections with other nerve cells and their joint activities. One can easily imagine a "cell assembly," in the sense of Hebb, with variable synaptic transmission tendencies between the neurons involved in this assembly. When these activation patterns become increasingly complex, one need not necessarily give up the visual idea, but conceive all of that as organized in a much more comprehensive, multiply layered and more complicated fashion.

Crick and Koch (1990) have attempted to illustrate their neurobiological conception of consciousness via the image of a Christmas tree with nearly an infinite number of lights. Even if the similarity between the brain and a Christmas tree does not necessarily suggest itself, I like this image, because it actually allows bringing several known features of brain activity into a graphic model. In the following, I wish to further extend Crick and Koch's model in order to develop a visual image of the neural processes underlying psychological functioning.

So let us imagine a Christmas tree with nearly an infinite amount of tiny lights, approximately a thousand billion. Each light represents a nerve cell. If a nerve cell is activated, the light is lit up, if inactivated, it is invisible. The lights are connected with one another in a highly variable fashion and may switch (stimulate or inhibit) each other on and off—depending on the kind and degree of their connectedness. A nerve cell's activation is not just represented merely by the fact that it is lit but that it flashes to a special rhythm. A neural activation pattern is represented by the nerve cells being involved in this activation pattern flashing to a synchronized rhythm (principle of connection through synchronization).

The light bulbs have a different color according to the cell type and function of the nerve cell. Apart from its general constitution, the nerve cell's function also depends on where it is localized in the brain. The different brain areas are represented as being different parts of the tree. For instance, if the lights in the region representing the limbic system are involved in an activation pattern, this means that it is associated with a quality of emotional experience.

Other brain areas have something to do with awareness or conscious attention. There are different areas for different achievements of awareness, such as the perisylvian region for verbal-syntactic achievements, the right posterior parietal lobe for spatial-visual ones, parts of the thalamus for selection, and the pre-frontal cortex for setting priorities, etc. (Birbaumer & Schmidt, 1996, p. 536). The activity of cell assemblies involved in a joint neural activation pattern together with the lights representing these brain structures by the same flashing rhythm, is accompanied by the experiential quality of awareness. So there are always those parts of the mental activity conscious that are involved together in a joint activation pattern with these awareness-producing neural structures. The respective lights flash in a joint rhythm.

On top of that we can imagine that these lights differ in being especially bright and in that different degrees of awareness are represented by different levels of brightness of the lights. The amount of lights capable of assuming the brightest level is limited per time unit (limited capacity of the short-term memory). Due to their being in this special functional state, the respective activation patterns are subject to special characteristics, namely those which differentiate conscious from unconscious processes.

There are always many activation patterns simultanusly activated which differ from each other by a different flashing rhythm. Not all, but many of the activation patterns can potentially assume the highest level of brightness. The processes represented by them enter the state of consciousness at that moment. This model illustrates that there are always many mental processes concurrently going on. Only a small portion of these is in the state of awareness at any given time, and this state can switch from one activation pattern to another. The way this functions is that it becomes activated or directly addressed by one of the activation patterns (contents of consciousness) being currently in the functional state of awareness. Not every pre-ingrained activation pattern, however, can be addressed by the currently conscious ones. One condition for that is that it must have been at least once before on the highest level of brightness. So it has to already be a part of the conceptual memory.

In conditioning, two already established synchronous light groups (UCS and CS) would begin to flash in a joint rhythm. This would constitute a new activation pattern that may be activated both from one and also the other original activation pattern. In more complex learning several light groups would be connected with one another by an overlying joint rhythm, and new, previously inactive light groups, or ones heretofore tied into other assemblies, would additionally flash in the same flashing rhythm, resulting in a qualitatively new light and flashing pattern.

When I speak of attractors at a later point this is exactly what I have in mind, the visual image of such light (neural) assemblies connected by a joint flashing rhythm. With the actuation of a neural activation pattern corresponding to an important goal, this activation pattern spreads out by "encompassing" more and more light assemblies strewn throughout the tree in its overlaying flashing rhythm. These light assemblies are each connected by a certain flashing rhythm with one another and correspond to certain memory contents, emotional responses, perceptual and behavioral tendencies. By this they are all connected with one another to a goal hierarchy. This higher-order activation pattern can be activated bottom-up and top-down. The "tendency to be infected" with a joint flashing rhythm is based on previously ingrained paths (synaptic transmission tendencies).

It is easy to imagine in such an almost infinitely large light tree that many light assemblies composed of different colors and spatially distributed in quite a different fashion simultaneously flash in their own particular rhythm. Of all these light assemblies, one is distinguished by being especially bright (being in awareness). Activation patterns corresponding to a control hierarchy in the sense of control theory are tied together to a joint pattern by the flashing rhythm of that activation pattern which represents the superior goal of the hierarchy. Goals or attractors thus have the ability to "infect" other activation patterns with their flashing rhythm, and to tie them into their flashing rhythm. Several patterns which distinguish themselves from each other by a joint flashing rhythm correspond to simultaneously-parallel activated control hierarchies or to that which I will later call "**motivational attractors**." Such an image allows an almost unlimited number and complexity of simultaneously actuated activation patterns, as we have to assume for the actual brain activity. Additionally, this image allows the depiction of the principle of hierarchical as well as that of parallel-distributive organization of neural and mental processes, something that due to our considerations thus far is a necessity.

This image also implies that psychological activity is active on its own; as long as an organism is alive, its nervous system is characterized by its auto-activity. Because of their connections the activity of nerve cells is organized in patterns. The strongly pre-ingrained neural activation patterns are those that are the most easily activated. With no outside stimulation coming in the strongly pre-ingrained activation patterns become spontaneously active. So psychological functioning is characterized by auto-activity. The human is not dependent on stimulation from the environment in order to become active. A psychological process does not begin with a stimulus as conceptualized by S-R-psychology, but instead begins with and is comprised of the activity of pre-ingrained neural activation patterns.

Therapist: So could we say then that the standard psychoanalytic situation in the setting of a couch with a therapist sitting reservedly behind the supine patient represents a rather consequent approach, since the psychoanalyst creates a situation that offers the patient rather little stimulation from the environment? One would have to expect then that the brain becomes active on its own, namely in the sense of the strongly pre-ingrained activation patterns. This would actually be the ideal situation for studying the mental processes of an individual. The same basic thought underlies the importance psychoanalysts give to the analysis of dreams. As a matter of fact, dreams are the purest expression of the brain's own activity without external stimulation. Aren't projective test methods such as the Rorschach test and the TAT (thematic apperception test) also based on the same fundamental idea? The less a situation is structured by certain prescribed perceptual contents, the more one can ascertain about the psychological auto-activity.

Psychologist: It might lead us too far from the topic we have been pursuing if I get into detail about my views on the standard psychoanalytic situation, on dream analysis and on projective tests. We would actually lose the thread we have been following throughout our conversation. Yet it would be tempting to discuss your questions from the perspective of the model which I just attempted to illustrate, using the image of a tree strung with lights.

At the least, let me make a few short comments. Your conclusions seem plausible at first glance. However, you must consider that the situation in which a projective test is given, and the standard psychoanalytic situation both limit the perceptual and behavioral space of a test person or patient in a specific fashion. The person's spontaneous behavioral tendencies in these situations might possibly not even get a chance to come through, and what one learns about that person might be more about their dealing with this restricting situation than any specific information about their perceptual, behavioral and emotional response tendencies under conditions where they can be freely unfurled. Nevertheless, what a person does in this situation, how he or she deals with it and what kind of issues they talk about, certainly says something about that person. Yet the question is how representative this sample of behavior is for the person's real spontaneous psychological activity under conditions where it could actually unfold freely.

Perhaps it is a shortcoming of my light tree model that it does not simultaneously illustrate that all psychological activity from the onset is inseparably interlinked with the interaction between individual and environment. The neural activation patterns develop out of the active interaction with the environment. Piaget (1981), whose concept of schemata largely corresponds to the activation patterns I am speaking about, made this fact, that the cognitive structures evolve out of the active interaction with the environment, the core issue of his entire epistemological conception. If we cut off a person from his well established interactions with the environment, or greatly limit them, we create a situation which certainly does not correspond to the natural psychological activity.

We can see this best if a person is completely cut off from all environmental stimulation by placing them in a "camera silens," that is a room so completely dark and so extraordinarily well insulated that a subject is unable to even hear his own voice. Additionally, the person is slightly fastened so that no feedback from movement is created. Such a situation, in which the exchange with the environment is artificially interrupted, is endurable only for a short time. Many persons get into panic conditions even if they otherwise have no claustrophobic tendencies. After a longer time, many suffer hallucinations. Being finally in contact with the environment again through one's senses is generally experienced with great relief.

To make a long story short: I believe there is more to be learned about a person's perceptual, behavioral, and emotional response tendencies when he can be observed in his natural environment, or at least in an environment characterized by a richness of challenges, than if one cuts him off from his natural interaction with the environment. In a projective test such as the TAT, with its various cards with very different stimulus characteristics, this seems to be better realized than in the standard psychoanalytic situation. Murray (1938, 1943, 1951) the creator of the TAT, along with Piaget (1937) and Lewin (1935, 1936), was among the first explicitly supporting an interactional conception of the relationship between individual and environment. His construct of "themes," resulting from "needs" of the individual and "presses" from the environment, was the first interactional construct in psychology for which, at the same time, a measuring method was conceptualized along with it (Murray, 1943). In fact, the TAT later on proved to be very reliable for measuring motives (McClelland, 1958, 1985).

For us here, perhaps the assessment of the standard psychoanalytic situation is more relevant as it also serves as a therapeutic setting. The patient is protected from perceptions allowing for as much space as possible to be made in his consciousness (short-term memory) for memories, as well as for associations and fantasies. But all this can only be drawn from the conceptual memory. Contents of the implicit memory, including the implicit emotional memory, can actually not be activated this way. They must be activated bottom-up by situations similar to those present during their first formation. The standard psychoanalytic situation in fact provides what could arguably be seen as the poorest possibilities for this, because of all therapeutic settings it so severely limits itself by such a heavy reliance on the verbal communication channel. It is actually only the quality of the therapist's voice and his other non-verbal behavior at the beginning and end of a session which may directly activate implicit contents of memory. When considering the great importance of processual activation as a precondition for changing contents of memory I see the standard psychoanalytic situation as offering especially poor possibilities for this.

So overall, I would not share the conclusion you have drawn from my light tree model. Your conclusion does point to a potential weakness of this image though, namely that the environmental context of mental processes is not sufficiently expressed.

Therapy researcher: Your light tree appeals to me regardless, as it represents a better metaphor than these computer metaphors that are used again and again, either explicitly or implicitly in cognitive psychology. The brain in fact does seem to function much differently than serially working computers. In particular, I like that your picture so nicely illustrates the simultaneousness of many mental processes in a way that only one of them each moment is fully consciously ongoing and several others are running with varying degrees of consciousness.

In addition, a Christmas tree allows for quite different associations in parallel than does a computer. With respect to mental functioning it is not so "cold" and rational as a computer metaphor. Something which has always bothered me about the terms cognitive psychology and cognitive psychotherapy is that there are overtones of rational and non-emotional associations in them. I like that you speak of mental processes and neural activation patterns rather than cognitive processes, because in these terms emotional and motivational qualities are not set off from any cognitive qualities that in my view do not exist in and of themselves.

When, for instance, would a mental process be cognitive in such a sense that it would be useful to emphasize that as its main feature? Even working on a mathematical task which is certainly a rational activity is indeed inseparably connected with emotions. For one person it is connected perhaps with satisfaction, for another with desperation, and still a third with weariness. If, however, it is not the exclusion of emotions justifying the predicate "cognitive" then: Which mental processes are non-cognitive in order to distinguish from them the cognitive ones? Obviously with the term cognitive we want to point to the qualities in mental processes that have newly emerged only after the development of the neocortex. But which of a human's important psychological processes are ongoing without the participation of the neocortex? The terms "cognitive psychology" and "cognitive psychotherapy" appear to me either redundant or, if meant to be a demarcation from emotional or motivational, questionable. The attribution cognitive does make sense in demarcation from a psychology that did not deal at all with the internal processes of the human being such as the behaviorist S-R-psychology. We have indeed surmounted the necessity for such a demarcation.

Actually, I prefer to use the term cognitive as an abbreviation that comes in handy for mental processes containing symbolic information processing. This is useful, for example, as a differentiation from sub-cortically controlled affective processes. Yet, as

an attribute for an entire psychological approach, the term cognitive is too much associated with problematic connotations for me. In your image of the light tree I like that
it does not contain such questionable connotations although it does include quite some
knowledge from those sciences that are also called "cognition sciences."

Yet I think your model also raises some questions: The existence of one activation
pattern creates at the same time limiting context conditions for others. What happens,
for instance, if goals are concurrently activated, which exclude each other? What occurs
if consciously and unconsciously different goals are pursued? A simultaneity of processes
cannot be infinitely possible after all. I mean not just quantitatively but also qualitatively.
There are indeed processes which exclude others. Surely it has to be determined which
of the activated processes will get their chance, and which will not. It is, after all,
unrealistic to assume that all a person's goals are in harmony with one another. If one
assumes a principle simultaneity of mental processes, perhaps explicit ideas regarding
the compatibility and incompatibility of these processes need also be developed, together
with some more explicit ideas in the case of incompatibility.

Psychologist: You are definitely right about this. Your demand for more explicit
ideas on the compatibility of psychological processes in fact puts me into quite a sweat,
psychology has so far not focused on this, and no wonder because the subject of the
simultaneity of mental processes has only been explicitly addressed in the last decade.
However, I have my own ideas about that and I will attempt to substantiate them by
referring to empirical findings.

You have, however, latched onto another point that I do not wish to ignore, namely
the danger associated with today's—often termed cognitive—psychology that emotions are always considered only secondarily. Particularly in psychotherapy where we
deal with problematic emotions and their modification, this of course should not be
that way. Even I have so far not addressed emotions expressly but have only mentioned
them in conjunction with other subjects. This might give rise to a false impression
regarding the significance emotions have for psychological functioning. At several points
I actually wanted to talk more about emotions only to discover that this would lead us
away from that red thread we are following. Now I would like to finally take the occasion to embed emotions into the considerations we have thus far covered.

2.21   The Emotional Quality of Mental Functioning

Emotions are of fundamental significance for psychological functioning. Phylogenetically and ontogenetically, an affectively determined behavior control has existed long
before the development of something that could be called cognition. I am referring to
cognition now as performances linked to the phylogenetically newer parts of the brain.
Affective regulation mechanisms are part of our inherited species-specific brain. They
belong to the hardware of the brain and need not be learned anew by every individual
of the human species (MacLean, 1970). From a psycho-biological perspective the innate affective regulation mechanisms have a significant survival function, both for the
individual and for the species. On the individual level, the inherited affective regula-

tion mechanisms direct mental processes, without any delay and second thought, towards goals that are crucial to survival. In living together with other members of the species the expressive behavior connected to the basic affects serves the social regulation of interaction. Affective signals in the environment trigger need-relevant behavior. Already in 1872, in his book *Expression of Emotions in Man and Animals*, Darwin had placed the expression of emotions into exactly this context (Ekman, 1973).

While culturally different practices of upbringing convey very different norms for which emotions should, or may be expressed, in which way, in which situations, one can find in all cultures the same basic patterns of facial expression corresponding to certain affects. Among these inter-culturally invariant affective expression and response tendencies that were found time and again in studies on facial expressive behavior are surprise, joy, anger, sadness/depression, fear and disgust. There is agreement among researchers of emotions on the fact that at least these six emotions can be considered innate response patterns, each characterized by a certain physiological response pattern, certain action tendencies, including also a certain expressive behavior, and a certain subjectively experienced emotional quality (Tomkins, 1962/1963, 1970, 1981; Ekman, 1971; Ekman & Friesen, 1975; Izard, 1977; Scherer, 1984; Frijda, 1986; Lazarus, 1991). These emotions are termed **primary emotions**. They have their basis in older mammalian brain structures (MacLean, 1970). The spontaneous non-verbal expression of these emotions is regulated by these older brain areas, while newer brain structures underlie the culturally determined emotional expression (Buck, 1984). Such newer brain structures do not replace the older ones, but overlay them and supplement them with new possibilities for regulation (Blanck, Buck & Rosenthal, 1986).

While other emotions such as contempt, shame, guilt, interest, and embarrassment are expressed in similar ways in most cultures (Ekman, 1989), they are, however, not considered primary emotions by most authors, because they already allude to more complex cognitive evaluations. Such **more complex emotions** include, for instance, also pride, gratitude, longing, embarrassment, jealousy, and remorse. They are conceived of as combinations of primary emotions and termed **secondary emotions**.

Proceeding not from expressive behavior but from neurophysiological research findings, Panksepp (1989) arrives at four to five emotional regulation systems with a fixed basis in the brain. To be sure that any semantic ambiguities are avoided, he characterizes these systems using several terms for each:
1. exploration—expectation—curiosity—researching,
2. anger—rage
3. anxiety—fear
4. separation—sadness—sorrow—mourning—suffering—pain—agony—fright and
5. possibly, but empirically not so well substantiated as the others, a "social play" regulation system.

According to Le Doux (1989), a more direct signal transmission and processing takes place in these affective regulation systems than in the symbolic information processing in the neocortex. The meanings do not have to be semantically decoded but are immediately given. Signals activating one of these regulating circuits lead directly to very specific action tendencies before there has even been time for cognitive appraisal of the situation. So primary emotions are triggered without involving consciousness, lead to physiological reactions, cause certain behavioral tendencies and manifest themselves in expressive behavior before a process of appraisal can even take place into which the contents of the individual long-term memory become integrated. The automatically triggered affects take possession of the consciousness and direct the entire psychological activity into a certain direction (for instance fight or flight), but they are not a product of conscious information processing. In contrast to the deliberate conscious action control they can be viewed as a phylogenetically older form of behavioral control.

I call these automatic primary emotional reactions triggered without the participation of higher cognitive processes **affects**, in differentiation from other emotions. Most emotions experienced by us cannot be seen as affects in this sense because considerably more complex appraisal processes based on contents of the conceptual long-term memory are integrated in these. Affects have three clearly recognizable functions: They **appraise** the present relationship of the individual to his/her environment regarding fulfillment or endangerment of innate needs; they **motivate** for certain behaviors, such as fight or flight, and energize them; and they have a **communication function** in social interaction. With modifications these functions also apply to more complex emotions.

The affects as basic forms of emotions are not yet based on self-acquired memory contents. In the course of development each individual makes emotional experiences that become the contents of his personal memory. According to Greenberg, Rice and Elliott (1993), the invariants of these emotional experiences are stored in the form of **emotional schemata** containing not only the emotional response tendencies but also the triggering circumstances which have been acquired by direct experiences or by observational learning. Following my previous comments on the memory, we can view emotional schemata according to Greenberg, Rice and Elliott as contents of an **implicit emotional memory**. The consciousness has no access to these schemata. They are activated automatically bottom-up by relevant triggering circumstances and then influence experience and behavior. In this sense phobias, for instance, might be conceived of as emotional schemata.

Today it is assumed "...that the memory for the emotional significance of events is actually mediated by brain structures other than those for the events themselves... That conditioned fears oftentimes persist throughout months and years and are extraordinarily resistant to changes through conscious insight could also lie in the fact that they are based on an **implicit emotional memory** which is mediated by brain structures operating independently from the declarative knowledge memory" (Goschke, 1996 a, p. 402).

Structures in the limbic system, particularly the amygdala (Menzel & Roth, 1996) play a central role for the storage of emotional connections. There are quite a number of neurophysiological facts indicating that the storage of emotional associations is to be viewed as a memory form of its own for which brain areas other than those in which the contents of the conceptual long-term memory are stored are in charge. To me this appears so relevant for the understanding and the therapy of emotional disorders that I would like to read to you word for word what the neurobiologists Menzel and Roth write about that:

"These close connections between the limbic system, especially the amygdala, and the memory system are also confirmed in animal studies. If a test animal is punished in the presence of a signal (for instance a tone) not only does it avoid the punishment but also displays a fearful reaction: It becomes stiff, blood pressure and pulse rate increase, harmless stimuli may then trigger panic-like reactions. If the connections of the appropriate diencephalon brain area (for instance the auditory nucleus of the thalamus) with the neocortex are severed then the learned avoidance reactions disappear (for instance running into the corner of the cage), but the fear responses continue to emerge. If on the other hand, the amygdala is destroyed, then the fear responses disappear while the learned avoidance reactions are not affected.

Recently we have seen reports of studies on three patients where the first had a damaged hippocampus, the second a damaged amygdala, and the third had bilateral damage to both areas. Conditioning experiments were then performed with these patients. The experiments corresponded to the schema of classical conditioning: As CS, the patients were offered different color stimuli or tones, among which one stimulus was repeatedly paired with a very loud noise (a fog horn) as UCS leading to a frightened reaction. Following that, the patients were asked which one of the color or tone stimuli were paired with the frightening stimulus. The skin conductance response was simultaneously measured, which in healthy test subjects increases strongly in the short-term as part of the reaction of the autonomous nervous system to the UCS.

The patient with the bilateral damage of the amygdala was able to pinpoint exactly which stimulus had been paired with the UCS (the frightening stimulus) yet he showed no SCR. So he had not developed any fear or fright reaction and lived through the events 'emotionless.' Conversely, the patient with the bilateral damage of the hippocampus could not tell anything about the stimuli paired with the UCS, yet displayed a clearly increased SCR. So while his emotional memory functioned, his declarative memory failed, which could be expected given the lesion to the hippocampus. The patient thus experienced fear and fright without knowing why.

So the amygdala is essentially involved in the connection between emotions, on the one hand, and learning/memory, on the other ... Predominantly the lateral nucleus is in charge for the representation of the fear memory" (Menzel & Roth , 1996, pp. 273/274).

Therapist: If in mental disorders, such as phobias, the different components of the disorder, namely the physiological response, the open behavior, and the subjective experience are stored together with the phobia-relevant thoughts, ideas and memories etc., in different memory systems, then that holds consequences for the therapy of such disorders. Earlier, we had already spoken about there being varying ways of accessing the different forms of memory. According to these findings, except by talking it should not be possible to exert any influence at all on emotional response tendencies stored in the implicit emotional memory. Conversely, a decrease of the emotional component alone by bottom-up triggered experiences should not necessarily change the avoidance behavior and the thoughts and ideas associated with the phobia, as these procedural and conceptual contents of memory may possibly not be activated effectively enough via a bottom-up activation so that a changing influence on them could be exerted. This would speak for a scenario where all components should be targeted with individual interventions specifically tailored to them.

Therapy researcher: There are examples for that in therapy research. In fact, something which has proven to be a source of constant irritation in therapy research has been just how little correlation is found in the treatment of anxiety disorders between the changes in the measures for avoidance behavior, for the subjectively experienced fear and for the physiological fear indicators. One wanted to measure the construct "anxiety," and for that a high internal consistency between the various operationalizations of anxiety would be desirable. It was mostly regarded as a measurement problem. Obviously though, this is not just a measurement problem but a substantial dissociation between the different components of an anxiety disorder. The findings on the various forms of memory presented by you let me see these low correlations in a different light than before.

Psychologist: Let me return to the emotions. The findings I talked about pointed out that existing emotional response tendencies may be connected with new eliciting situations. It is, however, not only the associations between emotions and triggers that change by experiences, but also the emotions themselves. Our abilities for emotional responses in adulthood, even in early childhood already, are much more differentiated and complex than the innate affects. Some of the more complex emotions I have already listed as examples.

The newly developing cognitive abilities are one of the reasons for the differentiation of emotions in childhood. The appraisal of the momentary relationship between individual and environment is one of the main functions of the emotions. With growing cognitive abilities this appraisal naturally becomes more complex (Sroufe, 1979, 1984). Izard (1978) also sees the differentiation of emotions in conjunction with cognitive differentiation, yet holds the view that the developmental influence between cognitions and emotions is reciprocal, which means that new emotions which develop in the process of adaptation also function as a motor of cognitive development.

In my opinion Campos and Barrett (1984; Campos et al., 1983, 1989) justifiably criticize that the ascribing of the development of more complex emotions to the development of more complex cognitions is incomplete because it ignores a very essential factor, namely the relatedness of the emotions to the individual's goals. According to Campos and Barrett, and especially Lazarus (1991) too, emotions are an appraisal of the momentary relationship between the individual and the environment **with respect to activated goals**. With the goals differentiating, the emotions differentiate too. Goals, according to Lazarus, are to be conceived of as desired individual-environment-relations. Lazarus views psychological activity, including emotions as principally environmentally oriented. According to him, each emotion corresponds to a specific transaction between the individual and his environment. Lazarus calls these transactions associated with certain emotions "Core Relational Themes (CRT)." Table 2.1 lists fifteen different emotions together with their corresponding Core Relational Themes.

The fact that the individual experiences himself in this specific relation to his environment is the result of an appraisal process that will be addressed more in-depth by me a little later. The positive or negative experiential quality of an emotion depends on whether the relationship between the individual and the environment means the fulfillment or non-fulfillment of a wish or goal. Wishes or goals are implicitly contained in the CRTs. One feels angry and hurt when one has been insulted by someone else, but one feels only really angry if one wants to be actually respected and positively regarded by the other person. If a person is feeling indifferent towards the other, then that other

Table 2.1:
Assignment of individual emotions to particular "Core Relational Themes"
taken from Lazarus (1991, p.122).

Anger	A demeaning offense against me and mine.
Anxiety	Facing uncertain, existential threat.
Fright	Facing an immediate, concrete, and overwhelming physical danger.
Guilt	Having transgressed a moral imperative.
Shame	Having failed to live up to an ego-ideal.
Sadness	Having experienced an irrevocable loss.
Envy	Wanting what someone else has.
Jealousy	Resenting a third party for loss or threat to another's affection.
Disgust	Taking in or being too close to an indigestible object or idea (metaphorically speaking).
Happiness	Making reasonable progress toward the realization of a goal.
Pride	Enhancement of one's ego-identity by taking credit for a valued object or achievement, either our own or that of someone or group with whom we identify.
Relief	A distressing goal-incongruent condition that has changed for the better or gone away.
Hope	Fearing the worst but yearning for better.
Love	Desiring or participating in affection, usually but not necessarily reciprocated.
Compassion	Being moved by another's suffering and wanting to help.

person is unable to trigger real anger. One feels threatened and experiences fear only if a threat relates to something one really wants, etc.

Therapist: If a strict assignment between certain emotions to certain Core Relational Themes actually exists then it should be possible to draw conclusions from the emotions a patient experiences to his goals. Whenever we notice a strong emotional reaction in somebody, it would indicate that one of his important goals was addressed. This appears to me a very practical and useful heuristic both for everyday life and for therapeutic work. If we see somebody blushing without there being an obvious reason for it, we can conclude according to Table 2.1: "The person must have just perceived the situation that way that he failed to live up to an important aspect of his ego-ideal. Considering the nature of the ongoing situation or the topic dealt with, which aspect could this have been? Oh, I see, the person most likely places great value on being this or that."

This kind of conclusion does not seem trivial to me. Even when applied to myself. For instance, if I had just completed a telephone conversation with a patient, and then I catch myself shortly thereafter as I am whistling to myself, relieved, applying this heuristic then, I could ask myself which goal may I have seen so seriously endangered before, that I am now so relieved. Perhaps it would become clear to me that I was much more concerned about the therapy of this patient than I had admitted to myself before. I would also have to admit to myself that apparently I had a very strong personal desire to successfully treat this patient. I may not have been aware of the strength of this desire and the extent of my concern. I am realizing it only now in my own, not consciously controlled, emotional reaction to the phone call.

This heuristic could also be used as a diagnostic tool in explorations or while performing therapy in order to find access to desires and fears of which the patient is unaware. In our first dialogue we discussed in detail the mechanism of motivational clarification, which is all about the patient becoming more clear about his actual wishes and fears determining his experience and behavior. The emotions are an important part of his experience. We can take a certain part of his experience, a specific recurring emotion, and ask ourselves which important goal is affected while he is experiencing this emotion. The contents of Table 2.1 might serve me as a heuristic to assist the patient in elaborating his feelings with respect to a certain core relational theme by himself. In fact, many times I have proceeded similarly in my therapies even without yet having the listings in Table 2.1 available to me as a means and what you report from research on emotions is quite congruent with my therapeutic experiences.

Psychologist: In accordance with the contexts addressed, Lazarus designated his theory as "cognitive-motivational-relational theory of emotions." I have already dealt with the motivational and relational aspect, the cognitive aspect still remains. The cognitive aspect refers to the **appraisal of the individual's transaction** with the environment. Lazarus distinguishes a primary and a secondary appraisal. The primary appraisal refers to the motivational aspect of the emergence of emotion, the secondary appraisal predominantly refers to the aspect of coping and to the context of the transaction. Each of these two forms of appraisal is comprised of three components.

The components of the **primary appraisal** are
– **goal relevance**: relevance of the transaction for one of the individual's goals. Situations not relevant for any of the individual's goals do not trigger any emotions.
– **Goal congruence** or **incongruence**: transactions experienced as an approximation to or fulfillment of personally relevant goals trigger positive emotions. Transactions counteracting important goals or thwarting them lead to negative emotions.
What feeling the person actually experiences depends upon further appraisals.
– **The form of ego-participation**: This appraisal depends upon the ego identity or the self which the individual has developed up to this point: What is important to him, what are his most important values? This appraisal component thus refers to which **personal values of the individual** are affected. Lazarus himself distinguishes six value categories, but one might also make other distinctions here. His six categories are: self-esteem and respect from others (How am I regarded by myself and by others?), moral value, ego-ideal (How would I like to be?), meaning of life (What is it that makes my life meaning ful?), other people and their well-being (How are persons affected who are significant to me?), and individual life goals. This appraisal component is important for the **quality of the emotion** that the person experiences.
A person feels anger for instance when he or she is hurt in their need for self-esteem and respect; guilt, when he or she has transgressed a moral imperative which they feel obligated to; shame, if that person has deviated strongly from their ego-ideal; pride, if a person feels heightened in his or her self-esteem or social respect. Sorrow, depression or a subdued mood is experienced in the event of the loss of an important part of a person's ego-identity; happiness if one feels secure in all important aspects of one's ego identity. By this we can already see how difficult it is to be consistently happy, because for that a large number of requirements needs to be fulfilled at the same time.

We can also see that it is easier for somebody who has the ability to focus on where things are going well to be happy, and looking away from where things are not going so well.

The three components of **secondary appraisal** are:

- Attribution of **responsibility**: Who is to **blame** in conjunction with a negatively appraised event; who gets the **credit** for a positively appraised one? Or is nobody responsible because it was a coincidence? For the emotion anger to emerge, for instance, it requires our being able to hold somebody responsible for a negative event and that if this person had acted differently, then things would have turned out differently. One can then be angry at another or at oneself. Pride requires that a person gives himself credit. An individual is not proud of a positive event that occurred without his having anything to do with it, instead one may experience perhaps surprise and joy or gratitude if someone else deserves the credit.

- Assessment of the **coping potential**: This appraisal is only relevant in the case of negatively appraised transactions, yet it is even more important for the emergence of the actually experienced emotion. How do I assess my chances for being able to behave a certain way towards this situation? Do I trust myself to handle the situation, to cope with it, to turn it to the better and to prevent serious damage from occurring? So, for these appraisals the individual's control expectations play a decisive role.

  Lazarus distinguishes a form of coping that refers to coping with the situation (**problem- focused coping**) and a form coping that refers to the mastery of the just emerging emotion (**emotion-focused coping**). If, for example, I trust myself to fend off an attacker easily, fear will not arise in me, but perhaps anger or contempt. If I know that I can easily handle emerging feelings of anxiety because I have succeeded in doing so many times before, I will probably not experience strong fear, even if the conditions are otherwise there for them to develop. It is obvious that the assessment of the coping potential strongly overlaps with the concept of self-efficacy expectation by Bandura (1977 a) which we addressed many times in our first conversation. High **self-efficacy expectations** generally have a moderating influence on negative emotions.

- **Future expectations**: This assessment differs from that of the coping potential by its longer time perspective for one, and also in that it gives stronger consideration to subsequent circumstances in the environment. In line with Bandura's terminology (1977 a) one might speak of **result expectations**.

In our first dialogue we talked a lot about the significance of the induction of improvement expectations for an improvement in well-being already at the onset of a therapy. The assessment of the transaction-specific future expectations has obvious relevance for the emergence of general improvement expectations. If the future expectations regarding a core relational theme, the significance of which for the patient expresses itself in strong theme-related emotions, improve, this should promote the general improvement expectations and vice versa. If we succeed in inducing general improvement expectations in the patient by appropriate means, as we discussed them in our first conversation, then this should have an effect on the intensity of his negative emotions experienced, the lowering of which would in turn logically promote the general improvement expectations.

Figure 2.14 presents a summarized schematic illustration of Lazarus' theory of emotions.

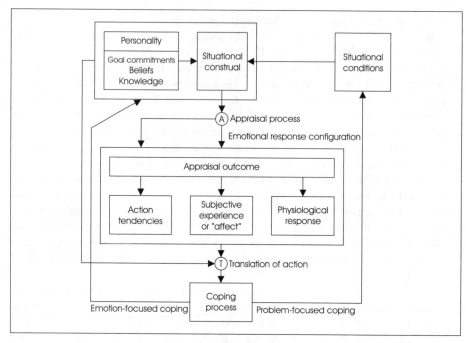

Figure 2.14:
Model of the cognitive-motivational-emotional system according to Lazarus (1991, p. 210).

The goals and expectations of the individual person are carried into the objectively extant situational conditions. This yields the subjective perception of the situation. The appraisal process, with respect to the appraisal components just described, simultaneously results out of what the person brings into the situation in terms of goals and expectations. This produces the subjective meaning of the transaction for the person. It goes hand in hand with experiencing a certain emotional quality and triggers certain action tendencies as well as physiological reactions. Included in the automatically triggered action tendencies are also coping mechanisms learned so far. How a person will actually behave is in turn determined by his or her goals, expectations and tendencies that have already influenced the individual's situational perception. The coping focused on the emotion itself leads to a reappraisal of the transaction, the situation-oriented coping exerts influence on the situational triggering conditions and can thereby change the foundations for the emergence of this emotional response.

This entire process goes on mostly automatically. The person does not have the feeling that he or she decides this way or that way at a certain point, but the emotion is simply being there. It is experienced as given and normally there is no consciousness for how much it was generated by oneself by specific appraisals. It is the same as with perception. The fact that cognitive appraisal processes play such a crucial role in the emergence of emotions does not therefore mean that those are conscious processes.

In most cases though, the cognitive appraisal also contains some conscious processing. A person is wondering, for instance, whether somebody might have wanted to hurt himself deliberately or whether that happened to him by mistake, and this has a clear effect on the emerging emotion. He might also ask himself whether the goal relevance is actually as great as it initially appeared to him during the automatic appraisal. This means whether a deleterious remark by another person really means that one has to be seriously feeling insulted in his self-esteem or respect etc. Lazarus refers to such processes as reappraisal. In the course of the emerging emotion they can already lead to a reappraisal so that the emotion about to emerge does not come to full development.

2.22 The Therapeutic Change of Emotions

Therapist: Now I feel on familiar ground. In psychotherapy we work with such appraisal processes all the time. The cognitive therapies in particular place their entire emphasis on changing those cognitions that accompany the emergence of emotions and causally underlie them. We try to identify and work on bringing out which automatic appraisals the patient practices. Once such appraisals are de-automated and remade conscious they are checked, for instance, by a "Socratic dialogue" for their rational tenability, with the goal, of course, to shake them up. Many aspects of Albert Ellis' rational emotive therapy aim at questioning the goal relevance of situations triggering strong negative feelings in the patient. The value of self-esteem is, for instance, explicitly acknowledged, yet whether one can really respect oneself only by receiving constant confirmation from others, is questioned. New, more rational ideas are developed containing different appraisals, along with an effort to automate them as much as possible by rehearsal. So the goal is to specifically work on revealing the problematic appraisals and replacing them with new ones that would no longer lead to the same emotions. Cognitive therapies attempt to change both appraisal components, the primary appraisal under the motivational aspect, and the secondary appraisal.

Most likely the therapeutic experience that one cannot achieve long-term changes of the appraisal of the coping abilities without the patient having made real mastery experiences, has led to the fact that over time almost all cognitively-oriented therapists have also integrated behavioral techniques into their work.

If behavior therapy leads to a change in negative emotions, then this can most likely be ascribed to a successful modification of the coping component of the secondary appraisal. The development of a self-efficacy expectation for being able to cope with a feared situation corresponds in Lazarus' theory on emotions to the change of the coping component in the secondary appraisal. It makes sense that such appraisals, because they are based on expectations, can be best changed by real experiences. In behavior therapy the procedure oftentimes focuses on both coping components, on the emotion-focused and on the situation-focused coping.

A good example of emotion-focused coping is one part of the treatment of panic disorders according to Margraf and Schneider (1990): In order to instigate a reappraisal, physiological sensations are deliberately aroused in the patient that he had so far interpreted as harbingers of a panic attack. This is also a good example for a bottom-up processual activation of those processes that need to be changed. The tendencies for physiological reactions are part of the memory. They are, however, not part of the conceptual, but part of the emotional memory. These tendencies cannot be changed alone by talking because these response tendencies stored in the emotional memory cannot be addressed top-down.

An example for situation-focused or problem-focused coping would be when a therapist rehearses with a patient how to better cope with difficult social situations. The self-efficacy expectation this builds for these kinds of situations should, according to Lazarus' theories, lead to the patient experiencing less fear when he or she encounters such a situation the next time. It seems to me that the mastery-oriented therapeutic procedures we spoke about in our first conversation have an effect on the emotions experienced by the patient via a change of the coping component. Especially in the treatment of phobias, to me this appears to be a central mechanism.

On the other hand, the therapeutic factor of intention change or motivational clarification elaborated by us in our first round of discussion seems to start with the primary appraisal, thus with the appraisal of a situation with respect to the goals activated in therapy. Every goal change should have effects on the emotions according to Figure 2.14. If, in a patient who was always very keen on making everything right for everybody, therapeutic conversations, for instance, succeed in deactivating this goal or in making it less important to him, then it should no longer matter as much to him if he makes a mistake or fails at something. In general he should be able to be more relaxed while being with others, because he is not constantly watching to see that an important goal might be potentially jeopardized. In this case the appraisal of the goal relevance would have changed.

It should also be possible to change the type of ego-involvement by verbal reflection. Because the neural activation tendencies underlying the main values should be content of the semantic and episodic memories for the most part, and should thereby lend themselves to being addressed principally from the short-term memory, that means from that which is momentarily conscious.

Goal and value changes should not just have effects on very restricted situations but also on the experience and behavior in a broad spectrum of life. Lazarus' theory on emotions clarifies how such value and goal changes take an effect on the emotional experience. It appears to me that this theory of emotions is a valuable addition to the expectancy-value theories. While these theories refer to how behavior changes as a consequence of value and goal changes, Lazarus' theory on emotions explains how changes of the value component have an effect on the emotions.

Therapy researcher: You have just created a very plausible link between Lazarus' theory of emotions and the expectancy-value theories. I suppose we could also create a similarly plausible tie to control theory which has so far served as a fundamental view of mental functioning in our conversation.

According to control theory, the interaction between individual and environment is continuously monitored with respect to deviations between goals and perceptions. As soon as an incongruence is detected, the mental activity directs itself towards its elimination or reduction. This assumed continuous appraisal of the transactions with respect to incongruities between perceptions and goals corresponds exactly to the appraisal of congruence in the emergence of the emotions listed by you earlier as the second component of the primary appraisal. If the transaction is congruent with the goals, positive emotions appear, if it is incongruent, negative emotions are triggered.

So incongruities in the sense of control theory are accompanied by negative emotions. They have a twofold effect: They direct the mental activity towards eliminating the incongruities, and they trigger negative emotions. Which negative emotions these are depends on further appraisal processes. These again are determined by the individual's goals. These goals determining the other appraisal components are not identical with that goal with respect to which an incongruence appraisal occurred. The emergence of emotions is thus regulated simultaneously by several goals: One leads to the incongruence appraisal, the others take an effect on the remaining appraisal components. All activated goals together determine which emotions the person actually experiences. So when trying to understand the emergence of emotions, we also have to assume that there are always several control hierarchies simultaneously activated.

2.23 Goal-Regulated Versus Emotion-Regulated Behavioral Control

I am very pleased that Lazarus' theory of emotions lends itself to being so compatible with control theory because in my view it was the consideration of emotions that control theory had been lacking. I felt this to be a great deficit particularly with respect to applying this theory to psychotherapy. However, I see Lazarus' theory of emotions not just as a compatible addition to control theory, but also leading beyond control theory. What I mean by that is:

An emotion consists of three components: certain action tendencies, the subjectively experienced feeling and certain physiological reactions. So if an emotion is triggered, certain action tendencies are also triggered. These are controlled by the emotion and not by the goal with respect to which the incongruity was identified. In the case of negative emotions, two action tendencies coexist: one which is goal-controlled and one emotion-controlled.

With the goal-controlled action tendency I am referring to the psychological activity directed towards the elimination of the identified incongruity. This action tendency is oriented towards producing perceptions congruent with the goal, the failure of which underlies the emotion.

With the emotion-controlled action tendency I am referring to the one that is part of the emotion itself. Strong rage, for instance, is associated with a strong tendency toward aggressive actions. A person expresses the rage in facial expression, gesture, words and actions. He or she furiously slams doors shut, swears at the person who elicited the rage, attacks that person verbally, or maybe even physically. This infuriated behavior may even be the complete polar opposite of that behavior possibly most well suited to achieve the goal, the failure of which underlies the rage.

Let us take an everyday example most of us have probably experienced ourselves. Living together in a relationship, one wants to feel safe and secure, respected, cared for and loved. The mental activity in being together with the beloved partner is, among others, directed toward producing perceptions congruent with these goals. One day, the partner does or fails to do something which leads to a perception entirely not in the sense of these goals. For example, he forgets a very important appointment or disregards something very important for the other. So the result is an incongruity assessment with respect to important goals. Exactly which emotion will result as a consequence of this incongruity is determined by further appraisal processes. At any rate, disappointment, anger or rage are all possibilities. Let us assume, the person gets very angry. In such a moment it is very difficult to suppress the behavioral tendencies directly associated with the rage. Depending on his temperament, the individual may scream at the partner, make insulting remarks, use swear words that perhaps he would otherwise never use in connection with a beloved person and the like. Certainly all these behaviors are not suited to create perceptions in the sense of the goals he actually has in this relationship. So something is happening here which exactly counteracts the basic principle of control theory. The realization of the incongruity leads to the opposite of what control theory predicts.

I think that given all these considerations it becomes clear that control theory alone is unable to sufficiently explain human experience and behavior, although it certainly does adequately grasp an important aspect, namely that of the basic goal orientation of psychological functioning. But it needs to be extended by theoretical ideas that account for the function emotions have in the overall mental functioning, and that do not merely consider them as an epiphenomenon. The emotions are anything but an epiphenomenon of psychological functioning. As I have attempted to explain with my example, they are partly autonomous determinants of this functioning.

A person's behavior is thus not just controlled by his long-term, higher-order goals but also by his emotions. Once strong emotions have been elicited, they become a determinant of their own in the psychological functioning. While this determinant is of temporary nature in comparison to the long-term goals, strong emotions are nevertheless a very powerful behavioral determinant in the moment in which they are activated.

Psychologist: Your explanation plays right into my ideas. What you just said is exactly the reason why I will later, after having introduced you to the concepts of dynamic system theory, familiarize you with the concept of "emotional attractors." By this I understand a temporary determinant of mental functioning which in addition to, and to some extent in conflict with the long-term determinants, which I will refer to as "motivational attractors," exerts an influence on psychological functioning.

Such a concept seems to be especially important for psychotherapy because a therapist often actually has to deal with "unreasonable" behavior which seems absolutely incongruent with the patient's long-term interests or goals. I could for example explain much of the phenomenology of "borderline disorder" (Clarkin, Marziali & Munroe-Blum, 1992) with the interplay of motivational and emotional attractors. With respect to the patient's long-term wishes, especially in his interpersonal relationships, we can observe incongruence appraisals again and again, partially because these wishes are unreal and partially because the patient does not behave as if he wants them fulfilled. The strong emotions triggered by these incongruence appraisals then determine his or her experience and behavior for a while. In these phases the person's behavior is impulsive and oftentimes destructive. It is in fact controlled entirely by his or her impulses and not by his long-term goals. As soon as the emotional condition recedes, the long-term goals will regain control and will again determine the experience and behavior until a new strong incongruence is identified and the emotional-impulsive regulation of psychological activity is gaining control again. This is how it comes to the emotional instability so characteristic of this disorder. Something similar could also be true for many more mental disorders. Perhaps we can return to that more in-depth at a later point when all this will have been embedded in a more coherent view.

2.24 Emotion and Nonverbal Regulation of Relations

I wish to point to yet another aspect of emotional behavior control which plays a crucial role for the interpersonal regulation of relations outside and inside of psychotherapies. What I mean is the emotionally-controlled expressive behavior. Previously I mentioned that the primary emotions are accompanied by certain facial expressions. Emotions involve motor-expressive activation patterns enervating the facial muscles in such a specific fashion that a certain emotion can be ascribed to a certain pattern of muscle contractions (Ekman, 1989). This facial expression belongs to the automatically triggered action tendencies which constitute an emotion together with the subjectively experienced feeling and a specific physiological activation pattern.

But the experiencing of emotions is mostly embedded in a social context. The conscious and unconscious goals activated in the respective social situation overlay the automatically triggered emotional expression tendencies. The facial expression is consciously controllable. We can deliberately smile, or make a surprised, shocked or scornful face. This willful behavior is determined by our respective conscious and unconscious goals activated in that situation. There are subtle differences demarcating a voluntary facial expression behavior from one that is involuntary, emotionally controlled. With micro-analytic methods such as the "Facial Action Coding System (FACS)" (Ekman & Friesen, 1986) such differences can be revealed and an "honest" emotional smile can be distinguished from a fake one (Ekman, 1985; Ekman, Friesen & O'Sullivan, 1988).

Among all the nonverbal communication channels, facial expression is the one which can be relatively most well consciously controlled. It is the one that can be most successfully placed in the service of a conscious intention. Many studies on this have been carried out investigating what makes one recognize whether or not someone is consciously lying. Zuckerman, DePaulo and Rosenthal (1986) did a meta-analysis of 35 studies that looked at which information was used by tests persons to best recognize whether somebody is telling the truth. The face revealed the least (effect size ES = .05), the voice, without considering content, revealed a little more (ES = .20) and body language/posture from the neck downwards revealed even more (ES = .43). Surprisingly, lies could be best recognized based on verbal content (ES = .70). In cases where the test persons had many communication channels for the assessment available to them, similar to the situation under natural conditions, the effect size was even higher, registering above 1.

In psychotherapy we need not protect ourselves from a patient consciously lying, in doing so he only does damage to himself. But the studies on deliberate lying tell us something about the conscious controllability of the various communication channels.

Accordingly, what a patient expresses with his face is usually closer to those intentions and emotions nearer to his consciousness than what he expresses via the other nonverbal channels. We gather more about intentions and emotions further away from a person's consciousness by the manner in which he says something and from his body language. This is even more true for the lower part of the body than it is for the upper part (Ekman & Friesen, 1974). Therapists should, therefore, learn to explicitly pay attention to their patients' body language and manner of speaking as this will better enable them to help the patient gain access to what he or she has so far not been consciously aware of.

Aside from that, conscious lying is a very specific communication situation. In normal everyday life we are hardly ever clearly aware of what we express with our face. This is not surprising because we normally have no continuous feedback for that. After all, we cannot have all interactions occur before a mirror. We can, however, much better observe the face of our interaction partner. Much more is happening on that face than we can consciously perceive with our naked eyes. Considering the great number of nonverbal communication channels, if we compare this multitude with the narrowness of our consciousness, then it becomes clear that much more is continuously nonverbally communicated than we are consciously able to perceive. However, that does not mean we do not perceive or process what was sent. Nonverbal communication research demonstrates to us that we do indeed respond to that. Thus we must have perceived it. The largest portion of what is nonverbally communicated is perceived implicitly and is not consciously processed. The implicit mode of functioning is of extraordinary significance for the interpersonal regulation of relationships.

If we find ourselves under the influence of a strong emotion, our emotional action tendencies, as a rule, spontaneously express themselves so clearly in our face that they practically cannot be missed by others, and this is also most likely their biological function. In your previous example describing the couple, the one partner's rage, for instance, would have been literally written all over his face. Such primary emotions have something unvarnished about them. Naturally, they do not by any means tell the entire truth about the relationship, but are momentary reactions that may evaporate very quickly in order to leave the behavior control again to the long-term intentions. But as a short-term emotional action tendency it may even happen that we make an expression of contempt towards a beloved person even if we actually have a completely different attitude towards that person.

Subconsciously, our emotional reactions may also be reflected in our facial expression even if our voluntary and automatically controlled behavior in the service of certain goals is supposed to simultaneously express something different. While we mostly succeed in bringing our involuntary emotional expression quickly back under voluntary control, the emotional reaction has most likely already been subconsciously registered by our interaction partner and may influence his or her further behavior.

Nonverbal expressive behavior is a very powerful means by which to provoke a reciprocal behavior in the interaction partner (Scheflen, 1974). If someone smiles honestly at you, that means emotionally controlled, it is very difficult not to smile back. If somebody really cries, one feels a tendency to turn to him and comfort that person. These innate behavioral tendencies have a crucial function in the regulation of social interaction, the biological function of which Darwin has already pointed out (see above). Apart from that, the same emotions the observed person is momentarily expressing nonverbally can be elicited in an observer by the process of identifying. One need only observe a movie audience while they are watching an emotionally moving scene in the film to see in the faces of the audience which emotions are being seen on the screen.

A patient can see in the face of their therapist whether or not he or she is empathic. What the patient reports is accompanied by a facial commentary that may very often express contempt, disgust, and rage, but also joy. If none of that is reflected in the therapist's face, he or she is internally rather untouched by what the patient experiences, and it is very likely that this is unconsciously perceived by the patient (Krause, 1997, see also following).

So in our nonverbal expressive behavior there is an interplay of expression controlled by activated goals, conscious and unconscious, and emotionally controlled expression. A complex mixture that cannot be easily interpreted may result from that. The same is true, by the way, for our overall behavior. When an emotion becomes very strong it tends to dominate the entire psychological functioning. In such moments the expressive behavior is unequivocal. It is also unequivocal when conscious and unconscious goals are largely congruent and there are no emotions exerting a discordant influence on the expressive behavior. But in all other cases, the expressive behavior is an ambiguous mixture from these more or less consistent influences. In the various communication channels: facial expression, gesture, voice quality, manner of speaking, breathing, posture, and movements of the upper and lower body, etc., different things can be expressed simultaneously, resulting in a vast variety of possible expressive patterns. This is even more true if we consider that with our facial expression alone we are able to send mixed messages. Larger still is the multitude of what is more or less consistently communicated if we also add the semantic and pragmatic communication aspects of the verbally expressed (Watzlawick, Beavin & Jackson, 1969).

When we experience an emotion—this need not necessarily become conscious—there is, at least for a very short time, an automatically triggered action tendency associated with the emotion in the facial expression. This can be very quickly "recaptured" by the expressive patterns controlled by the higher-order goals so as to not be consciously perceived by the interaction partners. We are equipped with the innate ability to recognize the facial expression patterns, especially those of primary emotions, in a flash, and to react to those equally fast and automatically. Both perception and our reaction may happen completely outside of our consciousness. Oftentimes these processes are much too quick to even be able to lead to conscious perceptions (Merten, 1996).

Earlier we spoke about unconscious perceiving and learning (section 2.15) so it should no longer surprise you that such unconscious perceptions have been encountered not only in tachistoscopic experiments but also and especially in natural interaction situations. We now know something about these processes since we have been able to document natural interactions on film and analyze them via a frame by frame analysis with slow-motion instant replay providing something like a time-microscope. One gets to see a world, much the same as like under a real microscope, a world that we were unaware of before due to our conscious perception. Our unconscious analyzers always had knowledge of that but were unable to share it with us. People have always been controlled in their interactions by such unconscious perceptions but only in recent times have we elaborated a knowledge and awareness for this through new scientific methods (Merten, 1996).

Due to the findings reported earlier on implicit learning we have to assume that perceptual, behavioral, and emotional response tendencies for the regulation of our interactional behavior are largely stored in the implicit memory and through that have an effect on our experience and behavior. As far as the possibilities of changing these determinants of our behavior are concerned, the same applies as does for the other contents of the implicit memory: They can only be changed if they have been processually activated bottom-up before. In an activated condition they may either be changed by non-confirming implicit perceptions or can be made the subject of conscious attention, thereby being brought step-by-step under conscious control so that they may perhaps become automated again later in a changed form. At any rate, the interactional behavior of a person cannot be changed long-term solely by talking.

Therapy researcher: You have ascribed the nonverbal regulation of interactions to the implicit perceptual and memory processes. This makes perfect sense to me because normally—with actors being probably an exception—there is no conscious learning or even training happening in this respect. One can also hardly ascribe nonverbal behavior to procedural learning because who would learn to consciously smile or look sad? A person need not learn these nonverbal behaviors the way one learns to ride a bike or to type on a keyboard. They are given to us already as potentialities. But obviously they can be improved—I am thinking once again of the actor—by conscious rehearsal. Patients too should be able to learn something in this respect through practicing if it appears necessary. In social skills training, for instance, one focuses very distinctly on nonverbal expressive behavior.

2.25 Nonverbal-Analog and Verbal-Digital Communication Have a Different Neural Basis

I still, however, have a question regarding the neural basis of the nonverbal regulation of interactions, specifically because it is obvious that a part of that behavior, such as the encoding and decoding of primary emotions, does not need to be learned, but is already pre-existing in the brain as a tendency toward certain neural activation patterns. It would appear then that this is located in a certain area of the brain, much the way there is a region for language. You already mentioned earlier that there is some indication that sub-cortical parts of the brain, especially the limbic system, play a crucial role as a neural basis for primary emotions. Does this also apply to the neural structures underlying the nonverbal regulation of interactions? I believe I once read that the two sides of the brain play different functional roles in that. Is there something to all this?

Psychologist: Thanks for reminding me. There have been many studies on the different functions of the two hemispheres of the brain, and the findings are, both with respect to emotions and to nonverbal information processing, very interesting and fit in well with the views so far developed. They clearly point to the two sides of the brain having different functions in the processing of emotional and nonverbal contents on the one hand, and verbal contents, on the other.

Our knowledge on **hemisphere specialization** is derived from studies of patients with unilateral brain damage and also from experiments with normal subjects who were presented with different stimuli to the left and right visual field or into the left or right ear. The rationale behind this being that stimuli from the right ear or the right visual field are primarily projected to the left side of the brain, whereas stimuli from the left ear and the left half of the visual field are processed by the right side of the brain. So if one finds lateral differences between the ears or the sides of the visual field with respect to the processing of emotional stimuli, one can draw conclusions about the function of the brain hemisphere situated on the opposite side.

For **auditory** stimuli the experimental design of dichotic listening (see section 2.15) is utilized. Typically, for example, text spoken in varying emotional intonations (happy, sad, angry, neutral) is offered into one ear and into the other, text spoken in a monotone voice. The test persons are to asses the text with respect to emotional quality and content. Using such an experimental design, Ley and Bryden (1982) found that for the assessment of the emotional tone of voice, the right side of the brain dominates, and for the correct reproduction of the semantic content, the left side. Safer and Leventhal (1977) found that during dichotic listening, test persons attending to the left ear paid more attention to the emotional intonation, and those listening with the right ear paid more attention to the content.

In studies on **visual** stimuli, predominantly faces with a certain emotional expression were presented separately to the right or left visual field. The test persons were told to assess as quickly as possible whether the emotional expression was congruent with the referent face (for example Strauss & Moscowitch, 1981). In many studies it was found that the assessments were faster and more accurate when the presented faces were shown to the left visual field. So the right hemisphere of the brain is superior to the left with regard to the speed and accuracy of the processing of emotionally-toned stimuli, independent of the quality of the senses.

Based on an overview of studies performed up to that point on the lateral differences in emotional information processing, Strauss (1986) arrived at the following assessment summarizing the research status: For emotional behavior predominantly controlled by sub-cortical areas of the brain, such as the spontaneous expression of primary emotions, there are no lateral differences according to studies with brain damaged persons. Functional differentiation of the brain hemispheres occurs only at the higher cortical levels. A functional differentiation, however, does not simply mean that the right side of the brain is in charge of the emotions and the left is in charge of the contents, but that both sides participate in emotional processing, yet their contribution is qualitatively different. The right hemisphere is responsible for the processing of complex patterns that are difficult to code verbally, such as nonverbal information like facial expressions or the quality of voice. This side particularly specializes in the holistic, gestalt-oriented information processing. In contrast, however, the left hemisphere is concerned with the linguistic and analytical processing of emotional material. In most feelings that arise under natural conditions, both forms of processing are involved.

This is to say, in direct response to your question, that the nonverbal information processing, and with that the nonverbal regulation of interactions, does in fact take place predominantly on the basis of neural processes in the right hemisphere. Significantly better **decoding ability for nonverbal information** is found for the right hemisphere, be it for facial expression, gesture, posture, quality of voice etc. Rosenthal and associates in particular have conducted many studies on that (see the summary by Rosenthal and Benowitz, 1986). In cases of damage to the right hemisphere, the non-verbal information processing is much more strongly affected than in situations of equivalent damage to the left hemisphere. The stronger the emotional quality of the nonverbal signals, the more pronounced the lateral differences.

The **encoding of emotional expression** takes place predominantly in the right hemisphere as well. Emotions are more strongly expressed with the left side of the face than with the right. This difference is not discernible with the naked eye. However, if the left side of a photographed face bearing a certain emotional expression is observed with a mirror placed along its vertical axis, then this artificially produced symmetrical face has a clearly stronger emotional expression than if you were to do the same with the right half of the face. Borod, Koff and Buck (1986) offer a review of the neuropsychological studies of the facial expression and also report on their own experimental studies regarding this topic. Based on these, they describe the particular information processing of the right hemisphere as nonverbal, holistic, synthetic, gestalt-oriented, specialized towards the recognition of patterns, visual integration and multi-modal integration.

In a comprehensive attempt to integrate all existing empirical evidence on the de-coding and encoding of facial expression, on lateral differences in facial expression and on the emotional quality of voice, Tucker (1986) arrives at the conclusion that the right and left hemispheres each specialize in a different form of information representation:

"Verbal cognitive representation entails the substitution of an internal code, a word, for sensory experience... A linguistic code is essentially an arbitrary substitution for the original information. This representational format offers important advantages to an information processing system over the analog representation that occurs in the initial, iconic or echoic, representation of concrete perception. In computer terms, a digital, substitutive code is relocatable, its semantic packages portable from one area of memory, or one brain, to the next. In this form, the substitutive code can be organized and processed according to fixed and repeatable rules, such as those of algebra and grammar. The capacity for repeatable, regularized cognitive operations is essential to complex instances of human cognition and may be intrinsic to the left hemisphere's operation...

Nonverbal cognitive processes involve a fundamentally different form of internal representation: They are analogical. There is no transformation of the continuous sensory data into a discrete, substitutive code; rather, the internal representation of the information is an analog of the sensation, mirroring the environment. An image retains the sensory quality of the sight or sound, and the cognitive processing of the image must occur through analogical, as opposed to logical or propositional, transformations...

The analogical nature of the right hemisphere's information processing may be important to an understanding of the nature of the information transfer in nonverbal communication. Buck (1982; Borod, Koff & Buck, 1986) suggests that the nonverbal communication operates through a biologically shared signal system, rather than the socially or culturally shared system of language... The analogical form of the information representation causes the message to reflect its meaning in a continuous fashion... The speaker's intonation conveys information not in an arbitrary code, but through mirroring an internal emotional state analogically...

The analogical nature of the data transfer is particularly important on the receiving end. The perception of the message requires an internal representation of the information; because the message is a concrete and continuous reflection of the sender's affective state, the simple mental representation of this information in the process of perception tends to elicit the corresponding affective state in the receiver. With verbal representation there is an inherent distance between the semantics of the message and the perceiver's affective response that is afforded by the indirect, substitutive nature of the verbal code. With nonverbal communication the analogical format of the information allows the communication to elicit emotion concretely and directly" (Tucker, 1986, pp. 265/266).

Therapy researcher: This sounds almost as though it was written by Watzlawick, Beavin and Jackson (1969), only they wrote about what takes place **between** people, whereas Tucker writes about what occurs in the brain. In my eyes their distinction between digital and analog communication seems to correspond exactly to both representational forms of information processing in the brain described by Tucker. Analog information processing seems to correspond more to the mechanism of the right hemisphere, and digital, verbal information processing more to that of the left hemisphere. So the right hemisphere is more in charge of the analog, nonverbal communication, and the left hemisphere, the verbal communication.

Psychologist: As a broad tendency, this is true. But the difference in sides should not be conceived such that one side of the brain strictly could only do this and the other side only that. What we have here is more a gradual specialization that evidently begins to develop already in earliest childhood (Turkewitz, Gordon & Birch, 1965; Carmon & Nachshon, 1973; Brown & Jaffe, 1975; Tucker, 1986). If one side of the brain fails, its functions can be taken over in time by the other side. But actually, it is not so much the specialization of the hemispheres in and of itself that is relevant for us, but more the fact that there are two different forms of information processing in the brain which are associated with differences between nonverbal and verbal communication as well as emotional versus rational information processing.

Therapist: I have discovered yet another reference to what we have been talking about. Don't these two forms of representation differentiated by Tucker largely agree with the differentiation between the perceptual and conceptual memory by Perrig et al. (1993) which you reported on earlier (section 2.12)? Doesn't their "associative response function" largely correspond to the analogical representation and processing mode and their "interpretive function" to Tucker's verbal representation mode? Isn't it possible that the implicit or perceptual memory could be more the basis for the analog and nonverbal communication and the conceptual and explicit memory that for the verbal communication? These references seem very obvious, at least to me.

At any rate, I think there is more and more evidence of there being two different kinds of mental processes with different neural foundations: Attributes such as conceptual-verbal-analytical-rational could be used to refer to one type, and perceptual-implicit-nonverbal-analog-emotional-holistic-intuitive to the other. Each of these two types have their specific advantages and disadvantages. Moreover, the first seems more associated with consciousness, whereas the second kind of processes occur unconsciously. But this should also not be understood in the sense of a strict categorization, but more in the sense of a tendency. Most of all, that these processes are in close exchange with one another and cooperate with respect to the individual's goals in sharing the work appears to me to be a specific strength of psychological functioning.

For me, as a therapist, a very important conclusion arises from this. In mental disorders emotions always play an important role. The emotions are much more closely tied with the implicit-analog-nonverbal mode of functioning than with the conceptual-verbal-analytical mode. In psychotherapies, the conversation almost always plays a central role. In a conversation both modes of functioning are activated, however the conversational partners' attention is mostly focused on the content and is thus confined to the conceptual-verbal mode. For the changes to be brought about, however, the other, the implicit-nonverbal-analog mode of functioning is more relevant due to its close association with the emotions. So above all, a therapist has to learn to focus his attention on those processes going on in this implicit-nonverbal-analogical mode of functioning. It is predominantly in this area that the therapist must bring about changes if he or she wants to change the patient's emotional experience. From this perspective the therapeutic factor of processual activation discussed in our first dialog appears even more crucial. Above all, a therapist has to learn to perceive, to think and to act processually if he or she wants to fully exhaust the potential inherent in psychotherapy.

Given all these considerations, it seems to me that many forms of psychotherapy have a general tendency to place too much weight on verbal communication. It may be much more difficult, or impossible, to gain access to the many contents of the implicit emotional memory in need of change from the verbal mode of functioning than it would be via the implicit analogical communication channel. Though I certainly do not want to throw the baby out with the bath water. For psychotherapy, the conversation is as indispensable as the conceptual mode of functioning for psychological functioning in general. Yet most therapists' conscious attention is probably occupied too much by this communication channel and mode of functioning, in order for the implicit analogical processes so important for the change to receive sufficient attention. I think most therapy training programs should pay more explicit attention to these processes.

2.26   The Significance of Nonverbal Communication for Psychotherapy

Therapy researcher: I can still come up with a whole list of research findings to add to this that would serve as grist for the mill of these conclusions. In therapy research there have also been studies done on the significance of nonverbal communication which fit well into what we just discussed, but have even lead beyond that. Perhaps this would be the right moment to report on those. Then you will have a moment to relax.

Psychologist: That would not be so bad, I do have a dry mouth from talking so much, so please take your time reporting on these findings.

Therapy researcher: There are three groups of research results relevant to our context. Some refer to therapists, some to patients and others finally to the therapist-patient-interaction.

Nonverbal Therapist Behavior

Let me first begin from the **side of the Therapist:** In our first conversation we talked about the qualities which should characterize the therapist-patient relationship in order to achieve a successful therapeutic outcome. Included therein is the patient having the feeling that the therapist is interested in him, understands him, is committed to him and makes a trustworthy impression. Many of these characteristics are summarized in the concept of **empathy** (Hogan, 1978). The significance of the therapist's credibly communicated empathy to the patient for a successful therapeutic outcome can be considered proven (Orlinsky, Grawe & Parks, 1994). What, in fact, is it though that makes a patient perceive his therapist as empathic?

Research on empathy reached its peak in the seventies. Many different methods were developed to measure empathy according to a therapist's verbal statements (Matarazzo, 1978). Yet Haase and Tepper (1972) were able to demonstrate that nonverbal behaviors such as eye contact, a forward leaning, sitting posture, and physical distance were much more critical for empathy assessment than were verbal statements. Researchers working on nonverbal communication defined empathy as "the ability to detect and describe the immediate affective state of another ... the ability to receive and decode affective information" (Danish and Kagan, 1971). Kagan and coworkers developed the "Affect Sensitivity Scale" for measuring empathy thus defined. Using this scale, longer interaction sequences between client and counselor were to be assessed on the basis of the verbal and nonverbal information with respect to which feelings were expressed by the person being assessed. Rosenthal and associates (Rosenthal et al., 1979) developed the "Profile of Nonverbal Sensitivity (PONS)" test. In the PONS test, sequences of video or audio tape only 2-seconds long are presented, from which all semantic information has been removed, and the test person must assess which emotion was supposed to be expressed either by body language, facial expression or quality of voice.

Tests like this that were used to measure the encoding and **decoding abilities** of therapists for nonverbally expressed feelings. Physicians active in the normal medical care system who showed greater aptitude at correctly decoding nonverbally expressed emotions had patients that were more satisfied with the treatment, which manifested itself both in direct statements about satisfaction (DiMatteo et al., 1980) as well as in their having a higher influx of patients (DiMatteo, Prince & Hays, 1986). A physician's sensitivity to a patient's body language and the patient's satisfaction were found to have an especially high correlation. Therapists demonstrating better decoding ability in the PONS test were judged by their supervisors to be more competent therapists (Rosenthal and Benowitz, 1986).

Generally however, clinical psychologists, psychiatrists and similar professional groups did not distinguish themselves by an especially high nonverbal sensitivity in the PONS test. The best nonverbal sensitivity was found among actors, students of nonverbal communication, and among art students. Women, more so than men, have a greater sensitivity in their perception of negative emotions. Older children and adults are more accurate than younger children in their assessments. This applies especially for visual nonverbal information. The ability to correctly identify intonation obviously develops prior to the visual decoding ability.

Individuals with a high sensitivity for nonverbal expression are, on average, more well adapted and maintain a more democratic and encouraging interaction style, are more extroverted, more well liked, and are assessed by acquaintances, partners or supervisors as being more interpersonally sensitive. These findings are based on dozens of studies that Rosenthal and Benowitz (1986) reported in a summary. A high nonverbal decoding ability is thus a highly desirable personality trait.

In the studies by DiMatteo and associates previously mentioned, the nonverbal **encoding ability** of therapists and physicians was also examined. This ability proved to be even more significant than the decoding ability. Physicians and therapists who are able to express a certain feeling intentionally, in a fashion unmistakably interpreted by the assessors as exactly this feeling, have a greater influx of patients and are more positively evaluated by their patients and supervisors. Being able to express oneself emotionally seems to be a specifically important ability for therapists.

Different persons, and of course different therapists, differ significantly in their nonverbal decoding and encoding abilities. According to twin studies, the different degree to which these abilities exist appears to be partially innate (Zahn-Waxler, Robinson & Emde, 1992). A natural, extraordinarily high, nonverbal ability for expression and sensitivity contributes greatly to what we call "charisma" (Friedman & Riggio, 1981; Riggio & Friedman, 1982). Most likely, many "psycho gurus" draw predominantly from this reservoir. Fritz Perls could be seen as the prototype of such a charismatic therapist possessing a high nonverbal perceptual and expressive ability.

For therapists not blessed by nature with a generous supply of this ability, it may be of some comfort to know that these abilities can be improved through specific training (Sanson-Fisher & Poole, 1978; Robbins et al., 1979). On the other hand, it would seem important to note that such a training should be done by therapists already performing therapies and not before, because if this is done in preparation, as a "dry run," the effects from training seem to vanish again (Hornsby & Payne, 1979; Kauss et al., 1980). Systematic observation of therapists' nonverbal communication behavior and its change should therefore strictly be a part of psychotherapeutic training, and especially of supervision.

What specifically should be paid attention to? The findings on this have been unmistakably confirmed by many studies time and again. A summary can be found in Harrigan and Rosenthal (1986). Therapists should be seated with their upper body tilted more towards the patient, arms open, hands held loosely in the lap, and should nod with their head again and again while the patient is talking. The therapist should underline his own statements with gestures, as a vivid gesture is positively perceived. Therapists doing so are much more positively assessed by their patients than are therapists who are slouched in a chair with their arms crossed in front of their chests. The legs should not be crossed, but relaxed and open.

All aspects of therapists' behavior have been studied as independent variables. The studies found interactive effects between the variables as well. The forward leaning, sitting position has an even more positive effect when utilized in conjunction with the legs in a relaxed, open posture, and the effect of nodding the head is greater with open, as opposed to crossed, arms. So it is not only the individual behavior itself, but also the consistency of the behaviors. A forward leaning, sitting posture with crossed arms, sends an inconsistent nonverbal message, just as much as nodding of the head with a leaned back body posture and crossed arms. These combinations are seen as more negative than positive by the patient.

When leaning forwards toward someone, it is evidently perceived as a desire for greater closeness and as more attentive and interested. Apart from that, a forward leaning body posture communicates a greater action tendency, that is a greater willingness to become active on behalf of the other. Open, relaxed arms signalize greater accessibility than when one puts up a barrier with crossed arms. An unshielded, forward leaning upper body, therefore, signalizes openness, desire for closeness and engaged interest, supported by a nodding head, as a sign of participation and receptiveness.

The intonation of the voice is also a very important nonverbal communication channel. It was predominantly Blanck, Rosenthal and Vannicelli (1986) who conducted fundamental studies on this. They technically filtered all the semantic information from therapist-patient interviews. From among 21 therapists, both female and male, the researchers analyzed 101 interviews **with** the patient as well as 218 interviews in which the therapist spoke **about** the patient, who was receiving either in- or outpatient care. Sequences of twenty seconds of text from both kinds of interviews, the content of which was incomprehensible, were presented to raters for evaluation of the intonation. A polarity profile with the following ten pairs of opposite attributes was used for the rating:

warm—not warm,
nervous—not nervous,
hostile—not hostile,
empathetic—not empathetic,
liking the patient—not liking the patient,
professional—not professional,
competent—not competent,
optimistic—not optimistic,
dominant—not dominant,
honest—not honest.

A factor analysis for the ratings of the direct patient-therapist interaction resulted in four orthogonal dimensions independent of one another, according to which the intonation quality varies, namely,

warm/empathetic,
professional/competent,
afraid,
honest.

The factor analysis of the intonation in the statements **about** the patient resulted in a more differentiated seven factor solution. The first four factors matched those just listed. The three additional factors were hostile, optimistic and dominant.

The intonation can be assessed surprisingly reliably from 20-second long sequences of conversation lacking any semantic information. The agreement among the raters lies at around .90. The consistency of the intonation over the duration of an interview is also surprisingly high, especially when the therapist speaks directly with the patient.

Some of the results are hardly surprising. The voices of the female therapists were assessed as warmer, more nervous and more honest, but less professional/competent. This part of the results matches gender role stereotypes and probably tells something about the assessed persons as well as about the assessors.

In my eyes, an important result seems to be that a professional/competent intonation in the direct patient-therapist interviews was significantly correlated with the patient's improvement expectations. This finding appears relevant to me in conjunction with our considerations on the induction of expectations of positive improvement outlined in our first dialogue. A professional/competent intonation can contribute to the induction of such expectations. Therefore, in the training of female therapists, special attention should be placed particularly on their learning to adopt a professional/competent intonation, contrary to the gender stereotype.

This is all the more true as female and male therapists judged by their supervisors as interpersonally especially competent or less competent differed from each other most notably in this aspect of intonation. Interestingly, however, this was only the case for the first phase of the interview. In a later interview phase, those therapists judged by their supervisors as especially competent had a markedly warm, rather than a preponderantly professional intonation. Apart from that, therapists judged as more competent or less competent, differed in that those judged more competent revealed a less nervous intonation in their conversations with the patient.

While reading the research report by Blanck et al., I was surprised at how much can be inferred solely from the intonation. For instance, based on the intonation in the first twenty seconds of an interview, one can, from the combination of the attributes warm, hostile, nervous, dominant, optimistic, almost certainly already predict whether a therapist was speaking **about** an in- or outpatient. When talking about inpatients, the therapists had a significantly more nervous, hostile and dominant intonation than when speaking about outpatients. In the conversations **with** inpatients, the therapist's intonation contained significantly only more nervousness. Obviously a therapist feels emotionally more challenged and distressed by patients in an inpatient setting and that manifests itself in how he talks about and with the patient. In addition, according to findings from other studies, the intonation is considered to belong to the "leaching" communication channels (Ekman & Friesen, 1969; Ekman, Friesen & Scherer, 1976; Zuckerman, DePaulo & Rosenthal, 1981). Intonation reveals one's emotional mindset especially clearly, without the awareness of the respective person.

There is still another finding from these studies which appears to me important for therapist training. Therapists speaking **about** their patient in a somewhat cold, explicitly non-nervous, overly professional and dominant intonation were also talking **with** their patients rather coldly, dishonestly and in an overly professional manner. So it seems that a general attitude towards the patient reveals itself in the intonation. It should, therefore, make a difference to instructors and training schools in which tone of voice patients are talked about in case seminars, supervision groups, etc. The patient should be talked about in a similar fashion as one would talk to the patient, namely in a professional and competent manner, but at the same time warm, empathetic, honest and concerned.

The aspects of nonverbal behavior discussed by me: body posture, gesture, nodding, and intonation are basically voluntarily controllable, but are usually automatic and unconsciously ongoing. Therapists in training, if their nonverbal behavior is not already that way, need to learn to consciously control these behavioral aspects until they automatically achieve their implementation. The influence of these nonverbal signals is much too powerful to be ignored. If therapists are not sending these nonverbal messages to their patients, much of what they have to say may be in vain no matter how sensible the content may be. Both interaction partners may be completely unaware of these processes, but these processes account for a considerable part of the eventual resultant therapeutic outcome (Krause, 1997). I consider the described nonverbal messages to the patient to be very important for his receptiveness, and this has been proven to be an important link between therapeutic intervention and outcome (Ambühl, 1991; Orlinsky, Grawe & Parks, 1994).

After all you previously mentioned on the specialization of the hemispheres, these results, which were gained independently from that, seem very plausible. Nonverbally, one speaks, so to say, to the patient's right hemisphere and thereby addresses much more easily his or her emotions. One emotionally comments on whatever it is that is being verbally exchanged with him, addressed to the left hemisphere. If the verbally and nonverbally sent messages match one another, one should usually have the greatest influence on what is happening in the patient's brain as a result of these messages. I pointed out "usually" because sometimes one may achieve a desired effect especially with targeted, inconsistent messages, namely in a situation where one, by doing so, is responding to inconsistent messages of the patient. This might be the working mechanism of the so-called "paradoxical interventions."

Nonverbal Patient Behavior

Nonverbal decoding and encoding ability has also been studied on the side of the patient. Rosenthal and Benowitz (1986) conducted their own research on the **decoding ability** among different kinds of patient groups and also reported on the results of other researchers. The findings can be quickly summarized: The ability to correctly decode nonverbal information is, on average, significantly worse in psychiatric patients than in normal persons. The more disturbed the patients, the more this is the case. Compared to normal persons, the difference for tone of voice is smaller than for facial expression and body language.

Also negatively affected is the learning ability with regard to the tasks of the PONS test. Whereas normal persons clearly improve from the first to the second half of the PONS test, the performance of patients barely improves. Normal persons benefit greatly when information from one channel (intonation, body language and facial expression) is enhanced by additional channels. Their performance improves with each added channel. In patients this is not or only very slightly the case. The more information there is to decode, the more their performance drops in comparison to normal persons. The possibility that these findings are due to differences in intelligence was ruled out.

The ability to correctly perceive other people's emotions is a very important basis for the regulation of interactions. A continuously false interpretation or lack of awareness with respect to the feelings of persons one lives together with must lead to difficulties in the relationship because the other partner feels not understood. It is so far unclear to what extent the observed deficits in the ability to empathize in individuals with a mental disorder are the cause of their disorder or just an accompanying symptom. What is obvious, however, is that these deficits are an essential aspect of a mental disorder and thereby merit therapeutic attention. So far we know little about how much this disability might (re-)improve in the course of psychotherapy. Appropriate scales have so far not been included in studies on therapeutic effectiveness. It is very likely that deficits in the ability to empathize vary in size and possibly in type for different disorders. The findings reported by Rosenthal and Benowitz indicate that the deficits in schizophrenics and patients with severe personality disorders are greater than those in neurotic patients, but only very gross distinctions are made in these studies and they do not correspond to those distinctions made by today's standard diagnostic categorization systems.

From the existing results we can only conclude that the nonverbal regulation of interactions in people with mental disorders merits explicit therapeutic attention. When patients experience unsatisfactory relationship situations over and over again, the reduced ability to perceive their partner's emotions might be one contributing cause. This can make living together very difficult for the partners. In psychotherapy, relationship difficulties are usually associated with the conscious and unconscious intentions of the participants involved, and are thus seen from a motivational perspective. Nonverbal communication research, however, argues in favor of such difficulties being also partially based on a deficit in ability.

In communication training programs favoring such a conception, emphasis for the most part is given to verbal communication, though it is still questionable how much nonverbal deficits improve by a verbally-oriented communication training. It might very well be that the nonverbal deficits require special attention and therapeutic measures explicitly tailored to them. Given that, it seems to me much more research is required before we will be able to give empirically founded answers to these questions. Nonverbal communication would have to receive greater attention in therapy research than has so far been the case.

There is, however, one research group which placed nonverbal communication in psychotherapies at the center of their research questions. This group, Rainer Krause and his colleagues at the university of Saarbrücken, Germany, came up with the only extant research results on the encoding of emotions among persons suffering from mental disorders. There is no research on this available using the PONS test, or none known to me at any rate. The studies by Krause and his associates focus on interaction situations that were either established for the purpose of the study, or on real psychotherapies. They refer to the expression of facial affect analyzed with the EMFACS, a variation of the previously mentioned FACS (Facial Action Coding System) by Ekman and Friesen (1986).

In order to study the facial expression of emotions outside of psychotherapies, Krause and associates created the following situation: "Two persons of the same age, gender and approximately the same educational level, previously unknown to one another, met together at our research institute and discussed politics for 20 minutes; specifically with the goal of reaching agreement on which of the four most important problems should be solved over the course of the next year in Germany. One of the partners was either healthy or suffered from schizophrenia, from colitis ulcerosa or a functional spine ailment with a neurotic etiology in the sense of a conversion. The control group consisted of healthy people interacting with one another. Since the patients, including the schizophrenics, did not interact openly in a psychotic fashion, their partners did not realize that they were speaking with an 'ill' person" (Krause, 1997, p. 74).

Figure 2.15 summarizes which affects were facially expressed by which experimental groups how often.

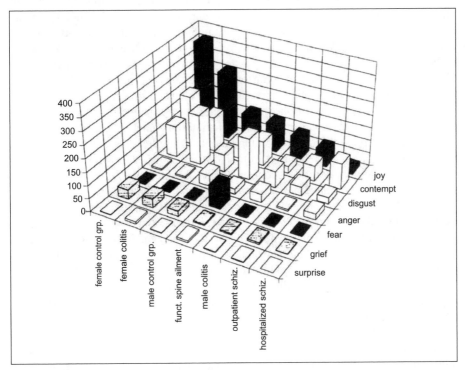

Figure 2.15:
Varying frequencies of the affect expressed by various clinical groups and by control groups not having a disorder. The height of the columns corresponds to the frequency with which the respective affect appeared in the facial expression during a 20 minute conversation on politics.
Figure taken from Krause (1997, p.81).

At first glance, the results again show a very clear gender difference: More emotion was expressed among women talking to women than among men talking to men. The reduced amount of affect expression in healthy men among themselves is a situation-dependent, gender-specific role behavior. The expression of joy in particular is more frequent among women. As soon as men talk to women, their facial expression becomes more animated. These findings confirm a general everyday life experience: The atmosphere in groups and when socializing is more comfortable when women are present. Perhaps things would really change in politics and business if women played a greater role in it. At least we find a solid empirical basis for such an expectation in the findings on nonverbal regulation of interpersonal relations.

It is surprising how much disgust and contempt regularly come across in the facial expression, the reason not being only that much in politics deserves disgust and contempt; this is also the case with other topics. From that we can conclude something very important about facial expression. The emotions expressed in the face are, to a large extent, not directed towards the immediate interaction partner but represent a commentary on what has just been said. Disgust and contempt in such a social situation refer to different manners of distancing oneself from what has just been discussed. If the negative emotion is directed at the conversation partner himself, thus representing an evaluation of the current relationship situation with regard to important interactional goals being violated at that moment, then the interaction partner is normally looked at. The largest portion of the emotions expressed in conversations however, is dedicated to whatever is talked about at the moment. This expression is determined by impression management (Schlenker, 1980). It is a part of a self-representation toward the other person relative to the discussed topic. This function of the facial expression plays a crucial role in people's emotional coordination of interactions with one another. The interaction partner can accept the other's self-representation nonverbally by displaying facially empathetic emotions (see above). Yet he may also present himself as being untouched by the other's facial expression behavior, or he may distance himself from that with his own expression. The extent to which this unconscious nonverbal coordination is accomplished between two or more persons we also refer to in common language as "personal chemistry."

In patients with minor disorders, such as the functional spine ailment, the emotional expression in and of itself is not reduced. It differs from that in healthy persons by there being a frequent, simultaneous existence of positive and negative affects, such as contempt/joy or contempt/rage that may very well be conflictual. These patients are the only group also expressing fear in this situation.

Schizophrenic men, and most distinctly the hospitalized schizophrenics among them, express much less affect, positive affects in particular, than do healthy men (Krause, Steimer, Sänger-Alt & Wagner, 1989; Steimer-Krause, Krause & Wagner, 1990; Steimer-Krause, 1994). The same applies to patients with a severe psychosomatic disorder such as colitis ulcerosa (Frisch, Schwab & Krause, 1995). Their joyless expression is certainly an understandable articulation of a life without much joy, but it also leads to that their life remains joyless as the patients infect their healthy interaction partners with their emotional expression (Figure 2.16).

This takes us from a separated consideration of the therapist's and the patient's sides to looking at the interaction between two partners, and thereby to the therapist-patient interaction.

Nonverbal Therapist-Patient Interaction

In analog form, similarly to Figure 2.15, Figure 2.16 shows the emotional expression of the healthy conversation partners as they interact with a patient from the different disorder groups. In a time span as short as twenty minutes, the interaction partners just about completely adapt to the communication style of a severely disturbed patient.

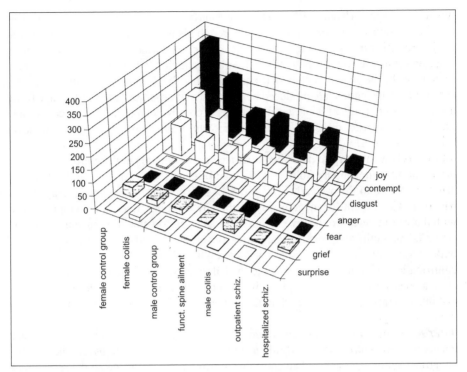

Figure 2.16:
Varying frequencies of the affect expressed by healthy persons while interacting with patients having different disorders. The height of the columns corresponds to the frequency with which the respective affect appeared in the facial expression of a healthy person during a discussion with a conversation partner suffering from a clinical disorder.
Figure taken from Krause (1997, p. 82).

A person interacting with a schizophrenic will himself behave like a schizophrenic in terms of facial expression after only a short time. So there is actually a nonverbal coordination taking place. This, however, does not result in the patient adapting to the healthy person, but the reverse.

Accordingly, the contention could be made that more severe mental disorders are accompanied by a loss of the ability to flexibly adapt the nonverbal behavior to varying interactional situations. To phrase it in your terms, one might say that the patient's nonverbal behavior is like an attractor drawing the nonverbal behavior of the interaction partner into a certain interaction pattern. Similar to how you spoke earlier about emotional and motivational attractors, one might perhaps speak of an "interpersonal attractor." Someone who has deliberately tried to maintain his otherwise animated interaction behavior while interacting with a schizophrenic knows just what power such an attractor may exert.

According to the findings by Krause and associates, patients with severe disorders often display an especially distinguished affect in their facial expressions denoted by its frequency. Krause refers to this affect as the "leading affect." "For schizophrenics this 'leading affect' is definitely contempt, for colitis patients–at least for the male ones–it seems to be disgust" (Krause, 1997). The patient may either infect his interaction partners– even his therapist–with his leading affect through his nonverbal behavior, or trigger a reciprocal affect in response to that. So the interaction partner is placed into a certain emotional mindset by the patient's nonverbal behavior, due to which he responds reciprocally to the patient's behavior (Scheflen, 1974). Stable interaction patterns largely controlled by the patient are produced by this, which the therapist can only escape from through conscious effort. Unless a person has expressly been trained to perceive such interaction processes, these processes go on mostly without either partners' awareness.

Therapist: What you just described reminded me very much of the conception of the therapeutic relationship by Sullivan (1953) and Beier (1966). As early as 1966, Beier already referred to the nonverbal regulation of the relationship between therapist and patient as "The silent language of psychotherapy" and described the therapist's task with the, at the time, provocative sub-title: "Social reinforcement of unconscious processes". The entire empirical research on nonverbal communication reported on by both of you, appears to have been conducted not until after that, but is essentially a confirmation of what Sullivan and Beier had already formulated earlier based on their clinical experiences. This example shows that clinical experience can lead to valuable insights even if empirical research in the respective field has not yet begun.

Therapy researcher: I agree with you completely. Sullivan, with his interpersonal conception of mental disorders (Sullivan, 1953) and his view of the psychotherapeutic situation (Sullivan, 1954) had an enormously stimulating influence on the research in the field (Grawe-Gerber, 1992). The classification systems for interpersonal behavior developed on an empirical basis in the meantime, the so-called "interpersonal circle models" (Kiesler, 1983; Benjamin, 1993) date directly, via Leary (1957), back to Sullivan.

Strongly influenced by Sullivan, the psychiatrist Ruesch, together with Bateson (Ruesch & Bateson, 1951) developed a theory of interpersonal communication that eventually led to the renowned work on the double-bind theory of schizophrenia (Bateson, Jackson, Haley and Weakland, 1956). Later, Bateson, together with Jackson, Haley and Weakland, began to examine the communication of schizophrenic patients in conjunction with the communication in their families (Jackson, 1968). The view of human communication developed from that, as depicted by Watzlawick, Beavin and Jackson (1969), is surprisingly congruent with the one empirically established only later on the differences between verbal and nonverbal communication. You have pointed to that previously. The communication therapy and system therapy approaches, such as those by Haley (1963, 1976), Minuchin (1967, 1974) or Selvini-Palazzoli, Boscolo, Cecchin and Prata (1977), can all be traced back to these roots.

The entire interpersonal view of psychotherapy as it is put together in the handbook by Anchin and Kiesler (1982), is permeated with Sullivan's spirit. Nonverbal communication research, the findings of which we discussed here, in my view, leads to therapeutic conclusions largely congruent with those views already developed by Sullivan, which were, of course, expressed in a slightly different language.

Therapist: That is what I meant earlier. Sullivan and his student Beier talk about a therapist having to behave "antisocially" in therapies with patients with interpersonal disorders. Behaving in a way as suggested by the patient's nonverbal behavior is exactly what the therapist should not do. Sullivan maintains that the patient's nonverbal behavior is controlled by his important goals, that includes his avoidance goals as well. For the patient, nonverbal behavior is a means particularly well suited for keeping the therapist away from his wounds. The research results you just reported on confirm that the patient exerts a strong controlling influence on his interaction partners with his nonverbal behavior. So therapists have to really behave "antisocially." They must absolutely not allow themselves to be infected if they wish to lead the patient out of such an interaction pattern.

Yet Sullivan looked at nonverbal behavior only with regard to its motivational significance. The findings you reported on indicate that nonverbal behavior should also be viewed under the ability aspect. A patient communicating so emotionlessly must perhaps relearn how to communicate emotionally in a more animated fashion. Maybe that would require his becoming emotionally infected by his therapist. According to the empirical findings, female therapists are, on average, more qualified for that than male therapists. So perhaps patients communicating very emotionlessly should be brought into contact with a female therapist who is especially lively in her emotional communication, and who consciously tries to not become infected by the poor emotional expression of the patient, but to infect the patient with her emotionality. If we imagine specific neural activation patterns, mainly located in the right hemisphere and associated relatively closely with emotional activation tendencies as the basis of nonverbal behavior, a positive effect on the patient's interpersonal behavior and on his emotional state could possibly be exerted just by such a targeted nonverbal influence without this behavior having ever been a topic of explicit discussion. On the other hand, I have never heard about such a thing having been tried anywhere systematically.

Yet this alone would not sufficiently allow for the fact that the patient's nonverbal behavior is determined by goals. With his own interpersonal behavior, a therapist might purposefully deny or interfere with the relationship patterns initiated by the patient with his nonverbal behavior. According to Lazarus (1991), one would then have to expect negative emotions to evolve in the patient because he is hindered in the achievement of his interpersonal goals and these also include his avoidance goals. The therapist would have to simultaneously influence the patient's evaluation processes in order to prevent emotions that might result in the patient dropping out of therapy or closing himself off from the therapist. We already talked about that earlier, how important it is that a therapist combines problem actuating interventions with active resource activation. The same applies for such nonverbal interventions. The therapist could, for instance, while nonverbally behaving in a specifically non-reciprocal fashion, verbally emphasize, and thereby confirm, the patient's strengths and individual goals.

It seems to me that on the level of nonverbal interaction there is a rich diagnostic and therapeutic field open to a therapist who has learned to perceive nonverbally, and who has the skills of good nonverbal encoding abilities. In our first dialogue we talked about the concept of tests by Sampson and Weiss (1986) whereby a patient tests a therapist during therapy with respect to confirming his or her most central fears by virtually inviting the therapist to behave towards him or her in line with these fears. It appears plausible that the patient uses mainly his nonverbal behavior for this. It would, therefore, be important for the therapist to carefully reflect and emotionally code his or her response, especially on the nonverbal level. The therapist should respond exactly **not** in line with his first action tendencies, as those are exactly the ones suggested by the patient according to his fears, but instead should use these action tendencies diagnostically in order to respond in a well considered fashion. This requires that he opens himself up to such influences by the patient and pays attention to it.

This I can imagine only when the therapist has previously developed a concept about what the patient's main fears might be and with what kinds of tests he or she might be confronted with as their therapist. Caught off guard, without mental preparation, one might be barely capable of conceptualizing sufficiently well considered response messages. Therefore, I imagine such therapeutic work taking place only on the basis of a, at a minimum, rudimentary case conception. Even if I do appreciate disorder-specific procedures—we have accumulated sufficient reasons for that in the meantime—I have always maintained a certain skepticism towards disorder-specific manuals according to which one should be able to perform a therapy without a case conception. The processes on the level of nonverbal interaction we just discussed could not possibly also be conceptualized in a disorder-specific manual and, as a result, would then not become the focus of therapeutic attention. The consideration of these processes does however demand explicit, conscious attention, especially because these processes are normally going on unconsciously, even on the part of the therapist.

Therapy researcher: In the meantime, findings from Krause's research group have appeared which can be viewed as an empirical confirmation of such a conception. In a pioneering research project, Krause and his associates, using the EMFACS, analyzed 12 fully-videotaped, 15-hour-long therapies of different orientation (psychoanalytic, client-centered, cognitive-behavioral) with different therapeutic outcomes with respect to the nonverbal regulation of therapist-patient interaction. First results of these analyses were reported in Krause (1997). Krause and his associates first determined the leading affect, i.e. the most frequently displayed affect by the therapist and the patient in the first therapy session with the EMFACS. Then they placed the leading affect of patient and therapist in relation to one another and established three groups based on that:
1. Both display a positive leading affect.
2. Both display a negative leading affect, however, it need not necessarily be the same affect.
3. One has a positive, the other a negative leading affect.

Regardless of the therapeutic orientation, the best therapeutic outcomes occurred in the therapist-patient relationship patterns in group three, and the worst in group one. If a therapist allows himself to be seduced by his patient into the nonverbal exchange of positive emotions throughout the entire first therapy session, then that is most likely an indication that the patient's experiential activation of problems has been avoided, because that should be accompanied by negative emotions.

Krause reports on a detailed case example of a female patient diagnosed with "panic disorder with agoraphobia" who had previously undergone an unsuccessful behavior therapy, and whose following clarification-oriented treatment, examined in the project, was completed unsatisfactorily as well.

Figures 2.17 and 2.18 illustrate the facially expressed affects of this patient and the therapist over the entire course of therapy.

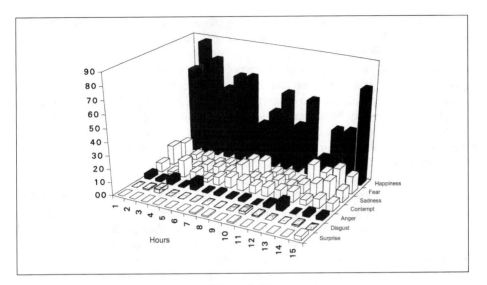

Figure 2.17:
Expressed affect of the patient diagnosed with panic disorder with agoraphobia over the
course of a 15-hour clarification-oriented therapy.
Figure taken from Krause (1997, p. 91).

Throughout the entire therapy the expression of joy largely dominates, a little more
so for the patient than for the therapist. In the follow-up processing of the sessions,
although the therapist described the patient's behavior as a "smiling mask," and decided

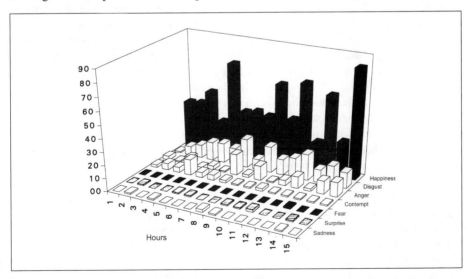

Figure 2.18:
Expressed affect of the therapist over the course of a 15-hour clarification-oriented therapy
with a patient diagnosed with a panic disorder with agoraphobia.
Figure taken from Krause (1997, p. 91).

that her greatest problem was her lack of aggressions, he did not succeed in either escaping the affects induced by her or relating to her non-reciprocally by behaving "antisocially."

Evidently, the patient's problems were not limited solely to the DSM diagnosis of panic disorder with agoraphobia. Her regulation of emotions and relationships not included in the diagnosis must be conceived of as an important problem on its own and should have obviously been approached therapeutically. This would have required a problem actuation by inducing and provoking negative emotions. Yet, under the powerful influence of the patient's nonverbal expressive behavior, the therapist was unable to follow through with that.

This therapy can be viewed as an example of a missed or failed problem actuation. We can also see by this example that actuating the problems identified with a DSM diagnosis is not always sufficient, as this type of problem actuation had probably already been tried with the patient in the preceding behavior therapy. Based on additional information coming later, Krause interpreted this patient's nonverbal behavior as a manifestation of a strong attachment desire not allowing her any detachment and autonomy. According to that, the unconsciously experienced incompatibility of security and autonomy should have been made the focus in this therapy, and that would have meant actuating the fear of loss of security itself in therapy through "antisocial" responses to the patient's excessively joyful behavior on the part of the therapist. We are able to integrate this "researched-informed case study" nicely into what we discussed in our first conversation on the potential significance of conflicts and the treatment of patients suffering from agoraphobia (section 1.25). Krause's case example supports the view that unconscious conflicts may play a crucial role in agoraphobias as well.

This example also allows us to see that even where a clarification-oriented therapy is indicated, it may fail, because it does not succeed in overwriting the problem-relevant schemata stored in the implicit memory with corrective experiences, even in those cases where the respective schemata were activated in the therapeutic relationship. Obviously, in this patient, her exaggerated joyful behavior had an avoidance function. Through his nonverbal behavior, the therapist would have had to induce, over and over again, perceptions incongruent with this avoidance schema. Only by doing so, could a real problem actuation have been reached with regard to the presumed unconscious conflict. The therapist then would have had to direct his patient's attention to her emerging negative emotions in order to work together with her on an awareness for the determinants of her negative emotions, and thereby also on an awareness for the determinants of her previous avoidance behavior.

The change of intentions that would have been necessary was obviously never achieved in this patient. This case can be seen as an example that problematic motivational constellations can have a sustaining function for mental disorders. Without effective change of this motivational constellation, the symptomatology can be maintained even if the therapist otherwise uses well established interventions to work on the disorder-specific conditions sustaining the symptoms.

I believe that an identification of such sustaining conditions can only be achieved within the scope of a case conception that accounts for the entire range of individual characteristics of the patient. Such case conceptions must also systematically consider processes exerting their influence on the symptom in the implicit mode of functioning.

This case is, at the same time, an example for the powerful influence of the processes going on in the implicit mode.

The fact that the therapies of group three achieved the best outcome indicates that non- reciprocal therapist behavior may efficiently assist a patient in escaping his well established emotional response patterns (see also Kiesler, 1982 a, b). Across the entire twelve therapies examined, Krause found a correlation of .69 between the relationship pattern in the first therapy session and the therapeutic outcome, as defined by the success ratings by the therapist and the patient and other outcome measures. This is an almost unbelievably high correlation given that it was applied across various types of therapies. Additionally, it refers to a connection of the therapeutic outcome with an aspect of the therapy process which has almost never been considered thus far in therapy research, and which the actors themselves are largely unaware of.

Correlations of such unusual magnitude usually cannot be confirmed in independent replications. This remains to be seen. If, however, other studies could confirm that predictions of therapeutic outcomes of similar magnitude are possible, based on what is nonverbally happening in the first therapy sessions, then this would necessarily lead to far reaching consequences. It would mean that the nonverbal interactions in psychotherapies are of greater significance than the technical interventions, because correlations approaching these in value have never been found for the latter. As a result, training for perception and control of these processes should be rated much higher than has been the case so far in most therapy training programs.

That the interactions in the first therapy session are already so highly correlated with the later therapeutic outcome points to the fact that an interaction pattern may establish itself already at the beginning of therapy which has great significance for the later course of therapy. This means that the first therapy session should be prepared with utmost care. It would be ideal if the therapist were to already have as much information as possible beforehand on the patient's relationship behavior. Principally, this might be achieved by videotapes of diagnostic intake examinations. This would allow the therapist to prepare himself mentally for possible unfavorable relationship patterns into which he could be drawn, and come up with a well reflected relationship strategy for such a situation.

The responsibility for establishing a favorable therapeutic relationship with respect to all of this lies with the therapist, and he or she must realize it in the patient's interest, even if it means making the patient feel uncomfortable for a time. Initially the patient is completely unaware of these processes, therefore he or she has no responsibility whatsoever for this particular aspect of the relationship. On the other hand, not all of the success-relevant aspects of the therapy can be made transparent to the patient in the beginning. The therapist has no other choice than to take responsibility in a situation where the patient himself is still unable to do so.

Therapist: I think both of your reports on the findings about nonverbal communication lead to encouragingly concrete therapeutic conclusions. Although some of that might perhaps not stand on stable footing, nevertheless it seems to me that we have received quite a range of suggestions and ideas for therapeutic training and practice that actually already deserve to be implemented without one having to still wait for further results.

If I now look back over the course of our second conversation, I must say we have put a great deal behind us. We have combed over major areas of general psychology: perception, memory, learning, emotions, and from there have even touched on one of the most important areas of social psychology. In the meantime I have taken great pleasure in viewing the phenomena and problems of psychotherapy from this, at least for me, entirely unaccustomed perspective. However, what I still feel to be missing is one of the great areas of general psychology which should, in fact, be especially relevant for psychotherapy, namely motivation. While we touched on motivational aspects here and there, most clearly in conjunction with emotions, we have never made them a main topic.

According to Powers' model, the goals of control hierarchies play a powerful role in mental functioning. Earlier you had approximated it in this way: "All mental processes are directed towards producing perceptions congruent with certain goals, and that is to say always several goals simultaneously. So an individual's experience and behavior is essentially controlled by several intentions at all times." You mentioned this before we dedicated our thoughts so thoroughly to perceptions, memory and learning, the emotions and nonverbal interactional behavior. We know much more about mental processes now. We know that there are always many processes running parallel to each other or with one another and that only one or a few of those are conscious, the others, however, are unconscious to varying degrees. But we have not yet dealt with the goals by which these processes are controlled. The entire question of motivational determination of mental functioning seems to remain murky.

Should we maybe turn to this question now? For me at least this is the greatest open question that I still have.

Therapy researcher: I agree this topic should be the next one. You actually had some time to rest. I am sure, judging by your previous comments, that you have some ideas on how one might conceive the motivational determination of mental functioning. Could you maybe now present your ideas to us?

Psychologist: I actually wanted to still say something about the functions of cognitions in mental processes in order to not leave out any of the important aspects, but maybe I will find another occasion later in another context. Apart from that, I also believe that the question of motivational determination is one of high priority and merits our full concentration.

Part 3: Determinants of Experience and Behavior

2.27 Who Controls Our Mental Life?

To address the question of which motives drive mental processes I would like to return to the first part of this conversation where I introduced you to Powers' control theory. Powers termed the seventh regulation level of the control hierarchies the "program level." This is the level where our intentions are implemented into reality. Staying with the terminology we used in the first dialogue, one could also call this level the "realization level." It is the level of intention realization.

Our wishes need not adhere to the conditions of reality. Similar to our thoughts, they may transcend the restrictions of time and space, the possible and the impossible. Thoughts and wishes are free. Unfortunately, this is also true of fears. They also need not halt at the conditions of reality, but oftentimes exceed what may realistically, or is likely to occur.

For wishes to be realized they have to pass through the bottleneck of reality. For optimal realization they have to be transferred into a mode of psychological functioning which is tightly in tune with the actual real life conditions. Freud termed this functional mode the "secondary process," differentiating it from the primary-process-related mental functioning, which does not stick to the restrictions of the possible, such as our dream life, for instance. Secondary processes are connected to the waking consciousness.

In their conscious realization, wishes become concrete goals and intentions, and from intentions, they turn into plans and actions. We experience goal setting, planning, decision making and action as something that we ourselves control. But who is this "our selves?" Who am I? Can we also control our own wishes and fears ourselves?

We all experience this differently. Wishes and fears emerge spontaneously. At times, we can push or chase them away, but we do not experience them as generated by us in the form of a consciously set goal. Even our emotions are usually not experienced by us as something we ourselves generated. We experience them as a part of us, but not, or at least only partially, as a subject of our conscious control. The same applies for our perceptions and memories. They are also experienced by us as something controlled by whatever is perceived and recalled, and not as something that we essentially created ourselves. We are able to consciously direct our attention towards something, and in doing so feel that we influence what we perceive. Yet whatever we perceive within the focus of this attention, we perceive as something set, as something that is not controlled by us, but by the "actual" situations. What we experience is for us "the" reality.

Yet, we know from what we discussed before that at least our perceptions, memories and emotions are, to a large extent, controlled by ourselves and not just by the external situations, such as the emotions for example, which are controlled by our goals and appraisals. "The" reality is thus "in reality" one largely created by ourselves in line with our neural activation tendencies. Included in those are predominantly also motivational tendencies. Our experience, our subjective reality, is a goal-controlled interpretation of the "objective" reality independent from us. The experience or feeling of our self is blind to this self-contributed portion.

Another important constituent of our feeling of self is the consciousness that I am the originator of my actions and cognitions. As I now sit before you, I know that I could raise the index finger of my right hand if I chose to. I also know that I could willingly direct my attention to this or that, that I could bring to mind my workroom at home, or where I had my last vacation, or that I could even think about the Pythagorean theorem.

If I imagine raising my index finger right now, an EEG electrode appropriately placed in the area of the cortex responsible for this movement would actually demonstrate on an electroencephalograph the appearance of a so-called "activation potential" (Kornhuber & Deecke, 1965) several hundred milliseconds prior to beginning the movement. The same happens if I only imagine this movement, but do not actually follow through with it. What triggers this activation potential preceding the movement? As the originator of my actions, I naturally presume that it was triggered by my decision. This presumption is, however, mistaken. In reality, the temporal sequence is exactly the reverse.

"Approximately ten years ago, making use of the existence of activation potentials, Benjamin Libet performed sensational experiments investigating the relationship between the activation potential and the planning of voluntary actions ('volitional acts') (Libet et.al., 1983). In these experiments, test persons were trained to **spontaneously** make a decision—in a set time frame (1-3 seconds)—to bend one finger of the right hand, or the entire right hand. While doing so, they were watching a kind of oscilloscope clock whereby one rotation of a point moving around the dial equaled a period of 2.56 seconds. The area of rotation was divided into distances of 107 milliseconds. At precisely the point at which the test persons made the decision to move, they had to memorize the position of the point in the rotation on the face of the 'clock.' In another series, memorizing whether they had made the decision prior to, or following the stopping of the rotating point, which is considerably easier for the test persons, was sufficient. For all test subjects, the activation potential was measured, i.e. filtered from the EEG.

It was found that the activation potential usually preceded the 'volitional decision' by 550 ms (with a minimum of 150 ms and a maximum of 1025 ms). In none of the cases did the activation potential occur precisely at the same moment in time with the 'volitional decision,' or even following it. Most experts view this as an indication that the brain has begun preparing for a movement long before the test person ever has the feeling that he **wants** to move finger or hand. So accordingly, the volitional decision cannot be the trigger for the volitional act even if we subjectively have that impression" (Roth, 1995, p. 264/5).

Movements such as the raising of an index finger can also be triggered with the aid of electrodes by stimulating the corresponding areas of the associative cortex. If the respective person is then asked why he raised his index finger, he will answer that he wished to do so. It is, therefore, possible to create the subjective experience of a volitional decision by "artificially" triggered neural activity. The subjective experience occurs a few hundred milliseconds after the electrical stimulation. Evidently this is the time span needed by our brain to create the quality of a subjective experience. Already in 1978, Libet found that from the beginning of the stimulus up to the conscious perception, approximately 300 ms pass. Our brain, however, filters out this seemingly consistent delay between physiological process and subjective experiencing, leaving us with the feeling that our experience and what is happening physiologically is simultaneous.

If movements are induced by stimulation in sub-cortical areas, the individual concerned does not feel that this is a voluntarily conceived movement. He or she may say the movement occurred by mistake or has even happened against their will, or even deny that a movement occurred at all. So the experienced quality of volition is tied to neural activation patterns in the neocortex.

What we find out by experiments about the components of our experience, such as perceptions, memories, emotions, and actions is thus very different from how we subjectively experience these processes. For perceptions and emotions which we subjectively experience as something happening to us, our experience does not reflect how much we create them for our actions. We are lead to believe that there is an authorship that does not actually exist the way we experience it.

We have to abandon the idea that what we experience as "I" represents the central controlling organ in our mental life. The experience of "I" is an experiential quality like the taste of lemonade. That taste is an emergent quality consisting of the simultaneous stimulation of sweet and sour receptors (see section 2.2). Our experience of "I" is an emergent quality of the totality of neural processes going on in us. Our "I" is not the monitor and ruler over these processes, but is their product. Neural processes with certain functional traits are experientially "marked" with the quality of awareness, others are marked with the quality of volitional acts, yet others with the quality of feelings. I explained this to you earlier using my "light tree" metaphor (see section 2.20).

So underlying our wishes and fears are neural processes with distinct functional characteristics. If, in addition, these wishes or fears are also associated with the quality of awareness, there are different neural processes with different functional characteristics activated than if the wishes or fears remain unconscious. According to this view, it is quite obvious that there may be wishes or fears that are not, or do not become conscious. In that case we should perhaps no longer refer to them as wishes and fears, but instead as approach and avoidance intentions in order to demonstrate the differences in functional characteristics of the underlying neural processes expressed in the different experiential quality. In both cases, however, we have neural activation patterns or activation tendencies with motivating, i.e. direction giving and energizing functional qualities. In similar fashion, I already differentiated feelings from emotions. I speak of emotions regardless of whether they manifest themselves in subjective experience as feelings, and I speak of feelings when an emotion is consciously experienced as a certain feeling.

Intentions are characterized at the neural level by the fact that pre-frontal and limbic centers are involved in the respective activation patterns (Roth, 1995). I already pointed out earlier that the empirical basis behind statements about complex neural processes is less well-substantiated than the basis of simple perceptual and memory processes. Nonetheless, in the meantime, neurobiologists have progressed so far that they are able to correlate not only circumscribed perceptions, but also more complex subjective experiences with very specific brain processes. For instance, Posner and Dehaene (1994) have been able to clearly establish a connection between a certain state of neural activation in the brain with the subjective experience of "attentive expectation."

So intentions, i.e., those neural processes which give a certain direction to the other neural activity, and which energize the behavior resulting from it, may be associated with the experiential quality of pure wishing, but also with that of firm will, and they may be conscious or non-conscious. When intentional activation patterns are activated, they have, by definition, an effect on mental functioning, whether conscious or unconscious. When associated with the experiential quality of awareness, it means that a neural activation pattern with different functional characteristics is activated than would be without this experiential quality. The specific possibilities connected with conscious perception and behavioral control result from the specific neural activation pattern and not from the subjective experiential quality of awareness. We experience it this way, but the special functional possibilities of conscious behavioral control and the experiential quality of awareness are both emergent qualities of the underlying activation pattern, similar to the way that the taste of lemonade is an emergent quality of the joint activation of sweet and sour receptors.

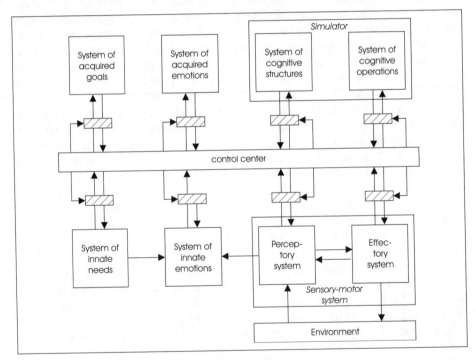

Figure 2.19:

Structural model of the psychological regulation system according to Becker (1995, p.83). Between the control center, to which a central control function and the consciousness function is ascribed, and the various subsystems, there is an "information regulator"(small, cross-hatched rectangles) which—like the aperture in a camera—controls the information flow from the subsystems to the control centers, and thereby their influence on the entire system.

The control center is able to vary this influence. In this model it, therefore, represents the "superordinated system."

If we conceive of mental life as being a product of the interplay of 100 billion nerve cells connected in the most manifold ways, able to stimulate or inhibit one another reciprocally, then there is neither the space nor the necessity for any homunculi exercising certain functions in mental processes, such as decision making, goal pursuit, etc. Freud's ideas of psychological entities such as the Ego, Superego and the Id that, in a way, each pursue their own goals, does not agree with the view I presented to you. Homunculi like this are also not necessary to conceptualize such phenomena as repression, defense mechanisms, conflicts etc. I will go into that later.

Even in recent psychology, such homunculi continue to be conceptualized. The computer, the most favored metaphor of cognitive psychology models, literally invites this. This tendency can be found even in models that are otherwise close to my ideas, and that have adopted a lot of knowledge from psychology.

One of these models which I find especially well elaborated comes from Becker (1995). Becker and I assume a rather similar systems view. He too connects Powers' control theory and Epstein's theory of self (see below). His model is both a functional and a structural model. Following Ford (1987), he distinguishes seven functions of the psychological regulation system: a command function, comparative functions, a control function, an action function, an information gathering function, an energizing function, and a central coordination function (consciousness, attention, and volition). In addition, he designs a structural model with a controlling center at its core. Figure 2.19 describes this structural model.

Table 2.2 lays out which functions are attributed to the various subsystems of the structural model.

The function of the control center is described by Becker as follows: "As the name says, the 'center' is the preeminent switchboard of the whole system and responsible for the coordinated running of the mental processes as far as they are subject to aware-

Table 2.2

Functions of the different subsystems represented in the structural model illustrated in Figure 2.19 according to Becker (1995, p.84).

Subsystem in Figure 2.19	Functions
System of innate needs	Command function
System of acquired goals	Command function
System of innate emotions	Comparative function
	Energetic regulation function
System of acquired emotions	Comparative function
	Energetic regulation function
Perceptory system	Information function (with reference to the outside world)
	Command function
System of cognitive structures	Information function (with reference to the outside world)
	Command function
Effectory system	Control function
	Action function (with respect to motor skills)
System of cognitive operations	Control function
	Action function (with respect to cognitive contents)
Central control	Central coordination, consciousness, attention

ness, ... In the language of system and regulation theory, it represents the **'superordinated system'**" (Becker, 1995, p. 86).

Becker's model is a well elaborated, scientific version of a very common assumption, which is that our consciousness is the central control over our mental functioning. It directs our attention and makes the decisions. It is the actual master of mental functioning corresponding with our experience. One might justifiably refer to Becker's control center as the individual's "I."

As I just explained, the concept of mental functioning I presented to you arrives at a different view of consciousness and of what we experience as the "I." According to this concept, there is no central control in mental functioning. All psychological phenomena are a result of the interplay of neural processes possessing certain functional characteristics. Our experience of a supervising and controlling "I" is an experiential quality generated by all these processes together; however, this experience reflects the actual control conditions in mental functioning in a distorted fashion, similar to the way our perceptual experience distorts the actual functional characteristics of the perceptual process.

Just as much as "the" I or Ego or "the" consciousness does not exist as a central control entity, according to this concept, "the" unconscious also does not exist. I should have made it sufficiently clear that in my conception unconscious processes are ascribed a very important role; however, there is no psychological entity of "the" unconscious that could be distinguished from another entity as "the" consciousness. There are no entities at all, but only functional characteristics with particular neural foundations. The neural processes underlying these functions are distributed throughout the entire brain. If certain brain areas are destroyed, certain functions are lost because these nerve cells were a necessary component of the neural activation patterns with these functional characteristics; one cannot state, however, that these brain areas are "the site" of these functions. In many cases these functions can be taken over after a while by other brain areas.

Through a comparison with Becker's model, I can explain some of the special characteristics of my own view of mental functioning.

An essential difference is that in my conception parallel simultaneity of many processes is a principle characteristic of mental functioning. The view that at any moment many mental processes are running simultaneously has far-reaching consequences for the entire view of mental functioning. One is the great significance of non-conscious processes, because one of the special characteristics of consciousness is that only very little can simultaneously find its place in it. It also yields conclusions for the regulation of the simultaneity, something I will go into in more detail later. And in addition, an essentially different view results from it with respect to the position of consciousness in mental functioning. Ultimately—to get right to the point—it also leads to an entirely different view of mental disorders and this again has consequences for the conception of psychotherapy. But I am jumping too far ahead with this.

The different conclusions which Becker and I arrive at must have to do with the foundations we refer to. I have mainly focused on experimental research on the basic foundations of psychological functioning, such as perception and memory and also, where it was suggested, have considered current neurobiological research which is also based mainly on an experimental approach. Becker refers more to research findings from differential and personality psychology. He hardly refers at all to experimental research and research on basic psychological functions. In pointing out these differences, Becker's conception might be seen more as an attempt at categorization, mine more as an attempt at explanation. My opinion is that the views could supplement each other, but the conceptions are incompatible with respect to the point I just brought up. My ideas on the determination of mental functioning differ from Becker's.

Therapist: I find it more difficult to grasp your view of what constitutes the experience of "I" than to comprehend Becker's idea of a control center. But you yourself already mentioned that the idea of consciousness as a control center is the more common one. It seems reasonable to me that it need not necessarily be preferred over yours. If, according to your conception, the conscious "I" is not the main determinant of psychological functioning, what is it then that determines what a person experiences and does?

Psychologist: Of course I had expected this question, and in responding to it I will proceed in several steps. The first will sound quite familiar to you in light of what I mentioned earlier. The following steps will, however, take us beyond the framework we have created thus far.

2.28   Motivational Tendencies and Schemata

In connection with conditioning, I previously introduced an experiment done by DeCasper and Fifer (1980) in which they showed that newborns already exhibit a demonstrable preference for the voice of their mother. An infant will do everything he or she can to hear the voice of his or her own mother rather than that of a strange woman if the opportunity arises (section 2.16). This demonstrates how, from the very beginning, our behavior is determined by intentions. A newborn is obviously already capable of recognizing his or her mother's voice and has a preference for it. Otherwise, the research findings by DeCasper and Fifer would be unexplainable. The newborn must already possess a perceptual tendency for his or her mother's voice, which functions, in the language of control theory, as a standard for comparison with the actually heard voice. So, even at the age of three days, a rudimentary perceptual schema exists that is neurally represented by an already ingrained activation tendency.

There exists by that time even more than just this perceptual tendency. The newborn has also already learned which behavior he or she can use to produce this perception. So a rudimentary action schema also already exists. Apart from that, the newborn becomes active on his or her own so as to produce, through his own behavior, an obviously intended perception. At the moment the infant attempts to suck with a certain speed, his/her psychological activity is determined by a certain intention, namely that of hearing his or her mother's voice. This is already a fully completed circuit in the sense of control theory. The behavior is directed towards generating perceptions that are congruent with a certain goal.

This example presents us, in a way, with the nucleus of a "**motivational schema**" that plays a great role in every person's life. We are created in such a way by nature that we bring a need for attachment to one or a few trusted persons with us into the world (see in more detail section 2.39). If this were already studied, or could possibly be investigated, a newborn would most likely attempt to produce not only his mother's voice but also other perceptions that he or she is able to make with his senses at that time, such as the mother's smell. Later, the mother's smiling face would also belong to the preferred perceptions.

We might perhaps refer to the superordinated goal of such a developing motivational schema as "being in contact with mother." "Mother," of course, need not necessarily stand for the biological mother, nor must it be female. For many years "being in contact with mother" will remain an important source of motivation for the child. When the child has perceptions in agreement with this superior goal, he feels satisfied, safe and secure and is joyful. At the age of five a child still normally demonstrates strong fear if his mother is suddenly missed. If missing becomes a constant condition, fear becomes desperation, depression and eventually apathy (Spitz, 1946). "Being in contact with mother" is thus a transactional state in the sense of Lazarus' theory on emotions which is very strongly intended by small children.

In the course of development, this motivational schema common to all people now becomes individually differentiated. The relational rules of the respective special mother-child dyad are assimilated to this schema. Most of those processes are initially occurring nonverbally and become part of the implicit and emotional memory. These early childhood experiences stored in the memory can, therefore, not be recalled via codes only to be developed later such as the verbal code, as is generally true for the contents of the implicit memory. They can, however, be activated bottom-up and thereby play a crucial role in how a person shapes his later relationships. For this, on the other hand, we have no consciousness. Whether or not we are spontaneously attracted to a person is most likely very strongly determined by an unconscious, bottom-up activation of such motivational-interpersonal schemata that originated very early in life.

While the motivational schemata is differentiating itself more and more, all of its components continue to develop, that means not only the perceptions and actions assimilated to this schema, but also the goals. So over time there can be many possibilities for how to realize the goal component of a motivational schema. Along with the differentiation of the goals, there is also a differentiation of the emotions that continuously accompany the activity of a motivational schema. Perceptual tendencies, action tendencies, emotional response tendencies and motivational tendencies are also included in a motivational schema. The latter, the intentions, are the ones connecting all these parts to a functional unit. The neural activation patterns representing the intentions have the particular functional characteristic of being able to force their "flashing rhythm" upon other activation patterns (section 2.20). That distinguishes their determining function in mental activity.

A motivational schema corresponds to Power's control hierarchy. The schema is hierarchically ordered in an increasingly differentiated fashion through the assimilation of more and more experiences. There are more and more subordinate goals for the superordinate goal of "being in contact with mother." When mother is otherwise absorbed, talking to other adults, working at her desk or taking care of other children, then perhaps screaming, romping and similar behaviors are tried out for getting back into contact with her. If mother is actually accessible at the moment, it is perhaps more advantageous to go to her with a picture book in hand and a particular expression on the face as she likes to tell stories using these books.

Perhaps while playing later on, the child catches sight of the picture book. This perception activates the neural activation pattern representing the motivational schema "being in contact with mother." Mother, however, perhaps has company at that time so "telling stories from the picture book" does not represent a realizable subordinate goal at that moment. In the meantime, the child has a whole range of possibilities to aid him in realizing the intention of "having contact with mother." In this situation perhaps, "romping" is chosen if it has proved to be successful in the past for realizing this intention.

As long as the mother's physical proximity is required by the child for realizing the intention of "being in contact with mother," then every time mother is absent for a prolonged time, if this does not follow a certain rule that has become part of the schema, it leads to an incongruence signal and to a feeling of nonfulfillment. In this situation the child might perhaps ask again and again: "When is mommy coming back?" and much to the chagrin of the supervising persons, is incapable of concentrating for a longer time on something else.

So motivational schemata initially develop around the fundamental needs brought into the world by every person. The word stem "*movere* = to move," poignantly expresses the essence of these schemata. They "move" mental activity; they impel it in the direction of certain goals. Goals are the desired relations between the individual and environment, the achievement or approximation of which is accompanied by positive emotions and their absence or impediment, by negative emotions, as discussed by us earlier in conjunction with Lazarus' theory of emotions (section 2.21). Therefore, needs do not exert influence on the psychological functioning in an abstract form but via motivational schemata whose goal components, from the outset, are defined by certain relations to the environment which were experienced in the course of life.

These relations are represented by the memory traces of neural activation patterns that have actually taken place. Motivational schemata are intentional tendencies, and these tendencies are based on memory traces ingrained over the course of life. On the other hand—briefly discussed by us earlier (section 2.16)—people are genetically pre-differentially prepared for acquiring certain neural activation patterns.

Mental activity then is directed and energized by motivational schemata, which are spontaneously active. Intentionality is perhaps the most important fundamental quality of mental functioning. As long as there is any neural activity, it is intentionally oriented. The deeper the neural connections representing the schema are ingrained, the more easily the schema can be activated bottom-up or top down, that is to say, the more likely it will determine the psychological activity also in the future.

2.29 The Significance of Motivational Schemata for Psychotherapy

Therapist: According to what you just said, motivational schemata would, in fact, have to be thought of as the crucial determinants of psychological functioning. If the strongest pre-ingrained motivational schemata most likely also determine the future experience and behavior, then it is quite obvious that we must activate and change these schemata in therapy if we hope to achieve that a patient changes his behavior and emotions on a long-term basis. We would then need to discern which of his motivational schemata lead to the problems which brought him to therapy, as these could be the most promising targets for the therapeutic intervention.

Psychologist: That sounds obvious. I do believe, however, that this is only partially correct because I did not say that motivational schemata are the only determinants of psychological activity. Earlier when discussing emotions, I already pointed out that, once triggered, an emotion may become an independent determinant of mental functioning, regardless of the schema, the activation of which lead to the emotion (section 2.21). I referred to these semi-autonomous determinants as "**emotional attractors**" (section 2.50). I mean that we can, in a similar fashion, also conceive of psychological disorders as semi-autonomous determinants of mental activity. Once they have emerged, they exert an independent influence on the mental life. In anticipation of the terminology of dynamic systems theory, which I would still like to familiarize you with, we can term these determinants "**disorder attractors**" (section 2.51). I also once earlier mentioned rather in passing that interpersonal processes may become a partially independent determinant of mental functioning because they cannot be unilaterally influenced at will as one would like. We might call these determinants "**interpersonal attractors**" (2.52).

For psychotherapy, I believe that these four types of attractors, namely:
motivational attractors,
emotional attractors,
disorder attractors and
interpersonal attractors,
are the most relevant determinants of psychological functioning. We must systematically consider all of these four types of attractors for the explanation and treatment of mental disorders. According to my theoretical ideas, therapies which only attempt to change the patient's motivational schemata will not fully exhaust the total potential of psychotherapy, if they do not outright fail, because they do not give sufficient consideration to these other determinants of psychological functioning.

With these limiting comments on the significance of motivational schemata for psychotherapy, however, I do not in any way want to narrow the significance they hold for the understanding of normal mental life. A person's life is most strongly influenced by his motivational schemata. In every moment of an individual's life the motivational schemata largely determine what the respective person does, thinks and feels. Naturally, the fortune or misfortune of an individual is also determined by events over which he has no control over. In the case of a person unlucky enough to have to lead his life in a war torn area, that person's experience and behavior is largely determined by circumstances well out of his control, regardless of his motivational schemata. Such determinants of human life lie beyond the reach of psychotherapy. With methods like posttraumatic stress disorder treatment or pain therapy, psychological measures may help in easing suffering imposed on people by such external determinants, but the main application of psychotherapy lies in helping where people, due to their motivational schemata, do not make use of actually accessible possibilities for a better life or even bring about their own misfortune.

My opinion is that motivational schemata hold a central importance for the emergence of mental disorders. Once a mental disorder has developed, the neural activation patterns representing this disorder turn into an independent determinant of psychological functioning which one has to account for with interventions specifically tailored to the special dynamics of this disorder. It no longer suffices to just exert an influence on the constellation of motivational schemata that lead to its emergence. With a disorder, a new situation has been created, an emergent phenomenon of its own quality and dynamic that must be influenced by disorder-specific interventions in order to alleviate the situation that has developed. Of course, it would not be very smart just to alleviate this situation without asking oneself how that situation arose, and without taking any precautions to be sure it will not arise again, but those are two different tasks. I think a therapist should give due recognition to both tasks in most cases (section 2.51) if he or she wants to offer optimal help to the patient, at least according to my theory.

Therapy researcher: Doesn't your view lead to a conclusion similar to that which we arrived at in our first conversation? The motivational schemata yield the motivational context of a mental disorder. Influencing that context requires intention changing interventions such as, for instance, motivational clarification. Solving the problem developed on this basis is a different task, that requires mastery-oriented interventions and those require problem- and disorder-specific know-how. Due to your theoretical considerations you arrive at the conclusion that, on the one hand, one should consider and change the motivational context of a disorder, and on the other hand, exert an influence on the disorder itself. In our first dialogue we arrived at quite a similar conclusion based on psychotherapy research and its findings, namely that psychotherapy usually requires both working on the right and on the left bank of the Rubicon.

Yet also with patients suffering so severely from a certain disorder that it has to be the initial focus of treatment, there must be something that drives them to a new behavior. A disorder-specific treatment can, therefore, also not be successful without the successful activation of existing motivational tendencies, in the service of which the changes take place. Apart from that, the disorder did not develop out of nothing, but is a product of the patient's mental activity essentially determined by his motivational schemata. Therefore, motivational schemata have, even if they are not the only determinants of psychological activity, definitely a very great significance for psychotherapy. So it is important for me that we devote ourselves more in detail to the question of how motivational schemata can be recognized, activated and therapeutically used or changed.

2.30   Therapeutic Change of Motivational Schemata

In our discussion I already pointed out that the schema construct enjoys growing popularity in psychology and psychotherapy alike, and this from authors coming from originally quite different orientations (section 2.1). Yet, not everyone using the term schema means motivational tendencies by this, as you do. Strictly speaking, in most concepts the term schema does not refer to the motivational aspect of psychological functioning. Beck (1967), for instance, refers to certain characteristics of cognitive functioning. The term schema is used in psychology and psychotherapy in such different ways that one has to take a very close look in each case at what the individual author understands by a schema.

Läderach and Verdun (1995) offer an overview on the many different ways the term schema has been used in psychology and psychotherapy. There are those, for instance, who understand a self-schema or a body-schema as an image that the respective person has of himself or his body. Others conceive of a schema just as you do; not as a content, but as a regulating process. I think one should only use the term schema in the latter sense. If one means the content, then perhaps it is better to speak of image. There is no doubt that by schema you understand a process, because your concept of schema strongly overlaps with that of control hierarchies in the sense of Powers. According to that, Gallagher (1986), for instance, makes the distinction between body schema and body image.

In psychotherapy, I have so far never encountered the term motivational schema. There are, however, two schema-theoretical conceptions which come at least close to your understanding of a motivational schema, even if they use other terms for that. I think we should take a closer look at these two conceptions.

In our first conversation I already made detailed reference to the therapy concept by Greenberg, Rice and Elliott (1993) as an example of motivational clarification work. Yet at that time I had not touched on the theoretical basis for their therapeutic procedure and I would now like to do this because what Greenberg et al. write on schemata and their changes sounds partly as if they, in fact, had been present in our conversation. I will read excerpts to you because it best emphasizes both the similarities and also the differences of their ideas and conclusions compared to yours. I will comment in between the quoted material on those parts of the text which appear to me especially noteworthy with respect to your thoughts. I would like to begin by mentioning that Greenberg et al. speak of emotional schemata and not of motivational schemata, although in their description of such schemata the reference to goals plays an indispensable role. So here is the text on their understanding of an emotional schema:

"We will use the term emotional scheme rather than emotional schema (Note: Piaget already made this distinction as he wanted to distinguish action schemata from other schemata). This emphasizes the goal-directed, action-oriented embodied nature of our view of emotion. The best representation of this view is Pascual-Leone & Johnson's (1991) neo-Piagetian notion of schemes. They define them as **goal-directed, functional units**, ultimately addressed to the environment **to negotiate the meeting of some need**. According to them, schemes possess both a releasing component and an effecting component, providing a set of conditions for cueing the scheme to apply and the set of desired performance effects of the scheme, respectively. In this view, schemes are activated by appropriate cues, and this leads to their application.

As well as guiding what is perceived and done, adaptive schemes are also open to accommodation or change. **They both direct experience and are changed by it** as they **actively interact** with incoming information. At output, schemes interact with new incoming information to allow a variety of appropriate responses to a variety of new situations. The person acts flexibly but according to a plan. Thus, **schemes are nonconscious mental structures** or modules that interact with incoming information to determine both what is perceived and experienced and to provide the framework for our responses to the world. **They are our core means of organizing both our experiences and our responses, and they change by accommodating to new experience.**"

Up to this point I am unable to distinguish Greenberg et al.'s description of an emotional schema from what you understand by motivational schema. The following paragraph shows that while an emotional schema, in their sense, has the same components as a motivational schema in your sense, the component placed in the foreground as a schematized sum of previous experiences is, rather, the resultant emotion and not the goal component as in a motivational schema.

"Schemes that affect people's psychological well-being (and therefore are the focus of therapy) are those that represent self-in-the-world emotional experience. It is these self-in-the-world integrative **cognitive/affective/motivational/relational action structures** that we henceforth refer to as emotion schemes. **They are the targets of our therapeutic work**."

Without saying this explicitly at this point, Greenberg et al. are moving exactly within the realm of Lazarus' cognitive-emotional-motivational-relational theory of emotion that you referred to earlier when discussing emotions in so much detail (section 2.21). All the thoughts developed there can be easily connected with the therapeutic concept by Greenberg et al. It is not by accident that Greenberg et al. only peripherally make reference to Lazarus' theory of emotion despite the almost literal overlap in the characterization of the approach. Lazarus strongly emphasizes the secondary appraisal in the development of emotions, above all the coping component. That would suggest mastery-oriented procedures as a therapeutic consequence, yet those play almost no role in the therapy concept and the concrete therapeutic procedures by Greenberg et al. In this respect, the authors remain quite true to their humanistic origins. The theoretical foundation they refer to, however, actually does not at all suggest neglecting the mastery aspect. Instead, both clarification-oriented and mastery-oriented procedures would result as therapeutic consequences from that theoretical foundation. Greenberg et al. only present the clarification-oriented implications.

"In our view what is crucial about emotion schemes is that although they involve cognition, they go beyond purely representational cognition to include emotion, motivation, and relational action as well. They are not simply conceptual and classificatory in nature, but rather, they are embodied organizations of sets of anticipations and reactions. Thus a client enters therapy with a nonconscious emotion scheme that, when activated, generates a feeling of, say inadequacy. The client may not be aware that a situation has activated the inadequacy producing scheme and may say 'I just feel bad' or 'I don't know why I reacted in that way.' Or a client may anticipatorily feel inadequate in imagining situations that do not necessarily call for such a response. The inadequacy emotion scheme is either activated out of awareness or is overly accessible and anticipatorily guides behavior. It is schemes like this **that need to be accessed** and restructured in therapy. Self-in-the-world emotion schemes that generate feelings such as feelings of being inadequate, or of being unlovable or insignificant are all highly affectively laden structures, which, when evoked, result in feelings of sadness, shame and disappointment."

Here it becomes clear that the emotional component, and not the motivational component, is placed in the foreground. According to Greenberg et al., emotional schemata are emotional response tendencies. This requires that the individual has continued to make the same emotional experiences regarding the fulfillment of certain needs so that finally the emotional response tendencies are directly activated and no longer the original intentions. It is here, I believe, that your view deviates from the one by Greenberg et al., because intentions are spontaneously active and by themselves impel the psychological activity in a certain direction, while emotional response tendencies require a situation to activate them. Upon closer inspection, it almost seems to me as though an emotional schema, the way Greenberg et al. refer to it, is a sort of hybrid between your motivational schema and that which you earlier referred to as emotional attractor.

"The point of therapy is not to use reason or evidence to change purely cognitive schemes (Beck, 1976; Ellis, 1962). Rather, it is to change the complex cognitive, affective, motivation, and relational action components of emotion schemes. Thus, an emotion scheme that generates, for example, disappointment in relation to lack of support, involves not only the expectational belief that 'no one will be there for me.' It also involves an action tendency such as to withdraw and curl up into a self-protective ball, a feeling such as emptiness in the pit of the stomach, and a desire to be comforted. This whole response complex is activated when the scheme is activated. Emotion schemes essentially contain internal representations of our need-related action tendencies to appraised situations in a form that produces a response when applied. They lead us to anticipate experience and to react in line with past experience. Once activated, they are the cognitive/affective/motivational structures that produce relational actions. These internal structures come to form our core sense of experienced self. Once activated, they provide the referent for our conscious mental state. They produce what is like to be oneself, providing a sense of an embodied self that can or cannot be attended to and consciously represented."

I feel these passages are valid for your motivational schemata and likewise for emotional schemata. The formulation that schemata are "need-related action tendencies" appears worth noting. In addition, Greenberg et al. expressly state here that our consciousness and feeling of self is determined by the schema structure. This congruence with what you said earlier on that should also be noted.

"The foundation of the self lies in the affectively toned expressive and sensorimotor patterns of early life that are represented internally in these emotion schemes and begin the process of ordering experience (Stern, 1985)."

Here, I assume, you would say that the early life experiences manifest themselves in motivational, rather than emotional schemata, although in this early stage affect and motives are barely distinguished.

"These emotion schemes ultimately come to involve a representation of the lived situation, including a representation of the stimulus, its appraisal in relation to a need, the belief or attribution about the self in the situation, and the affective response to the appraised situation."

The appraisals listed here are all among the primary appraisals according to Lazarus. At this point, the relatively little attention paid to the coping component in the realm of secondary appraisal becomes obvious, although, as will still be made clear later, Greenberg et al. do not completely ignore it.

"In our view the organism has a strong tendency to construct these emotion schemes from affect-laden experiences involving need satisfaction or frustration. According to emotion theory, emotion emerges as a function of appraisals of match/mismatch between situations and need, goals or concerns, and our appraisal of our ability to cope with the situation. Emotions are thus most strongly evoked when we are unable to meet our needs or when we succeed in doing so. Thus emotion schemes are constructed in relation to situations that frustrate or satisfy needs, goals, and concerns. Emotion schemes that are central in personal and interpersonal functioning, as we have suggested, go beyond purely conceptual propositions and beliefs. They are instead complex cognitive/affective/motivational internal organizations that guide constructive information processing and produce relational action. They provide the referent for self-awareness and are the basis of our conscious experience of ourself" (Greenberg et al., 1993, pp. 66—68).

In this passage one could actually substitute motivational schemata for emotional schemata in all places. This would change the content of the passage in a way that you could probably fully agree with it, but for Greenberg et al. the passage would then have the emotional component too little in the foreground.

Psychologist: You understood very well what I mean by a motivational schema. Your comments actually fall right in line with my view. I am now interested about which role, according to Greenberg et al., emotional schemata play for the development and treatment of mental disorders.

Therapy researcher: For now, once again I will let Greenberg et al. respond themselves, and then I will summarize:

"When a scheme is activated, it guides both pre-attentive and attentive processing and produces anticipations and responses that have been forged from past learnings. What people experience and how they respond now are generated by their schemes. First, as described above, if the information generated by these schemes is not attended to and synthesized, the organism, unaware of its own reactions, is ungrounded by its own experience and is disoriented. However, these schemes themselves can generate dysfunctional responses as a function of traumatic and damaging experience, or as a function of the construction of maladaptive or imbalanced internal representations of self, other and world. For example, a schematic representation that views the world as threatening and the self as vulnerable, when activated, will generate experience and behavior consistent with this view. If the scheme generates shame, this experience will govern the person's behavior. Thus, schemes based on traumatic or negative learning histories can produce primary emotional responses that are dysfunctional in new contexts. Thus, currently feeling shame or fear at exposing one's own feelings or views to others results from a history of having been shamed or threatened for having revealed one's feelings or views. Therapists need to help clients evoke and symbolize maladaptive responses in therapy, and once these responses are in awareness, they need to be restructured, not specific thoughts and beliefs" (Greenberg et al., 1993, p. 86).

With this last remark, the authors obviously distinguish themselves from cognitive therapists who wish to change "specific thoughts and beliefs." I would not agree with this distancing, because the modification of automated appraisals should, according to Lazarus' theory, have considerable effects on the emotions. According to our considerations so far, it is important that these schemata are really activated if one wants to change them, and that should always be in conjunction with emotions. Whether one directs the patient's attention to the emotion, or to the automated appraisals leading to this emotion, most likely will not make that big of a difference as far as the effect is concerned.

For Greenberg et al., the most important thing for a therapeutic change is essentially that the patient learns to perceive and accept his true emotions. Their most important therapeutic tool for doing that is directing the attention.

According to their assumptions, dysfunctional emotional schemata are predominantly maintained by four characteristics of psychological functioning determined by these schemata:

1. The environment is selectively perceived in line with the schemata. The individual responds to this segment of the environment in the sense of his schema and continuously supplies himself with experiences that confirm his schema. One who feels unloved, sees signs of rejection everywhere.

2. The environmental information is perceived as distorted in the sense of the existing perceptual tendencies. Events actually not confirming the existing schema, therefore, do not lead to corrective experiences. One who feels insecure and threatened, experiences neutrality, or only attempted support, as being left alone or as criticism.

3. The individual avoids exposing himself to new experiences. Greenberg et al. also assume that emotional experiences are largely stored in the implicit memory. Individuals tending very strongly towards abstract conceptual information processing have no access to these emotions. They are able to talk in an abstract way about their not trusting anybody, but they do not feel it in that moment. Emotional schemata therefore must be processually activated bottom-up in order for the patient to be able to focus his attention on that. Only then can there be corrective experiences that change the schema.

4. If an emotional schema is activated, the individual may be so occupied by the emotions triggered that he has no more information processing capacity left with which to process any extra, non-confirming information. Therefore, it will only result in a reliving of the emotion, but not in a corrective experience.

I find these views to be quite compatible with those developed by you. If emotional schemata in the sense of Greenberg et al. are conceived of as neural activation patterns, then by and large we would arrive at similar statements, and I believe we would also arrive at similar statements if we wanted to explain why problematic motivational schemata oftentimes do not change by themselves.

According to Greenberg et al., there are six working mechanisms contributing to therapeutic changes:

1. A therapeutic relationship in which the patient feels secure and protected. This decreases his interpersonal fears and frees up information processing capacity. The patient has more capacity available to allow him to focus his attention on his inner experiences.

2. The patient focuses his attention on his internal experiences, those experienced truly at that moment and not on what he reports verbally. These direct experiences may be new to him and are very immediate. Such immediate experiences are especially well-suited for changing existing expectations.

3. Stimulation and activation of the emotional schema via bottom-up activation of episodic and emotional memory content with non-verbal exercises opening up access to the implicit memory contents.

4. Encouraging the patient to expose himself to real fearful situations previously avoided in order to help him make new experiences on which he can concentrate conscious attention in order to initiate a restructuring of expectations.
5. The therapist creates situations in which the patient behaves in a new fashion, such as expressing feelings never previously expressed. This may, for instance, be a dialogue with a deceased parent. This behavior in itself would be a new experience. In these experience-activating exercises however, the patient can also be brought into contact with the ways in which he avoids or denies such experiences in order to protect himself. By doing so he may not only work on a more conscious concept of important emotions towards certain persons or things, but also on his own mechanisms for avoiding uncomfortable feelings.
6. The patient may make corrective experiences regarding emotional schemata in the here-and-now interaction with the therapist if such schemata become activated in the therapeutic setting.

I believe that these therapeutic components in the conception of Greenberg et al. on the modification of emotional schemata can all be very well backed up with what we have discussed so far. They may be applied to motivational as well as to emotional schemata. If we consider schemata as neural activation tendencies, then for changing these schemata, above all else, it is important that these activation tendencies are actually activated. Of those just listed, points 3-6 all refer to measures for activating such existing neural activation tendencies. That is an expressed emphasis of the therapeutic concept.

Given that nonverbal and emotional experiences are largely stored in the implicit memory, great value is placed on a bottom-up activation. This precisely matches up with our considerations on the psychology of memory. The procedure is directed towards bringing out the patient's emotions that are associated with the particular schema to be changed as strongly as possible. According to Lazarus' theory of emotions, strong emotions are experienced when the goal component of the appropriate schema is activated. When strong emotions are triggered in the procedure suggested by Greenberg et al., it means in your view, an important motivational schema has been activated. This creates the necessary requirements for a schema to change.

A second important component of the procedure is directing the patient's conscious attention to what he does and experiences in the moment the schema is activated. According to our psychology of memory considerations, this is exactly the way by which implicit memory contents can become part of the conceptual memory. As soon as they have become part of the conceptual memory they can be called into the working memory in order to be consciously processed there. They may become subject to conscious consideration or ideas, they may be included in plans and become the object of voluntary decisions. Creating contents of consciousness for these previously unconscious processes is, therefore, a precondition for effective action control in the sense of Kuhl (1994).

Promoting and practicing new conscious action control and assimilating as many new experiences as possible in various real situations to the newly formed conscious action schema by reflective abstraction in the sense of Piaget (1976), is no longer part of the therapy concept by Greenberg et al. This represents for me an unnecessary limitation of this concept. The existence of new contents of consciousness cannot be expected to be a sufficient condition for effective action control in all patients.

A third component of the conception by Greenberg et al. lies in the verbal processing of the newly formed contents of consciousness with the goal of a "satisfactory," that is non-conflictual integration into the patient's self-image. This would bring the procedure of motivational clarification to a close.

But as I just mentioned, by this alone a satisfying realization of the now conscious goals might still not be achieved. For this purpose the interventions directed towards motivational clarification could be supplemented by mastery-oriented therapeutic procedures. In my view there is no plausible reason for withholding such support from a patient if the motivational clarification, and possibly intention change as well, have by themselves not produced a satisfactory solution of the important problems which necessitated engaging in therapy.

In my discussion I limited myself to the **therapeutic conception** by Greenberg et al. In their book they also describe in detail the therapeutic procedures which may be used to realize the individual components of the conception. In my eyes this is a therapeutic procedure with a solid foundation in basic psychological research. The therapeutic mechanism of this procedure can be well explained using the concepts derived from basic research that you revealed to us piece by piece. At any rate, it is not surprising to me that psychotherapy outcome research has found these procedures and similar ones to be effective (Greenberg, Elliott & Lietaer, 1994).

Therapist: The example of this therapy concept made me realize for the first time how considerations founded in basic science may actually lead to an in-depth understanding of the mechanisms of a therapeutic procedure. In our first conversation I was already impressed by how you placed the therapeutic mechanism of motivational clarification into the Rubicon model, which explained its position in the context of the spectrum of the various therapeutic possibilities.

I have a much better understanding now **what motivational clarification actually means psychologically** and **how** it affects the mental life. In the future, when I am planning to initiate and promote a motivational clarification process in a patient it means for me that I must first activate the problem-relevant neural activation patterns which represent the respective motivational schemata. I should especially look for possibilities to activate them bottom-up, this is to say by concrete sensual experiences, so that implicit contents of memory are also activated. Prior to, and while I do this, I should also seek to activate positive motivational tendencies in the patient that become the basis for our cooperation. These already existing tendencies must become the determinant of his therapy behavior, which is to say, they have to motivate the patient to deal with the uncomfortable feelings associated with the processual activation of the problems and to direct his attention to what becomes processually activated.

Focusing the patient's attention on what he does and experiences during the processual activation of the motivational schemata would be my next important task. My goal must be to create the conceptual contents for the new perceptions the patient makes. For that, I should use already existing possibilities. I should then try to achieve that he exposes himself to as many experiences as possible that relate to the newly formed contents of consciousness. Or he should learn to more and more easily relate his experiences that he makes anyway, for instance, experiences with me in the therapeutic relationship, to these newly formed contents of consciousness. The contents of consciousness should become an easily activated content of his conceptual memory, ready to be voluntarily recalled at all times, so deeply ingrained that it can also be easily activated spontaneously by appropriate situations.

As this content of consciousness refers to a neural activation pattern with strong motivational and emotional components, it remains part of a process with strong intentional tendencies. My goal must be for the patient to replace the previously unconsciously pursued intentions with conscious goals, which enable him, if he recalls them into his consciousness from the conceptual memory, to exert a conscious, voluntary control over his behavior in specific situations. The more he has successfully exercised this conscious control, the more strongly the newly formed neural activation patterns become ingrained, and the less voluntary effort will eventually be required for him to continuously behave in a new fashion. The newly ingrained activation patterns are, of course, also associated with new emotions. By these emotions I might be able to judge whether or not we were successful in establishing new positively evaluated activation patterns because their activity should be accompanied by more positive emotions than was previously the case.

Putting it into these words might make it sound a bit complicated, but I realize that I am able to move around more easily in this new world of ideas, and I find this satisfying.

There is only one point that remains rather unclear to me. That is the question as to which motivational schemata I must activate if I wish to promote the patient's motivational clarification process as efficiently as possible. How do I identify the motivational schemata that are to be changed?

Psychologist: The practical significance of this question is indeed immediately clear to me. But how you should actually proceed in practice, I frankly do not know. I had hoped that perhaps the two of you would have some answers or at least ideas on that.

Therapy researcher: I previously announced that there are two therapeutic concepts utilizing a construct very similar to your motivational schema. We have only discussed one of these conceptions, namely the emotional schema by Greenberg, Rice and Elliott (1993). The other concept, which I have yet to introduce, offers something specifically to address the question you have just raised. What I mean is the construct of the **relational schema** or the interactional schema by Grawe (1986), and also the method of schema analysis elaborated by him and his associates (Grawe et al., 1996).

Therapist: Oh yes, of course, I know that. I guess that I must have been a bit too much in the world of "experiential therapy" to bridge that gap, but now I see what you mean. You seem to know the concept better than I though, therefore I think you should try to connect this concept with our previous considerations.

2.31 Motivational Schemata and Relational Schemata

Therapy researcher: In his report *Schema Theory and Interactional Psychotherapy* Grawe (1986) describes a concept of schema largely corresponding to your idea of a motivational schema. "For psychotherapy, the most important component of the schema construct is its **motivational** component. This is the part of the schema construct which energizes the mental processes and gives them direction. Activation of a schema means that the psychological activity is directed towards generating perceptions consistent with the schema's goal component... The idea that psychological activity is determined by schemata means that human beings are, by nature, and at any moment, striving towards certain goals. As long as there is some sort of psychological activity, it is focused on generating perceptions in line with the schemata activated at the moment. We are always searching for those situations, or we create those, which are relevant to our schemata, and we try to reproduce ourselves in our transactions with this situation according to our schemata" (Grawe, 1986, p. 2/3).

Grawe particularly emphasizes the transactional character of the schema construct, namely that schemata evolve from the individual's active exchange with the environment, and that they, themselves, are directed towards bringing the individual into certain intended relations with his or her environment. So, goal components of schemata are relations with the environment desired by the individual. Therefore, they correspond to the core relational themes which Lazarus (1991) combined with certain emotions in his theory of emotions (see also section 2.21). Grawe too maintains that there is continuous appraisal of the momentary individual-environment relations taking place with respect to these transactional goals which produces the emotions always accompanying psychological activity. So Grawe's concept of schema is a motivational/cognitive/emotional/relational conception like that of Lazarus and that of Greenberg, Rice and Elliott (1993). The components are the same, only the emphases are somewhat different.

Grawe holds the goal component to be that which ties the schema to a functional unit; for Greenberg et al. it is emotion. Seen from this angle, Grawe's schema construct corresponds exactly to your motivational schema. What Grawe's conception is missing, however, is a reference to the psychology of memory and neural foundations that played such an important role in the derivation of your schema construct. I mentioned earlier that I find it much easier to relate to a neural activation pattern than to a schema, and that is why Grawe's schema and your motivational schema, represented by a neural activation pattern, are not the same for me.

Also, Grawe does not speak of motivational schemata, but of **relational schemata**. He emphasizes the relational aspect, particularly relations to others. For him, schemata represent the most important foundations determining interpersonal relations. Schemata are used to continually bring people into particular kinds of interpersonal relations. That is why Grawe's relational schema allows us to establish a connection between your motivational schemata and schema concepts which refer to interpersonal relations.

Such an affinity between motivational schemata and interpersonal relations is obvious, because an individual's most important motives do indeed relate to goals which are realized in interpersonal relations. The intended individual-environment relations are mostly specific patterns of interpersonal relationships, such as "being admired by others," "being superior to others," "feeling close to somebody," etc. Motivational tendencies, action tendencies, perceptual tendencies and emotional response tendencies all belong to this schema. If we formulated all these components for a motivational schema, we would, at the same time, obtain a schematized description of an interpersonal pattern. When this schema is activated, the individual tries to bring himself, in line with his ingrained action tendencies, in relation to others in such a way as to realize the desired interpersonal relation. Certain perceptual tendencies are simultaneously activated, i.e. expectations as to how others will respond; at the same time certain emotional response tendencies are activated, i.e. tendencies to emotionally respond a certain way to the other's behavior. The emotions are associated with action tendencies that include how one will in turn respond to the other's behavior.

So, in the expectations and tendencies of a motivational schema whose goal component refers to interpersonal transactions, certain recurrent patterns of interpersonal processes are schematized. The components in these interpersonal patterns are the person's own behavior determined by certain wishes or fears, the other person's response behavior and one's own reaction to this response behavior. These components correspond to the relationship patterns, as defined by the role relationship models (RRM) by Horowitz (1989) and the core conflictual relationship themes (CCRT) by Luborsky (Luborsky & Crits-Christoph, 1990). Reliable measurement methods exist for both of these constructs (Luborsky & Crits-Christoph, 1990; Horowitz & Eells, 1993). Therefore, these may also be considered reliable methods for measuring relational schemata, or, if you will, motivational schemata as well. In my view, the CCRT method in particular measures important components of a motivational schema and could, therefore, be employed for measuring the most important motivational schemata of a patient, although actually more for research purposes, since this method might, in fact, be too time consuming for everyday clinical practice.

Therapist: Grawe and his associates, however, approach the assessment of relational schemata differently. They have developed a method called schema analysis specifically designed for application in the clinical practice rather than in research (Grawe et al., 1996). This method should also be particularly suitable for the assessment of motivational schemata as you conceive them because it has one advantage, it is predominantly focused on the assessment of the goal component of the motivational schema.

While listening, I suddenly realized that I see an essential aspect of emotional schemata in Greenberg et al.'s view as a disadvantage of their concept. How can this concept assess whether, and when a patient systematically **avoids** certain relations to his environment? In this case he would, in fact, not experience the emotions which would arise if he got involved in this situation. Therefore, proceeding from his emotions, we are not able to identify those areas which he tries to exclude from his experience and behavior. Yet according to my clinical experience these avoided areas are especially important in therapy. This is where I see a plus for Grawe's schema concept and the method of schema analysis. In schema-theoretical case conceptions, according to Grawe et al. (1996), the assessment of schemata which are aimed at avoiding certain emotions plays a crucial role.

It would be too boring for me to simply present to you how Grawe et al. proceed in their schema-theoretical case conceptions, so instead I would like to try to combine this approach with your previous considerations on motivational schemata and to develop a conception of motivational schemata specifically tailored to clinical practice from that.

2.32   Intentional, Avoidance and Conflict Schemata and Their Significance for Mental Disorders

Intentional Schemata

Using the example of the newborn, we saw earlier that motivational schemata develop around a person's basic needs. With growing experience, the individual develops more and more sub-goals and means (capabilities) for realizing the superordinate goal. The more differentiated the hierarchic structure of a schema becomes, the more possibilities the individual has to satisfy the need behind the motivational schema. People with well established motivational schemata, therefore, have more possibilities for satisfying their needs. They experience positive emotions more often, feel better and are happier in general. Well developed motivational schemata can, therefore, be considered the foundation for sound mental health.

The motivational schemata developing around the basic needs are aimed at striving, creating, bringing about something or achieving a desired state. They are characterized by a positive tendency "towards something." We may therefore call them **intentional schemata** (*intendere* = to strive for) or also **approach schemata**. The foundation for the development of intentional schemata may not only be innate needs but also values acquired in socialization, particularly by identification learning.

People with badly differentiated intentional schemata have, in a way, a reduced "potential for happiness." These may be people who have learned to be satisfied with very little, whose level of aspiration regarding need satisfaction is relatively low. These people will not lead an intensive life and they will find relatively little fulfillment, however, they will also not suffer intensely from negative feelings resulting from incongruities between their perceptions and goals.

On the other hand, for individuals whose level of aspiration regarding need satisfaction is high because they were quite spoiled as children when they were required or able to contribute very little to their need satisfaction by themselves, but whose abilities—components of their motivational schemata—are badly developed, the situation is quite different. Those people are unable to achieve their lofty goals by their own means later on. That is why in these people negative emotions are constantly elicited, the quality of which depends on what attributions the individual makes regarding the source of incongruities between their wishes and their actual perceptions.

These individuals run the risk that the negative emotions become a main determinant of their mental functioning, thereby worsening the conditions for need satisfaction by yet another step, because a large portion of their psychological activity is then no longer directed towards the realization of positive intentions. That is why the intentional schemata develop no further, the production of negative emotions continues, the psychological activity is even more determined by these emotions etc. This constellation may develop into a fruitful, however initially still unspecific breeding ground for mental disorders. Whether, or which kind of a diagnosable psychopathological disorder may develop from that depends on many influences and cannot be predicted without knowing the specific constellations of the individual case.

Once a certain mental disorder has developed, however, it will largely absorb or determine the psychological activity. The disorder is, in a way, constantly supplied from the still existing, or rather increasing incongruities regarding need satisfaction.

If, in such a constellation, a therapist limits himself by approaching the disorder with solely disorder-specific methods, a long-term improvement would be highly unlikely, because the breeding ground for the development of the disorder in fact still exists and would definitely contribute to its perpetuation. Even if one were successful in changing the specific disorder, there would still be no satisfactory therapeutic outcome, as the low need satisfaction would continue to produce negative emotions.

In such a case the therapy should therefore combine disorder-specific interventions with interventions aimed at advancing the intentional schemata in order to improve the patient's means for need satisfaction. The more effectively this is achieved, the less chance there is of negative emotions arising. This could be considered a therapy which eliminates the real source of the disorder. So even a largely mastery-oriented therapy can be a "causal therapy." This constellation also demonstrates that a mastery-oriented therapy need not necessarily always be, and definitely need not merely be, a disorder-oriented therapy.

According to my clinical experience, such constellations are especially difficult to treat, because it is not easy for a grown adult to make up for something which was lacking in his childhood. Schemata are developed in active exchange with the environment and that requires time. Due to this, the further development of underdeveloped schemata is hard therapeutic work, work that is emotionally even more difficult for a therapist, since patients such as these, with their underdeveloped relational schemata, are also unable to give a lot in the relationship but do, however, have high expectations with respect to receiving something themselves from that relationship. As a therapist, one has to be very careful in such therapies not to be too occupied with negative emotions the patient elicits in oneself. Otherwise, things might very easily slide into an exchange of negative emotions which perhaps only happens nonverbally and not consciously, but this entails negative impacts for both sides. Earlier we discussed the nonverbal exchange between therapist and patient (section 2.26). In these therapies it is very difficult not to become infected by the patient's continuous dissatisfaction and the negative emotions constantly elicited by him. In this case to behave "asocial" as suggested by Beier (1966) means to nonverbally communicate in an emotionally positive fashion, that is to say, to turn to the patient physically, to maintain a warm empathetic expression in the voice, express positive emotions in the face, to smile a lot etc. This may be very difficult and demanding if no reinforcement from the patient is received for this. It is, however, exactly this nonverbal and "undeclared" communication which might be suited to subconsciously satisfy some of the patient's relational wishes so that, at least in the therapeutic setting, there are less negative emotions triggered in him or her over time. This would create a positive basis for the further course of therapy which then, however, would have to include more than just a carefully considered shaping of the relationship.

Avoidance Schemata

The constellation more frequently encountered in clinical practice, however, is one in which the problem is not simply that the patient's intentional schemata are not well enough developed, but that need satisfaction is impeded by the activity of avoidance schemata. A person's basic equipment includes not only the "towards something" intention but also the "away from" reaction. Fear, disgust and contempt all belong to the primary innate affects and are associated with the "away from" action tendency. Flight, defense, and avoidance are components of a living organism's repertoire crucial to its survival. One avoids what hurts. That need not be pain in the literal sense, but anything triggering aversive sensations. So one also avoids incongruities between goals and perceptions in the sense of control theory, because these are associated with negative emotions.

The essence of control theory that "psychological activity is directed towards creating perceptions in line with goals..." implies the logical continuation: "...and towards avoiding any deviations from these goals." Neural activation patterns aimed at avoiding certain perceptions, therefore, belong as much to a person's basic equipment as do his intentional schemata. Psychological activity is continuously directed at avoiding deviation from certain goals, and consequently, is simultaneously determined by approach and avoidance tendencies.

Anticipatory and reactive avoidance should also be conceived of as a basic form of motivational schemata. Avoidance schemata form around a negatively defined goal, an individual-environmental relation that is to be avoided. The negative emotion which would emerge if the goal of avoidance was jeopardized or not achieved would then also be avoided. Because of this, Grawe (1986) has termed these avoidance schemata "negative emotional schemata." Actually, I find the term "avoidance schema" to be more consistent, because according to our ideas, it is primarily an incongruence between goals and perceptions that is avoided. Although the incongruence is always associated with negative emotions, the resulting emotion consists of more appraisals than solely the appraisal of incongruity. The incongruence appraisal is a requirement for the formation of the emotion, but alone, and in of itself, not a sufficient definition of its quality. That is why it makes sense that primarily the incongruence, and not the negative emotion is avoided. On the other hand, this distinction is only theoretically significant, because it more or less all boils down to the same thing whether one avoids a certain environmental relation or the emotion triggered by it. Over time, the goal of avoidance and the negative emotion are so tightly associated with one another that they have the same functional significance.

How do avoidance goals form? Above all, they may develop around painful experiences. "Once bitten, twice shy." Painful experiences, especially those resulting from a continuous or long-term life constellation, may become the negative goal component of an avoidance schema. They correspond to "wounds" (Beier, 1966) which the individual protects through more and more extensive avoidance strategies. Over time, the avoidance strategies assume a more and more anticipatory avoidance character, as an avoidance schema also develops in the direction of greater differentiation through assimilation. Avoidance schemata are characterized by the feared relation with the environment and the emotion associated with it normally not being experienced. The goal component of avoidance schemata can always only be inferred. Earlier, at one point you used the image of stars sending out light and "black holes." Intentional schemata would equal the stars, the black holes would equal the avoidance schemata.

The influence of an avoidance schema not only affects the behavior, but also the experience. Neural activation patterns not compatible with the goal component of this schema are actively inhibited. This also includes thoughts and other cognitions. An elaborated avoidance schema, therefore, has the effect that the respective components of experience, that is perceptions, memories, thoughts and feelings are, in fact, not consciously experienced.

The control over conscious attention is one of the most important tools serving motivational schemata. The goals of intentional schemata benefit from this control in that they can be pursued by means of conscious planning, decision making and action control. If the goal components of avoidance schemata are consciously represented these possibilities of conscious attention may also be used in the service of avoidance goals, for instance, in the situation of a mountain climber making careful preparation against accidents prior to his ascent.

The conscious attention, however, may not be used in the service of avoidance goals which are not consciously represented, because they are part of the implicit memory. The psychological activity is determined by the avoidance goal, while the avoidance intention and its effects are not directly represented in the consciousness. That which is being avoided is also avoided from becoming conscious. Entering consciousness would be associated with incongruities and those are avoided. So the functional meanings of the actually ongoing mental processes are not directly represented in consciousness. Yet, since people have a need to understand what they do and experience (see section 2.37), the individual tries to construe some meaning for what he or she does and experiences. This meaning, however, is not an appropriate representation of what is actually happening, but rather an interpretation in line with existing motivational tendencies.

From these considerations we can gather that the conscious cognitions have multiple functions in psychological functioning. First, they reflect what is and what happens. This can be termed the **reflective function**. At the same time, however, to a greater or lesser extent, they are always an interpretation of what is and what happens in the service of motivational tendencies. They are always inner perceptions in line with certain goals, thus always also having an **interpretative function**. Furthermore, cognitions have the important function of controlling behavior. The more the interpretive function of the cognition prevails over the reflective function, the less effective the individual's action control is in the respective situation, as then the **controlling function** is based on premises not congruent with the objective reality.

Accordingly, an essential function of psychotherapy should be making sure that the patient's cognitions appropriately represent the actual determinants of his action and experience, as this is required for an effective action control in the service of his goals. In my view, this is the primary task of a **clarification-oriented therapy**. I would like to remind you of what you mentioned earlier about the therapeutic approach by Greenberg, Rice and Elliott (1993): Through focusing of conscious attention on the actually ongoing internal processes, especially the emotions, new contents of consciousness are to be created which appropriately represent these processes. It is then tacitly assumed that the requirements for an effective action control are fulfilled. The concept of motivational avoidance schemata sheds additional light on this process. Directing conscious attention to the ongoing processes possibly very directly contradicts the avoidance goals, and has to, therefore, take place against the "resistance" of these avoidance tendencies.

This is no homunculus resisting here. It is the basic principle of psychological functioning that mental activity aims at generating perceptions in the service of approach and avoidance goals. Someone attempting to generate perceptions contradicting this basic principle will inevitably elicit negative emotions and increased psychological activity in the service of the activated avoidance goals. The therapeutic modification of motivational avoidance schemata can only be achieved against resistance, because it takes place against the natural direction of psychological activity.

That, however, is actually no great secret. A phobia may be conceived of as an avoidance schema. If, through exposure therapy, one diametrically works against the direction of the psychological activity which is determined by this schema through the concentrated generation of perceptions counteracting this direction, then one has to expect both strong avoidance tendencies and strong negative emotions. This example demonstrates again just how important it is for such therapies to activate positive resources of the patient as much as possible in order to strengthen the approach intentions in competition with the avoidance tendencies. Given that, the modification of avoidance schemata plays quite a crucial role in both clarification and mastery-oriented therapies.

Earlier, we learned from you that even monkeys acquire avoidance schemata, not just by direct experiences but also through observational learning. This is all the more so among humans. In particular, learning by identification in children, which you reported on earlier, should be important for adopting negative values around which avoidance schemata may then develop. Quite often I have seen children who have adopted a parent's fear of animals. Of course in the same fashion other fears may also be adopted. Even those that are not verbally expressed by the parents but that the child senses through emotional infection. Such nonverbally transmitted negative values are likely to be stored in the implicit memory. They will then unconsciously exert an influence on the experience and behavior because they are not accessible as a conscious content. If such a person is asked for the reasons behind his behavior, he can actually only give an answer that has the character of a rationalization, because the real reason is not accessible to him.

Avoidance schemata restrict the individual's realm of experience and thereby impede the development of positive intentional schemata. For instance, if over the years a child, verbally and nonverbally, receives the message from her mother and/or father: "You must never leave me, without you my life is empty, without you I die;" this person would very likely have feelings of guilt later in life just by fantasizing about living a wonderful life independent of the parents, and as a consequence would already stymie such strivings from the beginning. By avoiding experiences which one can make only by discovering life alone and independently, many positive intentional schemata would be impeded in their development. The successful weakening of avoidance schemata through therapy clears the way for new experiences and makes room for the advancement of intentional schemata, restricted in their development until now. Their development will improve the patient's possibilities for realizing her needs and positive values. The successful treatment of avoidance schemata can, therefore, clear the path for an even longer lasting positive development, which might possibly no longer require the support of a therapist.

After all we discussed, we may say that psychotherapy essentially achieves a great deal of its effects by weakening motivational avoidance schemata and promoting positive intentional schemata. The weakening of avoidance schemata can be brought about by either clarification-oriented or mastery-oriented procedures. Mastery-oriented procedures are indicated more when the patient is aware of the avoidance intention. Clarification-oriented procedures are indicated when the patient is initially still unaware of the functional significance of an avoidance schema, that means if she still has no awareness of where, how and to what extent her experience and behavior is determined by such avoidance intentions. Promoting intentional schemata requires therapeutic work on the right bank of the Rubicon. Developing an awareness of avoidance schemata requires work on the left bank.

Conflict Schemata

Approach and avoidance schemata may be so closely intertwined with one another that they can be conceived of as a functional unit. Such a functional unit may be called a **conflict schema**.

As an illustration let us take the aforementioned case of the patient whose becoming more independent from her parents is hindered by the induction of guilt feelings. It is likely that the messages: "You must not leave me/us alone," etc., were predominantly transmitted during the time that the patient was making strides towards gaining independence. The independence intentions are coupled with feelings of guilt through these recurring processes. This coupling can occur through temporal contingencies, but also on a symbolic level. Whenever future wishes or desires to do something independently emerge in the patient, to go on a trip with friends for example, the neural activation pattern representing the feelings of guilt is activated. All this exercises an impeding influence on the not yet fully activated neural activation pattern representing the desire for independence. So the latter is suppressed in experience and does not exert an effect on the behavior.

Tied to her parents through her feelings of guilt, the patient has fewer and fewer perceptions congruent with her intentions for independence. This has a two-fold effect:
- According to control theory, the incongruence signals regarding the independence goal have the effect that the psychological activity becomes increasingly focused on generating perceptions in the sense of the independence intention either way. At the neural level, the approach activation pattern is triggered; in experience the person feels stronger desires for independence again.
- The second effect is the triggering of negative feelings produced by the incongruence appraisal in the sense of Lazarus' theory of emotions. This might be rage towards the parents, for instance. Both effects lead to increased independence intentions in experience and behavior.

Yet, the more strongly the neural activation pattern representing the independence intention is activated, the more strongly the synaptic connections to the neural assembly representing the feelings of guilt and the avoidance intention associated with that are activated. At a certain activation level this activation pattern in turn regains control, inhibits the independence intention anew and the cycle enters into a new round.

So a conflict schema has two components counteracting one another, an approach or intentional component, and an avoidance component. I have attempted to schematically illustrate a conflict schema in Figure 2.20.

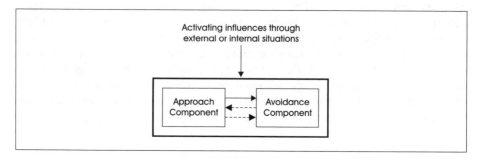

Figure 2.20:
Schematic illustration of a conflict schema. Solid line arrows refer to activating influences and dashed lines to inhibiting influences.

If the approach component becomes activated by certain situations, it will in turn activate the avoidance component. The latter exercises an inhibiting influence on the intentional component. The more successfully the avoidance intention is realized, the fewer incongruence signals there will be with respect to it, but the stronger the incongruence signals regarding the approach component will be. As a consequence the influence of the avoidance component on psychological functioning decreases. With the growing incongruence signal regarding the approach component, the latter becomes more strongly activated again. The incongruence signal is also associated with negative emotions, such as rage towards the restrictive parents in our case. The emotion itself is associated with an action tendency which in this case supports the independence intention. The intentional component is, therefore, simultaneously less forcefully inhibited and more strongly activated. This exercises an inhibiting influence on the avoidance component. The intentional component begins to re-exercise more influence again on the psychological functioning, which, in turn, leads again to the activation of the avoidance component, and the cycle begins again.

In a way, a conflict schema resembles a "neural swing" from which there seems to be no escape for the patient. From the outside it is obvious what the therapeutic solution of such a conflict should look like: The intentional schema should be reinforced, the avoidance schema weakened. In our case example this might perhaps not even be that difficult because it involves a conflict rather close to consciousness. The activation pattern would have to be turned around in therapy. The activation of the avoidance component should activate the intentional component instead of the other way around. This necessitates the creation of a new activating arrow from right to left in Figure 2.20, i.e. new neural connections should be created and ingrained. This requires a strong activation of the guilt feelings, over and over again, with all the restrictive consequences of the avoidance schema, until this elicits the independence reaction associated with rage. What must be achieved is that merely thinking about the restrictions and the very first signs of guilt feelings already produce independence intentions in the patient which will then exert an influence on her behavior and lead to truly new, thus far avoided, experiences. In all likelihood she would then realize that the fears associated with her avoidance schema do not materialize, and her independence would take on realistic shape and dimension.

The changed behavior of their daughter would also confront the parents with new experiences. They would most likely make the experience that their fears of being completely left alone would not materialize. Personally, in clinical practice I would temporarily include the parents in therapy, since their fears may as well be seen as a therapeutic problem which can only undergo long-term change by activation and corrective experiences. The more successfully the parent's fears would be alleviated, the lower the amount of guilt feelings retained by the daughter. She would also no longer need to dissociate herself from her parents through her rage as much, and that would further decrease her parent's concerns, thereby increasing perceptions congruent with positive wishes on both sides.

While not unrealistic, the case described is unfortunately not very representative for therapeutic practice. The reason for choosing this case is that by being so close to consciousness, the conflict is easily comprehended. Yet, conflict schemata are often characterized by the fact that the patient has little or no awareness of it. This is perfectly understandable looking at the origin of such conflicts.

When can one be so badly hurt? When can strong negative emotions such as disappointment or shame be elicited? This is above all the case when a wish that is of great importance to oneself is activated. A person is easily disappointed in a situation where he wants something very badly and is dependent on another person for getting it. The feeling of having lost face is stronger when it is very important to a person how he is viewed by others. It is easiest to be hurt when one feels needy. That is why the nuclei of conflict schemata emerge mostly in childhood when one is still very needy and dependent on the interpersonal environment for fulfillment of one's most important needs.

To comprehend how conflict schemata emerge let us imagine the following interpersonal constellation: A small child naturally strives for the proximity and the protection of a primary caretaker, for the sake of simplicity, let's say the mother. The child is born with this need. Over time this motivational tendency assimilates experiences telling the child how he or she can best realize the intention "sensing mother" or "being close to mother." Normally, a regularity develops in the interpersonal exchange of child and mother relationship which can be somewhat controlled by the child, that leads to a realization of the closeness intention.

This regularity in the actual interpersonal processes manifests itself in the child in the form of expectations and tendencies. The congruence between these components of the closeness schema and the actual interpersonal exchange enables the child to have a certain control over the realization of his or her desire for closeness mostly because there is a complimentary intentional care and protection schema activated in the mother that is accompanied by feelings of love for the child. The regularities of the mother/child relationship patterns, which are always accompanied by positive emotions on both sides, result from the activity of these intentional schemata, which are complementary and related to one another.

However, let us imagine a mother whose mental activity is very strongly determined by intentional schemata other than a care-taking schema for her child. Let us assume, it is her first and only child, a daughter. Apart from her being a mother, she is perhaps a person whose mental activity is strongly focused on gaining attention and admiration. She has perhaps established herself in a professional situation where she has so far been able to realize this intention very well. Her entire life, even her relationships were arranged in that fashion. Even the child, this big new event in her life, serves her in attaining attention and admiration. In situations where the child serves this intention, she turns to her child with a love suited to attracting admiration and attention from other adults. In the moment the child experiences this happiness which is not within her own control.

This happiness, however, is not of lasting duration because the mother's affection is adjusted not towards the child's needs, but towards the mother's own. When the mother feels like it, she pulls her daughter close to her and, for a moment, creates great intimacy. But then she "vanishes" suddenly back into her own world with her other plans, beyond the child's control, and is not accessible by her daughter. The closeness that the child longs for ends abruptly and uncontrollably every time, even while the need for attachment is still strongly activated. It is not the daughter detaching herself from the mother, since she feels safe and protected again, rather the mother terminates the interaction regardless of the child's need. Again and again the child experiences the terrible disappointment of this need for a secure closeness. The daughter's disappointment is possibly not even perceived by the mother because she leaves the child in other people's care. On the outside, it appears that the child grows up in a world where everything seems taken care of.

The uncontrollability of aversive events belongs to the most traumatic experiences people undergo, and try the hardest to avoid (see section 2.36). According to Kelly (1957), the entire mental functioning is focused on establishing predictability and controllability. Perceptual expectations and action tendencies serve exactly this purpose. For the child, the everyday interpersonal pattern described means that, unexpectedly and uncontrollable by her, she will be disappointed again and again in her most vital needs. The only control that the child can gain over this violation of her attachment need is to withdraw from an unprotected intimacy with her mother and to make herself inviolable by anticipatory avoidance. An avoidance schema develops with the goal "avoid being rejected and disappointed in your desire for closeness."

However, the neural activation patterns thus far formed around the intentional schema "be close to mother" are not erased with this. They maintain their potential for being activated by relevant situations, memories etc. Accordingly, in the future, when mother is present two neural activation patterns will be simultaneously activated, exercising a conflicting influence on her experience and behavior. Logically, the goals of the intentional and the avoidance schema appear to exclude one another, however, the mental life functions according to a both-and principle rather than according to an either-or principle.

Both activation patterns may simultaneously, and with variable weights have an impact on the behavior. If mother is not yet close, the activation of the intentional closeness schema predominates. When the situation becomes more intimate, the avoidance schema becomes more and more strongly activated and prevents the desire for closeness from ever being satisfied, but it simultaneously prevents such a terrible, uncontrollable disappointment in the relationship with mother from happening ever again. The non-fulfillment of the desire for closeness is now happening under the child's control, and no longer determined by uncontrollable changes in her mother's behavior. The child gets close to her mother in a way that no longer allows real intimacy.

In interpersonal communication an inconsistent or even contradictory relationship can be established because there are many communication channels available by which messages can be sent simultaneously. Verbally, one can strive for closeness while the nonverbal behavior is simultaneously directed towards an avoidance of closeness. Or, one part of the nonverbal behavior may express the desire for closeness while other channels are employed for avoiding closeness. The behavior appears "somehow" inconsistent, but in a way that is very difficult to express verbally, because, in fact, for the most part an analog communication code is used so that these messages are indeed perceived and processed, but this does not happen consciously. After all we learned about perception, memory and nonverbal behavior, we can presume that something like that is possible.

Only a small part of what we just described is represented in the mother's and the child's consciousness. The causal interpersonal processes happened in the child's very first years of life. The experiences made in this time for the most part no longer exist later in the form of retrievable contents of the conceptual memory for the child and, therefore, cannot be called into consciousness. Yet, as contents of the implicit memory they have become the foundation of large parts of the child's interpersonal behavior. A person affected by such experiences is in a way, "memory blind" to the original causes underlying his or her own experience and behavior. Later on, the daughter may not know why she behaves in such a way in relationships. Most likely she does not even know that she prevents experiences of closeness by her own behavior, and how she does this. The same happens with the mother, she may find after a while that she has a difficult child without knowing why. In her relationship with her daughter she continues to make perceptions which are incongruent with her own motivational schemata. The daughter is no longer suitable for showing off. Rather she develops into a fault. The mother also has desires for intimacy towards her child that are no longer satisfied. Motherhood has become a rather disappointing experience for her. The daughter senses these feelings and realizes that she is a disappointment to her mother. She attributes the reasons for that to herself and this localization of the cause matches her mother's. This has negative effects on her just developing self-esteem (see section 2.40).

Therapy researcher: The circumstances described by you might also lead to the development of a mental disorder. Individuals who have not succeeded in developing a secure attachment pattern to a reliable care-taking person in the first years of life are more likely to develop a mental disorder of some kind in their later lives than are individuals having a secure attachment pattern (Schmidt & Strauss, 1996; see also section 2.39). Although exactly what kind of disorder might develop depends on many other influences, conflict schemata such as those you described certainly represent a fruitful breeding ground for mental disorders. At any rate, one should not be surprised if the daughter in your example possibly develops a depression later on.

Therapeutic Modification of a Conflict Schema

Therapist: Let us assume this to be the case and that today I have this daughter as a patient. Let us assume that she suffers from an acute depression. The discussions we had in our first conversation suggest that I would first have to devote myself to the acute disorder, this being the immediate reason for starting treatment. I would have before me an individual with an acute depression, low self-esteem, an obviously rather bad relationship to her mother, and a history of failed or only attempted, not even fully developed partner relationships.

I am going to ignore the considerations that would have to be made and realized under the aspect of resource activation and the induction of positive expectations for improvement and instead limit myself to the aspect of treating the problem.

I would have to begin by assisting the patient with her most acute problems, seeking to get her out of her acutely depressed state with depression-specific therapeutic interventions such as those developed by Beck (1967) and Klerman, Weissman, et al. (1984). The acutely depressed state of the patient means she is not in good condition to actively participate in the modification of a conflict schema that has become part of her personality very early in her life, and which to a large extent, is underlying her interpersonal experiences.

So first, one would have to focus on a **mastery-oriented**, **disorder-specific** procedure. If this succeeds in getting the patient out of her depressed state she will most likely acquire a certain trust in my being able to help her.

To most patients the question of how they came to be afflicted with this disorder makes sense. It would probably not be very difficult to motivate this particular patient to pursue this question and to direct her attention to her interpersonal relations. Most likely, the patient would bring up the bad relationship to her mother on her own, and might even articulate strong negative feelings towards her mother which she can easily back up with concrete examples of their interpersonal exchange over the past years.

Talking about these issues, however, would be more of an occasion for me to convey to the patient that I feel with her and I am on her side, and that I take her feelings seriously. Yet, I should not delude myself that the topics brought up by her, accompanied by these feelings, actually mean that relevant conflict schemata are activated. The feelings articulated by her should be viewed as a commentary on what she reports, and my commenting empathetically and nonverbally on this commentary is especially important for our relationship (see section 2.26).

This would all be an activation of recallable conceptual memory contents. It would not be a processual activation of the conflict schema, the two components of which I described earlier. If I wanted to change this conflict schema underlying her unfortunate interpersonal experiences, and ultimately her depressive tendencies as well, I would have to search for ways to **processually activate** it. The activation would have to be **bottom-up**, and not top-down, proceeding from the contents of her consciousness. Situations would have to be either looked for or created, or existing situations suited for activating the desire for closeness would have to be utilized in order to also activate the avoidance strategies.

This might be done, for instance, via the **therapeutic relationship**. My constant empathetic care towards her would probably be something that she missed so painfully from her mother, and it might, therefore, be something suited to activate the intentional component of the conflict schema. On the other hand, I would also have to consider the possibility that the avoidance component becomes simultaneously activated, aiming at protecting the patient from disappointments regarding her desire for closeness. The patient will, therefore, most likely behave in a way which makes it difficult for me to constantly and empathetically express my care towards her. She will respond highly sensitively to even the most minor signs of having no time for her, of disinterest, neglect or even rejection, because she has very strongly pre-ingrained perceptual tendencies for that. Thus, I would have to pass many "**relationship tests**" in the sense of Sampson and Weiss (1986; see sections 1.28 and 1.29) in order to gradually reduce her fears accompanying the avoidance component by **corrective experiences**. The weakening of the avoidance component would have to be my main goal in this second, **intention-modifying** part of therapy.

When I say part of therapy, I am not referring to a temporally separated section of therapy, but to a component of my procedure. All of this would most likely already take place parallel to the disorder-specific treatment of her depressed condition.

The more success I would have in weakening the avoidance component by corrective experiences in the implicit mode of functioning, the more I could attempt to direct her attention towards her desire for closeness. This would have been difficult to do earlier because the attention is under the control of the motivational schemata. Therefore, the still dominant avoidance schema would have assured that the desire for closeness did not become the center of conscious attention, as this would have allowed the deep pain associated with the non-fulfillment and rejection of her desires for closeness to become a conscious feeling.

In a relationship—not just in a therapeutic relationship, this could, of course, above all be a partner relationship, with a partner who would succeed in passing the relationship tests of the patient—in which the desire for closeness were activated bottom-up and not disappointed, the negative emotions that were biographically associated with the desires for closeness and later avoided, now may also be experienced as a conscious feeling. This would be required for a conscious reappraisal consistent with the primary and secondary appraisal components according to Lazarus (1991), and another essential step in the direction of establishing new neural activation tendencies is accomplished with this. In the change process of the conflict schema, this would be a **clarification-oriented** part.

The conscious representation of the desires for closeness would be the basis for the patient consciously controlling her own relational behavior consistent with her desire for closeness, for behaving in this new way in real relationships, and assimilating new experiences to the intentional closeness schema, since the path would now be clear for a self-sustaining, further development of this important motivational schema whose development was stifled from such an early point in the patient's life. According to the terminology used in our first dialogue, this part of therapy would have an **intention-realizing** emphasis.

If I had to give a quick and compressed sequential description of the problem-oriented procedure in this therapy utilizing the terminology we have developed so far, it would look as follows: First, in a **mastery-oriented** phase, the disorder would be approached with interventions that have proven to be successful with such disorders. Concomitant with that, one part of the conflict schema, the desire for closeness, would be **processually activated** by **shaping the therapist-patient relationship** complementary to her desire for closeness. This leads to the activation of the avoidance component of the conflict schema which manifests itself in the form of **relationship tests** in the therapeutic relationship. Passing the relationship tests leads to corrective experiences in the implicit mode of functioning and thereby to a **change in intentions**: The neural activation pattern representing the avoidance schema is "overwritten" with **corrective experiences**, i.e. new neural paths are established and old paths inhibited, leading to the overall outcome that now situations related to closeness no longer lead to the same neural activations. This causes the weakening of the influences inhibiting the neural activation patterns that represent the closeness intentions. The closeness intentions gain more influence on psychological functioning by this and can manifest themselves in the form of conscious desires. A clearer, conscious motivational state is created by **motivational clarification**. In the sense of an **intention-realizing** procedure, the desires for closeness may now become a conscious goal component as part of a self-actively, continuously developing intentional schema.

This case, which was constructed by me and is not so untypical for clinical practice, demonstrates rather well that therapists should be experienced in moving around on both banks of the Rubicon landscape. With a solely mastery-oriented therapy one would do as little justice to the patient as with a solely clarification-oriented therapy. For the conceptualization of this therapy I essentially had to take into regard all the working principles we have so far discussed.

This case also demonstrates that special training is necessary to recognize and modify conflict schemata. A conflict schema is not as obvious as a mental disorder that can be diagnosed according to the criteria of the DSM/ICD. A conflict schema may be easily overlooked by the therapist, especially by one who limits herself to what the patient claims to be his or her problem. The nature of a conflict schema is such that the patient is unable to pinpoint it as a problem because mostly he has no awareness of it. Conflict schemata are usually largely unconscious.

Based on my clinical experiences, I do not believe that unconscious conflict schemata play a functional role in all mental disorders and need to be included in therapy. Many of the findings from therapy research you reported on in our first dialogue seem to speak against that as well. On the other hand, conflict schemata relevant to the treatment are also not a rare exception in my clinical experience. I think that in any intake examination with a psychotherapy patient the therapist should be attentive to any signs indicating the existence of an important conflict schema. I would hope that therapy research might provide us with more confirmed criteria for that. In our first conversation you raised hopes that this could be accomplished in the near future, as several research methods are now available for that. I hope you are right.

Therapy researcher: Motivational schemata appear to be a very fruitful and suitable construct for therapeutic practice. You have not been so actively involved in any of the topics discussed by us as you are in this one. The therapeutic treatment of conflict schemata indeed seems to utilize all the working principles that I derived from therapy research findings in our first conversation. Earlier you presented an easily comprehendible connection of these working principles with the ideas about the psychological functioning developed by us in the second dialogue. This was actually our stated goal. Don't you think we have come close enough to our goal now to allow us to do a final inventory, and perhaps discuss what all this means for therapeutic practice?

Therapist: You took the words right out of my mouth. I actually have the urgent desire to let everything settle and think all this over in peace and quiet, and then come together again in a third dialogue later on in which we draw practical conclusions from the discussions in our first two dialogues.

Psychologist: Given the time I needed for my presentations, I find it rather embarrassing to say this, but I find it is still too early for that, we are not that far yet. I do believe one can view the motivational schemata as the immediate determinant of what we do and experience. This is the reason why, without doubt, they are especially important constructs for psychology and psychotherapy alike. We have to change a person's motivational schemata if we want to change his experience and behavior.

However, can we indeed view motivational schemata as the "ultimate" determinants of mental functioning? What actually determines which motivational schemata develop how strongly in a person? Don't motivational schemata themselves have to satisfy certain criteria? And which criteria would these be? Where do these standards emanate from? So far we have not said much about the content aspect of goals. Should we be satisfied with leaving the question of which goals the mental activity is oriented to unanswered? Is it not inevitable that at the highest hierarchy level the question about which are the contents of motives does arise?

Looking at the totality of schemata, doesn't the entirety of the schema activity have to follow some organizational principles so that mental life does not become chaotic? Couldn't it be that a better structured schema activity goes hand in hand with an overall better mental functioning, and that perhaps mental disorders in particular are accompanied by inferior organizational characteristics of the schema activity? We have continuously addressed the simultaneity of many psychological processes, doesn't this simultaneity have to be organized in some fashion? Does, for instance, the principle of hierarchical organization of mental functioning cease to be valid for motivational schemata? And if many control hierarchies are synchronously activated, are they really supposed to be simultaneously-parallel active to any degree regardless of the type and direction of the activated control hierarchies?

Therapist: I have the funny feeling something lies ahead for us, it sounds as though you saw a rather long list of topics ahead of you. I have to admit, however, my capacity for absorbing all this will be exhausted sometime in the near future. It just becomes too complicated for me. I cannot make use of such complicated concepts in my practice anyway.

Psychologist: Perhaps it will not become more complicated, but simpler. Imagine we are hiking up a mountain. We have already seen many overwhelming things and are both full of impressions and exhausted. Should we really not complete the last, much smaller part to the summit and miss the view and overview that is the big payoff for all our efforts? Is it not possible that from up above, having the entire overview, everything that one was unable to put together into a consistent image on the way up without this entire overview becomes integrated into a greater simplicity and harmony?

To stay with this image, in discussing the motivational schemata we have reached the eighth or ninth level of Powers' model. What Powers referred to as principles determining the standards on the program level would be our motivational schemata. Powers, however, sees the necessity of still another level above the level of principles. He refers to it as the system level or the level of self. Behind the conception of such a highest regulation level lies the idea that an organism represents a wholeness or a unit and because of that, all ongoing processes have to be coordinated in some kind of fashion for the benefit of the entire organism.

For our purposes, Powers' ideas about the system level do not tell us much. The same goes for his ideas about the level of principles. It is, therefore, time to "change theoretical horses" and to select one having qualities more suited to the last part of the journey. Yet before I saddle that horse, I would like to just make sure about whether you would like to continue with this last part of this journey or whether you wish to stop.

Therapist: You leave us practically no choice. If I do not participate now, I would eventually burst from curiosity about what I might have missed. I really do not wish to do that to myself, so please continue.

2.33   How Can the Simultaneity of Several Goal-Oriented Mental Processes Be Theoretically Conceived?

Psychologist: I really feel it would have been a pity if you had chosen to give up right in the middle of this, because we are now at a point in our second dialogue where we will proceed from the phase of differentiation to the phase of integration.

If we look back on what we have discussed about perception, the memory, the emotions, nonverbal behavior, and lastly, about motivational schemata, we see that one particular recurring feature of mental functioning is recognizable in all these areas: there are always several different mental processes simultaneously ongoing. While there is not so much simultaneously finding a place in our consciousness, we have seen that conscious perceiving, thinking and acting are only special modes of psychological activity ahead of which many pre-attentive processes are pre-instated, and parallel to which, many other processes are ongoing in another mode. Earlier we termed this other mode of mental processes the **mode of implicit functioning**, because the neural connections underlying these processes seem to be stored in a form of memory other than the conceptual memory which our rational information processing is based on.

All the research areas we have thus far dealt with have yielded evidence for the significance of this implicit mode of functioning. Different terms have been applied to it by researchers from different areas. Psychologists such as Perrig, Wippich and Perrig-Chiello (1993) working in the field of the psychology of memory distinguished it from the conceptual interpretative function by calling it an "associative reaction function;" perceptual research predominantly makes the distinction between attentive and pre-attentive processes; research on emotions and on nonverbal communication distinguishes between an analog and a digital code (Tucker, 1986; see section 2.25; see also Paivio, 1986, 1991). Depending on the psychological function examined, the qualities of the implicit mode of functioning have been described somewhat differently, but the descriptions have considerable overlap, allowing us to say: Whatever aspect of psychological functioning is researched, we find evidence for there being at least two qualitatively different modes of functioning: an implicit and an explicit/conceptual mode, with the second one (but not the first) always being accompanied by consciousness. Instead, the implicit mode of functioning is characterized by the possibility that many more processes can be simultaneously ongoing and not only one.

All of these areas of basic psychological research we have mentioned so far lead to the conclusion that the simultaneity of goal-oriented processes is one of the most obvious features of psychological activity. This conclusion cannot be dismissed, nor is it by any means trivial.

I think that a key to understanding human mental life lies within these facts and that the door to a new understanding of mental disorders and psychotherapeutic processes of change may be opened with this key, and these are exactly the questions which have brought us together. Although these facts are spread across rather broad areas of psychological research, the question as to how to conceive this basic feature of psychological activity is what leads us into new psychological territory. Not that others before us have not sought to explore this territory, but for now they are still pioneers. Mainstream psychological research and theory formation has not yet devoted itself to this subject.

What I still wish to bring into our discussion is related to the theoretical conception of this issue. Later on we can think about whether or not the concepts which try to account for these issues yield practical conclusions for psychotherapy.

First, I would like to introduce to you an author who developed a personality theory that matches so well with what we have been discussing that one might even think the theory was developed just for this purpose. This is all the more astonishing as the author makes almost no references at all to the basic ideas which have lead to our views so far. That, in and of itself, has confirmed for me that one can reach strongly overlapping and supplementary views on mental functioning from very disparate starting points.

The author is Seymour Epstein. Throughout a period of over 20 years, Epstein (from Epstein, 1973 through Epstein & Morling, 1995) has developed a personality theory which he termed "**Cognitive-Experiential Self Theory (CEST)**" (Epstein, 1990, 1991 a). Based on this theory he repeatedly devotes himself to questions which are highly relevant for our endeavors such as considerations on unconscious mental processes (Epstein, 1983, 1994), on the differences and conflicts between rational and intuitive information processing (Kirkpatrick & Epstein, 1992; Epstein, Lipson, Holstein & Huh, 1992; Denes-Raj & Epstein, 1994), on the relationship between the self and emotions (Epstein, 1993 a), values and the self (Epstein, 1989), on the significance of biographical experiences for the development of the self (Epstein, 1991 b; Catlin & Epstein, 1992; Epstein 1993 b), to conflict, stress, coping and symptom formation (Epstein & Katz, 1992; Epstein 1993 c), to traumatic neuroses (Epstein, 1991 b), and to questions of psychopathology and psychotherapy in general (Epstein, 1987).

Perhaps the best way to explain Epstein's theoretical approach is to present the individual components he used for naming his theory to you in succession.

2.34 Two Modes of Functioning of Psychological Activity and Their Specific Mechanisms: The Implicit and the Rational Mode of Functioning

Cognitive-experiential refers to two different systems of mental processing, a cognitive-rational system and a cognitive-experiential system. Table 2.3 presents a more specific description of what is meant by "experiential system" and gives a comparative juxtaposition of the features of the experiential and the rational processing systems.

The list clearly demonstrates that the experiential mode of functioning is largely congruent with what I just summarized as being implicit, whereas the rational matches what I referred to as explicit. This allows me to use the term "implicit" system in place of "experiential system."

The rational mode of functioning lends itself to being easily described in words. Expression and meaning complement one another. It is rationally, analytically, logically, verbally, consciously, sequentially, differentially, voluntarily controlled. The implicit mode is more difficult to describe verbally due to its special nature. It does not correspond to what we can describe denotative-rationally by words. I need not go any deeper into the rational mode of functioning, as it is fairly obvious what is meant by that. However, I would like to discuss the implicit mode of functioning a bit more in-depth so that we are as clear as we can be about its qualitative distinctiveness. First I will summarize what Epstein (1990, 1993 b, 1993 c) himself writes on it.

Humans share the implicit system with other higher life forms. It has developed over millions of years and, therefore, has a proven high adaptation value. It is neither superior to the rational system, nor inferior to it, but simply different. Each of the two systems have their advantages and disadvantages. At the simple level the implicit system allows, without much effort, a far more rapid, however, not very exact response. At the higher level, it is a source of intuitive wisdom and creativity. It relates to concrete situations and experiences in a holistic way, whereas the rational system can abstract from concrete things, and can detach itself from the actual situation thereby allowing delayed, accurately planned actions.

The implicit mode of functioning is strongly connected with emotions. Also included therein are "vibes," a diffuse "sensing," a quality also attributed by Perrig et al. (1993) to their "associative reaction function" (see Figure 2.12, section 2.12). Emotional reaction tendencies existing in the memory of the implicit system are situationally activated. If these are positively tinted, the result would be a tending towards the situation, if these are negative, it leads to an abandonment of the situation. This all happens in a flash, without conscious decisions. The individual experiences these processes as though he or she had responded to an external event. His own emotional appraisals, having gone into the perception of the events, remain unconscious to him. That is why what is consciously experienced is largely influenced by unconscious processes. The influence unconscious processes exert on the conscious mental functioning is, therefore, even more pervasive than assumed by Freud (Epstein, 1994).

In fact, in reference to Freud, Epstein distinguishes three different information processing systems:

Table 2.3:
Comparison of the rational and the experiential processing systems according to Epstein (1990, p.168).

Experiential system	Rational system
1. Holistic	1. Analytic
2. Emotional: Pleasure vs. pain-oriented (what feels good)	2. Logical: Reason-oriented (what is sensible)
3. Behavior mediated by "vibes" from past experiences	3. Behavior mediated by conscious appraisal of events
4. Encodes reality in concrete images and metaphors	4. Encodes reality in abstract symbols: Words and numbers
5. Rapid processing: Oriented toward immediate action	5. Slower processing: Oriented toward delayed action
6. Slow to change: Changes with repetitive experience, direct or vicarious	6. Changes rapidly: Changes with speed of thought
7. Learns directly from experience	7. Learns from symbolic representations of experience
8. Crudely differentiated and integrated: Associationistic, categorical, and organized into emotional complexes	8. More highly differentiated and integrated
9. Experienced passively and pre-consciously: We are seized by our emotions	9. Experienced actively and consciously: We are in control of our thoughts
10. Self-evidently valid: Experiencing is believing	10. Requires justification via logic and evidence

1. The primary processual system which Freud put on one level with the unconscious. This, for instance, determines what takes place in dreams.
2. The implicit system that comes close to Freud's preconscious, but which deserves a much greater significance than that assumed by Freud. It is the unconscious system which is actually influential.
3. The rational, secondary processual, conscious system.

With the aid of the graphic in Figure 2.21, Epstein (1991b) has tried to illustrate the relative significance attributed to these three information processing systems in psychoanalysis, in mainstream psychology and in his theory:

The "experiential" or implicit processing system is denoted in the figure as "preconscious." Epstein's theory distinguishes itself from psychoanalysis or mainstream psychology in that it attributes to this system, which is—while not completely separated from consciousness—not clearly conscious, the greatest significance for mental life. This system is characterized by its own mechanisms which differ from both those of the rational consciousness and the primary processual functioning as Freud put it.

According to Epstein, classical conditioning is one of the simpler events in the implicit reaction system. Tversky and Kahneman (1974) see "heuristics" as a more complex form of implicit information processing and for them, heuristics are a kind of "cognitive short-cut" people use in many natural decision making processes. These underlie many irrational reactions in everyday life. Short stories, so-called "vignettes," have often been used to research such reactions. Test subjects in such research are to

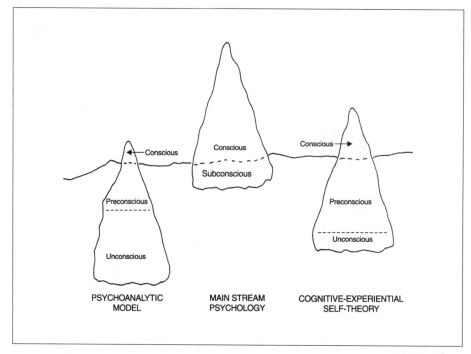

Figure 2.21:
Schematic illustration of the relative significance of three modes of functioning of the mental system in psychoanalysis, in mainstream psychology and in Epstein's personality theory. Figure taken from Epstein (1991 b, p. 66).

say how the protagonist in the story would react if confronted with an accidental misfortune, that means in a situation where no other person is seen to be responsible. Despite the obvious coincidence of the accident, however, the test subjects attributed more anger to the protagonist when it was clear he or she had done something prior to the accident rather than when he or she had not done anything; when this protagonist was free to make his or her decisions rather than somehow restricted; and when he had done something unusual rather than something normal, etc. Although they knew better, the test subjects made their judgments as if the protagonist had in some way been responsible for the accident.

Another frequently researched kind of irrational judgment is the so-called "conjunction error." This is when subjects rate the likelihood of two symptoms appearing at the same time more highly than the likelihood of each single symptom actually appearing alone. In a trial by Tversky and Kahneman(1982), 85% of the test subjects committed this error. This result has been repeatedly replicated under varying experimental conditions. Given the large number of relevant studies all leading to the same results, it can be viewed as undeniable (Fiske & Taylor, 1991) that people often use irrational heuristics in their everyday life decision making situations.

Other examples for the "irrationality" of the implicit mode of functioning are control illusions and unrealistic optimism. A control illusion is when someone believes his chances in throwing dice to be better if he throws them himself as opposed to leaving it up to another. I will return to that more in-depth later in conjunction with another part of Epstein's theory.

Unlike Tversky and Kahneman, Epstein views such irrational behaviors not as judgment errors which should possibly be eliminated, but as the result of a normal adaptive mode of functioning which differs from rational thinking. In their own experiments, Epstein and his associates found that the extent of "irrational" judgment errors depends on how much an implicit or rational information processing mode was activated in the experiment via instructions, priming, or other measures (Epstein, Lipson, Holstein & Huh, 1992; Kirkpatrick & Epstein, 1992; Epstein & Denes-Raj, 1992, Epstein, Heier & Denes-Raj, 1992).

So, what looks like an irrational mistake from the perspective of a rational system declared to be normal, can also be viewed as normal functioning in the sense of another mode of functioning which does not exactly follow rational principles. In connection with judgment behavior, one should maybe rather speak of "intuitive" decision making. In the kind of judgment situations investigated by Tversky and Kahneman, intuitive decisions are certainly not optimal, but they might have advantages over the rational mode of functioning in other decision making situations having different characteristics, for example it is necessary to quickly react in very complex situations.

There are other authors as well who do not see intuition immediately as a deficit, but as a mode of functioning of psychological activity also having its specific advantages. Yet, all authors had a difficult time positively defining this other mode of functioning, not just defining it as the absence of a rational analytic procedure.

According to Hammond (1988), it depends on the type of task to be solved whether a rational or intuitive procedure is more successful. He sees intuition as being more advantageous, the more information there is to be processed, the more complex the structure of the task and the more vague the content is, also, the less accuracy is required, and the less familiarity one has with the task. Hammond, however, views rational and intuitive information processing not as two different modes of functioning but as two extremes on a continuum.

For Dreyfus and Dreyfus (1986), the rational and the intuitive are two separate processing systems, as the first is symbolic and the second sub-symbolic. This conception strongly agrees with Tucker (1986), which I presented earlier in dealing with nonverbal communication, it also agrees well with the "dual-coding theory" by Paivio (1986, 1991) and with Epstein's view as well. Dreyfus and Dreyfus give special emphasis to the significance of experience. According to them, experienced experts utilize a more intuitive processing mode. The greater one's experience in an area, the more superior the intuitive processing mode is over the rational.

While also assuming two separate systems, Hamm (1988) views their activation not as an either/or, however. According to him, the best information processing performance results, for experts as well, when a person can rapidly switch back and forth between these two modes.

Caspar (1995) has empirically investigated the information processing of psychotherapists during an initial interview with respect to the utilization of intuitive and rational information processing strategies. Among other things studied, he looked at both experienced and inexperienced therapists. He found that experienced therapists proceeded more, not less rationally/analytically than inexperienced ones, in addition, they also realized positive characteristics of intuition to a greater extent. They thought more consciously, more complexly, used more meta-cognitions, more reasoning and more rules than the inexperienced, without this restricting the positive characteristics of intuition. So, one can obviously combine intuitive and rational/analytic procedures.

This would also correspond to Epstein's opinion. He sees the simultaneity of implicit and rational processes as representing the normal condition of psychological activity. This view of intuition also results from our viewing it as belonging to the implicit mode of functioning. According to our ideas from psychology of memory, intuition is based on neural processes different from those underlying rational thinking and action, and these processes have a different basis in the brain.

Frick (1993, p. 8) also arrives at this conclusion: "To account for the intuitions, there must be a part of the brain with the following properties:
1. This part of the brain produces information.
2. The results of the processing become conscious.
3. The processing in this part of the brain is not available to conscious introspection.
4. This part of the brain can know things that consciously are not known.
5. This part of the brain can operate without conscious initiation and direction."

The properties listed by Frick are exactly the same ones we have come up with for the implicit mental processes in the course of our conversation. Consequently, we can view intuitive deciding and acting as another property of the implicit mode of functioning not yet listed by Epstein in Table 2.3.

The opinion that there is a different basis in the brain for the rational and for the implicit mode of functioning matches up well with the conception that both processes are simultaneously ongoing. Many studies, such as those on dichotic listening, have shown us that this is actually the case. The distinction between the rational and the implicit mode of functioning strongly overlaps with that between a digital and an analog mental code by Tucker (1986), and the distinction between a verbal and nonverbal code made by Paivio (1986, 1991), who reports on many more findings on which roles these two different kinds of mental representations play in perceptual and memory processes, as well as on their interplay in mental functioning. Epstein's assumptions that
1. there are two different modes of functioning of psychological activity, and that,
2. both modes of functioning are simultaneously active,
is supported by a very broad empirical foundation.

Epstein associates a whole series of everyday life phenomena with the implicit mode of functioning. In his eyes religions appeal to the implicit mode of functioning. The ubiquitous existence of religion at all times and in all places is evidence for how much people feel that the special properties of religious thinking and practices appeal to them. The biblical history of the emergence of the world and the human being, the illusion of control through ritual, magic and prayers, the commonality that is felt in joint singing and prayer, the comfort in difficult life situations: this is all a fulfillment of basic human needs largely excluding the rational-analytic mode of functioning.

Even prejudices, superstitions, esoteric thinking and astrology are subjects that expressly call into question the rational mode being the only mode of functioning of psychological activity. The attraction of and demand for all these point to the fact that there are extraordinarily powerful influences at work. Epstein is decidedly of the opinion that psychotherapy should make use of these powerful influences by working with techniques that activate the implicit mode of functioning. The close connections the implicit mode has with the emotional and the immune systems may open a way to also influence biological processes by psychotherapy.

This view becomes even more plausible if we assume, as we have done throughout the entire conversation, that mental processes are represented by neural processes. Not only does this mean that one may change mental activity by influencing neural processes with medication, as has been proven beyond doubt for psychotropic and neuroleptic agents, but that the reverse influence is also possible. If we successfully alleviate a person's depression with psychotherapy, it means that we change certain synaptic connections by psychological means (Bohus & Berger, 1992). In so far as processes of biological illnesses are associated with events in parts of the brain that also play a role in emotional processes, it might become possible via this link to also psychologically gain influence on the courses of biological illnesses. Psychoimmunology is still young and would lead us too far afield were we to also go into that, but neural processes could be the link that enables us to relate psychological and physical processes to one another. There is greater likelihood that this can be done via older brain areas, than via the newest. The implicit, and above all, the affective system is phylogenetically much older than the rational. Therefore, it is likely that one can exert more influence on immunologic and other biological processes by influencing implicit processes than by modifying verbal-rationally controlled processes.

2.35 What Is the Self?

The second element of Epstein's cognitive-experiential self theory is the term "self." Epstein conceptualizes the self as a "personal theory of reality." The elements of this theory of reality are fundamental "postulates" derived from emotionally significant life experiences. Epstein distinguishes between descriptive and motivational postulates. Descriptive postulates are the ideas the individual has about the world and him- or herself. Motivational postulates are condensed experiences about what the individual has to do and to avoid to fulfill his or her basic needs.

Epstein assumes the postulates to be hierarchically organized and as having an effect on behavior via these hierarchies. The highest motivational postulates would correspond to the higher-order standards of the control hierarchies on the level of principles in Powers' model. At the same time there are what we previously termed motivational schemata. In his recent publications, Epstein himself uses the term motivational schemata rather than motivational postulates. He understands by motivational schemata exactly what I understand by it. So there is no danger of confusing the terms. The self, according to Epstein, is the sum of the individual's motivational schemata and his beliefs concerning himself and the world.

In conjunction with my comments on memory earlier, I already developed the view that, in a way, the organism can be viewed in its entirety as a theory about the world formed by a process of selection over millions of years (section 2.9). Epstein's view of the self as a theory of reality is based in an analog way of thinking. In the course of ontogenetic development, the self as a reality theory develops on the basis of the individual's experiences. The sum of tendencies and expectations formed by the individual while in pursuit of his basic needs **is** the self according to Epstein. He places the utmost value on the self not being viewed as a psychological instance of its own. His, initially somewhat strange sounding formulation that the self would be a theory of reality, obviously serves the purpose of keeping it from being viewed as a kind of homunculus which itself plays a role in psychological functioning. The self is not an end in itself but a personal theory developed by the individual for the fulfillment of his or her basic needs. The self is not an actor in psychological functioning but an expression for the sum of motivational and descriptive postulates forming an entity.

The self as reality theory refers to the implicit self, not to the concept that an individual has of himself. The self concept is part of the conceptual system. It feeds on the available contents of the conceptual memory. The "experiential self" need not be congruent with the self concept. The implicit self is more important than the self concept. If a therapy is successful in changing the implicit self, the experience and behavior will change, and that will also have impacts on the self concept. On the other hand, changes in the self concept, thus the recallable contents of consciousness about oneself, must not necessarily have impacts on experience and behavior. So it is important in therapy to focus on changing a patient's implicit self, rather than on what he thinks about himself. Nevertheless, what one thinks about oneself also has a process aspect. It is an action and this action is part of the implicit self. So, for instance, if we change the patient's automated thoughts about himself in therapy, we change a part of his implicit self along with it.

So according to Epstein, the self is not a regulating authority, and, therefore, does not mandate any standards. The standards for the motivational schemata are determined by basic needs common to all people. This contributes something new to Powers' control theory. For Powers, only the level of the self was left above the level of the principles corresponding to our and to Epstein's motivational schemata. If one wanted to combine Epstein's personality theory with Powers' control theory, an additional level above the motivational schemata would have to be conceived, namely the level of basic human needs. The self, however, would not be a regulation level of its own, but would be included in the connection between the need level and that of motivational schemata.

Therapist: Now this all becomes really captivating for a therapist. I believe that most psychotherapists also expect answers from a theory they work with about what it is that actually drives people. I suppose the fact that Freud never shied away from making firm statements on this has contributed to the great success of psychoanalysis. Not only does one want to know how man functions but also what moves him. The question of a person's motives can in fact be something that occupies us intensely in everyday life. Sometimes people cannot stop thinking about this until they feel they know why someone has done something in particular. One then has the feeling of having understood, and that is somehow satisfying. As a therapist I feel the same way. I want to understand why a patient behaves exactly the way he behaves. It is somehow frustrating to perform therapy without an understanding.

2.36 Basic Human Needs as Highest Standards of Psychological Activity

Psychologist: Epstein would completely agree with you because according to his theory, the need for understanding belongs to a person's basic needs. I will get into that in a little while, as I would like to present to you next what Epstein sees as a **person's basic needs** and which position they have in his personality theory.

As I already explained in other words, according to Epstein, the self is the individual's theory about what he or she has to and is able to do to fulfill, in the world in which he or she lives, his basic needs. The motivational schemata that a person develops represent his **implicit theory on what he must do to fulfill his needs**. The development of schemata takes place under certain life conditions. Therefore, the motivational schemata are a product derived from the interaction between the needs and the life environment into which a child was born.

In the course of the development of motivational schemata the child also acquires knowledge about the world and about himself in this world. Epstein refers to these elements of knowledge as descriptive schemata. He calls the knowledge about the world the world model, and the knowledge about oneself in this world the individual's self model. Especially important are the **beliefs** directly related to the basic needs acquired by the individual in the course of the development of his motivational schemata.

So the basic needs have a central position in Epstein's personality theory. In a way, they are the highest standards for all an individual's psychological activity.

I will not only briefly list the basic human needs assumed by Epstein, but also comment on them and explain their significance and substantiate their importance. The reason for doing so is that Epstein himself does not offer any detailed explanations as to why he thinks that these and not others are the most important basic needs. He limits himself to pointing out that Freud, Rogers, Bowlby, Kelly, Allport and others have also held one of these needs to be "the" most significant basic need. He does, however, not separate himself from these authors, but expressly refers to them, and he sees the great difference in his approach to be that he does not assume one central, but **four equally justified basic needs**. Those are the need for orientation and control, and the need for increasing pleasure and avoiding pain, the attachment need, and the need for self-enhancement.

In fact, the attractive properties of Epstein's theory result from this assumption of several, equally justified basic needs. Until 1990 he assumed only three basic needs. The attachment need (see below) was added later. This shows that his conception of psychological functioning in general does not stand or fall with the assumption of exactly these four needs.

Epstein's specific choice of needs may seem somewhat arbitrary given the effort that psychology put into developing the most complete lists and category systems possible for human needs. But I have thoroughly devoted myself to this question and think that the four needs posited by Epstein actually have a sound foundation in current research. Though this does not rule out that an additional need should perhaps be considered, or that the exact definitions might look slightly different. There is no final consensus in this respect.

I think this is a question of the objective one has in mind. For example, I think there are good reasons for assuming that such a thing as a basic need for exploration or discovery exists. This can be biologically substantiated and nicely explains what people do if their other needs are largely fulfilled and they are left up to their own devices. The importance that playing has for children can hardly be explained without assuming an innate tendency for exploring. It seems to me though that contemplating this particular basic need would bring no great gain for the purposes of psychotherapy. Perhaps many things relate to a need for exploration that one could also attribute to a need for orientation and control. So, considering the specific domain of psychotherapy, I see no necessity to postulate such a basic need. Should this prove to be desirable, however, one could easily add such a need to the other four without major changes to important parts in the overall conception.

Epstein's four needs are well chosen for psychotherapy. I will propose an alteration to one particular point, but otherwise Epstein's conception is consistent with what I myself find well substantiated for psychotherapy. Therefore, unless anyone here protests, I would like to save us from going into the many different conceptions of human needs in great detail (for instance Murray, 1938; Maslow, 1954; Gasiet, 1980; an overview can be found in Heckhausen, 1980, in Becker, 1995 and in Ford, 1992). This would certainly lead to a very long trip and eventually result in nothing more than us having to ultimately make a decision about which of the strongly overlapping conceptions convinces us the most.

Therapist: You have my agreement. My interest lies in the suggestions you came to following your having given this due consideration, and not in everything that has already been researched and discussed in conjunction with this question. Besides, I myself lack the criteria for making an informed decision in favor of one over the other. To do so, one would have to devote oneself to the subject far more thoroughly than is possible for us to do in this context.

Psychologist: So now I will present to you the four basic needs according to Epstein, one after the other, adding in references and research findings substantiating the significance of the respective need.

2.37   The Need for Orientation and Control

According to Epstein, the most basic human need is the need for **orientation and control**. Every person develops a model of reality to which he can assimilate his real experiences and try to maintain this reality conception which means, according to Epstein, his self. In other words: The person has a **need to understand and to have control**.

Depending on the experiences that the individual makes in life with respect to this need (predominantly in early childhood), he or she develops a basic belief as to how much life makes sense, whether predictability and control possibilities exist, whether it is worth it to commit oneself and engage in something. Rotter's (1966) construct of control beliefs refers to this basic belief.

These biographical experiences lead to personal expectations about to what extent this basic need can be satisfied. The standards for the later satisfaction of needs thus emerge as a product of innate needs and the societal as well as the individual life environment. The standards are the goal components of the motivational schemata developed by the individual around this need.

Epstein maintains that inherent in the basic need for control are also its prerequisites, namely the stability and coherence, or consistency of the system that assimilates the reality experiences (Epstein uses the expression "coherence," I use consistency to adjust for the terminology we used in our earlier considerations). I find the confusion of this very plausible requirement for efficient psychological functioning with the need for orientation and control rather unfortunate.

If the mental processes of a person are in themselves inconsistent, contradictory and conflictual, it very much affects the individual's ability to fulfill his needs. Biologically, it also affects his ability to survive and to reproduce. It is, therefore, to be expected that a human's phylogenetically developed psychological processing is equipped so that sufficient consistency and uniformity of the direction of mental processes is guaranteed. Especially if we assume a principal simultaneity of mental processes and consider that these must always account for several basic needs at the same time, we can expect sufficient **consistency** of these processes to be an indispensable basic requirement of effective psychological functioning. Due to principle considerations, therefore, we have to assume that psychological functioning is such that a sufficient consistency is guaranteed. Hence, there must be mechanisms for creating consistency, and mechanisms for preventing inconsistency. I do not think it is logical to conceptualize this as yet another need beside the others. Rather, this should be conceived as a basic principle of psychological functioning that is superordinated to all other individual needs.

My ideas deviate from Epstein's in this respect. After presenting and explaining Epstein's four basic needs, I will elaborate on this higher order principle of psychological functioning which I call **consistency principle**. For me it is the most basic principle of psychological functioning. I find it extremely important, especially for an understanding of mental disorders. That is why I distinguish the consistency principle from the need for orientation and control and will devote myself at this point only to the latter.

There is such an extensive amount of literature on the control need and on the control beliefs developed around this need that it makes no sense to even try to present a comprehensive overview to you. There are literally thousands rather than hundreds of research findings on that. Therefore, I am only going to touch on those points especially important for psychotherapy. An excellent introductory overview on the concept of control can be found in Flammer (1990), whereas Wegner and Pennebaker (1993) offer an overview on recent research trends dealing with the many aspects of mental control.

The extent of theoretical considerations and empirical research devoted to the concepts of control, control expectations and control beliefs alone indicates that these concepts refer to an undeniable part of human existence. In the words of Flammer (1990, p. 114/115) this would speak for assuming "an appropriate need, that is to say, to assume that people are spontaneously ready to come up with the effort to acquire, maintain and increase control. This need is not directed towards the possible effects per se but on their control...

I distinguish control need from basic need for control. The basic need for control is innate, but is always expressed in a concrete context, and refers to concrete subjects and goals. The individual has access to these concrete goals due to his socialization. One might also say that in the course of socialization, the basic need for control materializes in certain contents or goals, connects to certain scenarios and is thereby multiplied and specified. There are many control needs, but only one basic need for control."

What Flammer says here about the relationship between basic and specific needs, applies not only to the control need, but likewise also to the other three needs assumed by Epstein.

In his book *Action Regulation and Control*, Oesterreich (1981, pp. 130 & 132) backs up the assumption of a control need with biological considerations: "One must assume that every living creature or every species, respectively, strives to preserve itself or its own species respectively... It is all about actions... directing them in a such a way that a multitude of different action possibilities is preserved. Out of necessity, living creatures have a striving for survival, to be derived from that... is the assumption that more highly developed life forms strive for control. This entails adjusting the behavior so that the ability for regulation in the environment is preserved."

So control need is not only about exerting control in the current situation, but also about securing as large a scope of action for oneself as possible. "The control need is satisfied by the offering of as many free action alternatives possible, in as many important value spheres as possible. The person striving for control strives for scope of action; for reserves, to be able to achieve important goals if necessary. The control need can be satisfied by a currently existing control belief, it need not necessarily be the actual controlling" (Flammer, 1990, p. 117).

Obviously, people with the need to preserve as large a future scope of action as possible by saving up money, have a high need for control. The ability to manage money can be seen as the securing of a general scope of action "just in case." For other people, their relationship to money is determined more by the basic need to indulge in as many pleasurable experiences as possible. They spend their money, for example, on culinary joys, travel and other nice experiences. Others use money as a means for satisfying another basic need, namely that of self-enhancement by driving a flashy car, wearing expensive clothes, having an impressive house, etc. Those dependent on money for satisfying their attachment need are rather deprived individuals, but even that is not so unusual.

Diagnostic conclusions can be drawn from how somebody deals with his money to the relative priority of his basic needs. When some people do not understand what others do with their money, we can be sure that these people have different motivational schemata. This also demonstrates just how much we tend to project our own need-related beliefs onto others, and to assume our own need structure as the "natural one."

Positive control experiences, i.e. experiences which have enabled a person to successfully bring about effects by his own behavior in line with certain goals, according to Rotter (1966), lead to positive control beliefs, or, according to Bandura (1977 a), to positive self-efficacy expectations. One can see by the formulation I used that the assumption of a control need is a central one in Powers' control theory: Behavior is directed towards creating perceptions in the service of certain goals. Epstein's assumption that the need for control is one of a person's most basic needs should, therefore, already be familiar to us. While Powers never uses the expression "need," his entire model nevertheless presupposes such a need as a central motivation behind all mental processes.

Therapy researcher: According to what you just said, the control need is the need to be able to do something for creating and maintaining one's own goals. It thus refers to the competence aspect of mental activity. It would be a severe violation of the need for control to not be in control of something that is relevant to important goals. Thus, mental disorders which are naturally experienced by the patient as something he cannot control are always a violation of the control need. In therapy, whenever we give the patient something which assists him in coping better with his disorder or problems, or even solving them, we "cure" a bad injury to one of his most important basic needs.

Therefore, it is understandable that successful mastery of a problem in therapy, according to Grawe (1995), not only leads to an improvement of this specific problem, but also usually to a more general improvement in well-being, as one of his most basic needs is now better fulfilled. This explains a well-substantiated finding of therapy research: Disorder-specific therapies which limit themselves to helping the patient in mastering his predominant disorder have generalized positive effects on the patient's well-being if—but only if—the disorder-specific treatment has been successful. Many have been surprised at these far reaching positive effects of disorder-specific interventions. Looking at these findings under the aspects just mentioned, however, they are no longer surprising but correspond precisely to what one should expect.

Therapist: Is it not possible to apply an analog consideration to clarification-oriented therapies as well? In what you just said you emphasized the aspect of control, while in the beginning, you had spoken of the need for **wanting to understand** and to have control. In reality, understanding is indeed a requirement for an effective action control in most cases. If a patient doesn't understand what is going on with him, why he experiences things a certain way, why he behaves the way he does, then working on a better understanding in psychotherapy should also have a "curative" effect with respect to the violation of the control need. So better understanding should have as much of a curative effect on control need as better coping. "Curing by understanding" would, therefore, not only be a comprehensible slogan but an important working mechanism of clarification-oriented therapies.

Therapy researcher: Now that you mention this, a research result which had previously bothered me somewhat comes to mind that I feel I can now better understand. In a study by Meyer (1981), client-centered therapy proved to be somewhat more successful with psychosomatic outpatients than psychoanalytic focal therapy, though the psychoanalysts actually had better expertise in treating such patients and had developed a better understanding of their patients' conflicts.

Considered under the aspect of control experiences, this result makes sense. According to what we just said, the curative effect on the control need depends on the patient getting the feeling **that** he now understands better, not so much what he understands. The psychoanalytic therapists however focused on helping the patient to understand something very specific, namely his central conflict.

It may very well be that therapists who would like to help the patient to attain a certain insight run the danger of overchallenging him with interpretations (Henry et al., 1994). In this instance, the patient may make the experience that he or she is not having control because the control is exerted by the therapist and his interpretations and that he actually does not develop a better understanding. Rather, the patient makes the experience that there is something within him that he does **not** understand. If, however, the therapist always stays very close to the "core of the patient's issues," as in Sachse's (1992) concept of goal-oriented client-centered therapy for instance, increasing the processing depth of the conversation only in small steps, one can imagine that the patient will repeatedly have the experience that he now understands better. Every little improvement in understanding would be a positive experience in the sense of his need for control. This would actually have nothing to do with the therapist's case understanding. We already discussed that understanding the patient's conflicts may definitely help the therapist, especially in relating to him or her in the right fashion. Yet the therapist should always keep in mind—on the side of the patient—that the **experience of** understanding is more important than the **content of understanding**.

In this context, another research finding comes to mind confirming the special nature of the client-centered procedure: The Bern comparative treatment study by Grawe, Caspar and Ambühl (1990 b) I brought up in our first conversation yielded one result I had not yet mentioned. In that study, the patients undergoing client-centered treatment, and only those, had a remarkably strong increase in their internal control beliefs as measured with Rotter's internal-external scale. This increase even continued beyond the completion of therapy. This highly significant increase in the control beliefs must have been the result of better understanding, because the patients subjected to this treatment condition had not undergone any mastery-oriented therapy.

Under the aspect of the control need, naturally it would be most advantageous if the patient made both the experience of a better understanding and being able to actually exercise better control by mastering his problem much better. Together, these would probably have a cumulative, positive effect on the control beliefs.

Psychologist: So many significant correlations between control beliefs and mental health, tolerance for stress, well-being and self-confidence have been found that it is not possible nor necessary to go too deeply into all of these. These correlations have been confirmed so many times that they can be seen as well established. I mention here only a few particularly noteworthy correlations without going deeper into the respective studies. More detailed information can be found in Flammer (1990).

People having higher internal control beliefs are more satisfied with life and more resistant to stress. If one feels helpless in a situation, the same uncomfortable stimuli, such as noise or pain, are experienced as more uncomfortable than if one was exposed to the same stimuli with the awareness that one can avoid or alleviate them if desired.

Consequently, the person who goes through life with positive control expectations, with the feeling of being able to cope with difficulties and aversive things, should they arise, is not only better able to deal with stressful situations but also suffers less from them from the very beginning. High control expectations also have a definitive protective value and are an important component of mental health.

This also holds up in the negative sense. Not being able to control aversive events is oftentimes experienced even more uncomfortably than the aversive events themselves. When having the choice, people prefer to choose to inflict pain upon themselves over having to wait without any control over whether and when an expected pain stimulus will occur. This is important for an understanding of "neurotic behavior." A person with strong fears of rejection and disappointments may bring about what he fears through his own behavior rather than expose himself without "protection," i.e. without control, to the situations in which he might be rejected or disappointed. He, therefore, makes repeated experiences confirming his fears but makes these experiences under his own control, and that is easier for him to take than being exposed to them without the chance to have control.

People often behave irrationally regarding the satisfaction of their basic needs. In order to satisfy the need for a close relationship, for instance, it is required to make oneself dependent on another person to a certain degree. This opens the possibility for being hurt. Sometimes it is exactly those people with an especially strong desire for a close relationship who do everything to prevent closeness. This can be better understood if one considers behavior not only as determined by the attachment need but simultaneously by the control need. People are especially sensitive to the loss of control regarding things that are most important to them. Those wanting closeness very much, but not having high control beliefs in this respect, are especially sensitive to the violation of their control need and are, therefore, striving for control which may protect them from an uncontrollable disappointment. In the interest of her control need, the respective person behaves in such a way that her need for a close relationship will not be satisfied.

In my opinion, the satisfaction or protection of one need at the expense of another can contribute a great deal to the understanding of mental disorders. Later, I will give you a few more examples after I have discussed the other needs.

How do people respond if they are restricted in their need for control? One aspect of a person's control need is being able to do what one wants to do, even if one would actually not do it. If people are restricted in their possibilities for control they tend to respond with reactance (Wortman & Brehm, 1975). Whatever is prohibited becomes very attractive. If alcohol is prohibited, everything begins to revolve around alcohol. If the choice of a study program or the access to university seminars is restricted, everyone suddenly wants to do exactly what has been restricted. This can be used therapeutically: If a therapist prohibits a couple with sexual difficulties from having sex with one another for a certain period of time, then what was a "must" before may become a freedom that gives the situation an entirely different meaning.

Even aggressive acts and destruction can give oneself a strong feeling of effectiveness; to visibly cause something with one's own behavior. In situations where one experiences sheer powerlessness, destroying can, in that instance, have a liberating, positive meaning with respect to the frustrated need for control. To cause fear in others with one's own behavior may have the same function. Wherever the feeling of power-lessness and lack of self-efficacy spreads, there is an increased tendency towards vio-lent acts and destruction. In such situations, it is necessary to give the respective per-sons the feeling of being able to cause effects in line with their goals, utilizing behav-iors other than aggression and destruction. This will change the actual cause of the aggression, namely the violated control need.

Therapist: Similar reactions are found in patients. Some get into a state where they have the uncontrollable need to hurt themselves or otherwise cause severe damage to themselves. With respect to the need for increasing pleasure or avoiding pain, such behavior seems completely incomprehensible. Yet, according to what you just said, one may conceive of such behavior as a desperate attempt to cause an experience of one's own effectiveness. Given this, it can then be assumed that patients doing some-thing like that act out of a feeling of desperate powerlessness, that is to say, those are patients whose control need has been badly violated.

Psychologist: One can also feel paralyzed and not having any power in a conflict. Powerlessness caused in that way should lead to consequences similar to those caused by other severe violations of the control need. This can even happen at the animal level. I remember an experiment done in Pavlov's laboratory where a dog in a discrimination learning paradigm learned to react to a circle in one way, and to an ellipse in another. Then the circle and the ellipse were more and more closely approximated to one an-other, until the dog could no longer distinguish between them. Animals exposed to such a procedure got into such a tortured state of agitation that one may speak of ex-perimental neuroses.

Therapy researcher: This reminds me of the state of learned helplessness that Seligman (Seligman & Maier, 1967) and many other researchers produced in dogs, other animals and eventually in people by exposing them to uncontrollable, uncomfort-able stimuli. In the course of the experimental procedure, the animals obviously be-came convinced that their behavior had no effect on the aversive stimuli. This brought them into a state that Seligman compared with that of depression. In this state, test animals and subjects were no longer even able to use objectively existing control pos-sibilities. In people, the effects of an experienced helplessness strongly depends on their attribution of their lack of control. If they take it personally, if they assess it to be not only temporary, but chronic, if they think it is global and not just situation-specific, and if it is personally significant things that cannot be controlled, then experiencing lack of control can actually have severe effects on a person's state of mind that come close to that of a depression (Abramson, Seligman & Teasdale, 1978; Abramson, Metalsky & Alloy, 1989). In rats exposed to such a condition lack of control for a longer period of time, and only in those, massive ulcers were found following these experiments.

In my eyes, all this indicates to us that the need for control is an indispensable basic need not only in people but also in other higher living creatures, the violation of which may have severe effects on mental health.

2.38   The Need for Increasing Pleasure and Avoiding Pain

The second basic need is the striving to achieve pleasurable experiences and to avoid painful or uncomfortable ones. In other words, people strive for an optimal balance of pleasure vs. displeasure. This corresponds to Freud's pleasure principle: **increasing pleasure and avoiding pain.**

Pleasure and displeasure are inherent components of people's biological templates. This becomes even more obvious when we consider that our innate affective reaction systems are designed to produce these two experiential qualities. Pleasure and displeasure are perceived from the very beginning of our lives, and throughout life they remain the most important feedback in the development of optimally adjusted behavior. With their emphasis on the principles of reinforcement and punishment, behaviorists viewed the regulation of pleasure/displeasure as the most important psychological regulatory principle of all. At least in this respect, they seemed to agree with Freud.

Depending on the kinds of experiences a person has during childhood, he will come to see the environment as a source of positive or negative experiences. Over time, he will then develop an optimistic or pessimistic attitude or outlook on life. People who have become optimists by virtue of positive early experiences will typically also have acquired the goals and capabilities that allow for the continuous confirmation of these positive expectations. An optimist believes that the world is generally good and a source of joy.

The meaning of this basic need is obvious, and it corresponds entirely to subjective experience. Therefore, there is little reason to explain its significance any further. Instead, it may be more important to acknowledge that this cannot be the only basic need. Indeed, even Freud recognized this point. It became increasingly obvious to him that certain phenomena cannot be explained if the pleasure principle is assumed to be the only regulatory principle.

For instance, the recurrent nightmares reported by returning World War I soldiers did not seem to be wish-fulfilling, in the sense of the pleasure principle. In *Beyond the Pleasure Principle* Freud (1920), influenced by such observations, developed the concepts of the death instinct and repetition compulsion. The concept of repetition compulsion allowed him to account for phenomena that the pleasure principle alone could not explain; including, for example, recurrent nightmares following traumatic experiences.

Epstein, in contrast, conceptualizes such post-traumatic disorders quite differently. He views them as a continuous effort and failure to assimilate actual experiences into existing schemata. A person who sees the world as good, secure, and controllable may simply not succeed in assimilating to his implicit schemata the horrifying experiences witnessed in war. This also holds true for other traumatic experiences, such as rape, catastrophes, torture, and other violent acts. Psychological activity is continuously focused on the discrepancy between core beliefs and incongruent perceptions. Experiences that are emotionally overwhelming cannot simply be forgotten. Both the discrepancy itself and the adjustment of the schemata to the horrible reality cause anxiety. Because the experiences cannot be assimilated into existing schemata, they also cannot be "filed away" in memory. Thus, the memories repeatedly intrude into conscious awareness.

Three possibilities arise:

1. The traumatic memories are "split off." I will discuss such dissociation phenomena later when we focus on the consistency principle. Once split off, the memories are

not necessarily rendered "harmless." One might say they become a mental time bomb, ready to explode at any given moment.

2. The discrepancy between core positive beliefs and actual traumatic perceptions is alleviated as the positive schemata accommodate to the traumatic experiences. Once this is accomplished, the world will no longer be experienced as good, secure and controllable. Such a negative shift in core beliefs may have long-term negative effects on mental well-being. Catlin and Epstein (1992) reported on a study of Vietnam war veterans, where the progressive worsening of soldier's core beliefs over a 15 year time period was linked to the deterioration of their mental status.

3. The traumatic experiences are actively processed and assimilated into existing schemata, which—in turn—are also altered to some degree. As a consequence of such processing, the person may become a little "sadder and wiser" as Catlin and Epstein put it. This kind of change is promoted in therapies that are effective for the treatment of post-traumatic stress disorders.

These considerations actually do not belong in a chapter that deals with the need for increasing pleasure and avoiding pain. They have more to do with the first basic need and with the consistency principle. Nevertheless, these ideas suggest themselves at this point because they demonstrate that we cannot explain many clinical phenomena with the pleasure principle alone. The other basic needs may be less obvious, but they are indispensable for a full understanding of mental disorders.

Avoiding fear, pain, disappointment and other uncomfortable feelings plays a crucial role in the development of avoidance schemata. Such schemata, in turn, have quite an important function in the development of mental disorders. The attempt to avoid aversive emotions clearly plays a role in all mental disorders. Aversive emotions emerge when other basic needs are violated; positive emotions when they are fulfilled. In this sense the basic need is pervasive, permeating all of mental functioning.

The implicit assumption of such a basic need is reflected in a wide range of societal and social processes. Why do we give presents to our children? We want to make them happy. Efforts to make others happy are based on the implicit assumption that people are inherently motivated to experience joy. The assumption of such a motivation is also supported by the finding that happiness, as one of the basic emotions, is driven by a distinct biological system. Similar arguments could be formulated with respect to pain, disappointment and fear. The need for creating positive and avoiding negative emotions is so basic for human beings and other highly developed creatures that no theory of mental functioning can afford to ignore it. Without the assumption of such a need we would not be able to explain much of mental life.

2.39   The Need for Attachment

Although it was Aristotle who defined man as a *zoon politikon*—or social/political animal, meant to exist in the context of a community—it took a surprisingly long time until the attachment of a person to his fellow human beings was granted the status of an independent basic need. This has changed only recently. In his theory, Freud did not assume any independent need for attachment; anything having to do with the interpersonal domain was subordinated to the pleasure principle. For a long time, no psychologist took on the task of postulating or scientifically elaborating such a basic need. It is mainly due to the combined influence of Sullivan's (1953) interpersonal view of mental disorders and Bowlby's (1969, 1975, 1976, 1983) attachment theory that interpersonal needs finally receive the attention they deserve in psychological theory and research.

We already discussed the developments initiated by Sullivan, so I will now focus on Bowlby's attachment theory. This is also appropriate given that it was Bowlby who first postulated the child's innate need to seek and maintain proximity to a person who manages life better than the child himself. If this need is fulfilled, the child can be at ease and turn to other things, but if the attachment person is not within reach, psychological activity is focused on restoring proximity. The fact that small children seek proximity to one or more reference persons was interpreted by Bowlby as a **basic need for closeness to a reference person**.

Motivational schemata develop around this basic need that influence a person's behavior in relationships throughout life. The exact nature of these relationship schemata will depend largely on the availability and sensitivity of reference persons in early childhood. In a good relationship, the caregiver always provides a place of refuge, giving protection, security and comfort. What Erikson (1959) refers to as "basic trust" develops from this. According to Ainsworth (1982), who has performed the most important empirical studies on attachment behavior, a "secure base" remains important for a person's lifelong mental and physical well-being. For most people a partner relationship later takes over such a function. The kind of partner relationship sought and created later in life depends largely on the relationship experiences with early caregivers, which become manifested over time in his motivational schemata.

Bowlby summarized the core of his attachment theory in three postulates:

"1. If a person trusts that an attachment figure is available whenever he wishes, this individual will be less likely to have intense or chronic anxiety than another person who, for some reason, does not have such trust.

2. Trust in the availability of an attachment person, or the lack thereof, develops gradually in the early years—early childhood, childhood, and youth—and the expectations formed in these years remain relatively unchanged for the rest of life.

3. Experiences related to the accessibility and responsiveness of attachment figures that different individuals acquire in their early years are rather accurate reflections of experiences that these individuals have already made" Bowlby (1976, p. 246).

The expectations and trust Bowlby speaks of correspond to Epstein's motivational schemata and basic beliefs. The child internalizes early dyadic relational experiences. These later manifest themselves in his brain in the form of perceptual, behavioral, and emotional reaction tendencies as well as motivational tendencies. Bowlby calls the inner manifestation of these experiences the "inner working model." What he refers to as the inner working model corresponds to the role-relationship model by Horowitz (1989) and Grawe's (1986) relational schemata, which we talked about earlier.

"As an organizational pattern of ideas about oneself, of attachment persons, and of relationships, the inner working model provides a framework for how much someone expects closeness and security in a relationship with an attachment partner, and to what extent somebody feels he deserves care, love and attention, and can thus allow intimacy. While the model is generally open to allow for new experiences and changes, it does direct future expectations and experiences within intimate relationships, so that new experiences continuously impact the model in a stabilizing fashion" (Schmidt & Strauss, 1996, p. 141).

These quotes from Bowlby and other researchers in this field demonstrate that attachment theory can be integrated seamlessly with the ideas we previously developed. Attachment motivation may be regarded as a basic need, consistent with Epstein's ideas, and the "inner working model" may be viewed as the motivational and descriptive schemata related to this need. Perhaps it would make sense to further specify the nature of these attachment-related motivational schemata.

According to these ideas, unfavorable relationship schemata develop when proximity with the attachment person cannot be established, or when the attachment persons lacks "sensitivity." That is, when the reference person is either consistently unavailable or inconsistently-unpredictably available.

"Being rejected leads to the child's emotional alienation from the attachment person. The unpredictability of a caregiver makes the child overly dependent on the reference person; that is to say, the attachment system is chronically activated due to the fear of losing the attachment person. In an undisturbed attachment relationship, the child receives comfort, care and protection if he or she demands it, and can also pursue his or her curiosity and social wishes for new friendships without being unduly restricted or punished by the caregiver" (Grossmann, 1990, p. 232).

Ainsworth and associates (Ainsworth et al., 1978) developed a standardized observation procedure for studying how children reacted to separation from their primary caregivers. Children between the ages of 11 and 20 months were studied. Many other researchers later carried out empirical studies on attachment behavior utilizing this observational instrument (in this context, see overviews by Schmidt & Strauss, 1996; as well as Strauss & Schmidt, 1997).

Four repeatedly recurring **attachment patterns** emerged from these studies. These patterns might be viewed as reflections of children's emerging relationship schemata:

1. Children with **secure** attachment behavior. They respond to a separation from the mother with worry and immediately seek proximity upon her return. This attachment pattern is accompanied by a positive basic trust and enables the child to develop conflict-free intentional schemata to satisfy the need for attachment.
2. Children with **insecure attachment and avoidant** relationship behavior. They avoid, after a separation, closeness and contact with the mother and already fail to react to the separation with the apprehension that securely bonded children usually display.
3. Children with **insecure attachment and ambivalent** relationship behavior. These children are very anxious during the separation and, upon the mother's return, display behavior varying between aggressive rejection of contact and seeking closeness. After a separation these children are entirely focused on the relationship and not free to participate in any other activities.
4. Children with **insecure attachment and disorganized/disoriented** relational behavior (Main, 1991). These children react to both the separation from and the return of the attachment person with bizarre and stereotypical behaviors.

In the studies by Ainsworth et al. (1978), two-thirds of children displayed the secure attachment pattern. Nonetheless, a third of the children in a random (American) sample between 11 and 20 months of age already display relationship behavior strongly marked by avoidance and/or negative emotions. So even at such a young age these children have rudimentary avoidance schemata, which will disadvantageously affect the further course of their relationship experiences. About five years later, Main, Kaplan and Cassidy (1985) and Grossman and Grossman (1991) conducted follow-up studies among children whose attachment pattern had been researched when they were between the ages of 11 and 20 months. At the time of the follow-up, they were six years of age. The researchers were able to show that in about 80% of the children the attachment patterns had remained stable throughout this time. The studies revealed significant differences between children with secure and insecure attachment patterns at preschool age with respect to play behavior, social contact behavior, balance and fluency of communication as well as autonomy and self-trust (Erickson, Sroufe & Egeland, 1985; Grossmann et al., 1985; Main, Kaplan & Cassidy, 1985; Renken et al., 1989). The differences were always in favor of those children having secure attachment patterns.

What leads to an insecure attachment pattern? According to the studies by Ainsworth et al. (1978) and Grossman et al. (1985, 1989), it is the lack of availability of the primary caregivers on the one hand, and low "motherly sensitivity" on the other. Sensitivity means at least perceiving the infant's reactions and behaviors, interpreting them from the infant's perspective and not from one's own, responding promptly to the infant's behavior so that the infant experiences his behavior as effective (the child makes control experiences, as discussed in the section on the control need), and adequately reacting to the infant's developmental state. Infants with sensitive mothers reveal much less anger, respond much less anxiously and aggressively, and communicate in a more differentiated fashion.

So a person's relationship experiences made as early as the first months of life lay the foundation for relational schemata, which, in turn, exert an early influence on the child's later relationship behavior. It is very likely, then, that feedback processes confirm these early schemata. The availability, and particularly the sensitivity of the infant's primary attachment person has a decisive influence in this process. Sensitivity is the result of a person's own relationship experiences, including those from their early childhood. Benoit and Parker (1994) studied attachment styles among mothers using the adult attachment interview, a frequently employed instrument used for recording the attachment patterns in adults. Based on the knowledge of mothers' attachment styles, they were able to predict in 81% of the cases which attachment style the children exhibited. The attachment patterns of grandchildren were even predicted in 75% of the cases, based on the attachment style of their grandmothers! Main et al. (1985) came up with similar results as did Grossman et al. (1989). What comes to mind here are Goethe's words of Prometheus : "It is the curse of the evil deed that it has to continuously give birth to evil."

Therapist: All these research results confirm an experience long known in therapy practice; namely, that relationship patterns often continue across generations. These findings seem to suggest that a therapist should also, whenever possible, take a look at a patient's primary caregivers because important information may be gained by looking at them about relationship processes that the patient is unable to report on.

Attempts to find out about familial patterns by using genograms (McGoldrick & Gerson, 1990) also receive empirical confirmation from these results. Obviously, targeted interventions are frequently needed in order to disrupt such relationship patterns across generations. I can hardly imagine that the mothers and grandmothers in these studies had any awareness for these cross-generational patterns, and their children, naturally, had even less. These relationship experiences are entered into memory long before the verbal code that allows for conscious recall has developed.

What you just mentioned certainly has far-reaching implications for psychotherapy. We are typically completely unaware of these attachment patterns and relational schemata, which are so important for our later relationship behavior. These patterns can, in fact, only be stored in implicit, nonverbal memory. Evidently, they will later be activated bottom-up, because, as we have heard, they influence the relationship behavior on a long-term basis. Yet memory contents acquired so early can, in fact, later only be unconscious. And it really makes no sense to speak of suppression. Violations of the need for attachment occur predominantly in early childhood. They are coded from the beginning in such a way that they must be unconscious later. Truly, such people may not know as adults why they behave as they do in relationships.

Therapy researcher: I agree with you that the results of attachment research are of utmost relevance for psychotherapy. All the necessary consequences have by no means been drawn from that, and this really comes as no surprise. Two studies by Schmidt and Strauss (1996), and Strauss and Schmidt (1997), which were aimed at expressly making psychotherapists aware of this significance, have just recently been published. Both of these overviews are among the most interesting material I have read in recent times. In fact, they present quite new dimensions for the significance of the relationship aspect in psychotherapy.

Psychologist: This is exactly what I was getting at. The relevance becomes even clearer if we also include the research on adult attachment behavior. Over the last ten years this research has seen quite some explosive development. Numerous questionnaire and interview methods for recording adult attachment styles have been developed. Schmidt and Strauss (1996, p. 147) offer an overview of these methods.

Berman and Sperling (1994, p. 8) define attachment among adults in the following way:

"Adult attachment is the stable tendency of an individual to make substantial efforts to seek and maintain proximity to and contact with one or a few specific individuals who provide the subjective potential for physical and/or psychological safety and security. This stable tendency is regulated by inner working models of attachment, which are cognitive-affective-motivational schemata built from the individual's experience in his or her interpersonal world."

I think this can literally be adopted by us as a definition of the adult attachment need. According to this definition it becomes obvious that the adult attachment need can actually only be satisfied in the context of a stable partner relationship. In functioning partner relationships, both partners usually satisfy their attachment need reciprocally by each giving and receiving closeness, protection, and a sense of security.

I do not think I need to prove to you the great importence a well functioning relationship has for a person's happiness in life. The failure and the loss of a relationship generally are among the most painful experiences people endure, and may have a devastating influence on their well-being and mental health. People will take on almost anything to avoid such a loss: the worst devaluation of self-esteem, relinquishing control, accepting intense displeasure. This demonstrates the eminent significance of the need for a close relationship.

According to the definition by Berman and Sperling, the ability to create a good relationship is a direct function of a person's interpersonal motivational schemata. Interpersonal schemata may be of fundamental significance for psychotherapy. Whenever a patient is not in a happy relationship—something that can be relatively easily established—the therapist has good reason to focus on the patient's relational schemata.

Collins and Read (1990) have studied the connection between attachment patterns and the quality of a couple's relationship. They do not categorically distinguish the attachment patterns, but proceeded from three continuous dimensions, closeness, trust and fear. In combination, the two dimensions "allowing closeness" and "fear of being abandoned" turned out to be especially important to the quality of the relationship. Accordingly, persons having a secure attachment pattern have little fear of being abandoned and are able to allow closeness. Insecure-avoidant people can allow only little closeness and have a great fear of being abandoned, and insecure-ambivalent persons are able to allow closeness, but have a great fear of being abandoned. Figure 2.22 graphically illustrates these three types of attachment by placing them in a space that stretches between the two dimensions fear of being abandoned, and accepting closeness.

According to this and many other studies, it appears that a secure attachment pattern— the presence of well constructed intentional schemata for creating and allowing closeness and little fear of being abandoned—is an important requirement for a well functioning relationship and, at the same time, effective protection against the development of mental and psychosomatic disorders. People with insecure attachment patterns, however, are at increased risk for developing mental and psychosomatic disorders.

Therapist: When viewing attachment patterns from a therapeutic perspective, the insecure-avoidant attachment pattern corresponds to a "negative emotional schema," consistent with Grawe (1986), or that which we earlier termed conflict schema: Mental activity is no longer focused on satisfying the attachment need, but towards protection from any other damage. The strong predominance of avoidance in interpersonal situations prevents the development of motivational schemata that could create satisfying relationships. A therapist treating persons with such an attachment pattern can expect hard work. Not only is it especially difficult in such a constellation to achieve a good therapeutic relationship, but such a therapy would, in most cases, also have to have the goal of changing something about the patient's attachment pattern, as the problems which prompted the patient to seek therapy are likely related to the unsatisfactory fulfillment of his attachment need. For a patient with such an attachment pattern, establishing a good therapeutic relationship means much more than just creating good conditions for therapy. A great deal of the therapy will be spent on establishing a good therapeutic relationship. If the patient were able to give up his insecure-avoidant attachment pattern, through corrective experiences with the therapist, it would mean that very important motivational schemata would have been positively changed, giving him essentially much better possibilities for the future satisfaction of his interpersonal needs.

In line with these considerations, it would be much easier to treat patients with insecure-ambivalent attachment, because of the positive intentional schemata they have for satisfying the attachment need. All that is lacking is the trust in the security of the relationship. It would be mostly fears that would have to be weakened here. But even for those patients the therapy, for the most part, would have to be interpersonal in focus.

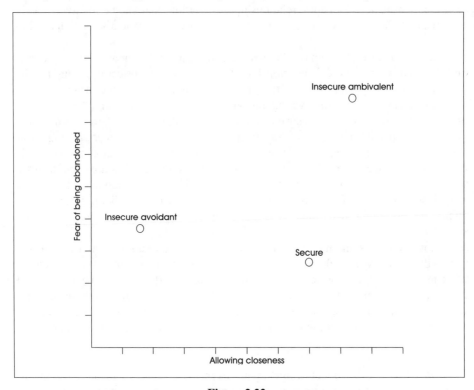

Figure 2.22:
Three different attachment patterns as a function of the two variables "fear of being aban-doned" and "allowing closeness" according to Schmidt and Strauss (1996, p.146).

It should be relatively easy to create a good therapeutic relationship with patients who have a secure attachment pattern, and the modification of the interpersonal sche-mata should be less of an issue for these people. If there are important basic needs unmet among those patients, these would most likely be ones other than the attachment need.

Psychologist: As discussed earlier, the particular difficulty in treating patients with avoidance schemata is that the avoidance strategies also prevent the respective wishes, fears and emotions from becoming conscious. Where such avoidance strategies con-cern the need for closeness, Bowlby refers to "emotional alienation."

"The information removed in emotionally alienated children and adults is of a special nature... What is removed in these pathological states are signals coming from within and from the outside which would usually activate an attachment behavior, along with accompanying thoughts, emotions and wishes and which allow one to both love and be loved... This form of exclusion is nothing other than repression. In the same way that Freud views repression as the main process of every form of defense, I view defensive exclusion. And further still, just as Freud pointed out that what is repressed may return at any time, I am emphasizing that a deactivated system is ready to be activated at any time" (Bowlby, 1987, p. 71).

According to our ideas about psychological functioning so far, one would have to put this a different way. The mental structures (schemata) formed around the need for closeness in insecure-avoidant persons are, for instance, not deactivated in potential closeness situations, but highly activated, and it is particularly this activation which prevents them from becoming conscious. It is because no intentional (approach) schemata, but only avoidance schemata have developed. The avoidance takes place in the implicit mode of functioning. Therefore, there is no awareness for the avoidance.

When somebody **does not** do or experience a certain thing, the reason may be that they have not developed a motivational schema in this area. However, the reason may also be that there is an avoidance schema activated in these situations. The latter would mean that the not-doing and not-experiencing have an active property. In persons with an insecure attachment pattern we have to assume an active avoidance of the act of becoming aware and not a deactivation of an attachment need. There is an interesting study by Dozier and Kobak (1992) concerning this possibility. They studied galvanic skin response as an indicator for emotional reactions during an adult attachment interview with youths. The teenagers, who, judging by their behavior in this interview, had to be seen as the insecure avoidant type, while verbally avoiding the attachment relevant topics, simultaneously demonstrated an increase in the GSR. With their implicit systems they responded to the topics associated with negative emotions; however, in the rational mode of functioning, they simultaneously excluded these topics from consciousness.

Therapist: Given all that we are discussing here, it would be extremely helpful for a therapist to know in advance whether she is dealing with a patient who has a secure or insecure attachment pattern. You mentioned before that there are numerous methods available for measuring attachment patterns in adults. With sufficiently economic instruments for therapeutic practice, one should actually be able to routinely assess a patient's attachment pattern prior to the beginning of therapy. This would leave a therapist prepared from the beginning for what awaits her in therapy regarding the relationship.

Therapy researcher: This is a good idea. I do not believe that this is already being done anywhere. For the most part, problems in the patient's relational behavior are commonly identified with the "Inventory of Interpersonal Problems (IIP)" by Horowitz (Horowitz, Strauss & Kordy, 1994), with the "Impact Message Inventory (IMI)" by Kiesler (1983, 1986; Kiesler et al., 1976), or with a self- or other assessment according to the model of the "Structural Analysis of Social Behavior (SASB)" by Benjamin

(1974). All three procedures are based on the "Interpersonal Circumplex Model," which dates back to Leary (1957). According to this model, interpersonal behavior is circularly arranged, with a horizontal axis having the two poles "positive vs. negative affect" and a vertical axis having the poles dominance/control vs. submission/dependence. In empirical studies, these two axes have repeatedly turned out to be the fundamental dimensions of the "interpersonal space," in which people can maneuver their interpersonal behavior. The IIP serves to locate the patient's interpersonal problems in this interpersonal space. Figure 2.23 illustrates how that might look.

The patient described has problems, for instance, with being too unfriendly and cool (avoiding closeness) towards others and simultaneously relating to them "from above"; that is, in a criticizing or aggressive fashion. We can assume that patients predominantly interacting with behaviors in the left part of interpersonal space have an avoidant attachment style, because they create and allow little closeness.

The IIP by Horowitz requires a certain self-insight and openness on the part of the patient because using this instrument, the patient himself is asked to describe his problems in relationships. The IMI by Kiesler and the SASB procedure by Benjamin do not focus on interpersonal **problems** but on overall interpersonal behavior. The IMI entails an assessment from a person who knows the patient well. As a result, it describes what kind of impression the patient makes on others. Naturally, this perspective differs from the assessment he himself makes with respect to his interpersonal problems.

The SASB procedure sets things up differently from the beginning. It is based on placing every single statement made by the patient in the interpersonal circumplex model. Therapists familiar with this procedure can quickly locate the interpersonal behavior of others in the interpersonal space. Additionally, the procedure considers towards whom the interaction is directed. Therapists having good command of this system need no other measures to characterize a patient's interpersonal style in clinical practice. All three procedures consider patients whose interactions are located in the left part of the interpersonal space as most likely to have insecure attachment patterns.

These procedures may be viewed as an aid in the identification of attachment patterns. They also have the advantage of measuring more than just this one aspect. Horowitz, Rosenberg and Kalehzan (1992) have found, for instance, that patients with interpersonal problems in the upper left quadrant of interpersonal space were less successful in psychodynamic therapies than persons with problems in other parts of interpersonal space. This makes good sense, because creating a good therapeutic relationship with an arrogant or unfriendly-aggressive patient is not easy. These patients are most likely difficult to deal with for all therapists, but this has not yet been established for other forms of therapy.

My description of instruments based on the interpersonal circumplex model was not intended to imply that we do not need more economic instruments to measure a patient's attachment pattern. The interpersonal circumplex model is suited to describe and classify the patient's attachment behavior, but it was not functionally designed for this purpose. Thinking about the patient's attachment need leads to a functional view of his psychological activity, which immediately suggests therapeutic interventions. Therefore, I think that the explicit consideration of a patient's attachment pattern is a valuable addition to previous interpersonal approaches to psychotherapy.

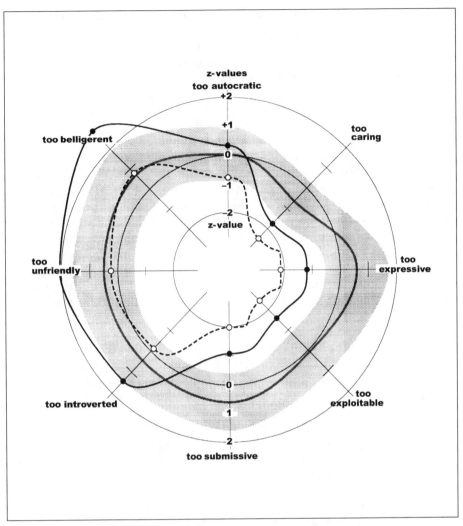

Figure 2.23:

Test profile of a patient in the IIP. The patient described assesses his behavior (prior to therapy) in his interpersonal relationships as too belligerent, unfriendly and introverted. The special nature of the individual patient stands out in this graphic representation against the background of the normal population (the circular zero-line) and a clinical reference group (gray curved band with the shaded area) corresponding to a standard deviation above and below the mean value of the clinical reference group. This form of illustration is called a "figuration."

Using a special "figuration analysis" computer program such figurations can be developed for measuring instruments of all kinds (Grawe & Baltensperger, 1998; see also legend for Figure 3.8).

This form of illustration can also be used for representing changes. The consistent black line connecting the points represents the patient's condition prior to therapy, the broken line, his condition following therapy. Following therapy the patient claims to have fewer interpersonal problems in all areas.

Psychologist: I would like to return once again to attachment research. Even among non-human primates the great significance of secure attachment is well established (Todt, 1995). According to animal research, the limbic system plays a crucial role in the regulation of attachment behavior (Capitiano, Weissberg & Reite, 1985; Steklis & Kling, 1985). I mentioned earlier that the limbic system plays a crucial role for the emotions as well. It seems that the regulation of attachment has to be attributed by and large to the implicit mode of functioning. Earlier we already speculated that the implicit regulation processes are likely to be connected to biological regulation processes rather than the rational mode of functioning. Therefore, one might speculate that the attachment system is associated rather closely with physical occurrences via the emotions and via the limbic system. Some empirical evidence does in fact exist for this. Gunnar et al. (1996) found a stronger cortisol reaction—considered to be an indication for stress—in anxiety-inhibited two-year old children following a psychological stress situation among insecure rather than the secure children. Strauss and Schmidt (1997, p. 6) write about the connection between attachment behavior and biological processes:

"In man as well, there is already some evidence for an interdependence between physiological processes and the attachment behavior system. Especially cardiovascular, immunological and endocrine reactions have been studied in this respect. As a result, attachment theory is given potential significance for the understanding of psychosomatic reactions..."

In addition, Strauss and Schmidt report on studies in which disadvantageous coping behavior was found in persons with an insecure-avoidant attachment style. So overall, there are many indications that particularly the insecure-avoidant attachment style is accompanied by risk factors for decreased mental and physical health, whereas the secure attachment style functions protectively with respect to such disorders.

Translating attachment style into the language of motivational schemata, it means that people who have developed conflict-free intentional schemata for establishing close relationships in their early childhood are much less susceptible to physical or mental health disorders later, whereas the early development of closeness-avoidant schemata or of conflictual interpersonal schemata later develops more frequently into disorders.

Therapy researcher: For mental disorders, such a connection is, of course, even more obvious than for physical disorders. Although research is still in its early stages, it can be seen today as already established that persons having an insecure attachment pattern are, by far, much more likely to develop mental disorders than persons having a secure attachment behavior. In the article by Strauss and Schmidt (1997, p. 9) there is, for example, a table listing eleven studies in which significant connections between attachment patterns and mental disorders were found (see table 2.4).

In light of such findings the question naturally arises whether very specific attachment patterns go hand in hand with very specific mental disorders. Strauss and Schmidt arrive at the following assessment regarding this question: "All in all, it appears unlikely that certain populations with defined mental disorders demonstrate specific attachment characteristics. For instance, in an analysis of studies on attachment quality and agoraphobia, De Ruiter and Van Ijzendoorn (1992) arrive at the result that agoraphobic patients are largely ambivalent in their attachments, compared to mentally healthy persons (compare also Thomson, 1986; Liotti, 1991). However, the ambivalent attach-

Table 2.4
Studies on the association of specific attachment patterns with mental disorders.
The tables were taken from Strauss and Schmidt (1977, p. 9).

Authors	Sample	Results
Dozier (1990)	14 schizophrenic, 28, depressive patients	increased attachment insecurity in both groups, more frequently among schizophrenics
Dozier et al. (1992)	21 schizophrenic, 18 depressive patients	among the schizophrenics, by comparison, more frequently distanced attachment
Carnelley et al. (1994)	25 depressive patients	attachment pattern predicts later interpersonal ability better than degree of depression
Harris & Bifulco (1991)	reanalysis of Walttharnstow study (225 women)	5 out of 6 attachment patterns were attributed to depressive patients, according to Bowlby (forced care = 60%)
Cole & Kobak (1991)	65 students (male and female) with eating disorders and/or depressive symptoms	eating disorders only-distanced pattern, depression only-ambivalent pattern, eating disorder + depression-both patterns
Fonagy et al. (1994)	85 psychiatric patients	90% insecurely attached, high proportion of unprocessed experiences of abuse in borderline patients
Patrick et al. (1994)	12 patients w/ borderline disorder, 12 patients with dysthymia	12 borderline patients vs. 4 dysthymia w/ complicated attachment: in 6 borderline patients vs.0 dysthymia patients indications for unresolved trauma
Sperling et al. (1991)	24 borderline patients	borderline patients in comparison to student population mostly insecurely attached; dependent attachment style in borderline population correlates with less pathology
Adam (1994)	132 psychiatrical symptomatic youths	80% insecurely attached, considerable portion suicidal
van Ijzendoorn (quoted in Scheidt & Waller, 1996)	meta-analysis of AAI-results	proportion of insecure attachment in clinical populations: 41% insecure-avoidant; 46.5% insecure-ambivalent; 12.5% secure; correspondingly in control group of "healthy individuals": 23.2% vs. 17.6% vs. 59.2%
De Ruiter & van Ijzendoorn (1992)	Overview on studies on agoraphobics	proportion of ambivalent patterns very high among agoraphobics, but not specific to the disorder

ment pattern played a role in the etiology of other neurotic disorders as well, so it was not specific to this disorder. As a result, according to current research, one can merely state that an insecure attachment will increase the susceptibility for developing psychopathological disorders—in this respect Bowlby talks about pathogenic development" (Strauss & Schmidt, 1997, p. 19).

Attachment patterns other than the secure type lead to the failure of optimal fulfillment of the need for a close relationship. Each of the insecure attachment patterns develops from violations to this basic need. This violation of the basic need for security and interpersonal protection most likely comprises one of the most important breeding grounds for the development of mental disorders. Some of the numbers listed in Table 2.4 speak very clearly for themselves: While in a normal control group, approximately 59% of the persons studied had a secure attachment pattern, the percentage in a mixed clinical population was only around 12%. Forty-one percent of the patients had an insecure-avoidant, and 47% an insecure-ambivalent attachment pattern. All in all, 88% of the clinically symptomatic patients exhibited insecure attachment patterns. In the study by Fonagy et al. (1994), the percentage of insecure attachment patterns in a mixed sample of psychiatric patients was very close to that figure namely 90%. The conclusion is, therefore, that mental disorders are almost always accompanied by an insecure attachment pattern or: In almost all individuals with mental disorders, evidence for violation of the attachment need can be found.

Certainly these statements are still too general. A priority should be established that the attachment patterns be better specified by more research. Most likely, the insecure attachment patterns need to be further differentiated. Pilkonis, Heape, and Proietti (1991), in an attempt to differentiate the various kinds of depressive disorders, for example, already differentiate six different insecure attachment patterns. Cole and Kobak (1991) found frequent insecure-ambivalent attachment patterns among patients suffering from depressive disorders and frequent insecure-avoidant attachment patterns among those with eating disorders.

Differentiations between various attachment patterns are, however, certainly most relevant for personality disorders. This is an emphasis of current research (see Strauss and Schmidt, 1997). Utilizing the SASB-model, Benjamin (1993) has specified the personality disorders of Axis II of the DSM on the interpersonal level in a very differentiated fashion, deriving therapeutic recommendations for the interpersonal treatment of the individual disorders. For a causal understanding of personality disorders it would presumably be constructive to empirically study what the attachment patterns are that produce the individual disorders, although as I said earlier, it is highly unlikely that individual attachment patterns lead to very specific disorders. Mental disorders are far too multi-causally determined. But such research indications may perhaps yield an understanding of which interpersonal experiences are more likely to result in such personality disorders and, in turn, we may then have some therapeutic information as to which kinds of interpersonal experiences one would have to work on with the patient and process in therapy so that his interpersonal behavior will undergo a long-term change.

Attachment research today has already contributed much to the empirical substantiation of one particular belief that many psychotherapists have long held: Namely that it is the change in interpersonal behavior that is responsible for long-term improvement following treatment. The reported results give more than enough reason that psychotherapists should explicitly and systematically dedicate themselves and their work not only to the diagnosed disorder but also to their patient's interpersonal behavior. The interpersonal perspective we discussed in our first conversation, according to the findings of attachment research, is as important for psychotherapies as is the disorder perspective. Both perspectives should definitely be considered in every psychotherapy.

Therapist: I fully agree with you, but changing attachment patterns is not an easy task for a therapist. This is not only proven by practical experiences prove that, but it is also suggested by the research results we just discussed. According to this research, attachment patterns develop very early and mostly in the context of long-term relationships. Deep memory traces develop, predominantly in implicit memory, which is the reason that patients, for the most part, have no conscious awareness for their own problematic interpersonal behavior. They know that they have relationship problems, but they almost never know how much they actively produce and perpetuate these difficulties. This all happens mostly without awareness.

Therefore, the therapist must initially take responsibility for any changes in interpersonal patterns before he or she is even able to have an exchange about it with the patient, simply because these interpersonal patterns will also have an impact on the therapy, and the therapist will be forced to react to the patient's interpersonal behavior with his own interpersonal behavior. But herein lies one of the great chances for psychotherapy. The decision will be made at the implicit interpersonal level as to whether activating the intentional and avoidant relational schemata is managed in such a way that they can be constructively used and changed in therapy. For patients having very unsatisfactory interpersonal relations, the therapeutic success is decided predominantly on the interpersonal level. This is not to say that these important processes must remain unconscious the entire time. But awareness of them cannot be regarded as the condition for their modification. That these implicit schemata become conscious is both an important tool and partially an outcome of therapeutic influence. When I think about what we have discussed concerning the significance of nonverbal regulation of relationships (sections 2.24-2.26) and about the significance of the attachment need here as well, then one might have to conclude that therapists should, above all, be trained to be relationship experts. Although I have always regarded the therapeutic relationship as important, the extent and clarity of this constitutes a new insight for me.

Psychologist: Perhaps we can return to the practical conclusions arising from this discussion at a later point. I would like to remind you that we are not yet finished with our discourse on basic needs. We have yet to discuss one basic need which many think plays quite a crucial role.

2.40   The Need for Self-Enhancement

"People want to feel good about themselves. They want to believe that they are competent, worthy, and loved by others. This desire for self-enhancement is regarded as so fundamental to human functioning that it was dubbed the 'master sentiment' by William McDougall (1932) and 'the basic law of human life' by the renowned anthropologist Ernest Becker (1971). Many other figures of historical (e.g., Allport, 1943; Cooley, 1902; Mead, 1934) and contemporary (e.g., Baumeister, 1991; Greenwald, 1980; Schlenker, 1985; Steele, 1988; Tesser, 1988) prominence have endorsed the belief that a drive to achieve a positive self-image is, in the words of William James (1890), a direct and elementary endowment of human nature" (Brown, 1993, p. 117).

The list of authors who place the need for self-esteem on the highest level of human needs could easily be extended. Alfred Adler (1920, 1927), for example, who regarded the drive for overcoming the inferiority complex as the most important source of human motivation.

If the need for increased self-esteem is such a central human motive then why is it that so many people have a low self-image and—worse still—why do such people often underrate themselves? Why do they tend to choose interaction partners that think negatively about them (Swann, 1990, 1992)? Why do they withdraw from relationships in which the other person rates them positively (De La Ronde & Swann, 1993)? Social psychologists have recently devoted systematic attention to this "puzzle of low self-regard" (Baumeister, 1993).

How does low self-esteem arise in the first place? Sullivan (1953) provided the following account. He wondered how a small child might respond in an inadequate relationship with a caretaker, where the child's needs are not met or only insufficiently met. In the child's world, there are only two alternatives in such a situation: Either I am good, and mother is bad; or I am bad and mother is good. For a small child who is entirely dependent on his mother, the first alternative would be far worse. The child would then be helplessly dependent on his bad mother, without hope that he can contribute anything to improving the situation. Consistent disappointment would be felt along with this, fear or anger toward the mother, and/or hopelessness. Relative to this other alternative seems to be better: If the child attributes his mother's behavior to his own "bad behavior," thinking that he is not worthy of being treated better, he could at least maintain hope that he might be able to change things. This would at least permit a certain feeling of control.

Thus, a small child whose needs are not satisfied by his caregiver will tend to view himself as the cause for this dissatisfying situation, and—consequently—he will feel bad and worthless. One might expect such interpretations and resulting feelings even in situations where the child did not actually receive rejecting messages from his caregiver. It seems more likely, however, that the child would receive such negative messages, given that an insecure, avoidant child is, in many respects, no joy for his mother. The mother has no awareness for the fact that her child's behavior is caused by her own lack of availability and sensitivity, and she will likely seek the reasons for the unsatisfactory relationship in the child. She might perhaps give the child signals through messages such as: "Why aren't you just like other kids? " She might also yell at the child or criticize him often. The child then internalizes these messages, through the process of identification, and in time develops a stable negative self-image and low self-esteem.

This account of the development of low self-esteem is entirely compatible with the assumption that people have a drive for positive self-regard. In order to meet this need for self-regard, however, people require a suitable environment. If we also consider that the need for increased self-esteem is just one among several basic needs wanting to be satisfied, we can explain—even without resorting to Sullivan—how it is that some people appear to do all they can to perpetuate their negative self-esteem.

This perpetuation of low self-regard is not actually a goal people have, but it is a means of serving other needs. The reasons for this apparent paradox are no more a secret than those of the person who—despite the need for a close relationship—behaves in a way that such a relationship never materializes. In both cases, it is likely that damaging experiences in the realm of a basic need have occurred. Avoidance schemata might then have developed, and one need is "sacrificed" in the interest of another. In most cases it is not possible to adequately understand human behavior if we do not consider the fact that all needs must be met simultaneously. In each case, we must consider the "total balance."

The "executive organs" of the needs are the intentional schemata, which developed as guides towards need fulfillment. These schemata must be sensitive not only to the needs but also to environmental contingencies. According to Epstein, the schemata are "schematized experiences," or hypotheses that predict how under certain conditions— for instance, given a particular mother—the respective need may be satisfied. If none of the attempted means prove useful, no rules arising from such means and experiences can be extracted. Consequently, no intentional schemata are formed.

However, it may not be the case that the environment that would facilitate schema-development is lacking. Instead, the individual's attempts to elicit need-satisfying reactions from the environment may be futile. As we discussed earlier, every futile attempt leads to negative feelings, such as disappointment. However, as we also discussed, humans also have a need to avoid negative emotions, especially when they occur without the possibility of control. Therefore, it is not surprising that the individual will develop schemata that enable him to avoid the disappointment of an unfulfilled need. Situations related to such a need will then no longer trigger approach reactions, but instead will activate avoidance schemata. Eventually, it may appear as though the person's behavior is aimed towards goals that are utterly incompatible with the respective basic need. The "gain" of such counterintuitive behavior becomes obvious when we consider the person's other basic needs: He avoids pain, and he exercises control.

These considerations illustrate the importance of differentiating between goals and needs. Without experiences to make them concrete, needs are not tied to specific goals. Goals are always related to the environment (including one's own body as a form of perceived environment). Goals are always related to something, which is true even when we speak of abstract goals within a schema. The "schematized" or abstract goals within motivational schemata are rules that are extracted from concrete experiences. If a person develops the goal of protecting himself from devaluation and disappointments, it does not mean that he has no need for increased self-esteem. It means that the individual has not developed experience-based goals that would lead toward the fulfillment of such a need.

Such goals might have been extracted as rules from positive, need-fulfilling experiences. However, if such experiences have never or rarely been made, then avoidance schemata are more quickly and more strongly activated than are the approach schemata. The neural activation patterns representing the avoidance schema will thus inhibit those representing the approach schema. Mental activity will then be determined by avoidance goals. These avoidance goals are not pursued in the interest of the need for increased self-esteem but rather in the interest of other basic needs, to avoid pain, to maintain control, and to have a close relationship.

However, the need for increased self-esteem does not simply disappear. Instead, strongly developed avoidance schemata might stand in the way of need-fulfillment.

The situation of people who actively perpetuate their low self-esteem is analogous to that of patients with insecure, avoidant attachment patterns. Thoughts, wishes, or fantasies that would raise self-esteem are blocked by avoidance schemata, as are behaviors that would lead to increased self-esteem. The respective impulse is simply shut out. Individuals with low self-esteem behave in a way that seems to suggest the presence of a drive towards the perpetuation or verification of a negative self-image.

"Self-verification theory assumes that as people mature, they learn that their relationships proceed most smoothly when others see them as they see themselves—even if they see themselves negatively. For example, people discover that those who develop overly positive appraisals may become disappointed and disgruntled with them. Through repeated exposure to this fact of life, people come to associate self-verifying evaluations with feelings of authenticity and non-verifying evaluations with feelings of uneasiness or bemusement. Eventually, these epistemic concerns become functionally autonomous (Allport, 1937) of the interpersonal or pragmatic concerns that originally produced them and people verify for either epistemic or pragmatic reasons. Thus for example, a man with low self-esteem may seek negative evaluations either because he fears the social consequences of being appraised in an overly positive fashion or because his past experiences have convinced him that he should expect to encounter such evaluations. Thus, both epistemic and pragmatic considerations may motivate people to seek self-verifying appraisals, even if this means displaying a preference for unfavorable evaluations" (De La Ronde & Swann, 1993, p. 149/150).

Our discussion here seems to provide support, then, for verification theory. The "puzzle of low self-regard" (Baumeister, 1993)—the apparently paradoxical fact that persons seem to actively perpetuate low self-esteem—fits nicely with our ideas so far, even with the assumption of a basic need for increased self-esteem.

For people with positive self-esteem, the assumption of a drive for increased self-esteem obviously does not conflict with the tendency to perpetuate the existing self-image. It seems that only the behavior of persons with low self-esteem needs to be explained. An appropriate understanding of this phenomenon is very important for psychotherapy, given that most patients in therapy have problems with their self-esteem. Indeed, most psychotherapists view the improvement of self-esteem as an therapeutic goal in its own right.

Therapist: According to your view, the active perpetuation of low self-esteem results from dominant avoidance strategies in the service of the attachment need, the avoidance of pain, the control need, and the consistency principle. If I as a therapist wished to achieve that the patient begins to think, act and feel in such a way that self-esteem is increased, I would first have to clear the way for the development of approach schemata. That is, I would first have to work on decreasing the avoidance schemata. The less influence these avoidance schemata have, the less the consistency principle would be violated through self-esteem-increasing perceptions. In your view, however, I could assume that self-esteem-increasing perceptions actually have a need-satisfying effect, even for people with a low self-esteem. Have I understood you correctly on this?

Psychologist: Yes, this is how I interpret current research on this issue. In fact, there is empirical evidence showing that people with low self-esteem still have self-esteem-increasing behavioral tendencies, even if they do not openly admit to it.

In experiments, individuals with low self-esteem have been given the opportunity to assess: 1. themselves, 2. persons with whom they share common characteristics, and 3. persons with whom they do not share common characteristics. This research has found that people with low self-esteem will typically rate those associated with them very positively. At the same time, they do not rate themselves or those who do not share characteristics with them positively. Persons with positive self-esteem do not have such tendencies. They typically rate their own achievements positively and those of others not positively (Brown, Collins & Schmidt, 1988). When persons with low self-esteem were made to believe that they shared characteristics, such as having the same birthday, with very attractive persons, then they rated themselves as being more attractive. Among persons having high self-esteem, such an "increased self-esteem based on another" does not occur. One might say that they do not need such a boost (Brown et al., 1992).

People generally tend to increase their feeling of self-worth by identifying with successful, attractive others (Cialdini & De Nicholas, 1989). Students refer to their college football team as "us" when the team has won but not when it has lost (Cialdini et al., 1976). According to Brown (1993) this tendency is especially prevalent among people with low self-esteem. National pride, identification with heroes and with sports teams, etc., may confer the advantage of an indirectly upgraded self-esteem in these persons.

These phenomena indicate that the need for increased self-esteem in people with low self-esteem is not simply absent. It would seem that this knowledge may be quite important for therapists wishing to connect with their low self-esteem patients. When working with such persons, one has to perhaps first look for possibilities to increase self-esteem indirectly, before they are ready to accept direct self-esteem increasing feedback.

Epstein and Morling (1995) argued that the implicit system spontaneously tends towards reactions that increase self-esteem, whereas the rational system tends to create a compromise between the need for increased self-esteem and the consistency principle (agreement of perception with previous experience). These views are actually empirically supported. Swann and colleagues (1990), for instance, undermined the dominance of the rational system by making their test participants choose a partner under severe time pressure. The potential partners differed in how positively they had been rated by the participants. Under time pressure, all participants chose those persons whom they previously had rated positively. With more time available, participants with low self-esteem selected partners who had previously been rated negatively. The tendency towards self-verifying behavior, then, seems to be more associated with the rational mode of functioning, whereas the tendency towards self-esteem increasing behavior seems to be more linked with the implicit mode of functioning.

This difference between the implicit and the rational functioning mode was confirmed in an independent study by Epstein and Morling (1995), using an entirely different approach. In their study, the degree of positive or negative evaluation by the potential partner is much more finely tuned. This more precise version allowed participants to choose, if they had sufficient time for rational processing, persons who previously had been rated as a little—but not much—better than themselves. This reaction was interpreted by Epstein and Morling as a compromise between the tendency towards increased self-esteem on the one hand and the verifying tendency in the service of the consistency principle on the other.

Epstein sees in this a confirmation of his general theory that behavior should essentially be viewed as a compromise between the satisfaction of different needs. Often, behavior serving one need would also benefit another or several other needs. However, the needs could conflict with each other, in which case the behavior would have to find a compromise between the various demands.

Therapy researcher: What you just mentioned about the different self-appraisal reactions in the implicit and rational modes of functioning might actually also explain why there is usually only weak convergence among behavioral tests, self-appraisals, and appraisals of a person's self-esteem by others(Savin-Williams & Jacquish, 1981). What is measured by self-esteem questionnaires should actually correspond to the components of the self-image stored in conceptual memory. As Epstein would see it, this explicit self-image need not be congruent with the implicit feeling of self-esteem that one can infer from the behavior and emotions of a patient.

The implicit by felt of self-esteem might be more important for what somebody really does in real situations than are the explicit appraisals in a questionnaire. Weinberger (1990) reported that motives inferred from TAT stories (these should correspond more to the implicit motives) predicted people's real behaviors in their lives far better than motives based on self-appraisals.

Maybe we can also derive recommendations for therapeutic practice from this; that is, perhaps therapists should predominantly focus on changing a patient's implicit self-esteem reactions. A better starting point for therapy might be found here, especially because—according to the results you reported—self-esteem-increasing reactions can be more easily activated in the implicit mode of functioning. Especially among people with low self-esteem one should perhaps first try, entirely by the implicit way, to exert a positive influence on the feeling of self-esteem. Thus, self-appraisals should not be brought up as a separate issue, but one should allow the patient to first make implicit self-esteem-increasing perceptions (consistent with the principle of processual resource activation).

Therapist: One particular question is still bothering me: Is it possible that the negative self-image a patient has of himself is totally realistic? People speak of a "a depressive realism." Should it really be our task as a therapist to cause patients to engage in positive illusions? Shouldn't it be generally seen as a positive characteristic for a person to be in touch with reality?

Psychologist: I have to disagree strongly. Positive illusions, in moderation, are correlates of emotional well-being. This is not only true for the need for increased self-esteem but also for illusions of control and unrealistic optimism.

It is true that many authors have taken the view that an undistorted perception of reality is a requirement for healthy personality development (Haan, 1997; Vaillant,

1977; Jourard & Landsman, 1980). At the same time, many facts contradicting this have come to light, rendering this view untenable. Overviews can be found in Nisbett and Ross (1980) as well as Fiske and Taylor (1984). The latter pointedly express the essence of their overview: "Instead of a naive scientist entering the environment in search of truth, we find the rather unflattering picture of a charlatan trying to make the data come out in a manner most advantageous to his or her already held theories" (Fiske & Taylor, 1984, p. 88).

An overview on relevant studies on this phenomenon can be found in Taylor and Brown (1988). The findings that most individuals have a tendency towards positive illusions are so numerous that I will not go deeper into individual research but rather give a short summary:

When people are asked to describe themselves, they choose more positive than negative attributes. Most people describe themselves more positively and less negatively than average. The majority of people, for instance, think of themselves as above average drivers. Logically, this is not possible. Most people, therefore, have illusions in this regard. In comparing themselves with others, most people use their positive features for the comparison and not their weaknesses. If they evaluate themselves with respect to personality dimensions, and were simultaneously appraised by an independent observer, the self-appraisal for most people turned out to be far more positive than the appraisals made by others. These transfigured evaluation tendencies are also applied to friends and partners in a somewhat diluted form. Even these are described as being better than the average.

A person is better able to recall positive information about oneself and to process it faster than negative information. Successes are more easily remembered than failures. In memorizing, test subjects described their achievements as better than they were. Negative self-aspects, if they cannot be overlooked, are downplayed in their significance. The things one does not do so well are described as relatively unimportant.

What I just reported refers to the majority of test subjects in the respective studies. The only exceptions to this self-esteem increasing trend are depressed individuals and those with low self-esteem. These people perceive positive **and** negative aspects about themselves in a much more balanced way, their self-appraisal agrees much more with that of outside assessors and they remember positive and negative self-esteem situations equally.

So it is the mentally healthy who have a distorted perception of reality with regard to themselves and not those of less sound mental health. Healthy individuals tend towards an increase in their self-esteem if given the opportunity. This certainly indicates a general basic need for increased self-esteem. Most people satisfy this need if given the chance. It is a sign of sound mental health if a person sees himself overly positively and appraises himself more positively than other people. The concern should be for those individuals who are not able to do that, and not vice-versa.

A therapist's goal, then, should not be for the patient to achieve an absolutely realistic view of self but to support him when he elevates himself, even if from an objective perspective that seems somewhat exaggerated. Of course, this has its limits and naturally this does not apply to patients whose disorder consists of elevating themselves continuously to an extent that they jeopardize their other basic needs, such as patients having narcissistic personality disorders.

Taylor and Brown also report on studies of unrealistic optimism. Most people, for instance, believe that they are less likely to be hit by misfortunes such as becoming ill with cancer, having a bad car accident, being the victim of a violent crime, losing a job, etc. This is also true for positive events. Most people believe that in the future, they will be doing well even if they appraise the prospects for others to be negative. The majority also believes that they are happier than other people; again, the depressed do not share this unrealistic optimism.

In general, then, one can conclude that people tend to "fool themselves" a great deal with respect to their basic needs. They delude themselves into thinking that their needs are in better shape than is actually the case. Presumably these thoughts and behavioral tendencies have a need-satisfying function (of course, only to a limited degree). That is, these skewed self-evaluations lead to feelings that are more positive than is actually justified.

However, by exerting a real positive effect, these illusions have the nature of a self-fulfilling prophecy. They put the person into a better state of mind. On average, in this state of mind they function better than without these illusions, and that improves their ability to satisfy their needs. This, in turn, brings them into a better state of mind... This self-perpetuating, positive feedback process appears to be an essential aspect of normal mental functioning. If this aspect no longer functions, because the illusions collapse in on themselves, it has disadvantageous effects on the mental activity and the resultant state of mind.

Once again, we encounter the great significance positive feedback processes appear to have in mental life. We encountered this phenomenon already in our first discussion, when we spoke about the induction of positive expectations for improvement and about resource activation. We saw, however, that positive feedback processes do not always lead to positive developments. As the development of anxiety disorders showed us, negative expectations also have a tendency towards self-fulfillment. Above all else, perhaps, mental disorders predominantly result from positive, but destructive, feedback processes, whereas psychotherapy, for the most part, may bring about constructive, positive feedback processes. I would like to return to this thought again at a later point.

Therapy researcher: There are many indicative that damage to, and a permanent non-fulfillment of a person's basic needs, is the most important breeding ground for the development of mental disorders. We have indeed observed a great deal of evidence and many indications in support of that. It now seems logical to me that change processes in psychotherapies ought to be viewed much more with respect to these fundamental needs than the results from psychotherapy research have suggested thus far. In our first discussion of conversations, in which we started with findings from therapy research, we really did not talk at all about what the therapeutic procedures mean with respect to the patient's fundamental needs. Right now I see this as a rather large gap in our previous thoughts on the mechanisms of psychotherapy. I still have to reflect more in detail on what our last considerations about the fundamental needs suggest as consequences with respect to an understanding of the mechanisms of psychotherapy.

Therapist: The same applied to me, but I am somewhat over-challenged to do this off the cuff, though it also appears to me that we should think about this issue in more detail.

Psychologist: I don't want to stand in the way, but I suggest that we first discuss the modification I had in mind regarding an aspect of Epstein's theory. This aspect refers to the interplay of the fundamental needs in mental life, and appears indispensable to me for an understanding of many psychological and psychopathological phenomena.

2.41 The Consistency Principle and Its Functional Significance in Mental Functioning

From a systems perspective the requirement for **consistency of mental processes** is most basic. Dissonance, conflict, and dissociation comprise the polar opposites of consistency. If psychological activity comes too close to these polar opposites, there is danger of a system disorganization or even collapse. Consistency is not a driving motivation of the individual in the same way that other needs are, and it cannot be regarded as equal with the other needs. Consistency is a basic requirement for systems to function. When this condition is violated severely, the system cannot be successful in the evolutionary selection process. Therefore, this requirement cannot be regarded as equal to the other needs but has to be viewed as the highest-order principle of mental functioning.

According to what was just said, psychological processes are directed towards simultaneously satisfying the basic needs of a person in the best possible fashion. If these various processes striving for need satisfaction do not counteract one another, and do not inhibit or prevent one another, they are consistent with one another. The more consistent the psychological processes, the more effective the need satisfaction. People who are very healthy and happy differ from others mentally not just in their being little damaged in their basic needs and in their well-developed approach schemata around their fundamental needs, but they also distinguish themselves in their ability to satisfy their needs in agreement with one another; that is to say, in a consistent fashion. If we were to define human happiness from the consistency perspective, then it would be a situation of "**being one with oneself and the world.**" Low consistency will always take its toll on an effective need satisfaction. A high degree of inconsistency means mental suffering and human misery.

Consistency refers to the holistic nature of the psychological system. "The potential to be whole and to function as an organized unit is not only mandatory for a system to exist and to self-regulate. The potential to function as an organized whole underlies the concept of a system" (Schwartz, 1990, p. 407).

Schwartz points out the etymological connection between "whole" and "health." Being "healthy" means as much as being "whole," healing means as much as making "whole." Making a person more "whole" means making his psychological processes more consistent. People who are ill, disturbed or beset with an impediment in their physical and/or mental well-being are persons whose self-regulation processes show inconsistencies.

When a person's consciousness becomes inconsistent, we view this as a rather alarming indication of a severe disorder. Any psychiatrist will interpret incoherent thinking as an unmistakable sign of a grave, oftentimes organically caused mental dysfunction.

Incoherence in the flow of consciousness over time is such a rare instance that most people take the coherence of their consciousness for granted. However, we know now that our consciousness is best understood as something that is created actively by certain neural processes, as something that fulfills a specific task in mental functioning. Consistency is a feature of our consciousness that is created continuously and actively, and that means simultaneous consistency and coherence over time.

A blackout following a severe alcohol binge demonstrates that coherence in the flow of consciousness requires the functioning of certain neural processes. Other forms of incoherence experienced over time are based on either organic brain disorders or, as in the case of multiple personality disorder or "fugue syndrome," they reflect the presence of severe mental disorders that are especially difficult to comprehend by average people. Among individuals who experience repeated brief failures of consciousness (for instance, due to sleep apnea or minor epileptic seizures), there is oftentimes no awareness for these "disruptions," because the brain "artificially" creates a continuity of the flow of consciousness. In similar fashion to how modern CD players can guarantee coherent musical flow across a disc—through techniques of extrapolation or over-sampling—our brain is able to create a continuous flow of consciousness despite such discontinuities.

Unless some major interference occurs, our neural activity is occupied with creating coherence in the consciousness over time. The fact that we also aim to create consistency among contents that are simultaneously present in consciousness has been confirmed repeatedly since Festinger's (1957) formulation of his "theory of cognitive dissonance."

"Until 1977, over 800 studies have been published. The variety of phenomena arising out of efforts to reduce cognitive dissonance is remarkable. The majority of this variety of phenomena concern the change in attitudes and beliefs when a decision made, forced agreements in actions one would otherwise not have made, new information about attained alternatives, contradictory beliefs or unexpected results of actions and their consequences have produced cognitive dissonance" (Heckhausen, 1980, p. 168).

Festinger himself already saw that cognitive dissonance or the drive for consistency resembles a core motivation that in some sense can be viewed as a fundamental need. At the same time, he knew that this drive for consistency cannot be equated with other needs. "Cognitive dissonance can be seen as an antecedent condition which leads to activity towards dissonance reduction just as hunger leads to activity oriented towards hunger reduction. It is a very different motivation from what psychologists are used to dealing with but, as we shall see, nonetheless powerful" (Festinger, 1957, p. 3).

Festinger's theory already contains the idea that the tendency towards dissonance reduction is greater the more important the coexistence of the inconsistent cognitive content is for the individual. In agreement with Festinger, Brehm and Cohen (1962) postulated that dissonant content must be relevant to the individual's goals if dissonance reduction is to occur. Festinger's cognitive consistency striving, then, resembles what I have described here as a drive for consistency of conscious content or consistency among mental processes. My view emphasizes the **consistency of the processes determined by a person's motivational schemata**. The beliefs that are based on such schemata are also included in my formulation.

The fact that my view of mental consistency includes but also transcends Festinger's drive for cognitive consistency can best be shown by examining the specific postulates of dissonance theory. For this purpose, I have chosen a list of postulates by Zajonc (1968, pp. 360—361):

"1. Cognitive dissonance is a noxious state.

2. In the case of cognitive dissonance the individual attempts to reduce or eliminate it and reacts so as to avoid events that will increase it.

3. In the case of consonance the individual acts so as to avoid dissonance-producing events.

4. The severity or intensity of cognitive dissonance varies with (a) the importance of the cognitions involved and (b) the relative number of cognitions standing in dissonant relation to one another.

5. The strength of the tendencies enumerated in (2) and (3) is a direct function of the severity of dissonance.

6. Cognitive dissonance can be reduced only by (a) adding new cognitions or (b) changing existing ones.

7. Adding new cognitions reduces dissonance if (a) the new cognitions add weight to one side and thus decrease the proportion of cognitive elements that are dissonant or (b) the new cognitions change the importance of the cognitive elements that are in dissonant relation with one another.

8. Changing existing cognitions reduces dissonance if (a) their new content makes them less contradictory with others, or (b) their importance is reduced.

9. If new cognitions cannot be added or the existing ones changed by means of a passive process, behavior which has cognitive consequences favoring consonance will be recruited. Seeking new information is an example of such behavior."

If we consider that the cognitions relevant for dissonance reduction (see above) are also goal-relevant cognitions—consistent with Brehm and Cohen's model—then many cognitive dissonances are actually constellations that we can also refer to as conflicts. Dissonance reduction would then be synonymous with a reduction of conflict tension. Much of what happens in verbal psychotherapies could be attributed to the points in this list. In therapy, attempts are made to change existing cognitions or to create new ones that alter previous evaluations. Eventually, a new view is created that is experienced by the patient as consistent or consonant. In light of this obvious connection between the postulates listed above and the process of therapy, one wonders why dissonance and related theories have never been applied fruitfully to psychotherapy. As we discussed in our first conversation, such a connection is exactly what psychotherapy could have used from psychology: A theoretically well elaborated and empirically supported conflict theory.

In my view, dissonance theory never inspired conflict researchers because of the following four reasons:

1. Dissonance research focused almost exclusively on contrived or artificially created situations, not on real-life conflict situations.

2. No connections were established to individual participants' uniquely important goals or motivations.

3. The research focused on content rather than processes.

4. The possibility for dissonance reduction that is most crucial for an understanding of mental disorders was ignored; namely, the elimination of one of the dissonant elements from conscious awareness.

This last and most important reason has to do with one of the major, decade-long exclusions made by psychology that I spoke about at the beginning of this dialogue (section 2.1): The exclusion of the great significance unconscious processes have for mental functioning.

This possibility of eliminating dissonant contents from consciousness was never articulated because the distinction between conscious and unconscious did not exist in academic psychology when dissonance theory was in its heyday. Similarly, the idea that processes eliminated from consciousness might impact mental functioning was inconceivable at the time.

A peek over the fence towards psychoanalysis could have been stimulating in this respect, but such a move was taboo at the time. Actually, it seems obvious that what psychoanalysis terms defense mechanisms are mental mechanisms of dissonance reduction. In fact, within the psychoanalytic drive model, this is conceptualized differently. In psychoanalytic thinking, the defense mechanisms serve to ward off fear that is triggered by conflict-laden impulses. It is the threat of these impulses becoming conscious that triggers the fear, and the "queen of all defense mechanisms"—repression—is used to ward off the content and/or affect which represent the drive impulse becoming conscious. This is not designated cognitive or mental dissonances, but actually the warding off of certain contents serves exactly the avoidance of unbearable dissonances that would emerge if the warded off impulses were accepted into consciousness.

It is obvious that the psychoanalytic drive model and Freud's meta-psychology, in many respects, do not agree with the ideas of mental functioning we developed here. Yet, if we think about what types of mechanisms the human mind might have developed to guarantee consistency of mental functioning, we quickly recognize the limitations of cognitive dissonance theory. While the mechanisms of dissonance reduction analyzed within this theoretical framework may also be viewed as possibilities for maintaining consistency, there are at least two more important groups of mechanisms that should be added.

These are **constructive mechanisms,** such as emotional and problem-oriented **coping** (Lazarus & Folkman, 1984). We mentioned these forms of coping while discussing emotions, but they also play a very important role in the constructive mastery of inconsistency tensions. They do not, however, contribute that much to the understanding of mental disorders. Instead, these coping strategies are all the more important for treatment. In addition to constructive coping, there are the **defensive, avoidant, or protective mechanisms.** Included in those is the avoidance of awareness or of the process of becoming aware. These avoidance mechanisms are what is referred to in psychoanalysis as defense mechanisms.

In his article "Repression" from the year 1915, Freud defines this as follows: "The essence of repression lies simply in turning something away and keeping it at a distance from the conscious" (Freud, 1915, here quoted according to the complete English edition, 1957, p. 147). This is a very open-ended definition. Instead of repression, Freud often used other terms such as suppression, inhibition, avoidance and many more others (Erdelyi, 1990). Even the term repression itself was not used consistently by him. In his early works, his tendency was to alternate this term with the general term defense. Later, after the formulation of his updated fear theory (1926), he used it increasingly, but not exclusively, in a more narrow sense as one of many forms of defense side by side with isolation, denial, rationalization, projection, response formation, intellectualization, undoing, and sublimation. Repression then referred to motivated suppression or forgetting (Singer, 1990a).

According to Freud himself, the result of repression was the unawareness of the repressed content or affect, but he did not necessarily view the process of repression as something unconscious. At many points he explicitly writes about conscious suppressing or repressing. He also assumed that this event might become unconscious over time through automatization. The assumption that the process of repression and all other defense mechanisms are regularly unconscious does not go back to Freud himself but to his daughter, Anna. In her book *The Ego and the Defense Mechanisms* (Anna Freud, 1936) she defined all defense mechanisms as unconscious.

I do not want to go into the individual defense mechanisms distinguished in psychoanalysis. These distinctions are not empirically founded, and they are difficult to separate from the psychoanalytic defense model whose views I do not share, for reasons already explained. Yet I would like to discuss the general mechanism of repression as a mechanism for **maintaining consistency**, which is very important for psychotherapy. The non-acceptance, elimination, or warding off of perceptions, memories, thoughts, or feelings from consciousness has been examined empirically, independent of psychoanalytic theory (Holmes, 1990; Shevrin, 1990; Kihlstrom & Hoyt, 1990). When I speak of **repression** in the following sections, I am referring to the empirically supported phenomenon referred to as "**repression**" in the literature and not to a term from psychoanalytic theory. In my view this phenomenon is very relevant for the understanding of mental disorders and for therapeutic practice. This phenomenon can also be integrated nicely with the concepts of mental functioning we have developed so far.

2.42   Mechanisms for Maintaining Consistency

Based on the ideas of mental function we have developed so far, what are some of the factors that can threaten or undermine consistency among psychological processes? Two major possibilities come to mind:

Threats to Consistency:
Incongruent Perceptions

A person's perceptions may deviate grossly and consistently from his important schemata, core beliefs, or convictions. His actual perceptions may deviate so strongly that they cannot be assimilated into existing expectations. In terms of control theory, such continuous discrepancies trigger a constant and strong incongruence signal. The experiential equivalent of such a discrepancy might be anxiety, for example.

According to Epstein, traumatic neuroses can be linked to such continuous discrepancies between actual perceptions or memories on the one hand vs. preexisting schemata/beliefs on the other. Trying to keep memories of traumatic experiences out of consciousness may be futile. They constantly push themselves into conscious awareness—even during sleep—because they cannot be assimilated into existing schemata; they cannot be processed and filed away in memory. In a sense, there is a persistent and persisting need for assimilation. Therapeutic procedures developed for post-traumatic stress disorder (PTSD) often promote this process of assimilation.

If traumatic experiences persist inescapably for a long time and affect important life spheres, the eventual result is that previous, more positive basic beliefs accommodate to these new, negative experiences. An example would be abusive experiences suffered during childhood that stretch across a long period of time. Not only do they lead to acute anxiety, but over time they also constitute severe violations of basic needs. Trust in close others is undermined, self-esteem decreases, and the violation of the need for control triggers helplessness and hopelessness.

However, it is not just the severity and duration of traumatic experiences that affect long-term outcome, but also the person's coping experiences after the event. Catlin and Epstein (1992) reported on a comparative study of Vietnam war veterans. Two groups in the study had been exposed to traumatic war experiences of similar severity, but both developed very differently over the long-term. One group exhibited short-term post traumatic stress disorder; the participants in this group coped effectively and continued to lead a mostly normal life. Over a period of 15 years, the other group gradually experienced a continual worsening in their well-being, as well as in their beliefs about the chances for the fulfillment of their basic needs. The first group may have successfully assimilated the horrifying experiences into the existing beliefs. The latter group, however, may have accommodated their schemata to the traumatic experiences.

The discrepancy-creating perceptions need not necessarily be tied to the external world. They may also involve signals from one's own body or from memory. In other words, memories can also trigger incongruence signals.

Inconsistencies between perceptions, memories, affective impulses and existing schemata may literally become unbearable. What happens when a person exceeds his "threshold of tolerance for inconsistencies?" The person may "flip out," "run amok," display a panic reaction, etc. It makes sense to assume that in the course of the long, ontogenetic developmental history of our mental system, warning signals of some form or other would have developed, so as to avoid complete panic reactions or systems collapse. Principles of evolutionary biology suggest the plausibility of such a "mechanism for securing consistency. "

Specifically, one possibility for securing consistency relates to the findings that parts of experience can be split off or "suppressed" from conscious experience. Consistency in conscious experience is thereby maintained. The person remains capable of functioning. However, there is a high price for preserving consistency in such a manner. Something that has great—albeit negative—significance for the individual's goals is excluded from conscious information processing; on a long-term basis, such exclusion may cause a great deal of damage. Whatever the excluded content may be, it no longer belongs to the realm of things the individual can control consciously. Consistent with this line of reasoning, Rogers saw the core of mental disorders in such suppression of dissonant perceptions. "Psychological maladjustment exists when the organism denies to awareness significant sensory and visceral experiences that are not compatible with the self-structure" (Rogers, 1951, p. 510).

Suppression does not mean that the neural activation pattern representing the perception becomes deactivated; there is no reason for assuming such complete deactivation. The neural pattern is and remains activated, and continues to exert influence on the individual's experience and behavior in the implicit mode of functioning. However, the pattern has escaped conscious control. It cannot be addressed directly by consciousness because it has not become integrated in conceptual memory. Therefore, in the absence of control by the individual, the pattern becomes activated "bottom-up" in appropriate situations or via activation of related neural patterns. The suppressed neural pattern cannot be activated voluntarily or influenced from the top down.

It is unlikely that the mechanism of suppression is employed solely as a last resort or emergency measure. The perceptions to be suppressed need not necessarily be extremely threatening. Instead, it appears that people differ on this dimension. That is, they differ in their tendency to maintain consistency by suppressing incongruent perceptions. I will elaborate on this point later.

Threats to Consistency: Schema-Conflicts

The second possibility of a threat to consistency relates to the simultaneous activation of several motivational schemata that are fundamentally incompatible with one another. Given that a minimum of four basic needs that simultaneously demand satisfaction can be delineated, the simultaneous activation of several motivational schemata represents the normality in mental life. To fully understand this, let us imagine an everyday life situation—a dinner with coworkers and one's partner in a restaurant.

Control schemata become activated as early as in the selection of a table, choosing of food and drinks, the choosing of topics of conversation, controlling of the conversation, and deciding when and how the occasion comes to an end. At the same time, schemata are activated for the increase or protection of self-esteem. This may be evident already with the question of what to wear for this occasion. The activation of the self-esteem schemata runs through the entire evening: How do I present myself to the others? How do I do in comparison? Is what I am saying sufficiently interesting, and do the others respond to that? Do others pay attention to me? Do they constantly ignore me? Am I able to impress the others? The need for a secure relationship and related schemata are also activated. How do I feel about myself in my relationship with my partner? Does he or she support me? Can I rely on him or her? Is there a bond between us? Can I support him or her? Can he or she feel appreciated and supported by me? Is there a sense of connection between us? All these schemata are activated, and we haven't even mentioned schemata for maximizing pleasure, which might have influenced our choice of a gourmet restaurant, our selection of wine, food, etc.

Thus, even an everyday life situation can become highly complex, challenging and demanding because of the motivational schemata one carries into it. It is not the situation in and of itself that is so complex. The complexity of the situation is determined by the person's motivational schemata. For one person, such an evening can be stressful, for another, very comfortable. The person who leaves the restaurant on such an evening feeling fulfilled and happy is equipped with excellent possibilities for "producing integrative behavior." I am referring here to people who succeed in effectively pursuing many goals at the same time, without sacrificing one for the other. This requires the presence of differentiated approach schemata for each and every basic need.

The more goals a person has developed for satisfying their basic needs, the more possibilities they have available for their fulfillment. As goals are formed, experiences and capabilities that facilitate goal realization will evolve in tandem. The more goals have developed, then, the greater the chances that many of these needs can be satisfied simultaneously. The capacity to satisfy multiple needs simultaneously also requires the ability to postpone needs temporarily, so that they may be satisfied more effectively at a later time.

The suppression of impulses not suitable at a particular moment may be viewed as a constructive form of repression. At any given moment, the range of perceptions and impulses exceeds the capacity of conscious processing. So there must be a continuous selection of content to be accepted into consciousness, and compatibility with what is already present in consciousness plays a crucial role for this purpose. One might say that there is a consistency guard at the threshold of acceptance into consciousness. This guard accepts only that which fits with pre-existing content. Under sufficiently secure circumstances, but to a limited extent, such content may also be new, strange, or unexpected. In this case, interest, curiosity and astonishment might be triggered. However, if the content is too discrepant compared to what already exists in consciousness, then—in the interest of consistency—it will not be accepted into consciousness. Framed as non-acceptance into consciousness, repression constitutes a ubiquitous part of mental life. Schwartz (1990, p. 406) also expressed this point:

"Concerning repression, the potential to check, keep down, hold down, or restrain information is not only present in all systems. Within certain limits, the potential to restrain information is essential for a system to be able to engage in pattern recognition and interpretation, which in turn enables the system to generate adaptive, organized responses to stimuli generated externally and internally."

Approach-approach conflicts—the simultaneous activation of several approach schemata—belong to the class of relatively easily resolved mental conflicts. **Approach-avoidance conflicts** and especially **avoidance-avoidance conflicts** put more of a strain on the requirement for consistency. Simultaneously wanting and not wanting something clearly violates the law of consistency. When discussing motivational schemata, you also spoke of **conflict schemata**. A conflict schema is defined as a built-in approach-avoidance conflict. Holding such a conflict in conscious awareness creates blatant cognitive dissonance, which, of course, is to be avoided. The simultaneous presence of conflict components in consciousness, then, is not permitted by our mental apparatus. The avoidance component of a conflict schema has its roots in violations of the corresponding basic need. Remembering such violations causes pain. Because of our striving to avoid displeasure, such unpleasant memories are avoided. The reason for the avoidance behavior, then, is also not represented in consciousness. Even the wish associated with the intentional component of the conflict schema is most likely kept from consciousness, because the conscious representation of such a wish would activate more memories of the painful feelings. The individual, therefore, has no awareness of both the approach and the avoidance component of the conflict schema.

The person must then devise alternate explanations for the behavior controlled by the conflict schema. This post-hoc explanation may then seem like a rationalization. Repression leads to the necessity for alternative explanations for one's own behavior.

Even if conflictual motivations are not present in consciousness, they exert an influence on behavior in the implicit mode of functioning. The implicit mode of functioning has far greater tolerance for inconsistency than does consciousness. For example, in nonverbal behavior, conflicting messages such as the desire for closeness and the need for protection may be expressed simultaneously. Behavior can be quite inconsistent, then, without immediately appearing disorganized. Through the many parallel channels of behavior, one may simultaneously express and pursue many different things.

Consequently, there is a considerably lower requirement for consistency in the implicit mode than in the explicit mode of functioning. Contradictory content may coexist and simultaneously influence behavior, which would not be tolerated in the conscious mode. There is not even a requirement for conscious vs. implicit mental processes to be consistent with one another. However, the more these processes are dissociated from one another, the more conscious goal pursuit is rendered ineffective.

Viewed as an automatic, unconscious and continuous censoring of contents (including wishes, fears, and feelings) from consciousness, repression leads to a dissociation of mental processes and lowers the control over them.

On a short-term basis, then, repression has a positive, consistency-maintaining effect on what is going on in the conscious mode of functioning However, on a long-term basis, it has a dissociative effect on overall mental functioning. In this latter case, the subsystems of mental functioning are less closely tied to one another; they are less in-tune with each other. In other words, there is much less communication between the various subsystems, which may impair the psychological system's overall regulatory capacity. Disrupting the regulatory processes in this manner may open the door for the emergence of mental or physical disorders.

These processes may trigger a chain of events that eventually leads to illnesses related to the violations of the basic needs. This chain may look something like this:

Certain basic needs are violated, mostly through early childhood experiences, but possibly also by trauma experienced later in life. Strategies are then developed to avoid further need violations. An example would be the development of an insecure-avoidant attachment style at the toddler age. The traumatic experiences are removed from consciousness either in the service of the consistency principle or in the service of pain avoidance.

Post-traumatic stress disorders (PTSD), where traumatic memories repeatedly invade consciousness, are a special example in this respect. You already explained this in some detail.

The approach and avoidance schemata evolved around the unmet basic needs determine experience and behavior predominantly in the implicit mode of functioning. They are not adequately represented in consciousness and, therefore, they are not consciously controllable. There are different premises underlying the consciously controlled processes, and those are directed towards different goals. All this results in a dissociation of processes transpiring in the implicit vs. the conscious mode of functioning. In addition, processes that are transpiring simultaneously in the implicit mode of functioning may be dissociated from one another. Such dissociation may be more pronounced when psychological activity is influenced by avoidance schemata. Two consequences can be delineated: At the behavioral level, such dissociation prevents the effective fulfillment of basic needs. The needs are less fully satisfied, which leads to negative emotions and impaired well-being. At the level of inner-regulatory processes, such dissociation triggers general dysregulation, which then facilitates the development of mental disorders. The specific type of disorder that may develop depends on the regulatory processes that were affected by the dissociation.

According to this line of reasoning, conflicts, avoidance of dissonance, and repression may play a central role in the development of mental and physical disorders. Thus, we can trace the emergence of disorders to violations of basic needs and resulting avoidance strategies.

Because of our inherent need for control, avoidance strategies may take on an increasingly anticipatory character over time. If avoidance becomes a habitual response even when need violations are only anticipated, the person's opportunities for goal pursuit and need satisfaction will become increasingly restricted. Yet, such avoidance will not reduce the importance of the respective need. The opposite is the case. To a person for whom failure is so terrible that he does everything to avoid it, achievements are obviously overly important. However, if achievement-related situations are avoided because of the threat of failure, satisfaction of the achievement need is no longer possible. An important opportunity for self-esteem increasing experiences is thereby eliminated. Over time, excessive avoidance inevitably leads to stronger discrepancies between wishes and actual experiences. The significance of the wish becomes increasingly stronger, but so does the fear of its violation. The avoidance then becomes even more pervasive. What we have here is one of those positive feedback loop processes, of which we have already encountered. Having started the cycle of avoidance once, a person is at risk of ever increasing avoidance, until the avoidance becomes automatic and eventually transpires without conscious awareness.

The more a person engages in such habitual avoidance, the more will his prospects for need satisfaction diminish, and the more mental inconsistency will exist. Inconsistency refers to the gap between unfulfilled wishes and actual perceptions. The pain resulting from this incongruence is reduced if the wish is no longer represented in consciousness. However, this only means that it is not influencing conscious functioning. In the implicit mode of functioning, the wish remains active, even if it is less evident in observable behavior. For instance, the repressed wish may continue to influence the emotional appraisal of situations.

Whether experienced consciously or having become unconscious, the gap between wishes and actual perceptions leads to continuous inconsistency-tension in the system. Because consciously experienced dissonance tends to be even more unbearable than inconsistency that remains unconscious, the elimination from consciousness contributes to short-term relief of acute inconsistency tension. However, the long-term prospects for tension reduction via actual wish fulfillment tend to be worse. In the long run, repression almost inevitably leads to an increase in inconsistency tension.

Repression leads to a dissociation of conscious and implicit processes. The processes are no longer synchronized in their goal orientation. Not only does this undermine effective exchanges with the environment, but it also results in reduced synchronicity of neural regulation; that is, there is less of an clear "order" in psychological functioning. The dissociated processes result in increased instability of mental functioning because it is less clearly driven by need fulfillment patterns. This condition of increased instability and decreased goal "orientedness" literally requires a new order. Later I will introduce you to the idea that mental disorders may be viewed as new structural patterns of neural or psychological activity. These structural patterns establish themselves in order to decrease instability. However, these neural activation patterns are no longer directed towards need fulfillment; instead, they "begin a life of their own" as factors that influence psychological functioning.

If these considerations are accurate, then persons who habitually tend to suppress uncomfortable content from consciousness might be at increased risk for developing mental and perhaps even physical disorders. Research has supported this hypothesis.

According to recent literature, persons who present themselves in questionnaires as relatively free from distress but simultaneously receive high defensiveness scores are referred to as "repressors." Such repressors demonstrate a gap among verbal self-description, nonverbal behavior, and physical reactions.

"They generally claim even less experience of negative affect than the low-anxious group. However, numerous assessments of stress reactivity including multiple psychophysiological indices as well as vocal, facial, paralinguistic, and objective task performance measures, all suggest that they are as anxious or more anxious than individuals who report chronic distress" (Weinberger, 1990, p. 372).

People who maintain consistency in consciousness at the expense of reality perception, then, are demonstrating inconsistency in their conscious vs. implicit modes of functioning. Empirical evidence also suggests that such dissociation of mental processes has a negative impact on physical regulatory processes:

"There is growing evidence that repressive individuals are at greater risk than either distressed or non-defensive ones for a variety of specific illnesses, including hypertension (e.g., Davies, 1970; Schwartz, 1990), asthma (e.g., Mathe & Knapp, 1971), and cancer (e.g., Jensen, 1987; Watson, Pettingale & Greer, 1984)... Although the mediating mechanisms are just beginning to be identified, there is evidence that repressive coping may be associated with heightened release of stress-related hormones such as cortisol ... and norepinephrine ... and with suppression of the immune system" (Weinberger, 1990, p. 374).

According to Schwartz (1990), directing attention away from a discrepancy between actual and desired values (for instance, between wishes and actual experience) puts an end to the normal feedback processes of mental life, but these processes are thought to be essential for regulating mental processes.

"Both negative and positive feedback serve to interconnect components so that the system can function (behave) in a self-regulating (self-moderating or self-amplifying), and therefore predictable, manner. If the information is distorted or misperceived, or, in extreme cases, disconnected altogether, the self-regulation engendered by the negative and/or positive feedback will be impaired or cease altogether...

Integrating all the above, it follows that repression (and self-deception) includes dysattention to negative feedback that is essential for self-regulation and, therefore, healing. Dysattention promotes a state of relative disconnection (e.g., a functional disconnection of the left and right hemispheres as proposed by Galin, 1974). This state of neuropsychological disconnection induces a state of psychophysiological dysregulation, which is expressed as disorder in biological, psychological, and social functioning. This disordered biopsychosocial functioning is hypothesized to contribute to physical, mental, and social disease" (Schwartz, 1990, pp. 408/409).

I have quoted the passages by Weinberger and Schwartz verbatim, because they show that repression is a significant phenomenon, even without the foundation of psychoanalytic theory. The assumption of a conscious mode of functioning in psychological activity mandates that one also assumes a nonconscious mode, and that concepts that delineate the relationship between the two are needed. The core of the model developed here is that there are at least two, if not three, modes of psychological activity. Without this premise, the simultaneity of multiple mental processes cannot be modeled.

The existence of more than one mode of psychological activity is more than just an assumption. I have supported this claim many times in our conversation (sections 2.12, 2.15, 2.25, 2.34). Similarly, the existence of an unconscious mode of functioning is not just a psychoanalytical assumption. It is an empirically supported phenomenon. The idea of a filter between events transpiring in the unconscious mode of functioning and consciousness is also not just a psychoanalytic assumption. Whether or not this filtering process should be referred to as repression is a question irrelevant to the existence of such a filtering process.

Empirical evidence for the existence of such a filtering process cannot be denied. A compilation of relevant empirical research results can be found in Holmes (1990), Shevrin (1988, 1990; Shevrin & Dickman, 1980), Erdelyi (1993), Bonanno and Singer (1993), Kihlstrom and Hoyt (1990) and Bower (1990).

It is also not just an assumption, but an empirically supported fact, that habitual repression is associated with an increase in physical and mental disorders (Blatt, 1990; Bonanno & Singer, 1990; Schwartz, 1983, 1990; Weinberger, 1990). Moreover, the kind of disorder a person develops also appears to depend on whether he belongs to the habitual repressors or to those persons who instead attend appropriately to inconsistencies and related negative feelings (Blatt, 1990; Bonanno & Singer, 1990).

One handicap of studies on the relationship between conscious and unconscious processes is that researchers in this area remain fixed on psychoanalytic theory and its "Übervater," Freud. This fixation is of a magnitude that is not beneficial to the unbiased formation of new ideas. By now, this discomfort is shared even by psychoanalytic researchers whose work is devoted to empirical studies on the phenomena of repression. Towards the end of the eighties, Yale university hosted a three-day conference with the theme, "Repression and Dissociation and the Warding off of Conflictual Cognitive Contents," which almost all leading researchers in the field participated in. A conference volume was produced, which can still be viewed as the best summary of accumulated knowledge on this topic (Singer, 1990 b). The majority of these researchers come from a background of psychoanalysis.

Upon reflecting on this research, Jerome Singer—organizer and editor of this volume and a psychoanalytically trained researcher himself—arrives at the following summary:

"Towards the end of the three-day conference from which this volume arose, one of us (JLS) ventured the seemingly blasphemous proposal that any future conferences on thoughts and behaviors related to warding off conflictual cognitive contents ban any reference to Sigmund Freud. Let historians of science or scholars of epistemology devote themselves to the endless task of ferreting out what the old sage really meant. We, as cognitive and personality researchers and clinicians, have new paradigms, new models of how experience is organized, new methods, and new skills for devising replicable psychometric or clinical tools for engendering and testing hypotheses. Perhaps we need to start where the cutting edge of our scientific enterprise lies and not fret about whether it is consistent with a body of presumed psychoanalytic theory, for which there is really no general agreement... Let us start by proposing models of the human condition that reflect the tremendously rich cognitive literature, the increasingly heuristic work on the differentiated emotions, and the new approaches to studying patterns of thoughts and behavior across the life-span" (Singer, 1990, pp. 488/489).

The interplay of unconscious or implicit and conscious mental processes evidently has great significance both for the understanding of mental and psychosomatic disorders and for an understanding of the processes transpiring in psychotherapy. Our empirical knowledge on this topic is still at an early stage. We have repeatedly referred to portions of existing knowledge that are relevant for psychotherapy; however, more knowledge is needed on the interplay of conscious and unconscious processes in the development of mental disorders. Our model of mental functioning should be open to being supplemented with disorder-specific concepts so that the formation of mental disorders could be understood from a coherent perspective, and that also a disorder-specific approach to these disorders could be modeled along with general therapeutic procedures.

Therapy researcher: A model comes to mind in this context that can be nicely integrated with the ideas developed so far. This model adds a disorder-specific aspect. Williams and colleagues (1988), based on a long series of experiments, relate the formation of anxiety disorders and depression to various processes of information processing.

According to their model, anxiety disorders form on a pre-conscious level. We have called this the mode of implicit psychological functioning. People who tend to have fears pre-attentively turn towards these threatening stimuli rather than fend them off. From a wide range of stimuli offered, they select those stimuli that have a threatening character. Conscious attention is predominantly directed towards those, i.e. it is mostly such contents that find access to consciousness. In order for this to happen, an unconscious selection of these contents must have taken place. "Normal persons" tend to ignore the threatening stimuli and do not select them for conscious perception.

Williams and colleagues assume that, in the fearful person, priming has already taken place for such threatening stimuli so that they are particularly easily perceived. People who tend to have fears constantly scan their environment for threatening stimuli and are, therefore, occupied with such situational cues. Naturally, this increases their level of anxiety, which in turn increases their tendency to pre-attentively select threatening stimuli. Anxiety results from a positive feedback process that starts on the pre-attentive level. Already at the pre-attentive level, an anxious person, due to the attribution of threat, does not first perceive the pain in the chest and then interprets it as a heart attack. Instead, the pain is immediately understood to be a heart attack.

Depressed people differ from normal ones, however, not in terms of pre-attentive level, but in the way they process consciously perceived contents. They apply more information processing capacity to the elaboration of content that is already perceived.

When they are in a depressed state of mind, they elaborate the contents perceived in that state of mind with special thoroughness. This leads to content that is exceptionally well encoded and thus easily recalled from memory. From there, these memories very easily find their way back into consciousness. Consciousness, therefore, is increasingly likely to be filled with depressive contents, which pushes the positive feedback process further forward. Even depression, then, may be part of a positive feedback process.

Fearful and depressed persons thus differ in their (non-conscious) information processing mechanisms. These mechanisms contribute to sustained anxiety disorders or depression. Whether or not they have causal significance for the formation of these disorders cannot be stated with the same certainty. Due to their perpetuating function, however, they definitely represent important parameters for the treatment of these disorders.

Psychologist: At any rate, what is important for treatment are mostly those conditions maintaining a disorder and not those which have led to its formation. The latter are only important for a disorder-specific treatment if they still have a function at the moment. The reason for this lies in our concept of neural activation potentials.

According to these principles, developmental processes are irreversible. Their traces in memory cannot be deleted; they can only be overwritten. One might perhaps wonder which memory traces should be overwritten once a disorder has developed. Is it sensible—or even necessary—to trace back the point of origin of the development and to begin with the overwriting there, or should one begin the overwriting with the most recently formed memory traces? At best, one would go back in the chain only as far as necessary in order to effect sustainable improvement in the patient's condition.

According to the logic of our chain, inconsistency-tension—repression—dissociation—dysregulation—disorder, the psychoanalytic idea of tracing the origin of problematic development has some merit. "Striking at the root of this evil," however, is a wise saying from the world of implicit psychological functioning rather than the outcome of a rational thought process. The conditions that perpetuate a situation need not necessarily be the same as those that have led to it. Once a ship has run aground, getting it afloat again is what is first and foremost. For this purpose, the current conditions need to be considered and not those that led to it, at least not if these no longer have anything to do with maintaining the current situation. If the ship ran aground because the captain was drunk, and he is still drunk, he will be replaced, not because he caused the accident, but because his condition has a functional significance for the current situation. In case of an accident or disorder, it is important to first attend to the situation that emerged and influence the conditions that currently have functional significance in maintaining it. Once that has been accomplished, one may also trace the origin of the problematic situation, but the rational reason for such work lies in prevention of future accidents/disorders. Only current functional conditions are important for influencing the current situation. Coping with the past has its goal in the future.

In psychotherapy, it is sensible enough to also focus on development of the disorder, but not with the expectation that concentrating on the causes will alleviate the disorder. Such an expectation would miss the fact that new neural connections were created over time, which may be activated on their own in many different ways, not just by the conditions that produced them. Once they have been sufficiently ingrained, newly created neural connections can be said to have functional autonomy. Allport (1937) assumed that psychological structures later acquire functional autonomy from their origins. However, he was unable to explain this fact. I think such functional autonomy is very well explained if we assume the existence of certain ingrained neural pathways that underlie mental activity. Such ingrained networks can then be activated from many sources. In their ability to be activated, they have detached themselves from their origins, which is only a different way of saying that they have become functionally autonomous. It appears to me that we must view mental disorders in the same way. And if that is the case, then we need to do justice to such functional autonomy by devising disorder-specific interventions.

2.43   A Model of Psychological Functioning

Therapy researcher: We seem to have come to an end now with the factors that influence psychological activity. At least I am somewhat relieved that you have not introduced any new factors for a while, since I would like to summarize everything once again in a broader context. If I take as my starting point Powers' control theory and his hierarchical model, then different levels of psychological organization would have to be differentiated beyond Powers' seventh level, the program level. Such additional differentiation would be necessary to integrate the ideas we developed in the third part of our second dialogue. The whole model might then look as follows (Figure 2.24):

If we conceive of mental life as the product of a hierarchy of feedback loops, consistent with control theory, then at the top is the **system's requirement of consistency**. The psychological system strives for consistency and attempts to avoid inconsistency.

One level below are the **most important basic human needs and fundamental beliefs**. Those are the needs for control, increasing pleasure/avoiding displeasure, the need for a close relationship/attachment and the need for self-enhancement/protection of self-esteem. These needs provide the reference values or standards for more specific motivational schemata. The arrows from the level of needs to motivational schemata may signify **top-down activation**.

Given the consistency principle as well as the existence of at least four basic needs—all of which strive to be fulfilled simultaneously—we can infer the necessity of a **parallel-simultaneous organization** of mental processes. Several motivational schemata are always activated simultaneously. The level of **motivational schemata** is also structured hierarchically. This aspect has been omitted from the figure to avoid unnecessary complexity. The simultaneously activated schemata are intentional or approach schemata (denoted by an "I" in Figure 2.25) and/or avoidance schemata (marked with an "A" in Figure 2.25), which may be more or less **consistent** or **in conflict**, respectively, with one another. Conflict schemata, as discussed earlier are marked with a "C."

The activated schemata exert joint influences on behavior. The simultaneous influence of multiple, even conflicted schemata, is possible because of the many behavioral

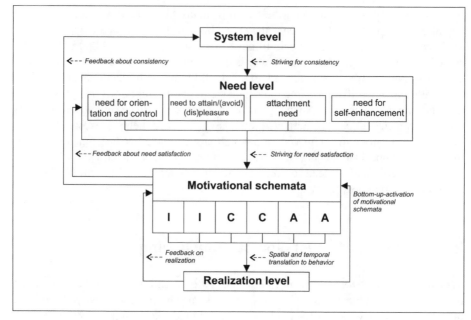

Figure 2.24:
A functional model of psychological functioning with four levels: realization level, level of motivational schemata, need level, system level.
I = intentional schema – C = conflict schema – A = avoidance schema.
Further elaboration of this is found in the text.

channels available to people. Their situational actualization requires that the motivational schemata, which are based on neural activation patterns in the brain, ultimately be transformed into muscle contractions, because this is the only way an individual can exert any actual influence on his or her environment. Beginning with the actualization level (Powers' program level), behavior has to be matched with the actual spatial-temporal (situational) conditions in which the individual currently exists. Conscious, planful action which is particularly sensitive in terms of recognizing and responding to situational reality, can also be classified as belonging to this actualization level.

Perceptions originating from one's own influence on the environment, as well as perceptions made independently of one's influence, are appraised in reference to currently activated motivational schemata (see arrow from actualization level to motivational schemata). These perceptions can also activate additional motivational schemata (arrow from the actualization level to motivational schemata). This corresponds to the idea of **bottom-up activation**.

Perceptions formed on the actualization level are continuously appraised in reference to one's needs and to the consistency requirement. The result of such comparisons can be a self-generated or—if occurring independently of one's own contribution—a "gratis" **need satisfaction**. This process can lead to a shifting of relative weights, from the level of needs to the level of motivational schemata. The result may be a deactivation of previously activated and a new activation of previously deactivated motivational schemata.

Many aspects that have received quite a bit of attention in our conversation are missing from Figure 2.24. For instance, emotions are missing, although we considered them to be crucial aspects of mental functioning. Also, the question of whether feedback confirms existing schemata or changes them is not clearly addressed here. No difference is made between different modes of functioning of psychological activity, between implicit versus rational-conscious information-processing. No clear differentiations are made between short-term versus long-term feedback processes (state vs. trait). Important terms that played a role in our previous discussions such as consciousness, the ego and the self do not appear at all.

I have attempted to depict in a sketch some of the most important functional relationships we discussed (see Figure 2.25). Unfortunately, the result is not as clear as I would like but that may well be a reflection of actual, existing complexity. Nonetheless, maybe the sketch can help us integrate the most important features we identified.

Let me begin to explain Figure 2.25 by commenting on the level of **needs**. Needs are thought to activate the motivational schemata developing around them. These schemata can be intentional (approach), avoidance, and conflict schemata. The continuous-line arrow signifies short-term **changes in need strength**, the dotted-line arrow signifies long-term need strengths. We can refer to these two aspects as the **state** and **trait** components. Thus, the dotted-line arrow corresponds to motives that are permanently activated, so that they exert a continuous or regular influence on behavior. The continuous-line arrow refers to temporal fluctuations in need satisfaction. If a need has just been satisfied, its influence will decrease for a while, and vice-versa, if a need has not been fulfilled in some time, it will exert a relatively strong influence.

I should also note that the level of need satisfaction manifests itself in the person's **emotional condition**. Here we also have to distinguish between long-term effects on **well-being,** versus short-term effects of need satisfaction (or dissatisfaction) on **current emotions**.

Activated motivational schemata and emotional condition both exert an influence on psychological activity. I have placed the motivational schemata and emotional condition together in one split box because they exert a joint influence on psychological activity. Between the schemata and the emotions I have placed a sort of "sliding lever" which may be moved to the left or right. By moving it to the right, the influence of the emotional condition becomes relatively greater in comparison to the motivational schemata, and vice-versa. This sliding lever refers to the ability the emotions have to break free as soon as they have reached a certain intensity. Although the emotions originate from feedback in relation to activated motivational schemata, as soon as they exceed a certain strength, they become **independent determinants of experience and behavior**, pushing back the influence of goals focused on need satisfaction for as long as this state continues (sections 2.24 and 2.50).

The joint influence of emotions and goals on behavior always occurs simultaneously in **both modes of functioning**, and, along with this, the influence in the conscious mode of functioning must pass through the bottleneck of the "**consistency filter.**" The consistency filter scrutinizes whether the processes concerned (wishes, emotions, etc.) are compatible with what is already in consciousness and conceptual memory. Whatever passes the consistency filter becomes content of **consciousness** and thereby determines conscious perception, thinking, acting and feeling. Thus, the motivational schemata essentially determine the contents of our consciousness.

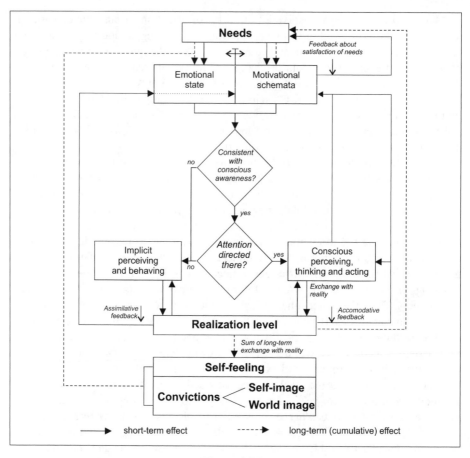

Figure 2.25:
Model of psychological functioning with consideration of the two different modes of functioning as well as short- and long-term influences. See text for further explanation.

Obviously the content of our consciousness is also influenced by real life situations, but these perceptions of actual events must also pass the consistency filter. Earlier, we attributed three functions to cognition, the content of consciousness: (1) A reality reflecting function, which I just discussed, (2) an interpretive function, appraising perceived events in reference to activated schemata, and (3) a control function. The arrow pointing from consciousness down to the bottom represents this control aspect. The content of consciousness becomes, by means of top-down activation, the starting point for consciously and voluntarily controlled perceptions and behaviors.

Even without the exchange with the environment, the motivational schemata and emotions receive feedback from consciousness. Space and time independent symbols may be used to represent these processes. The arrow pointing upward from consciousness to motivational schemata corresponds to conscious thinking, reflecting and deciding. An example would be when a person contemplates which of many wishes he should put into action. This is the process of selection, which was the topic of our discussion on the Rubicon model (sections 1.10-1.13), followed by the process of wanting, which is marked by the arrow pointing from consciousness downwards. If we look at just how little space this section takes up within the entire figure, perhaps it becomes clear why Heckhausen limited the explanatory value of his action-phase model with the following passage which you already quoted in the first dialogue:

"Wishing, selecting and wanting represent only the thin, uppermost layer on top of a series of basal motivation systems formed over millions of years, that have hierarchically built on top of one another. At any rate, it is the uppermost layer, the peak of the hierarchy.

At the lowest level are the automatic reactions of the autonomous nerve system, the endocrine and the immune system. On top of that there are pre-fixed movement patterns for specific, innate behaviors. Above that, primary drives which balance out disturbances to the bodily homeostasis. And on top of that are learned needs derived from primary drives that have become independent. And above that, all the primary affects such as happiness, grief, fear, anger, surprise and disgust enter into our experience, all of which, while deeply anchored in brain physiology, refer to the entire external and internal world of impressions and experiences, and can even be conditioned. On top of that, accompanying us is a constant striving to be effective in dealing with our close environment. And over that grow the higher, the social and cultural motives from which most of our wishes emerge if the lower systems are not necessarily occupied with alleviating homeostatic crises of our organism. And last, but not least, there is occasionally a little bit of selecting and a little bit of wanting that follows these wishes."

I think our second conversation has made it clear just how right Heckhausen was with his qualification of the processes of conscious selection and decision. Looking at what occurs in therapy, I am a bit concerned about how much we limited ourselves to this aspect of mental functioning, which concerns only a very limited, albeit important section of mental functioning. At the same time, we have elaborated on many of the aspects that Heckhausen listed, and perhaps even on a few additional ones. We may perhaps not subscribe entirely to his assessment that conscious selecting and wanting represent the peak of the psychological hierarchy. That is, consciousness, as we had discussed it earlier, cannot be conceived of as the highest determinant of psychological activity (section 2.27). Otherwise, the role Heckhausen ascribes to these processes in mental functioning correspond approximately to what I outlined.

Whatever does not pass the consistency filter is assigned to the **implicit mode of functioning**, which I deliberately placed closer to the emotions. In fact, as we have seen, the implicit mode of functioning has a **closer connection to the emotions** than to the rational aspects. Many things may occur simultaneously in the implicit mode of functioning. Several goals can be pursued simultaneously, even if not everything is moving simultaneously in the intended direction. The arrow pointing to mental processes in the implicit mode of functioning corresponds to **pre-attentive, nonconscious perception,** characterized by **high, parallel processing capacity** and **bottom-up activation of implicit memory content**. The arrow pointing downwards to the actualization level corresponds more to **intuitive acting** and non-consciously controlled aspects of behavior, such as large parts of **nonverbal behavior**.

Figure 2.25 depicts the limits of psychotherapy if one focuses on only the conscious mode of functioning. In fact, psychotherapy is usually about improvements of emotional states and other aspects of psychological functioning the patient cannot control consciously. These processes are all linked to the **implicit mode of functioning** rather than to the rational. What we referred to as **processual activation** in our first conversation refers predominantly to the activation of what is stored in **implicit memory** and thus concerns the implicit mode of functioning. Therefore, therapists must perceive, think, and act in terms of processes and not contents.

What takes place in the exchange with the environment at the realization level has both short-term and long-term effects. In the **short-term**, there is an appraisal with respect to activated motivational schemata. If feedback is confirmatory it can be **assimilated** to the activated schemata, and positive emotions result. In case of avoidance schemata, for instance, this emotion would be relief. Furthermore, every confirmation reinforces the previous **ingraining of the memory trace** underlying this schema. In other words: Each confirming feedback reinforces the existing synaptic connection weights of the neural activation pattern underlying the schema, so that in the future this schema may be activated even more easily.

Confirmatory feedback that becomes assimilated to activated schemata may have positive or negative change effects. It depends on the kind of schema involved. If it is an activated, problematic schema, confirming feedback leads to its becoming even more well ingrained. The problematic schema, and the experience and behavior determined by it, will be activated even more easily in the future.

However, if it is a positively assessed schema, **confirmatory feedback** may lead to a deepening of ingrained paths which were previously developed too weakly. The result would be that the schema may be more easily activated in the future and may gain more influence on the experience and behavior. This is also the rationale for **resource activating procedures**. The more a therapy succeeds in activating neural activation patterns that are positively assessed—that is what is meant by the term resource—, the better they will be ingrained, and the more influence they will gain on the patient's experience and behavior. This takes place independently of other therapeutic work.

Confirmatory feedback also has an effect on the approach component when **conflict schemata** are activated in therapy (see section 2.32). Because the goal of therapy as far as conflict schemata are concerned is the **strengthening of the approach component** and the weakening of the avoidance component, with respect to the weakly developed intentional component, the confirmatory feedback contributes directly to working on the problem. In most cases one will usually also have to target, and processually activate the second conflict component, the avoidance schema. This is to allow for accommodating to new experiences, but the path will be less uncomfortable for the patient and easier for the therapist, the more the positive conflict component becomes strengthened by confirmatory feedback. Such an **ingraining of the positive component of a conflict schema** follows, for example, if a patient puts his therapist through a "**relationship test**," and the therapist passing that test (see sections 1.29-1.31).

In most instances, however, the majority of the work in therapy will be the **weakening** of the **problematically appraised schemata** in their influence on experience and behavior. In the previous chapter we saw how negative the influence of avoidance schemata can be on a person's well-being. Thus, very often the goal in therapy will be to demolish or limit the influence of avoidance schemata, meaning that an accommodating influence should be exerted on problematic schemata. I depicted this influence in the figure with a feedback arrow leading both to the right side of the realization level and to the motivational schemata and consciousness.

Accommodating feedback means that the individual is not successful in terms of having perceptions that are consistent with his or her goals, and that is associated with negative emotions. Yet such a **"disturbance"** will also draw the individual's **attention** to it at the same time. As a rule, then, accommodating influences are associated with **consciousness**. There is conscious dialogue with the disturbance. This is the procedure which Piaget referred to as the beginning of **"reflective abstraction."** It is about **creating new neural paths.** The existing connection weights are overwritten with new ones. The newly established neural activation patterns must be so well ingrained through frequent activation that they can be activated more easily than the old problematic ones in the future. For a certain period of time this requires the conscious attention to support the newly establishing activation patterns until they are sufficiently established and automated so that they may be more easily, bottom-up activated in relevant situations. Problematic patterns, however remain traces in memory and when the newly established ones become weakened, the old ones may regain their former influence on experience and behavior.

In addition to these short-term effects, the processes just described also have long-term effects. Many similar short-term effects accumulate eventually to form long-term memory traces. In the figure, I represented such **long-term effects** by dashed-line arrows. There are five of these long-term kind of effects.

Events involving consciousness manifest themselves in the individual's **self-image** and the **world-view** on a long-term basis. I am referring to what Epstein termed the self-model and the world model. Long-term effects are fed into basic **convictions** with respect to the fulfillment of basic needs from both the processes in the implicit as well as the conscious modes of functioning. Overlapping, yet not identical to the self-image, is the **ego-feeling** a person lives with. It is fed much less by conceptual memory than is the self-image. It receives input particularly from implicit experiences the individual makes through his exchange with reality. These experiences are denoted by the downwards pointing, dashed-line arrows in the middle of the figure. What the individual has so far consciously thought and felt, i.e. the contents of his conceptual memory as well as what the individual did and experienced in the implicit mode of functioning, determines, apart from his self- and world view, also this ego-feeling which one lives with and which sets up the individual's relation to his environment.

These long-term memory contents are, on the one hand, products of motivational schemata via the links listed in the figure. On the other hand, they have an effect back on the schemata, penetrate them, become a part of them and codetermine how the individual feels on a long-term basis (left dashed-line arrow directed upwards to the motivational schemata and the emotional state). The long-term emotional state meant by this may be referred to as the individual's **basic feeling about life**.

In addition, the basic feeling about life is essentially also influenced by the long-term status of basic need satisfaction. If this is bad, the individual's basic feeling towards life will also be bad. A bad emotional state will have a negative effect on which motivational schemata are easily activated. In a depressed state of mind there are mostly depressed thoughts, etc. Additionally, the energizing of the motivational schemata and their realization is negatively affected, leading to experiences which, on a short-term basis, affect emotional status and the status of need satisfaction negatively, and the accumulation of this short-term negative feedback results in more long-term negative beliefs as well as in an even worse ego-feeling and feeling about life.

Again we are faced with one of those **positive feedback processes** that we have encountered several times in both the first and second conversation. Here I just described such a process progressively leading in a negative direction. From the same control and feedback processes, through reversed polarity of the emotional quality, a positive feedback process in the direction of an improvement of both need satisfaction and feeling towards life may, in quite an analogous way, also result.

Whether or not a **progressively positive or negative development** results, may actually depend on **relatively small influences** in one direction or the other. Therefore, a **dynamic** is at work that is not so obvious at first glance. What we have here is not a model of equilibrium, which tends towards maintaining the status quo. Rather, the model tends towards progressive developments in either a positive or negative direction. I find this to be an advantage for our purpose because the model explains quite well how the negative developments may grow into increasingly severe disorders, yet, it also shows the therapeutic starting points from which a progressive positive development of the kind we are striving for in psychotherapy can be initiated.

Together we have made an effort to avoid introducing any homunculi. Nowhere in my figure have I used the term "self." The self, according to this model is no distinct authority of regulation. If it makes sense to speak of the self at all, then the self is, according to this model, the totality of the elements listed in Figure 2.25. In a way, the figure **is** the self. The self is not mentioned in the figure because it is the entirety.

In order to familiarize ourselves with what this model implies about **at what points to begin in therapy**, just for fun, let's see what happens if we imagine changing ourselves into a therapeutic homunculus which gets lodged in the model at exactly the spot from where it can exert the greatest positive influence on the dynamics established in the model. Where exactly I, as a homunculus, would settle, is obvious clear: I would choose the box referred to as "realization level," i.e. I would view myself as part of the environment which the patient relates to in line with his motivational schemata and where the perceptions he makes proceed from. This does, in fact, correspond to the real influence I have as a therapist: I can exert an influence on what perceptions the patient makes.

Four arrows are available for me to influence. I can use the left arrow pointing upwards from the realization level to the processes in the implicit mode of functioning in order to activate neural activation patterns stored in the patient's implicit memory. This is my greatest opportunity for processual activation. The right arrow from the realization level to consciousness can be used for activating certain conscious processes in the patient by consciously, verbally communicating to direct his conscious attention to a point where there is new information for him. This may, for example, be the implicit processes that I triggered in him bottom-up just before, possibly in a nonverbal manner. These two vertical arrows refer to suggestions that come from me as the therapist. They are not reactions to the patient's behavior, but suggestions from me.

The two other arrows that are available to me for my work are the assimilation and the accommodation arrows. This concerns the feedback on the behavior the patient has just displayed. I may specifically confirm an activated schema and/or I may confront the patient with perceptions that may not be assimilated. I just described the effects that I can achieve with that, or the processes I can initiate, respectively. Thus I can

- exert an influence on the patient via the **implicit** and the **conscious** modes of functioning,
- I can specifically enable him to have **confirmatory** perceptions and/or confront him with **non-assimilable** perceptions.
- I may either **stimulate** him myself or **react** to his behavior.

My idea would be that I, as a therapist, am sitting in that little box referred to as the realization level, operating sort of a control lever which allows me to infinitely and variably mix and dose the aforementioned forms of influence in a smooth, continuous way, each in line with my particular therapeutic view of the situation at that moment. By flexibly combining all these available possibilities, one is, according to this model, equipped with a wide range of possibilities for exerting a beneficial influence on a patient's mental functioning.

My greatest **diagnostic** chances come from the two arrows pointing downwards from the patient's behavior to the realization level. By viewing me as the environment influenced by the patient in line with his motivational schemata and emotional state, I may draw conclusions for both from his behavior. His **nonverbal behavior** will tell me more about the less conscious processes going on in the **implicit mode of functioning**, whereas I can make usage of the verbal channel, transcending the limitations of time and space through the possibilities of symbolic communication, in order to obtain a possible wealth of information from the patient on issues that I myself am unable to observe.

Psychologist: I am amazed at what you managed to include in this sketch. What I particularly like is that at no point, in fact, did you include any central control authority. Mental life is simply the result of the interplay of a multitude of processes without there being any superior referee or controller anywhere. That is exactly my opinion. Your outline demonstrates that one can arrive at a model of mental functioning suited for psychotherapy without the underlying assumption of such authorities.

Therapist: I also like the model; as a therapist, I can make great use of this way of thinking about a patient. With the help of this model, I comprehend how conflicts and dissociation between mental processes are formed through violations of basic needs and through further development of more and more avoidance and repression. This eventually results in constant dysregulation and, in turn, can lead to mental or psycho-somatic disorders. What I also like is your image of the therapist who exercises her influence via activation of implicit and conscious processes as well as via assimilating and accommodating feedback, and is able to smoothly and precisely mix these influences to account for the particularities of the respective patient and situation. I can easily translate all this into tangible procedures.

Yet there were a couple of important points in our discussion that are not readily apparent in this summarizing sketch. I am a little concerned about whether these aspects will eventually get the attention they deserve once this model would be applied in therapeutic practice.

What I mostly miss is the aspect of functional autonomy of mental disorders that you pointed out earlier. How can the disorder-specific aspect be accounted for? The way you summarized this model just now—at least this is how I understand it—it can generally be applied to all people, at least to people of our culture. It is mostly a model of normal mental functioning and not a psychopathological model. While this model allows us to easily understand how disorders gradually develop, the model remains unspecific regarding the different types of disorders. To me as a therapist, however, it makes a difference whether I am faced with a patient suffering from an eating disorder, a phobia, or a depression as I must take into account the special nature of the disorder for the way I proceed. In therapy it does not suffice to comprehend what caused the disorder to develop. Yet, since the model is not concerned with **disorder-specific aspects**, we run the risk that they are not given sufficient consideration with respect to therapeutic consequences.

Regarding the **interpersonal aspect**, I have an analogous criticism. The model focuses on what takes place intra-psychologically. Yet interpersonal events cannot be reduced to intra-psychological processes. In light of the importance of interpersonal relations for a person's well-being, especially those produced by what we have discussed here, I have to ask: Wouldn't we have to work with a model in therapeutic practice which takes into account the special nature of interpersonal relations?

I am also somewhat concerned that in viewing psychotherapeutic problems from the perspective of this model the **capability aspect** of psychological functioning gets less attention than deserved. While I understand that this aspect is implicitly included at many points, it is not specifically mentioned and could slip too easily into the background. In our first conversation we saw how important being able or not able is for the aspect of intention realization. Therefore, this view should have a greater, explicit role in a model suitable for therapeutic practice.

As much as I like this model illustrated by your outline, a few things are still missing which I would like to see more strongly considered for use in psychotherapy.

Psychologist: I think you are right about the points left open by this model in this summary. These have played a greater role in our discussions than is demonstrated by your outline. We should make a greater effort to clarify these points a bit better. The advantages of the view which you just summarized, in fact, will not get lost.

In my opinion, before we develop such a model, some forethought should be given to just what purpose it might serve. This model is definitely satisfactory as a general model of psychological functioning. It really does not bother me that it is not simultaneously a disorder and an interpersonal model, because my expectation is not for one model to be able to simultaneously be useful for all purposes. As a psychologist devoted to basic science I am rather satisfied with this model, yet for the purposes of psychotherapy, I assume that it would be rather advantageous to work with a model attributing a high value to the disorder-specific aspect. What our model does not encompass thus far is the new quality of mental functioning which is added once a mental disorder has developed.

I have an idea as to how one could remedy the shortcomings you pointed out, but this would require that we dive into an entirely new world of thinking, and I do not know whether you are ready for that. Earlier you mentioned that you had enough now, and since then we have still continued. In dynamic systems theory there are concepts which might be useful for our purposes. Several times over the course of our discussion I mentioned that I would still like to address those. However, I admit that we took a lot longer than I initially thought, so I leave it up to you whether you wish to have another go at this, or whether we leave it at the present model. Certainly, we can already draw very many useful practical conclusions from the present model.

Therapist: This time I have to surprise you. I have learned something in the meantime. If we had quit at the point where I really felt like it, we would not have dealt with the basic needs and everything following thereafter. Now I cannot imagine how we could have done without all that. Especially for me as a therapist, our ideas on the basic needs and on the consistency principle were revealing and informative.

I am certainly not going to present any opposition this time when you say you still have a useful idea. This remains true even given the considerable bias I have against everything that calls itself dynamic systems theory, chaos research, synergetics or self-organization. I have yet to meet anybody who could explain to me in comprehensible terms how this all could be practically useful. I have always found this to be just a bunch of useless jargon. I just cannot listen to expressions like "postmodern constructivist shift" or the like; I just turn off.

However, I do not know you to be someone to express enthusiasm over terms without there being something behind it, so when you claim that these concepts might be useful for us, I will attempt to replace my aversion with curiosity. I do, however, request that you keep in mind that I am not a mathematician, and that I do not have great capacity for understanding all kinds of formulas. In addition, I also tend to have an aversion against anything that does not make sense to me.

Psychologist: I think I can set you at ease, I certainly do not intend to bore you with the mathematical foundations of chaos theory. Also, I am definitely not someone who maintains that these concepts could claim any superior validity or truth, or that they would be indispensable for that matter. For instance, the basic principles of self-organization are already included in the considerations we have developed without having used any terms from dynamic systems theory. Yet, there are a few concepts which might pinpoint even more concisely what we have developed in our ideas. The reason is that dynamic systems theory places the **time dimension** at its center. Thinking back to the very beginning of our first conversation, the questions all concerned processes that were temporally stretched, namely questions about the development and precipitation of mental disorders as well as about change or non-change in psychotherapies.

In the ideas we have been working on so far, we have conceptualized the human psyche as a system. Both our thoughts on neural functioning, and your summary demonstrate that it is an enormously complex system in which processes interact at different levels in a highly complicated manner. In addition, the system has its own dynamic. It activates itself, and is in constant exchange with the environment.

One of the most obvious properties of the system is that it develops. The multifaceted interactions within the system and with the environment produce changes. The psychological system develops continuously. In the course of this development something can emerge which creates a need for a psychotherapy, namely disorders of mental life. Psychotherapy starts at a certain point of a development, accompanies it for a time, and then leaves it to itself again. In the following, my goal is to focus on this developmental aspect by viewing mental functioning, mental disorders and psychotherapy from a developmental perspective. I would think it unwise not to consider here those concepts that were especially developed for modeling **the temporality of complex systems**.

Part 4: Mental Functioning From a Dynamic Developmental Perspective

2.44   The Concept of Self-Organization

At the beginning of our discourse on mental functioning we had posed the question: "Who controls mental life?" (chapter 2.27). We arrived at the conclusion that there really are no determining authorities in mental life, such as the ego, the self, the super-ego, the unconscious, etc. This is clearly demonstrated by your sketch (Figure 2.25). There are no central control authorities in mental life. There are only a large number of processes transpiring simultaneously and providing feedback to one another. These processes, however, produce behavior that quite obviously appears to be structured and oriented towards certain goals. This results in experiences in which we perceive ourselves as the ones who actually determine our actions. Isn't that a contradiction? Are we not to assume that mental life is determined by a structuring spirit?

This question has fascinated mankind since the beginning of existence. This question does not solely concern mental life, it concerns the entire order of our world. Who, or what has created this wondrous world? Isn't there necessarily a spirit that imposes structure behind the creation of the world? Isn't Genesis, as it is in the bible, much more plausible than the idea that everything formed out of a Big Bang of highly dense, but still undifferentiated matter? How should that have happened? How did life develop? The mind? Consciousness? Do we not have to conclude—especially if we look at the structuring capacity of our brain—that the brain was created from the outset with the purpose of achieving such capacities?

Of course, I do not want to go into the philosophical questions arising from this, as that would lead us too far afield from our goals. An animated discussion about these questions is currently going on, especially between neuroscientists and philosophers, caused predominantly by the great advances in neuroscientific research. If you have an interest in such questions there are some very exciting books (Popper & Eccles, 1982; Eccles, 1994; Edelman, 1995; Roth, 1995; Metzinger, 1996). I just wanted to point to the far-reaching implications these question raise for our image of the world and of man. My goal for our discourse is much more modest: I would like to introduce to you an image of mental functioning that requires no homunculi, not even if we wish to understand its development.

The capacity for developing into what it is, is already contained in the most important basic principles of mental life. We need no additional assumptions. Actually, what we have here are not mere assumptions but obvious facts:

1. The human psyche (mind) is in an **exchange with a system-external environment**. It receives energy and information from the environment and influences it in return. This is the basic assumption of Powers' model. All the while we have already been proceeding from this assumption.

2. There is constant feedback between the different psychological processes; a **negative feedback** and a **positive feedback**. A negative feedback cycle is the nucleus of control theory. The behavior is focused on decreasing or avoiding discrepancies between goals and perceptions. So negative feedback is also one of our previous basic assumptions.

We have also repeatedly come across **positive feedback processes**, encountering them as early as our first dialogue in conjunction with the induction of improvement expectations and with resource activation. There they had an influence in a positive direction. They were also to be found in conjunction with the role of expectations in the development of anxiety disorders, or generally in conjunction with the role of emotions in mental functioning. Certain thoughts, perceptions, etc., cause depressive feelings. In this state one tends to perceive and remember negative things. This leads to an even more depressive state of mind. While in this state, one perceives everything more negatively etc. Here, positive feedback processes have an effect in a negative direction.

Thus, we repeatedly encountered negative and positive feedback. They are ubiquitous in mental life and also have obvious anatomical and physiological substrates: The information transmitters in the brain, the nerve cells, have multiple connections with one another which they can use to mutually activate or inhibit one another. Negative and positive feedback, therefore, are not just a theoretical assumption, but have an unquestionable, evident neural foundation.

These few facts, or principles, respectively, already allow us to explain how structural patterns form, leading us to ask whether or not there has been a guiding hand somewhere along the way, led by a certain plan.

I would like to offer an easily comprehensible example, although it is still far from the actual complexity of mental life. The example is taken from Schulz and Hilgenfeldt (1994). If one takes a metal plate, evenly covered with dust, and by exposing it to sound of a certain frequency, sets it into an even vibration, over time, little dust heaps form as if "on their own." How does this new structure or "order" develop from the initial disorder? How is it that exposing the plate to sound leads to ordered structures?

The reason for this lies in the physical constitution of both the dust particles and the plate. The dust particles receive a jolt from below through sufficiently strong vibration of the plate, making them jump around on the plate. For particles lying on top of other particles, the force of the jolt is dampened by the other particles and, therefore, they jump less far.

Initially, when looked at macroscopically, the dust was seen to be equally distributed on the plate. Yet microscopically, it was observed to be minimally thicker in some spots compared to others. In these places the dust particles jump a little less far than in areas where the dust is somewhat thinner. If dust particles from the somewhat thinner layers land in these somewhat thicker places, any more momentum received by them is dampened by the particles beneath them. Therefore, they jump less far and remain together with those particles already in this place where the dust is somewhat thicker, and contribute even further to the dust which is piling up in this spot. Then this effect becomes even more evident. Over time the dust particles from the thinner layers collect in certain places and gradually form little dust heaps, while the thinner dust layers between the heaps gradually disappear. The thick layers become thicker, the thinner layers, thinner. The heaps that form over time are, therefore, the result of a **positive feedback process**.

Once dust heaps have formed, and the space between them is almost empty, a stable condition is reached, sustained by **negative feedback**. While the dust heaps continuously lose particles that are jumping away from their edges, these losses are made up for by new dust particles coming in from the almost empty spaces in between them. When the streams of particles in both directions are of almost equal magnitude, the system comes into a stable condition or balance. Because the individual dust particles continue to move through vibration, this is a **dynamic balance**. Macroscopically, however, this does not become evident. The system remains seemingly stationary in the established order.

At the beginning it would not have been possible to predict the order that eventually formed. Neither would it have been possible to say how many dust heaps would form, nor where they would form. Out of minimal initial differences, a new order with certain macroscopic properties gradually emerged by "**self-reinforcement**" of initially minor differences. Yet there is no great mystery to this whole procedure. It is simply a result of the initial conditions, of properties the particles already contain, such as mass and location. Thus, order has emerged on its own from the particles' defining features. This order has formed by itself without any plan behind it. This is the meaning of **self-organization**.

Using this example, I could similarly discuss a few other terms which are repeatedly used in conjunction with self-organization. What I just referred to as self-reinforcement, the positive feedback process, is also referred to as "**auto-catalytic process**." This is a frightening term which means nothing more than the possibility that through positive feedback, out of minimal differences, great effects may eventually emerge. A well-known example is the beating of a butterfly's wings in Brazil potentially leading to a hurricane in the Caribbean. Hurricanes in the Caribbean actually emerge in a less unlikely fashion and this is why they happen so regularly and frequently. Our small dust heaps are a far more realistic example to aid us in understanding how new structural patterns may emerge from small initial differences through positive feedback.

I could also say **attractor** instead of structural patterns, to introduce one of the most important terms of chaos theory. Our example makes it easy to see how the attractor acquired its name. It appears as if the dust heaps attract more and more dust particles. In our example, the dust heaps are attractors which the system moves towards, and in whose direction it develops through positive feedback.

From our example we know that the dust heaps do not really attract the other particles; it only looks that way macroscopically. In reality, the dust piles form as a result of the vibration influencing the individual dust particles. It is really the constitution of the individual dust particles, their mass and location, and the vibration all coming together, that form the dust heaps or "attractors." These influences, which lead to the development of a new structural pattern, are referred to as the **control parameters** of a system's state. Changing the control parameters has an effect on the system's structural pattern. If the sound frequency in our example is modified, perhaps it might not lead to the vibrating of the plate, and the system would remain in a state of disorder. So what is important is not only the characteristics of the dust particles but also **the interplay of control parameters**. The Greek word for interplay is "*synergein*," the processes discussed here then are also termed "**synergetics**." In a broader sense, synergetics means the science of the interplay of many processes in complex systems.

In the course of the positive feedback process triggered by the interplay of several control parameters, an ever increasing number of parts of the system are drawn into the attractor's sphere of influence. The graphic expression "**enslavement**" is used to describe this process. A newly resultant structural pattern draws other parts of the system into its sphere of influence, making them its slave by using them.

The formation of new structural patterns which could not have been predicted from the initial features, yet result from the positive and negative feedback of the initial features, is referred to as **emergence**. The dust heaps in our example represent such emergent phenomena. Emergence refers to qualitatively new features. According to our previous thoughts, consciousness, for example, might be conceived of as an emergence of mental processes that in themselves are not yet marked by the quality of consciousness.

Since I had promised not to complicate matters unnecessarily, I would like to ask you whether I was able to explain the meaning of the term self-organization.

Therapist: Following you through this has not been difficult so far. The example is indeed easily comprehensible, although I don't see why this jargon is needed when everything can be described just as well without these terms. The terms themselves, in fact, do not explain much. You have referred to physical laws to explain what occurs. Therefore, I am not at all sure why we even need new terminology.

Psychologist: I can see that, but this is not what I had hoped to achieve with this example. Whether or not we can use these concepts for our purposes remains to be seen once we apply them to mental processes. For now, I would be content for you to understand what is meant by these different terms.

Therapist: I am, of course, quite interested to learn how one can actually apply this to human behavior or mental processes, since I do have some doubts about that.

Psychologist: Perhaps we should carry out a small experiment so that I can give you a graphic description of the concept of attractors with respect to your own behavior. What is most important to me is that you familiarize yourselves with what is meant by an attractor and which role attractors play in mental life

2.45   The Concept of Attractor

I would like to ask you to participate in a little demonstration which will allow me to show you how the attractor concept can be applied to your own behavior.

I ask you both to please extend both of your index fingers outwards while keeping the other fingers bent down.

Now, bend one of the fingers while leaving the other extended.

Now, bend the extended finger and simultaneously extend the other one so as to make an opposing motion. Do it slowly so it does not take much effort.

This opposing pattern of movement can be viewed as a movement attractor. The speed with which you are bending and extending is seen as the control parameter.

Now, let's change the control parameter. Speed up the opposing movements, go faster and now even faster.

As you continue to do this, now look at what you are doing. Both of you started to "cheat." You are no longer making opposing movements, instead you are bending and extending both fingers at the same time.

You can stop now.

What did I want to demonstrate with this? Under the influence of the control parameter "speed" you involuntarily established a new structural pattern of movement coordination. As you reached a certain speed you were no longer able to move both fingers in an opposing way; instead, you unwillingly switched into another pattern of movement. This is similar to the situation where a horse, while trotting fast, has a tendency of switching into a different gear, namely galloping. Each gear has its own range of speed and for this range of speed, a certain gear is most energy-efficient (McMahon, 1984). This last fact is very significant for understanding the function of attractors for the system. I will go into more detail later.

This little demonstration makes it easy for us to see: You are also under the influence of control parameters, and with this, develop new structural patterns in your activity. We can assume that underlying your finger movements are very specific neural activation patterns. Under the influence of the control parameter "speed," a new neural activation pattern, a new movement attractor has just now established itself in both of you which has "enslaved" your voluntary movement behavior. The switch from one movement pattern to another without a gradual transition is an example of non-linearity, something that plays an important role in chaos theory. Continuous changes in the control parameter result in sudden transitions in the system's behavior, not in a gradual change analogous to the change to the control parameter. The system's behavior is stable across a certain range of variation in the control parameter. In a transitional area, previously established behavior becomes unstable, increased fluctuations within the system result, manifesting themselves in a heightened variability of the behavior, eventually leading to a non-linear, qualitative change in the system's behavior.

The inspiration behind this little demonstration comes from studies by Kelso and associates (Kelso et al., 1981; Kelso & Scholz, 1985; Kelso, Scholz & Schöner, 1986; Scholz, Kelso & Schöner, 1987). Utilizing experiments similar to that which I just performed with you, the various parameters of movement coordination were meticulously examined in a whole series of studies. If test subjects immediately begin to simultaneously extend and bend the fingers, then the increase in speed does not lead to destabilization of this attractor. The parallel movement represents a more stable attractor than the opposing movement. At a lower speed the opposite attractor is also stable, but an increase in speed initially results in a strongly increased variability of the movement coordination. The opposite attractor is not abandoned, but it becomes less stable. Such increased variability is the most important indicator that an attractor is becoming less stable. Another indicator of the attractor's stability is the time required for an attractor to find its way back to a stable condition following a disturbance. This is a very fast process for stable attractors, whereas it requires longer for unstable ones.

The latitude of the system increases with the instability of the attractor. The degree of enslavement is reduced. This brings about a fluctuation in the system's condition. These fluctuations are now strengthened by system-internal feedback processes, until the system falls into a new, stable condition.

In our example the parallel movement of the fingers is a very stable attractor which is not susceptible to disturbances and remains stable across all areas of the control parameter. If we think about this aspect of change in conjunction with psychotherapy, then it is difficult for such a stable attractor to be changed, whereas a less stable one, such as that of an opposing motion, would be much easier to change. The means of change is the alteration of the control parameter which is maintaining the dynamic balance of the parameter through its influence. One indicator which is also useful for therapeutic practice is the variability of the behavior one seeks to change. In a situation of very little variability we have a very stable attractor which would be difficult to change. At any rate, such a change would have to be carried out first by destabilizing this stable condition. In a case of greater variability of the behavior, it should be much easier to destabilize the behavior further and further, and generate those fluctuations that lead the system to fall into a new order through changes of the control parameter.

Attempts are often made to illustrate the stability of attractors by a landscape of potentials. Figure 2.26 places our demonstration directly in a landscape of potentials.

A stable attractor is represented by a ball in a steep and deep valley. It is very difficult to bring the ball out of this valley. The left, deep valley represents the opposing finger movement at slow speed. In this range of the control parameter we have a stable attractor. The decreasing stability of the attractor during increasing speed is illustrated by a less deep, and less steep valley. In this more unstable state, system-internal fluc-

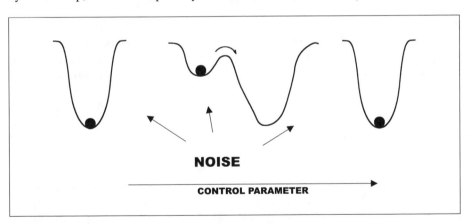

NOISE

CONTROL PARAMETER

Figure 2.26:
Illustration of a landscape of potentials for the change of movement attractors under the influence of the control parameter speed. In the left part, the system is in a state of stability (a stable movement pattern). In biological systems there are always fluctuations of the system's states (noise). This is illustrated in the middle part. Under the influence of a control parameter (speed, for example), the fluctuations exceed a critical value and the system settles into a different, qualitatively new state of fluctuation (right part).
Figure taken from Thelen and Smith (1995, p. 64).

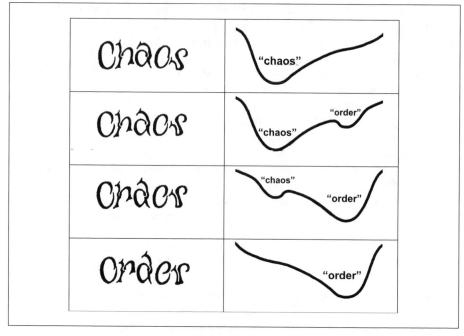

Figure 2.27:
Schematic illustration of the transition from one perceptual attractor (chaos) into another (order). On the left, the perceptual patterns; on the right, their illustration by a landscape of potentials.
Figure taken from Tschacher (1997, p. 64).

tuations, enforced by positive feedback, or few influences from outside, possibly suffice to get the ball out of the deep valley and cause it to roll into the neighboring, deeper valley. This valley then functions as an attractor of the ball in a very graphic way. The right part of the figure shows the stable attractor of the parallel finger movement also being very stable at high speed.

Similarly, Figure 2.27 depicts an example for two quite different attractors. Here we are dealing with perceptual attractors, namely the recognition of two words that are clearly written very differently.

Given our context, it makes sense that the relevant words be "chaos" and "order." The uppermost word is clearly legible as "chaos," the bottom one as "order." To the right of each word there is a deep valley which is supposed to characterize a stable point attractor. The two words in the middle, however, are less legible, which is expressed by two neighboring, differentially deep valleys next to the words, which are meant to express the two possible perceptual attractors. Here, only minimal changes in writing are necessary for the system to slip from one to another attractor.

Therapy researcher: By now it becomes clear to me that it is possible to apply the concept of attractors to very different phenomena. It appears to be a very abstract concept if it can be applied to both animate and inanimate systems.

Psychologist: For some purposes that is an advantage. Yet it can also become a disadvantage, of course, in that the concept then may be too non-specific for the individual phenomenon. Later on we will have to see how much of that concept can be applied for the purposes of psychotherapy. For now, however, I would like to use this advantage of the concept's abstract quality to explain to you more terms and principles of dynamic system theory, using another example from the field of physics.

It is an example frequently quoted, known as the **Benard-convection stream**. This can be observed at home when making spaghetti. Imagine placing a pot of water on a gas stove. At the beginning, the fluid—I view it now as a system—is in a state of complete disorder, in a thermodynamic balance. The molecules are equally distributed.

The flame first warms up the molecules at the bottom. Their heat energy is transferred to the upper molecules by collisions with them. This causes a transportation of heat from the bottom to the top throughout the fluid. Now, let's increase the temperature difference between top and bottom by turning up the flame, adding more and more energy from the bottom. When a certain difference in temperature is reached, the system all of a sudden displays a clearly, qualitatively different behavior than before: Hot streams of fluid flow to the top in regular, rolling waves, and cooler ones to the bottom. So what we have here again, is a non-linear change in the system's behavior during a continuously altered control parameter.

Just a moment before, the molecules were moving around in an irregular fashion. They were in a state of disorder, but now, all of a sudden, structured movement can be seen, namely rolling convection waves with a certain direction and speed. The fluid has taken on a qualitatively new state of order, an attractor. It enslaves the individual molecules. They are no longer able to move around erratically as they had before, but are drawn into a new, structured movement.

The convection waves are an emergent phenomenon arising from components already inherent in the system. The phenomenon is, therefore, "self-produced" from the properties of the fluid. The phenomenon, however, requires something very important: The system must be fed with energy from the system-external environment, only then can new states of order develop. Energy is continuously required by it (for mental or psychological systems that energy is information). This is the only way that a dynamic equilibrium can be maintained. Prigogine (1977) has, therefore, also referred to such states of order far removed from the stationary balance as "**dissipative structures**." They constantly use up system-external energy. Without this continuous influx, the state of dynamic balance would break down. From this perspective, all life processes are dissipative structures. Cessation of the collecting of energy from the system-external environment results in the breakdown of the many dynamic balances (attractors) in the organism, and signifies the transition from life to death.

Conversely, life coming into being is conceptualized as a qualitatively new, emergent phenomenon resulting from the characteristics of non-living material through self-organization. The development of new structural patterns through self-organization requires certain conditions. These necessary conditions are the control parameters. The most important control parameter for the convection waves is the temperature difference between top and bottom in the fluid, and this can be regulated by the gas flame. Yet the molecules also have to have certain characteristics as well. Their characteristics should also be conceptualized as context conditions necessary for new structural patterns to

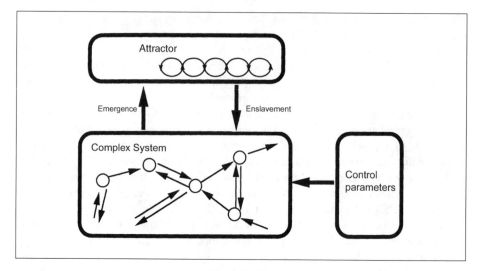

Figure 2.28:
Schematic illustration of a self-organized system according to Tschacher (1997, p. 49).

develop. So, there are relatively fixed conditions (constraints) required for certain states of order to form as well as variable control parameters whose influence can cause a certain phenomenon, such as convection waves under otherwise fixed conditions.

The most important connections assumed by self-organization theory are schematically represented in Figure 2.28. The bi-directional arrows in the part referred to as "complex system" symbolize the system-internal feedback processes. What is referred to as the "organizer" in the figure, I have previously called state of order, or attractor.

Therapist: You referred to attractors as new states of order and this makes sense to me. Both the dust heaps and the convection waves intuitively appear to me as being more structured than the conditions from which they emerged. But why on earth is a theory which claims to explain the development of new states of order called **chaos theory**? My understanding of chaos is the exact opposite of order.

Psychologist: This is a very justified question, and to answer it, I would like to return to the example we just discussed. What happens if we further alter the control parameter—the temperature difference in our example—under which the new phenomenon has formed? Under these changed conditions, the fluid changes its behavior again: Instead of the regular convection waves, turbulence appears. The convection waves start to change direction in an unpredictable way. Their behavior appears "**chaotic**" in the sense that it appears completely unpredictable. Yet, it is very important to distinguish this chaotic situation from the erratic, random movements of the molecules when we first began to heat the fluid. The turbulence is a new state of order which clearly differs from that at the beginning. The turbulence appears chaotic because it is unpredictable, but it is not random. In reality, it is precisely determined. The movement of the turbulence follows very specific laws that are difficult to recognize. Turbulence is referred to as **determined chaos**. Determined chaos appears anything but orderly; in reality, however, it is a new state of order for the system far removed from a condition in which the individual parts of the system behave randomly.

This is where our visualization fails and the point where mathematical abstraction begins to make sense. Chaos theory is actually an abstract mathematical theory and the distinction between a stochastic (random) chaos and a deterministic chaos is a mathematical one. I referred to the turbulence as a new state of order (attractor of the fluid), although it appears to be anything but ordered. In this case one speaks of a **chaotic attractor**. This, intuitively, seems to be a contradiction in and of itself, but it is really quite simple to understand how a system attains a state which appears chaotic, yet nonetheless follows a certain order.

To demonstrate this to you, I have to ask your permission to use a mathematical formula for illustrative purposes. While I know you are not entirely comfortable with too much math, I promise you will understand this formula. I also promise that this will be the only one.

Therapist: I guess this is a moment of reckoning for me, a corrective experience. I really did not imagine getting involved in any mathematical formulas when I signed on to this conversation. This is a sort of confirmation of my worst fears about what to expect from a basic scientist. Yet, somehow you have succeeded in preparing me for things I would have previously categorically denied. Perhaps, I should pay attention to the technique by which you accomplished that and maybe I could therapeutically learn something from it.

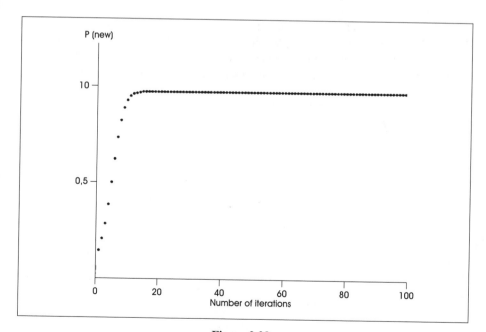

Figure 2.29:
Illustration of a positive feedback process with the starting state of p = .3 and the control parameter k = .5, which tends towards a point attractor of p = 1. Figure taken from Höger (1992, p. 225).

Psychologist: Your relatively calm reaction tells me you are ready and willing to accept my plan. You will not regret it because soon you will have grasped why chaos and order need not necessarily be contradictory.

I will now put the principle of positive feedback into a mathematical formula:

Let p be a value expressing a particular state of a system. Let us assume p to be linked to a positive feedback process. The next state of the system (p_{new}) always depends upon the state that the system was in just prior to that (p_{old}). Apart from that, the new state also depends on which influence was exerted on the preceding state. We refer to this influence as k.

We can now calculate each new state of the system (p_{new}) according to the following formula:

$$p_{new} = p_{old} + k \cdot p_{old} (1 - p_{old})$$

We assume p_{old} and k to be known. Then we can calculate p_{new}. The next step is that we insert p_{new} as calculated now as p_{old} into the right side of the equation, thereby being able to calculate the next following state of the system. This result can be inserted again into the equation as p_{old}. In this way we can continue to calculate which state a system, with a starting characteristic p under the influence of k will eventually have reached, after x number of calculations (iterations). The iterations express the feedback in the system.

Now we will do these calculations with actual numbers. For p we can assume an initial value of .3 and set k = .5. The results of the iterations are inserted in Figure 2.29. The y-axis includes the new value of p in each case and the x-axis, the number of iterations.

We can see that after relatively few iterations p already tends towards 1.

We may now insert any other values for p and k: as long as k falls within the range between 0 and 2, the outcome of our equation tends towards 1. No matter what initial value one begins from, after a certain number of iterations the state of a system with these parameters

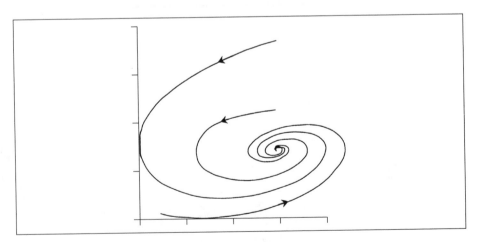

Figure 2.30:
Schematic illustration of a point attractor. Different trajectories lead from different initial conditions (points) to the same stable, final state.
Figure taken from Tschacher (1997, p. 9).

will always tend towards 1. Therefore, the state of p = 1 can be called an attractor of this system. From different initial states, the system continues to develop over and over again into a very specific state. Chaos theory speaks of a "**point attractor**" in such a case. There is one particular final state of the system which the system tends towards from all kinds of different initial states.

In Figure 2.30 such a point attractor is graphically illustrated in the form of trajectories through the space of potential states of a system.

In order for the system to move toward a very specific state, a point attractor, it requires that the value for k lies between 0 and 2. What happens now if the control parameter is continuously increased by inserting values into the equation of k = >2? An acceleration of the process leading to the value of 1 being achieved much faster could actually be expected. In reality, however, something else happens: with a value of k = 2.3 the results of our equation jump back and forth between two different values (see Figure 2.31). After a number of iterations, one continues to receive both the same results again and again. Without an external authority to set the pace the system demonstrates a regular periodical behavior. It fluctuates between two states in a certain rhythm.

If the value of k is increased even further, the number of potential values that result increases from 2 to 4, then to 8, then to 16. This phenomenon is referred to as a "periodically doubling cascading tree."

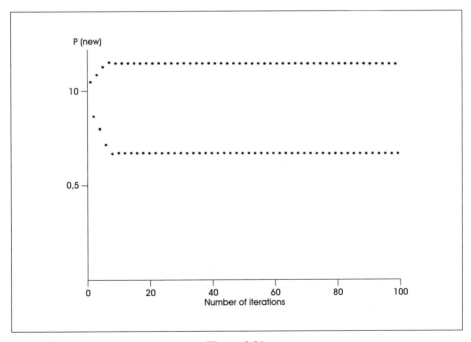

Figure 2.31:
Schematic illustration of a system fluctuating between two different states of order with a control parameter of 2.3.
Figure taken from Höger (1992, p. 225).

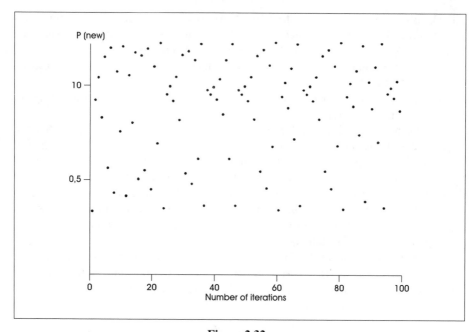

Figure 2.32:
Schematic illustration of a chaotic attractor:
With control parameter values greater than 2.57 the system seemingly fluctuates, entirely
unpredictably, independent of the smallest differences in the initial states.
Figure taken from Höger (1992, p. 226).

As of k = 2.57 no more fixed values can be predicted as resulting from the equation.
The results seem to be completely disordered. They may assume all kinds of values.
The value k = 2.7, for instance, yields the image shown in Figure 2.32.

The values jump from iteration to iteration in an apparently disordered fashion. The
result is now dependent on the most minimal differences in the starting conditions. For
instance, in the case of an initial-p of .10 a result entirely different from using an initial-
p of .11 is obtained. This represents a marked difference in comparison to the system's
behavior with k-values of below 2. In that instance, regardless of the initial value, the
iterations always tended towards one. When the iterations from our equation yield a
picture such as that seen in Figure 2.32, we speak of a **chaotic attractor**.

The states a system adopts, therefore, depend first on the control parameters, and
second, on the system internal feedback processes. Across wide areas of the control
parameters the system strives for a state of order which has earned its name. We can
call it a simple attractor. If we, for instance, view the dominant mood of a person as the
result of a multitude of control parameters and intra-psychological feedback processes,
then we can view the basic mood of a person which he continues to return to, following
situational detours, as a simple attractor.

The control parameters, however, may also move in areas, or the intra-psychological feedback processes may be so strong that the system fluctuates between different
states. The mood can then be "up one minute" and "down the next," or we simply speak
of "moody people;" people whose moods seem to change unpredictably to outsiders

and in the absence of any recognizable reason. In the clinical field this would correspond to the fluctuation between manic and depressive conditions. According to the considerations of chaos theory, such psychological phenomena could build up through relatively minor changes in external influences, which are then "autocatalytically" reinforced by system-internal feedback processes.

If one wanted to prevent such a back and forth between various states of order of psychological activity, in this case moods, one would have two points at which to begin. If one knew the control parameter of this mood attractor, one could try to shift it to a more advantageous area. The other point at which to begin would be the internal feedback processes. Since the intra-psychological feedback processes are based on neural activation processes, and these, in turn, depend on the synaptic activation transmission, it makes sense that one can influence these feedback processes not just via psychological, but also biochemical means, i.e. via medication (Bohus & Berger, 1992). In addition, the control parameter can be influenced by removing the patient from his previous environment. From this perspective the inpatient treatment of manic depressive patients with medication makes sense even if it would also perhaps be useful to try to exert more specific psychological influences on the intra-psychological processes and the control parameter. Again, in order to do so, one would have to locate and specify them.

For now it is still unclear which role chaotic attractors can play in human mental life. Possibly certain disorders, such as multiple personality disorders or schizophrenia, may be conceived of as chaotic attractors characterized by the fact that one state of order, rather unpredictably slips into another due to somewhat minor influences. Empirical research on that has just begun and faces major methodological difficulties.

Mathematical methods exist for deciding whether a time series with a value distribution such as that depicted in Figure 2.32 is based on chance or is the result of a deterministic-chaotic process. However, these time series statistical procedures require many reliable measurements which are performed in close, regular sequence over time. Such time series across relevant psychological phenomena are difficult to obtain.

Therapy researcher: That is true. For psychotherapy one would have to become involved in an effort of data acquisition hardly ever realized thus far, and at some point of course, a limit is reached as to just how much stress one can put upon a patient for research purposes. However, in the meantime, initial attempts have been made to approach clinical psychological and psychotherapeutic research questions with such methods. Tschacher (1997) and Schiepek et al. (1997) have performed such laborious time-series analyses for evaluating data obtained in psychotherapies. Tschacher and Grawe (1996) analyzed the development of the therapeutic relationship in different kinds of psychotherapies with respect to whether the relationship reaches a higher level of order over the duration of therapy, that is, whether, in fact, relational attractors establish themselves in the course of therapy. They really did find evidence of that. Not only did Tschacher, Scheier and Grawe (1997) confirm this finding for the majority of patients, but it was also demonstrated that both the absolute amount of order in the therapies and the increase of the level of order correlated with the quality of the therapeutic outcome.

These studies did not just view mental functioning but also the psychotherapeutic process as a dynamic system, and examined these with respect to the amount of order.

Certainly the results can also be interpreted from perspectives other than chaos theory, however, they can be viewed as first signs that there are new questions relevant for psychotherapy arising from this perspective, which may prove to be constructive.

Psychologist: This is how I see the current role for these concepts as well. So far, we are unable to rely on empirically sound knowledge when applying these concepts to questions of psychotherapy. At least I know of no findings that could be interpreted solely from the perspective of chaos theory. What I am presenting to you here, I view more as conceptual stimulation and not so much as sound and secure knowledge. Our question should be: Do these concepts open up perspectives which can give useful impetus for psychotherapy?

One potentially useful concept not yet presented by me so far is the **state space**. Attractors may be topographically illustrated. How illuminating the topographical representation of an attractor is depends upon what space it is illustrated within. The space set up by plotting within axes in Figure 2.32 obviously yields an illustration of a chaotic attractor which is only minimally enlightening. Only chaos is seen, no order. To characterize the state of a system by a graphically illustrated attractor, first, the **state**

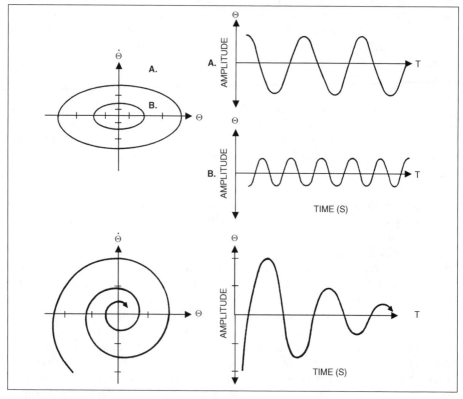

Figure 2.33:
Schematic illustration of the movements of a pendulum in a state space with the dimensions position and speed (left part of figure) vs. a reduction of amplitude over time (right part of figure).
Figure taken from Thelen and Smith (1995, p. 57).

space, whose dimensions should be the essential system components whose behaviors are to be illustrated, has to be conceptualized. Which components are necessary to describe the state of a system as completely as possible, but also as economically as possible?

For example, there are two ways a pendulum can be represented (see Figure 2.33).

One way is to depict the amplitude of the pendulum as set against time. This yields the illustration in the right part of the figure with the upper part showing a pendulum with no energy loss, and the bottom depicting a pendulum without added energy naturally dissipating its energy by loss of momentum.

It may also be possible to set up a state space within the axes position and speed. This will give us the illustrations in the left part of the figure. The movements of the pendulum can be viewed as a simple attractor, the attractor represented as a trajectory through the state space. This allows for the complete and economical illustration of which state the pendulum is to be found in at any given time.

It would also be very attractive, of course, if we could represent states of mental order or mental processes or even psychotherapeutic processes as trajectories across a state space. This would require knowing the critical components/dimensions of the corresponding system, because these would be the axes of that state space.

Therapy researcher: Even something like that has already been tried before. For instance, Tschacher (1997) has depicted the changing states of a patient the same way, as trajectories in a state space with the three axes tension, activity, and mood (see Figure 2.34). The choice of dimensions is based on analyses of semantic space obtained in polarity profiles. The depiction is based on 79 measurements. At each point in time, the patient made a self-assessment of her mood, activity and tension.

On the other hand, having such a figure to look at does not make us any wiser. Clearly, if a system contained more than three components the limits of visualization

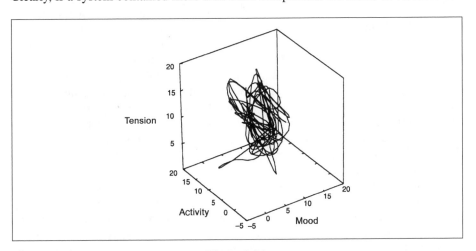

Figure 2.34:
Trajectory of the patient's states over a period of 26 days (79 measured time points) throughout a state space with the dimensions mood, activity and tension.
Figure taken from Tschacher (1997, p. 32).

would be quickly reached anyway. Therefore, I believe that the figures you and I have shown might perhaps be more useful in allowing us to visualize that there are different kinds of attractors, but that we should otherwise not get lost in the idea of a graphic illustration of attractors.

What we should, however, take with us from the idea of the state space is that one should have some knowledge about the relevant dimensions if one wants to describe states of order. Of course, the fact that the description should be as streamlined and economical as possible is an old scientific principle referred to as Occam's Razor long before the existence of chaos theory (Miller, Galanter & Pribram, 1960).

Therapist: Isn't there already a state space for interpersonal behavior that specifies relevant dimensions? Earlier you referred to the interpersonal circle model (see chapter 2.26), which included a state space with dimensions that allow us to economically describe interpersonal behavior. With her book *Interpersonal Diagnosis and Treatment of Personality Disorders*, Benjamin (1993) has shown how patterns of interpersonal behavior can be described by their positions in this state space. In this book the personality disorders according to Axis II of DSM-IV are characterized by a certain position in state space. Benjamin presumes that personality disorders develop out of interpersonal interaction patterns and that they manifest themselves specifically in interpersonal interaction behavior and that they are, by nature, ultimately interpersonal disorders. Fiedler (1995) also shares this view. In light of our considerations about basic human needs this also makes perfect sense.

The approach entails that each disorder be translated into certain interaction patterns and that these interaction patterns are all described in the same three-dimensional space. These three dimensions are:
1. Positive/friendly vs. negative/hostile affect,
2. Control,
3. Focus: Towards whom is the relational behavior directed?

One could view this "interaction space" in which these disorders are interpersonally defined as a phenomenon-specific state space for the description of "interpersonal attractors." The **interaction patterns** Benjamin describes might be viewed as **interpersonal attractors**. The picture that I associate with an attractor fits perfectly with these circumstances. Over and over again the patients slip back into the same kind of interaction patterns. Regardless of what kinds of relationships they enter, they are always tending towards a very specific interaction pattern. From different initial points offered by different interaction partners they always get into the same final state again. I find that Benjamin's description of personality disorders according to an interpersonal systematic comes pretty close to the goal of describing an attractor in a phenomenon-specific state space, even if Benjamin herself does not conceive interaction patterns as attractors.

The interaction partners of a patient with a personality disorder discover first hand in their own lives exactly what the expression enslavement portends in this context. They are, in fact, drawn into a certain interaction pattern and are very strongly restrained in their own freedom to behave in a certain way. Even a therapist treating such a patient is very tangibly confronted with these attempts at enslavement. At the same time, however, this presents a chance to exert an influence on the patient, and, over time, to destabilize the activated attractor. The destabilization would correspond to the accommodating feedback arrow in Figure 2.25. It would approximate our earlier concept of overwriting a strongly engrained neural activation pattern with new neural connections. Creating new neural connections could be seen as establishing a new attractor. Overall, we might consider neural activation patterns equal to attractors. While these different terms allow us to move in different worlds of ideas, we nonetheless mean the same.

Psychologist: You have moved ahead to the applications on psychotherapeutically relevant phenomena faster than I had planned. But the idea you just mentioned is pretty much the same I had just thought of. I am just a bit concerned that I may have created too great an impression of arbitrariness if I were to leave it at the previous explanations for the utility of the concepts of self-organization and attractor. There is more to these concepts than I have reported so far. I really did not get much further beyond an explanation of the terms. The examples used in describing the various concepts still had little to do with what predominantly interests us here. I think I should still add something before we finally turn to an attempt at applying all of this to the problems facing psychotherapy. Actually, I also wanted to focus on the developmental aspect, and I have not yet even gotten to that.

I would like once again to return to the example of the convection waves and point to an issue I had skipped earlier. This will then bring us to the concept of the attractor and its application to mental functioning.

2.46   The Function of Attractors in Mental Processes

If you place a pot of water above a flame, the temperature difference produces a **state of tension** in the fluid. The system strives to reduce this tension. This first occurs when lower molecules convey their heat energy to the top by colliding with other molecules. If the temperature increases, the system changes its behavior. The rising of the hot bubbles in the newly emerging convection waves represents a much more effective transfer of heat than if the heat energy is conveyed by colliding with other molecules. It is as if the system sought a way to decrease the temperature tension as effectively as possible, and had the idea that the convection waves would be an effective way to do so.

Of course, this is an anthropomorphized view. We assume that the fluid has something like a goal. In reality, there is only the interplay of certain physical laws. The "urge" that the system has to decrease the temperature difference corresponds to the second basic law of thermodynamics. The convection waves, under the physical conditions, i.e. the initial conditions and the control parameters, are an efficient means of temperature balance. They adhere to physical criteria. The developing state of order fulfills a physical function.

It is only a small step from here to the assumption that newly developing states of order fulfill a biological function in biological systems and a psychological function in psychological systems.

From this perspective we may view organisms newly emerging through mutations as new states of order of an ecosystem. What are the criteria for a new organism to fulfill its biological function? It is its survival and reproduction capability under given conditions (fixed constraints and variable control parameters). New biological states of order are selected according to criteria for their survival and reproductive capabilities. According to Darwin this is the way organisms emerge as more and more well adapted to a certain ecosystem.

Thus, systems' new states of order are **selected** according to certain criteria. We now switch with our ideas from the level of ecosystems to the level of organisms. Just as there are many coexisting states of order in an ecosystem that reciprocally need and influence one another—plants and animals—there are also many states of order in an organism that reciprocally require and influence one another: the heartbeat, the kidney function, coordination of movement, etc.

These states of order have also been selected by phylogenetic processes and to a lesser degree by ontogenetic processes. In higher developed forms of life the nervous system is a very important part of the organism. The states of order of the nervous system have also been phylogenetically selected according to biological criteria. The biological logic of complex nervous systems, however, lies particularly in the flexibility of their adaptation. This is why a great part of the selection of neural states of order takes place only in the course of ontogenetic development. So far, we have referred to neural states of order as neural activation patterns. According to this view, neural activation patterns are attractors that were selected according to certain criteria.

What criteria determine the selection of neural activation patterns? We will answer this question in a level-specific way. The question at this level is no longer about the selection of organisms, but about the selection of states of order of mental activity. Just as on the level of ecosystems, the selection takes place according to prescribed values. According to our previous thoughts in this dialogue, these values are the basic needs and the consistency principle.

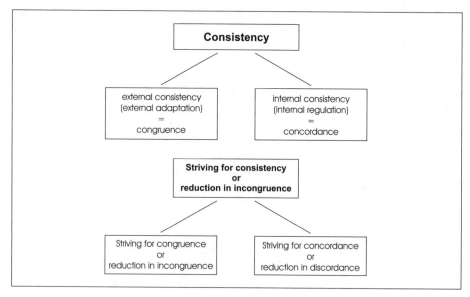

Figure 2.35:
Schematic illustration of the relationship between the terms consistency, congruence and concordance and the related processes.

A person's motivational schemata are the means for satisfying his basic needs. Psychological activity aims to create experiences that are consistent with the goal components of motivational schemata. Thus, basic needs are met, so the individual strives towards congruence. Previously we had referred to congruency as "external consistency" because it concerns the external adaptation of the individual. Thereby, we had distinguished it from "internal consistency," which might also be called concordance. In order to prevent semantic confusion, I have illustrated the relationships of the terms consistency, congruence and concordance in Figure 2.35. According to this figure, the striving for consistency—or for the reduction of inconsistency—represents the basic principle of mental functioning.

In placing this principle in a developmental perspective, we arrive at the following thesis on the basic principle of psychological development: **In ontogenetic development, psychological structural patterns are selected that effectively reduce inconsistency tensions**.

The ability to do anything—skillfully juggling several balls, for instance—requires certain neural activation patterns. If such activation tendencies were not ingrained in ontogenetic development, one would not be able to skillfully juggle. Motivation to do something—for example, to accomplish certain achievements—also requires certain neural activation tendencies. Only what one is able to do and what is actually done (to which one was motivated) can be selected. According to the consistency principle, when neural activation patterns are selected, there is always both **a capability and a motivational aspect**. Whatever one is motivated to do can only be selected if one has the ability to do it, because otherwise nothing would have occurred which could have been selected.

When I speak of neural activation patterns or of psychological structural patterns, then I mean both motivational **and** capability aspects. Earlier we referred to certain kinds of neural activation patterns as motivational schemata, in order to emphasize their causal influence on mental activity. Based on the ideas I just proposed, we now see that any motivational schemata that exist always have a capability aspect as well, because otherwise, they could not have been selected.

This is a response to the concern you expressed earlier, namely that the sketch in Figure 2.25 may not give sufficient recognition to the capability aspect. This can happen only if one has a limited understanding of motivational schemata. If schemata are viewed as ontogenetically selected attractors, the capability aspect is inseparably built in. There is less risk for us in speaking of a neural activation pattern than in speaking of a motivational schema, because clearly a neural activation pattern has to be in place for it to have an impact, and its actual existence means the actual existence of corresponding ingrained memory traces and this includes the capability aspect.

The idea that neural activation patterns are selected according to prescribed biological values was referred to as "neural Darwinism" (Edelman, 1987) by brain researcher and Nobel Prize winner Gerald Edelman. The ideas just presented by me mesh with Edelman's "Theory of the Selection of Neural Groups (TSNG)" (Edelman, 1987, 1989, 1995). I touched on the formation of neural groups via "reentrant mapping" one time previously, when I discussed the formation of cell assemblies according to Hebb (section 2.7).

Edelman's neural groups correspond roughly to what I had referred to as neural activation patterns. Those are cell assemblies linked together to one neural group by feedback ("reentrant mapping" in Edelman's terms) between different cell types specialized on different tasks. The perception of a chair (see Figure 2.9 in section 2.8), for instance, requires a reentrant mapping between different cell types. The reentrant mapping corresponds to what I had previously termed the connecting principle by synchronicity of activation (sections 2.8 and 2.20). Thus, the perception of a chair occurs through the activation of a neural group. We may also view a neural group as an attractor. Edelman's theory maintains that certain neural groups are selected from a population of neural groups by "differential reinforcement," quite analogous to the selection of organisms by differential reproduction. Selection criteria are biologically predetermined values. For Edelman these resemble our basic needs.

"In addition there is a connection between heredity and the selection of neural groups. In a selective system there must be a correlation between parents and their offspring which is greater than the background noise. In evolution this is secured by heredity, and in the TSNG, by synaptic changes. Neural groups which initially responded to a stimulus are more likely to react, on average, to a similar stimulus if it is offered once again; this likelihood, however, is influenced by value systems. In evolution the differences in the adaptation of different organisms to the environment lead to differences in reproduction, which, in turn, lead to changes in the population's genetic make up. In the selection of neural groups, differences in the kind of coherence, in synaptic structure and in neuronal morphology in the primary repertoire resulting from the encounter with different correlated signal patterns from the environment, lead to different reaction probabilities of the groups. These indicate the changes of the synaptic strengths. In one case there is differential reproduction, in the other differential reinforcement...

The natural selection has, astoundingly, created two entirely different somatic selection systems in the course of evolution both leading to recognition. If we accept this idea, the small loop of the selection of neural groups in the individuals of one kind, leads to different phenotypic behaviors. These different behaviors provide the basis for further natural selection in the larger loop of evolution. The relationship between the two selective systems, the somatic and the evolutionary, is mutual" (Edelman, 1995, pp. 143/144).

According to Edelman, a neural activation pattern corresponds to an activated neural group. Previously, we used the terms neural activation tendency and schema largely interchangeably. We could also add neural group as an equivalent term. A neural activation pattern would have the same meaning as an activated schema. It may simultaneously be viewed as an attractor, as a certain state of order of neural activity.

So, what we termed earlier as motivational schema we can consequently also call **motivational attractor**. According to Edelman's theory, those neural activation patterns are selected that have led to the reduction of an existing need tension. In the quote just cited this is the event referred to as differential reinforcement. Here differential reinforcement means the ingraining of neural activation tendencies.

Thus, attractors have a specific function within mental processes: They decrease tension. This is how they become ingrained. The more often a neural activation pattern has led to decreased need tension, the better ingrained it is and the easier it may be activated in the future. The expressions: "decrease of a need tension" and "inconsistency reduction" mean the same thing. If a person has perceptions that are consistent with an activated approach schema, he or she has need-satisfying perceptions.

Need tension does not indicate a purely intra-psychological construct. According to dynamic system theory, and Edelman's theory as well, the psychological system relies on a constant exchange of energy and information with the environment. Other than that, essentially no dynamic balances far from the stationary states of balance are possible. The attractor is a transactional concept (see below). Even when I talk about need tension, I mean a transactional concept. The needs are in constant interaction with the environment via the motivational schemata, which makes certain demands. These demands, however, attain their significance by the individual's motivational schemata. For the individual, the environment does not exist as an objective but as a subjective reality. This is one of the basic assumptions of control theory.

These statements are derived from Lewin's concept of life space (1926, 1934, 1935, 1936, 1951) in his field theory. For the individual the environment is a life space comprised of subjective meanings. "The psychological environment has to be regarded functionally as one interdependent field, the life space, the other of which is the person" (Lewin, 1951, p. 140). The different parts of the environment have a particular demand character, or "valence," for the individual. The valences in life space correspond to the individual's needs. "To a certain degree the statements: 'this or that need exists' and 'this or that formation possesses a demand character in terms of these actions are equivalent, since the change in needs certainly corresponds to a change in the demand character" (Lewin, 1926, p. 353). The needs correspond to states of tension in Lewin's model of the person. He speaks in this context literally of a "tension system" where there is a striving for a balance of tensions. According to Lewin, action goals have the character of "quasi-needs." "The effectiveness of an intention is essentially dependent on the strength or the importance for life: how deeply anchored the primary needs are to which the quasi-needs are connected" (Lewin, 1926, p. 370).

Linking Lewin's field theory with dynamic systems theory and Edelman's theory: Attractors are selected for their ability to decrease states of tension or valence, depending on whether one wants to focus on the person or on the life-space. At any given moment the system finds itself at a point in its life-space at which certain conditions exert an influence on it. Some of these conditions may be control parameters with respect to the system's position within the space of possible states it can be in. If we conceive of the system as basically being in development, it would be even more apt to speak of a "**developmental space**." The developmental space would be a life-space as conceived by Lewin, supplemented by the time dimension. Through the individual's own activity, and through external demands, increasing incongruities arise between goals and real experiences as well as discordance between the simultaneously activated goals. These inconsistencies which we have now discussed in detail would correspond to what I just referred to as tension.

Such tensions—as we already acknowledged—need not necessarily be experienced as states of tension. An unclear picture or a word not clearly written may even have a demand character, a valence for us to recognize something. The basic need for control and the desire to understand arises. If confronted with a picture having multiple meanings, a state of tension arises which is reduced by recognizing something in the picture. Figure 2.36 can serve as an example. It shows a well-known reversible figure-ground illustration.

After a short time, almost all people will recognize either an old, or a young woman. The recognition, however, takes decidedly longer than, for instance, recognizing a clear or unambiguous face. First, a state of tension arises, which is alleviated by a state of order. The perception strives towards a point attractor, a neural activation pattern corresponding to the perception of a young, or an old woman. If the person is told that one may

Figure 2.36:
An example of a perceptual object which creates a state of tension that can be alleviated by two different structural patterns. Explanation in the text.
Figure taken from Schiffman (1976, p. 253).

also recognize something else in the picture, it usually takes a while until another figure is perceived. The perception finds itself in an "area of enslavement" of the just previously established attractor. After the other neural activation pattern has also been established, we are faced with an oscillating attractor. From that point on, the perception jumps back and forth between one and the other state of perception. After both states of perception have been established, one can usually generate both of these voluntarily.

New states of order of psychological or neural activity, therefore, emerge through selection from a range of possibilities. These possibilities are determined by pre-ingrained activation tendencies and the actual circumstances that are suited to reduce an existing state of tension. It is a special constellation of external and internal conditions under which new attractors develop or are selected from already established possibilities.

With his principle of natural selection, Darwin assumed that selection makes the choice of those conditions which entail an optimal fit between organism and environment. Neo-Darwinism dismisses this assumption. The general assumption today is that conditions which fulfill certain constraints are selected. It need not necessarily be the optimal condition, but one which satisfactorily meets the present constraints. In ontogenetic development such constraints are, for instance, the individual's abilities, goals, personal history, as well as the situational conditions. As we saw with the example of the figure-ground illustration, several possible conditions may exist which satisfactorily meet the respective constraints. The following analogy from Varela, Thompson and Rosch (1991, p. 194) expresses this quite well:

"John needs a new suit. In a fully symbolic and representational world, he goes to his tailor who measures him and produces a nice suit according to the exact specifications of his measurements. There is, however, another obvious possibility, one that does not demand so much from the environment. John goes to several department stores and chooses a suit that fits well from the various ones available. Although these do not suit him exactly, they are good enough, and he chooses the optimal one for fit and taste. Here we have a good selectionist alternative that uses some optimal criteria of fitness. The analogy admits, however, further refinement. John, like any human being, cannot buy a suit in isolation of the rest of what goes on in his life. In buying a suit, he considers how his looks will affect the response of his boss at work, the response of his girlfriend, and he may also be concerned with political and economic factors. Indeed, the very decision to buy a suit is not given from the outset as a problem, but is constituted by the global situation in his life. His final choice has the form of satisfying some very loose constraints (e.g., being well-dressed) but does not have the form of a fit— even less so of an optimal fit—to any of these constraints."

Selection requires variation. If there is no variety of possible, available states, no suitable state can be selected. Both development and change require variability. Variability develops if the constraints—we might also say the control parameters— change. This will increase the degree of freedom the system has. It is temporarily less structured. This creates the opportunity for trying out previously untried spheres of possible states. Fluctuations in the system's state result. Such fluctuations, phases of increased instability, are both an indication and a requirement for a qualitative change in the behavior of the system. Of these fluctuations, one is selected that best meets the present constraints. Via positive feedback the fluctuation produces a new, stable attractor. Thus, change requires and announces itself by a phase of instability.

2.47   The Development and Change of Mental Attractors

We have now reached a point at which the question arises as to how the concept of attractors may contribute to an understanding of the development and treatment of mental disorders. The question of development and change brings the **time dimension** to the forefront. In order to obtain a concrete picture of the functional role of attractors in a temporal sequence of mental functioning, I would first like to give you an example that illustrates how one could conceptualize the relationship between control parameters and attractors with respect to the time dimension.

For example, I could have a strong "quasi-need"—an intent according to Lewin—to get from here to a different location as quickly as possible. One constraint might be not having any transportation available. Other constraints underlying my actual movements include the condition of my tendons and muscles, gravity, which has an impact on me (my weight), the condition of my route, the shoes I wear, and the state of my circulatory system.

In our development, each of us has developed certain attractors for moving: We may walk, hop, run, crawl, skip, drag our feet or limp, etc. Earlier I had mentioned the different movements of horses as attractors. Given my strong intent of getting to a certain place as quickly as possible, and given the constraints, the attractor "running" will probably be best suited to the situation unless I had just recently twisted my ankle or something akin to that.

Consequently, I begin to run; after a while I get a cramp in my side and become short of breath. My running loses stability, my stride becomes less regular, the attractor "running" becomes less and less stable. We know from before that increased variability is an indication for a transition in the behavior of the system. With increased voluntary effort, I run a little further under the influence of the control parameter "strong intention." Through my own activity, however, the control parameters impacting my movement behavior further change—getting into a critical area—above all, the state of my circulatory system. It eventually gets into a sphere in which my previous movement behavior traverses, in a nonlinear fashion, to a new state of order: I change my stride and begin to speed-walk. Through my own activity I have created a state of tension, namely the need to catch my breath or avoid pain which has an impact on me as a changed control parameter leading to the selection of a new attractor that meets the new constraints.

We can see something very important from this example, as it demonstrates something that fundamentally differentiates living systems and, above all mental systems, from our previous physical examples: **The attractors that were activated or newly established under the influence of particular control parameters have a reciprocal effect on the control parameters**. The values of the control parameters continually change under the influence of the attractors until they eventually get into a range that causes a non-linear transition in the behavior of the system. The result is either an entirely new state of order, if still no attractor is as yet stored in memory suited to the existing constraints, or an attractor already extant in the memory as an activation tendency is activated. The new attractor again has an effect on the control parameter in its own way—for instance in that one changes the situational conditions through one's behavior, sort of in the way a phobic person flees from the situation he fears—until one of the control parameters assumes a value leading again to a non-linear transition in the system's behavior, which then again changes the control parameters, etc.

This example illustrates why mental systems change their behaviors "on their own" and why from within themselves they develop new system states. Control parameters and attractors mutually impact one another. The control parameters of a psychological system are oftentimes attractors themselves. For instance, the circulation in our example can be viewed as an attractor of its own which normally maintains a stable condition through negative feedback. The movement attractor "running" influences this physiological attractor. The latter gets into a range in which there is an increase in the discrepancy between the value normally maintained by negative feedback and the current situation. We can view this discrepancy as a state of tension entirely congruent with the basic assumption of control theory: Psychological activity is focused on decreasing or avoiding Is-Should discrepancies. The state of tension, the over-challenging of my circulatory system, is alleviated by activating the movement attractor "walking."

Thus, in addition to external constraints, the basis for change and development of mental processes is predominantly the reciprocal feedback processes within the system itself, the **interdependence between attractors and control parameters**. What is to be viewed as an attractor and what as control parameters depends on one's perspective. Mental processes are usually simultaneously states of order under the influence of other mental processes that have an effect on these as control parameters, and are also control parameters for other mental processes. A mental attractor is also simultaneously a constraint for other attractors. When particular mental processes are taking place, this creates limiting and enabling conditions for other mental processes.

Previously I mentioned change and development under the influence of changing control parameters. By change and development I understand something completely different:

I speak of **development** if a **new state of order** of the system is being established. This requires that there is no attractor in memory that is suitable for the alleviation of the respective state of tension. In this "state of suspense" of psychological activity a particular state from among the natural fluctuations of the system is selected and reinforced through positive feedback, reducing the state of tension. Through this process, new neural connections are ingrained. Therefore, the behavioral possibilities of the system are extended through development. This need not always be positive. Mental disorders, in this sense, should also be viewed as new experiential and behavioral possibilities never experienced by many people. I will go into that more in-depth at a later point. For now we can summarize by saying that mental disorders may be viewed as emergent new qualities of psychological functioning and in that sense as attractors.

I speak of **change** when an already existing attractor is activated, when certain neural activation tendencies are already suited to reduce the respective state of tension. This is the case, for instance, if I select one movement pattern from among those available for transportation; for example, if I decide to run or walk. Such already extant attractors may be activated either bottom-up or top-down, as well as either in the conscious or implicit mode of functioning.

Activated attractors, in turn, serve as constraints for other mental processes. A newly activated attractor changes the conditions for future psychological functioning. This is why there are never ending changes in experience and behavior.

Memory is an essential concept in differentiating the previously discussed physical examples from psychological systems. Convection waves develop only if there is a certain temperature difference in a fluid, just as the dust piles of the metal plate form only if the dust and the plate are exposed to a sound of certain frequency which triggers a vibration. The states of order that develop are tied to the conditions (control parameters) that have created them. The waves leave no traces in the fluid that would lead to their being more easily generated next time. The state of order, in terms of its existence, is precisely dependent on these control parameters, and without them it does not come into being.

However, a neural activation pattern which was created under certain conditions (control parameters) for the first time, and which was ingrained by the alleviation of tension, leaves traces behind in the form of changed synaptic transmission weights. Over time, once it has been differentially reinforced by alleviation of tension, it becomes more easily activated, even by conditions entirely different from those which lead to its development. **The attractor stored in memory in the form of activation tendencies detaches itself from its developmental conditions. It becomes functionally autonomous** (Allport, 1937).

The functional autonomy of attractors from the conditions out of which they developed is of fundamental significance for the treatment of mental disorders. Mental disorders are new states of order of psychological activity. According to the ideas just discussed, at some point they must have been a suitable means for reducing an existing tension. Otherwise, they would not have been selected as states of order. However, once they have been stored as well-ingrained neural activation tendencies in memory, they have, through synchronicity, or "reentrant mapping" as Edelman put it, created connections to all kinds of other possible perceptions, thoughts, emotions, memories, etc., none of which have anything to do with the original conditions that led to their development.

Thus, mental disorders are no longer dependent on the original conditions under which they developed. They have become **functionally autonomous attractors** that may be activated in all kinds of different ways. The present activation possibilities are the ones that must be viewed as the decisive control parameters of an attractor. So, we must search for the control parameters of mental disorders in the present. It is the present conditions which must be influenced if one wants to remove the system from a disturbed state and bring it into another state of order. **For fundamental reasons the therapy of mental disorders requires a present-related, disorder-specific procedure**. The presently functional control parameters must be influenced in order to first destabilize the "disorder attractors," thereby freeing the psychological functioning of the patient from the enslaving influence of the disorder attractor, either by establishing a new, or by activating another, already existing state of order.

The present conditions functioning as control parameters may, however, also include the conditions under which a disorder developed, because they were in fact part of the newly establishing activation pattern at the time of the disorder's development. However, even if a particular inconsistency has been an important control parameter in the development of the disorder, that inconsistency may have been alleviated in the meantime by changes in the life situation or through development of new possibilities for a need-satisfying reduction of the inconsistency. Since it would not exist anymore, the inconsistency would, at present, no longer be a current control parameter. Yet the disorder attractor continues to exist independently, and many other possible parameters may activate it. The most important among those are the various components of the disorder itself; for instance, in agoraphobia the avoidance behavior, the response expectations, the self-efficacy expectations, the physiological components of fear, etc.

Therapist: The formulation: "I wanted to free you from the enslaving influence of a disorder attractor," would most likely resonate on some level with the majority of my patients. This is, in fact, what most patients experience: Their experience is of being dominated against their will by something they are unable to influence.

Yet, most likely, I would first have to explain the idea of a disorder attractor and, therefore, it would be good if you could first explain it to me. We have already discussed simple and chaotic attractors, movement, perceptual, motivational, and disorder attractors; earlier in our conversation you had also mentioned emotional and interpersonal attractors. That is indeed an inflation of attractors. Isn't there anything in mental life that one could not conceive of as attractors? What is left then of the content of the term attractor if it can be applied to all aspects of mental functioning?

2.48   Therapeutically Significant Attractors: Their Special Characteristics and Differences

Psychologist: Your statement about "attractor" being a very general term is quite correct, but this also holds true for the term "schema." One speaks in psychology of perceptual, behavioral, emotional, motivational, action, body and self-schema and that does not by any means exhaust the multitude of uses of the term schema (Läderach & Verdun, 1995). Still the term is considered to be very useful in cognitive psychology.

The term "neural activation pattern" is also a very general one. Actually, it was our contention that neural activation patterns underlie all mental processes. Would it not then be possible for us to speak of mental processes right away? What I am saying is that neural activation patterns, despite being equally abstract, is more specific than the term "mental process." I mentioned earlier why I prefer to speak of a neural activation pattern or of neural activation tendencies as opposed to a schema. There are some very particular ideas connected with the term neural activation pattern, namely: Various kinds of neurons connected with one another by different ways through variable synaptic connections which mutually stimulate and inhibit one another and which form neural groups or cell assemblies, etc. So it truly does make a difference whether I speak of a schema or of a neural activation pattern. The terms connote different realms of ideas, and one can be more useful for a certain purpose than the other. My preference for the term neural activation pattern also outweighs my interest in the term attractor, because I do not want to miss out on the advantages of the range of ideas opened up by neural activation patterns. Attractor is no substitute in this sense.

The term "attractor," in turn, implies still other images that also have their special merits. The term attractor includes the transition to new qualities of functioning; it demonstrates how continuous changes may lead to a sudden qualitative change, how new states may gain a dominating influence on the functioning of a system, how something of an entirely new quality may emerge from something already existing of different quality, how sudden transitions in a system's behavior may be explained, etc. The realm of ideas opened up by the term attractor has its specific merits especially for the aspect of change in psychotherapy.

Luckily, without too many difficulties, we can link the merits of the terms neural activation pattern and attractor by conceiving of neural activation patterns as attractors. The term attractor then becomes very general. Every mental process that attains a certain stability, be it reading or understanding of a word, recognizing a figure, imagining a melody, the feeling of fear, the suppressing of certain memories, swimming in a certain style, thinking in certain terms can be conceived of as an attractor. Attractor means that a process of a certain quality is established through positive feedback—usually in a split-second—and then determines a certain part of functioning. This process of a particular quality is based on a neural activation pattern. The better a neural activation pattern is ingrained, the more stable the attractor.

This means that at any time in mental functioning, a multitude of attractors are activated that mutually represent both constraint and control parameters for each other. New qualities of mental functioning emerge out of this complex interplay: If a person comprehends the mathematical principle of differentiating or integrating for the first time, a new state of order emerges, just like when one feels jealousy for the very first time. The more this state establishing itself for the first time reduces an existing state of tension, the more it is reinforced (consistent with Edelman) or selected from among other states of neural activity possible at that moment. This changes synaptic transmission weights, and, next time, a similar constellation of conditions will most likely activate the appropriate neural activation patterns a bit faster. The newly developing attractor becomes more stable. If a part of the network involved in the entire activation pattern is activated, the entire pattern is activated by positive feedback. Eventually the pattern may be activated via a large number of neural connections by many other activation patterns—practically without any delay. The attractor establishes itself with blinding speed in a split-second. It can be activated as a holistic state.

This is the basis of conscious experience: One content being in the state of consciousness, a neural activation pattern of the particular quality marked by consciousness, brings on another, and this one another again. The preceding and the momentarily consciously and unconsciously activated activation patterns are thereby always both constraint and control parameters for the newly activated or newly developing activation patterns. This creates coherence in our conscious experience. It is the result of self-organization. It is already a given part of the special character of the existing activation tendencies. Only activation patterns can develop that are compatible with the particular nature of already existing neural activation tendencies; much like the dust piles of our first example were explained by the unique nature of the particles (constraints) and the vibration (control parameter).

In addition to the specific realm of ideas opened up by it, the abstract nature of the term attractor confers yet another advantage. That is, it can be applied to mental, as well as other processes. An attractor may have quite different material foundations, as we have seen in our examples from physics, biology, and psychology. Attractor is an abstract, broad term which may be applied to systems of any kind, as long as they fulfill certain criteria.

We may, for instance, also speak of an attractor in the context of interpersonal systems. In this case, we move on a system level above neural networks and above individuals. In that sense, the term **interpersonal attractor** may be useful for the conception of interpersonal interactions. Because interpersonal interactions play such a great role for psychotherapy, the concept of attractor offers advantages for psychotherapy in that it allows one to remain within the same realm of ideas by speaking both of intrapsychological and interpersonal attractors. The expression neural activation pattern, on the other hand, cannot be so readily applied to interpersonal interactions, while the term attractor can.

This is one of the reasons for my introducing this whole world of terminology from dynamic system theory into our dialogue. This terminology actually allows us to cover all the phenomena of psychotherapy, because we always deal with dynamic systems, whether it be intra-psychological processes in the patients, the therapeutic relationship, or familial interactions. In speaking about intra-psychological processes, oftentimes it will be more of an advantage to speak of neural activation patterns because more concrete ideas about psychological activity are connected with this expression. But in some contexts the term attractor may also be appropriate for intra-psychological processes, especially in cases where one wants to express how a certain process begins to determine (enslave) psychological activity, and in cases when functional autonomy is to be emphasized.

The term "**emotional attractor**" may be quite appropriate if a momentary emotional state begins to dominate psychological activity; for instance, if a person has a sudden raging fit. At that moment, this attractor enslaves all mental activity. It is as if the motivational attractors usually determining the experience and the behavior are temporarily deactivated. While such an emotional state has developed in conjunction with activated motivational schemata, as we discussed earlier (section 2.21), once activated it has a functionally independent influence on mental functioning. While it is not a motive in the actual sense, it nevertheless becomes an important determinant of mental functioning. This functional autonomy may be expressed by the term attractor.

In conceptualizing new states of order in psychological activity also as attractors, we can also apply this idea to mental disorders. Of course, the **disorder attractor** is situated high on the hierarchic scale. The qualitative nature of the disorder results, on the one hand, out of its emergence from many other hierarchically lower attractors, and on the other hand, from its enslavement of other mental processes. This is also true for other attractors, such as for **motivational attractors**.

As I said earlier, one can distinguish many more attractors in mental functioning, but I believe that the four attractors we distinguished here are the ones most relevant for psychotherapy:
- motivational attractors
- emotional attractors
- disorder attractors and
- interpersonal attractors

I will now provide a brief description of the unique nature of each of these attractors.

2.49 Motivational Attractors

Motivational attractors and motivational schemata are identical. What we said earlier about motivational schemata (sections 2.28-2.30) also applies to motivational attractors. We may view intentional or approach schemata as attractors, which form as neural activation patterns are selected because they reduce need tensions and are reinforced by positive feedback. After a motivational attractor is established, it gains functional autonomy. It detaches itself from the functional context that was responsible for its development. This is true for all attractors, and this fact is of utmost importance for psychotherapy. Therefore, I would like to elaborate on this point.

I have encountered the term motivational schema in Epstein's work, and the term motivational attractor in the book *A Dynamic Systems Approach to the Development of Cognition and Action* by Thelen and Smith (1995). Surprisingly, the fundamental view of mental functioning developed in this book matches the one we have jointly developed here. That is surprising because Thelen and Smith arrived at this view of mental functioning based on entirely different research areas. Thelen and Smith are, in fact,

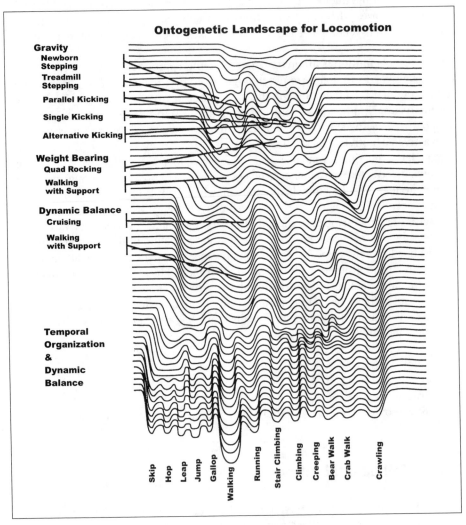

Figure 2.37:
Schematic illustration of the development of movement behavior as a series of potentials-landscapes according to Thelen and Smith (1995, p. 124). Thelen and Smith refer to this form of illustration as "ontogenetic landscape." Explanation in the text.

developmental psychologists and have predominantly devoted themselves to infant and early child development.

Thelen and Ulrich (1991) performed a series of very elegant experiments on the development of movement behavior in one-year-old children. The hypotheses tested and confirmed in these experiments were derived from dynamic system theory.

Infants' movements, such as kicking, can be viewed as attractors. Thelen and Ulrich studied how, out of the kicking movements, the ability for walking gradually develops, given the various constraints and control parameters. Every new movement behavior—for instance, the ability to alternately move one leg or the other—is viewed as a newly establishing attractor. The experiments proved that the ratio between muscle power and fat tissue accumulation in the legs is an essential control parameter for the development of the movement behavior. The variability of this ratio predicted, both with respect to the individual development over time and in a comparison among different children, when a child achieves the capacity for coordinated steps or walking.

A child's possibilities for coordinated leg movement can be illustrated as a landscape of potentials (see earlier examples, Figures 2.26 and 2.27). Each attractor is illustrated as a dip in the landscape. The inclination of the walls and the depth of the valleys represent the stability of the attractor and the width of the valley represents its variability. Within a wide valley there may still be several small sub-valleys corresponding to the different variations of a movement sequence.

Drawing such a potentials-landscape of movement behavior over time produces a developmental landscape. Figure 2.37 illustrates such an "ontogenetic landscape" for the development of movement behavior.

At the final point of this development—see the lowest landscape of potentials in Figure 2.37—a large number of attractors have developed, signaling the different possibilities of locomotion: hopping, jumping, walking, running, stair climbing, etc. Walking has become, by far, the most stable attractor, one that can be activated most readily. At an earlier point in time, however, crawling (far right, bottom) was the most likely and the most easily activated movement attractor.

Moving to the top of the figure, we see that there is a time with less pronounced attractors of leg movement behavior, whereas previously, more pronounced attractors already existed for certain kicking movements. This is a time when previously existing attractors have become unstable. The wide valleys signify great variability of the movement behavior without pronounced, coherent leg movement patterns. The most important reason for this transition time in movement behavior, which seems almost like a step backwards, is the increased accumulation of fat (weight gain) in the legs accompanied by still little muscle power. Children with higher fat accumulations begin later than other children with movement patterns that eventually result in walking (left bottom part of figure).

The actual movement behaviors are mostly controlled by the control parameters of neural development, muscle power and fat accumulation, and by their interactions, respectively. If these qualitative interactions change, qualitatively new movement patterns emerge.

The development of movement behavior has no obvious relevance for psychotherapy. Still, I wanted to show you this developmental landscape here, because this illustration conveys relevant ideas for psychotherapy, especially the idea of functional autonomy among the attractors.

The proportion of muscle power to fat in infants' legs is an essential control parameter for the development of walking. Once the capability for walking has become established as a stable attractor, this previously functionally very significant proportion no longer plays a role. The attractor walking has detached itself from the conditions under which it developed. Later, there are control parameters that have functional significance for this attractor other than those which were significant for its development. Later, the attractor walking may be activated by all sorts of other circumstances. It even becomes active on its own. Sometimes, one just feels like walking.

The same is true for motivational attractors: They may detach themselves from the original conditions under which they developed and then acquire "a life of their own." This is what Allport (1937) meant by "functional autonomy of motives." Once motivational attractors have established themselves, they may be activated from all kinds of different neural activation patterns, consciously and unconsciously, bottom-up and top-down.

When motivational attractors emerged, they were related to a particular need. They established themselves because they were suited to reducing an existing state of need tension. The behavior had functional significance with respect to this need. Later, however, behavior determined by this attractor may have entirely different functional significance. The need for pleasure may have impelled someone to begin cooking. If this person later becomes a chef in a hotel, the cooking may, in the meantime, have gained quite a different functional significance. Perhaps it no longer contributes to pleasure at all but now has become an aversive effort, yet, other control parameters now maintain this attractor. In wanting to influence such an attractor, one would have to exert an influence on the conditions presently maintaining it rather than the memories of the conditions under which it developed.

Thus, what has developed for the fulfillment of a certain basic need must not always necessarily remain a means for the fulfillment of the same need. This does not mean that each motivational attractor detaches itself from its function with respect to a particular need. Yet, if it keeps this function, then this represents a present function. It has this function, because it has it presently, not because the attractor has developed with respect to this function. Therefore, the current functions of motivational attractors with respect to the basic needs, to the consistency principle, and to other motivational attractors have to be studied in order to find out about the current functional significance of a certain motivational attractor. This might, for instance, be part of a clarification-oriented therapy.

Thelen and Smith take an analogous view of the development of motivational attractors and movement attractors:

"We can easily substitute a motivational landscape, therefore, for the locomotion landscape... Imagine that the hills and valleys ... (in Figure 2.37) ... represent not particular leg configurations but the relative strength and stability of the forces impelling or repelling the infant towards various stimuli or tasks. Let us assume that at birth, certain stimuli have acquired, through natural selection, particular valence values. Thus the furrows might present attractors for sucking when a nipple is in the mouth, or for warmth and physical contact, or for attending particular visual stimuli. Through learning in the manner we have described previously, not only may the behavior itself change but also the associations and strengths of the motivational drive propelling the performance of that behavior (Killeen, 1991). Additionally, the infant may learn to be a better perceiver of the stimuli that are associated with the motivational attractor.

That is, as infants move and perceive, as they explore the possibilities of the landscape, they meander among the various motivational basins ... (in Figure 2.37) ... This exploration allows them to sample and to be drawn in by various attractors and match their actions with the affective consequences. Through the processes of neuronal group selection ... these categories become associated with particular motivational attractors. Because of the emotional associations, they may subsequently attend to and remember the particulars of the perceptions and movements associated with that place on the landscape. When the emotional valence is not strong, any number of behavioral solutions may be good enough. Behavior can be flexible, somewhat determined by chance or whim, and diverse. When the emotional stakes are high, children will learn effective strategies quickly—they will be more focused, more quickly recruited, and less able to be distracted or perturbed by internal or external factors.

As an illustration, imagine that the furrows on the top third of ... (Figure 2.37) ... represent an infant's motivation to explore—to look, feel, and taste objects that can be reached and grasped. This is a compelling motivation, but of moderate strength, allowing infants to chose among several behavioral options, to move from one object to another, or to be distracted when a social opportunity intervenes or when they get hungry or sleepy. Within these moderate attractors, however, motivational strength will change. For instance, the motivation to put an object in the mouth for exploration decreases during the first year, as exploration with hands and eyes increases... Later, the motivational attractor associated with the mouth becomes associated with edible items; infants have learned to recognize a different category of things to be put in the mouth and to redirect the strength and goals of the motivational component. These changes are depicted as the hillocks changing depth and spread. Likewise, although infants may initially be attracted to very simple visual attributes, as they explore and acquire more complex categories of objects, other stimulus attributes become more compelling through their learned associations.

In contrast, let us focus on the series of valleys to the right of the attractor landscape. Imagine these are the motivational strengths of Bowlby's need for caregiver proximity. Although the behaviors subserving this attractor will change, the motivational strength starts strong and remains strong throughout. When this system is activated by the felt loss of caregiving, responses are rapid, strong, and not easily diverted. Other motivational drives are suppressed—exploration ceases, feeding stops—as all behavioral trajectories are sucked into this attractor furrow.

Thus, just as the real-time processes of perceiving and acting segue smoothly into the stuff of developmental change, so this motivational landscape, given only minimal initial biases, itself differentiates into a rich set of dynamic possibilities. The motivational landscape-potentials for perceiving and acting—lives in the same space as the behavioral state spaces. It is part and parcel of the same dynamic, just as the brain systems providing the affective valence are richly and densely interconnected with those of perceiving, acting and thinking" (Thelen & Smith, 1995, pp. 318/319).

We can view the furrows of such a developmental landscape as memory traces. The longer and deeper a furrow is, the more difficult it is to change the respective attractor. They are very well ingrained neural activation tendencies. In my view, it seems very important for psychotherapy that development is only related to one temporal direction: pointing forwards, from present to future. There is no reversing direction to the past. Our memory enables us, in a limited fashion, to transport images from the past to present, but the transport happens with tools of our present psychological functioning, under the influence of present motives, perceptual and thought categories, etc. Thus, memory always means transformation. Going back to the level of past functioning is not possible because the memory traces of the past were overwritten with newly ingrained neural paths. While the past was not erased, new neural connections have been developing on the basis of the earlier ones. Activation of neural activation patterns is only possible in the present. Only currently existing neural activation tendencies can be activated, not ones that have determined psychological functioning in the past.

Therefore, memories as well as current perceptions can be used in psychotherapy in order to activate attractors, but these attractors always refer to currently existing neural activation tendencies, not past ones. There are possibly memories that could activate activation patterns that are suppressed in the present by other attractors, but it is current valleys of the potentials-landscape that are sought, not past ones. Changing such attractors is only possible from the present to the future, not from the past to the present.

While these statements may seem obvious, I still wanted to explain them in some detail, because I have the impression that some therapists think one could jointly go with the patient back to past experiences to change something about the feelings which existed then, and that such a move would have an effect on the present. This view is incompatible, however, with the way memory works. The past has an effect on the present via memory in two ways: First, current activation tendencies represent manifestations of past experiences and second, past events may be stored in conceptual memory in a symbolic fashion. Such symbolically coded memory contents may be included in present-day mental processes and may enable access to past emotions.

Therapy researcher: It seems to me that past experiences are especially relevant for transference processes in psychotherapy. Content of conceptual memory may be activated in the therapeutic relationship through verbal communication, and content of implicit memory may be activated predominantly through nonverbal communication. Yet, we must remember that only activation tendencies that exist presently are activated, not those from the past. Particularly strong emotions could be activated by transference interpretations related to father and mother. Emotions very similar to those in the past may arise because they may not have been overwritten by new experiences in the meantime; nevertheless they are not the same emotions experienced by the child, because they evolve in a different context. They are embedded in a different attractor-landscape than in the past. Today, attractors that developed in the meantime function as constraints and control parameters, and therein lies a chance for therapeutic change.

In order to change the activation patterns underlying such feelings, one has to think from the present forwards. The existing activation tendencies must be overwritten with new experiences. Without new experiences that change the existing synaptic transmission weights, no change can be expected, and therein lies the important role of corrective experiences which a patient can make in therapy. Whether and how the existing activation tendencies are overwritten essentially depends on current behavior of the therapist and on other current, real interactional experiences.

Psychologist: The sum of one's current landscapes of potentials might be conceived of as one's life space, as Lewin put it. The motivational attractors play an especially important role in this context. Thelen and Smith also relate the developmental landscape to Lewin's concept of life space:

"For Lewin, behavior begins with a psychological force, a 'tendency to act in a certain direction' (Lewin, 1946, p. 796). People develop within a life space, a psychological field of various activities that have different motivational valences or potencies. The valence determines whether and how strongly people move toward the activity. Cognitive change, according to Lewin, results when people learn new pathways to their goal activities. Development, then, is an elaboration and differentiation of the life space, from the simple force fields of infancy, to the highly complex goal space of the older child and adult...

Motivational drive also played a predominant role in John Bowlby's classic work on attachment. Bowlby assigned the origins of attachment behavior to a 'felt need for proximity' to a caregiver. According to Bowlby this motivation is instinctive. It is built in because staying close to a caregiver gives immature animals an enormous selective advantage; they survive longer to differentially reproduce. Given this initial motivational bias, infants recruit different kinds of actions towards this goal, actions that change as infants mature. When infants are immobile, crying effectively keeps mother close by. As infants develop mobility, they can follow their mothers by themselves. Facial expressions, vocal gestures, and later, language, are all subsumed under this broad motivational umbrella: keep Mom nearby for protection and comfort" (Thelen & Smith, 1995, p. 313).

At the end of this quote Thelen and Smith have described the development of a motivational attractor. The superordinate goal remains the same; it is the means that change. The selection of new means takes place by differential reinforcement, through the decrease of need tension with respect to the basic need for a close relationship. The development of new motivational attractors is not completed in young adulthood but continues because constraints and control parameters change continuously.

Therapist: As a therapist, I think this last idea is especially important for me. In viewing psychotherapy from this developmental perspective, I encounter the patient at a certain point in the development of his motivation-landscape. On average, at this point in time there is a certain potentials-landscape of motivational attractors. I have two questions regarding the motivation-landscape:
1. How does this landscape refer to the patient's problems?
2. How can the existing landscape of potentials be used for therapeutic purposes and further developed?

Regarding the second question, I have to think about which of the intentional attractors, if activated, exert a positive influence on the experience and behavior of the patient from a therapeutic point of view. Particularly included are those motivational attractors that may have a positive influence on the patient's behavior in therapy. My goal should be to try to activate these motivational attractors as often and as strongly as possible so that they gain a stronger influence compared to that of more problematic attractors. We have previously referred to the activating of such positively assessed motivational attractors as resource activation. In my opinion, this expression is appropriate, even when seen from the aspect of attractors, because positive motivational attractors may be viewed as a patient's resources.

Posing the first question, however, presents difficulties with the expression attractor. The problematic motivational schemata of a patient are, according to our previous considerations, in fact, mostly his avoidance and conflict schemata. However, if the issue is specifically not to do something, to specifically not assume a certain point in a certain space, one can actually not really speak of an attractor, because this point in space, in fact, repels trajectories, rather than attracts them.

Psychologist: You are right. Therefore, Thelen and Smith consequently refer to such avoidance-'attractors' also as 'repellor' and not as attractor. According to them a landscape of potentials consists of attractors and repellors. If we remain with the image of a ball in a landscape of mountains and valleys and imagine the repellors as hillocks or mountains, we actually do get into difficulties: If the ball is at the top of the hill, it looks as though its state would be very unstable, in reality, a state of instability in a landscape of potentials is repeatedly represented as such. Yet, a repellor can, unfortunately, be very stable, and the image of the hill, unfortunately, does not distinguish between the state of instability and the function of repelling. This is a where the metaphor falls short.

Perhaps it might be better to conceive of attractors as magnets that attract and repel. The closer a system comes to the avoided state, the stronger the repellor repels. But even this image is incomplete as the direction of the repelling is not clear. Avoidance behavior, however, is usually very specific. The system, in fact, strives towards a certain state within the realm of possible behaviors. The latter, however, is determined by the avoidance of a state within the realm of possible experiences. The expression repellor, therefore, has its concealed risks. I prefer to speak of avoidance attractors. This takes into account that these attractors also determine a very specific behavior. In a potentials or developmental landscape, one might distinguish intentional and avoidance attractors by colors. I would assign the color black to intentional attractors and red to avoidance attractors. I do this because one whose life is controlled predominantly by positive attachment tendencies will more likely end up "in the black" in the balance of his life whereas one who largely avoids will end up "in the red."

Therapist: Do you have any more ideas as to how a conflict schema could be more graphically described using these ideas?

Psychologist: I do not, but there are others who have come up with ideas on this. Townsend and Busemeyer (1989) and Killeen (1989, 1991) have devoted themselves to conceptualizing conflicts in dynamic systems. Figure 2.38 reflects Killeen's (1991) suggestion as to how one could conceptualize a conflict (an approach-approach, an approach-avoidance, or an avoidance-avoidance conflict) in a potentials-landscape.

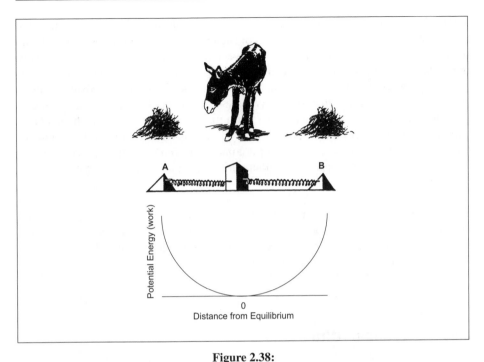

Figure 2.38:
Various possibilities for illustrating conflicts according to Killeen (1991).
Top: Buridan's donkey. Middle: forces having an influence on the donkey, illustrated by
springs. Bottom: potentials description of a conflict. Explanation in text.
Figure taken from Thelen and Smith (1995. p. 317).

The figure illustrates in its upper-part a problem which the philosopher Buridan already tackled quite some time ago: A donkey stands exactly in the middle of two hay stacks and cannot decide which he should approach and eat. Buridan's opinion was that the donkey will never move, because he was precisely at the point of balance between two equally strong forces which exert their influence on him. If he moves to one side, the force will become greater, pulling him from the other side, or—in the case of a repellor—the force becomes greater which repels him from this side. This is illustrated by the springs shown in the middle. In the lower part, the conflict situation is expressed by Killeen in a form already well-known to us, a valley situated in a potentials-landscape. The donkey is in the valley of a conflict attractor. To surmount the obstacle he has to generate motivational energy on both sides of the valley. As soon as he turns to one side, the force pulls him to the other side. Thus, his behavior oscillates back and forth between both goals without ever reaching one. This is indeed the situation we described earlier for a conflict schema. Even conflict attractors then can be imagined as valleys in a potentials-landscape; however, we would have to mark them by a different color in order to distinguish them from the intentional (approach) and avoidance attractors. Denoting them using a black/red pattern would be one possibility.

Therapist: The furrows of a developmental landscape as they are illustrated in Figure 2.37 would be colored in three different colors or patterns, respectively, to distinguish approach, avoidance and conflict attractors. It would indeed be nice if one could illustrate a patient's course of life in the form of such a motivational-developmental- landscape. If one could do so, this would yield a very good understanding of a patient in his or her development and current function. At any rate, one could possibly better detect at which point to begin so as to push this landscape of development in a positive way so that it can advance. From this perspective, the space before the patient—the future—presents itself as a developmental space with many open possibilities. The patient's current motivational attractors could be viewed as constraints of further development, but merely as constraints. They do not automatically represent the attractors of the future. I think this image opens up a rather optimistic, future-oriented perspective, and I like that.

Therapy researcher: It seems that this does not quite complete the landscape of development. We must not forget that we had also declared some attractors other than the motivational attractors to be therapeutically relevant. These would also have to find their place in the developmental landscape. The emotional attractors are, I believe, rather simple to include. I would like to focus on them next.

2.50   Emotional Attractors

Earlier we considered the emergence of emotions (sections 2.21-2.23) in the context of goal-oriented psychological activity. Emotions are based on continuous appraisals of mental functioning in terms of how compatible this functioning is with the motivational schemata. We can conceive of activated motivational attractors as being accompanied by emotions. Actually, emotions can be seen as attractors of their own kind.

When certain emotions are elicited repeatedly—in the sense of appraisals of goal-oriented activity—then the corresponding neural activation tendencies are ingrained ever more deeply each time. Once these patterns form, they become linked with other, simultaneously activated patterns, consistent with Edelman's reentrant mapping. These other activation patterns are primarily perceptions, memories, thoughts, and so forth, that are linked to simultaneously activated motivational attractors. Over time, these perceptions, memories and thoughts should acquire the capability to activate the emotional activation pattern on their own, even when no appraisal situation exists that would trigger the emotion. Thus, even an emotional activation pattern may detach itself from the context in which it originally developed and, to a certain degree, become a functionally autonomous attractor.

For most people, emotions stem primarily from appraisals of currently perceived, imagined, or remembered transactions with goal-relevant aspects of the environment. Therefore, the most important control parameters for emotional attractors are the appraisals specified in Lazarus' theory of emotions. Yet, when activation patterns become well ingrained and repeatedly linked with other activation patterns, emotions may eventually be activated without the presence of perceptual situations resembling the circumstances that first elicited the emotion.

In addition, an emotion that was originally triggered by ordinary, comprehensible appraisal processes (in Lazarus' sense), may be reinforced by positive feedback and eventually function as an independent motivational attractor, moving mental life in a direction different from the one dictated by simultaneously activated attractors. Thus, an emotional attractor can enslave momentary psychological activity. An example would be a person who has worked himself into a raging fit and can no longer be stopped. Ruled by his rage, he does and says things that are incompatible with his motivational attractors.

A hot-tempered person's constant outbursts of rage would be a good example of a strongly pre-ingrained, and therefore easily elicited emotional activation pattern. "Hot-temperedness" has the character of an emotional attractor that has become functionally autonomous. It can be triggered by all sorts of situations and, through positive feedback, attains an intensity that no longer seems justified by the situation. Another example is jealousy. There are also individuals who, through positive feedback, repeatedly reach euphoric states, even though the appraisal of the situation would not justify such emotions, given the person's goals.

Emotional attractors that have become functionally autonomous may cause considerable interpersonal problems. This is why therapists are so frequently faced with such attractors as a problem, even though the attractors are not strictly defined as mental disorders. By the standards of current diagnostic categorization systems, functionally autonomous emotional attractors are in a transitional area, compared to formally defined mental disorders. It is obvious that many mental disorders are characterized, in part, by emotions that have somehow become independent. This certainly applies to anxiety disorders and depressive disorders. Functionally autonomous emotional attractors also play a crucial role in personality disorders, such as borderline-personality disorder.

For a therapist faced with such attractors, the issue is predominantly one of identifying the relevant control parameters. The goal of therapy should be to change these control parameters or bring them under the control of the patient. This would require establishing new motivational attractors that overwrite the previous control parameters. The task here would be to more strongly ingrain already extant attractors or establish new motivational attractors. Therefore, therapeutic efforts should focus on changing the conditions that currently activate and maintain problematic emotional control parameters.

These control parameters may also be appraisals related to other motivational attractors. In this case the goal would be to influence these appraisals or the attractors themselves. Both mastery-oriented and clarification-oriented interventions could be used for this purpose. I think that for the treatment of emotional attractors we need ideas similar to those about destabilization of disorder attractors. I find it useful to recognize that emotions can themselves function as determinants of psychological activity, but I do not consider them equal in significance to motivational and disorder attractors. In my opinion, a therapist who knows how to change motivational and disorder attractors is also capable of addressing the functional autonomy of emotional attractors. Therefore, I would suggest that we focus primarily on motivational attractors, disorder attractors, and interpersonal attractors, and on their interactions with one another.

Therapist: Agreed. I am also particularly intrigued by the concept of disorder attractors because they are often at the center of what needs to be changed when clients present for therapy.

2.51   Mental Disorders as Disorder Attractors

Two points support the utility of viewing mental disorders as attractors:

1. Mental disorders are not variants of normal psychological activity. Rather, they are qualitatively different states of mental functioning. At the moment they develop, they are obviously products of a person's psychological activity. This means there are control parameters in mental functioning that produce qualitatively new ways of functioning, given certain constraints at the time. There is no denying that external circumstance may play an important role in the genesis of mental disorders; however, it is not the objective environment in itself, but subjectively represented reality that determines experience and behavior. Thus, it is a certain constellation of neural activation patterns that produces the qualitatively new mental functioning we refer to as mental disorder.

2. Once a mental disorder has developed and established itself, it enslaves a great portion of that person's mental life. In a way, it lives a life of its own, parallel to the individual's consciously perceived goals. It permeates the individual's mental life. It is not wanted, but it is experienced by the individual as something outside of his or her control. Its functional autonomy is painfully experienced by that individual as a loss of control.

The attractor concept expresses the phenomena of **emergence, functional autonomy** and **enslavement** with a special precision. This is one reason for conceptualizing mental disorders as unique attractors of mental activity.

The phenomena of emergence and functional autonomy must, however, be kept separate. The conditions leading to the development of a mental disorder need not necessarily be the same as those that later maintain it. An attractor detaches itself from the context that accompanied its emergence. It cannot be reduced to the conditions which brought it on. Therefore, I shall discuss the development of mental disorders and their functional autonomy separately.

The Development of Disorder Attractors

According to our preceding considerations, mental disorders must be conceptualized as a product of self-organization. At the moment of their development they must have been one of many possible states of psychological activity resulting from existing neural activation tendencies. As discussed earlier, there are actually biologically pre-ingrained tendencies for certain mental disorders. Humans and monkeys, for instance, have developed a genetically pre-ingrained tendency to develop a fear of snakes. A fear of other objects such as curtain rods or chairs, however, is very seldom. Also, people appear to have a genetically pre-ingrained tendency for the development of depressions and schizophrenia, since these disorders are seen in all cultures. Even personality disorders seem, at least in part, genetically pre-ingrained (Siever & Davis, 1991; McGuffin & Thapar, 1992). Twin studies have demonstrated that eating disorders are also largely pre-ingrained (Kendler et al., 1991).

Eating disorders demonstrate that there are not just genetically but also culturally and individually pre-ingrained tendencies. Bulimia appears more frequently in women born after 1960 (Kendler et al., 1991), and appears to be a phenomenon only observed in affluent western societies. Of course, such cultural influences must be somehow represented within the individual in order for an eating disorder to develop. Bulimic women have internalized the societal ideal of being slender to a greater degree than other women; they have a history of exaggerated preoccupation with body weight. This process can be viewed as an individual-level internalization of cultural control parameters. In addition, there are a number of other empirically documented individual control parameters that affect the development of bulimia: Lack of a positive father relationship, having low self-esteem, external control expectations, and being highly neurotic (Kendler et al., 1991).

Thus, there is an interplay of genetic, cultural, and individual constraints and control parameters in the development of the disorder attractor bulimia. It is a specific constellation of constraints and control parameters that together produces mental disorders such as bulimia. Most likely this is true for all mental disorders. All these control parameters and constraints exist as neural activation patterns at the moment of the disorder's first appearance. Under their influence, a qualitatively new neural activation pattern emerges—the urge to eat much too much at one time and to vomit afterwards.

This new neural activation pattern may be viewed as a neural group, in Edelman's terms, which is selected from among other possible groups. The conditions we just discussed are the constraints controlling the **quality** of the new neural activation pattern. Differential reinforcement and positive feedback are then required for the subsequent establishment of a new neural activation pattern. According to Edelman's theory of the selection of neural groups (Edelman, 1987, 1995) neural groups are differentially reinforced according to prescribed values. We regarded the reduction of inconsistency tension as such a value that is determined by the functioning of the psychological system.

The fact that fluctuations increase between different states of psychological activity is attributable to the absence of unequivocal motivational structural patterns determining psychological activity during such times of transition. Psychological functioning is inconsistent at such times, for instance, in that different motivational structural patterns block one another. Which one of these possible states is eventually selected is determined by existing constraints and the pre-ingrained tendencies. The new state of order has to meet certain requirements in order to fulfill its function of tension reduction. Reinforcement by tension reduction is necessary for a new activation pattern to form. Positive feedback among the components involved in the new structural pattern leads to the development of an attractor which strives ever faster towards a certain final state.

After the new neural activation pattern is stably established, reinforcement by tension reduction is no longer needed for its continued existence. Positive feedback has enabled it to become functionally autonomous and its individual components may now lead to its activation.

Thus, whether a certain mental disorder develops in a person depends, on the one hand, upon long-term, pre-existing, pre-ingrained tendencies. We may view these as risk or vulnerability factors for developing a particular disorder. On the other hand, the development of disorder requires an existing state of tension, an increased inconsistency in mental functioning, which then leads to the selection and differential reinforcement of a particular variation (or fluctuation) of psychological activity. The specific constellation of the fluctuation and the inconsistency tension may be unique in a person's life. Therefore, it is futile to follow up in retrospect to the "original cause" of the mental disorder. While such earlier circumstances have historic significance, they are relevant for treatment only if they also have functional significance in maintaining the disorder.

There are also good reasons to assume the existence of a long-term "breeding ground"—a continuous state of inconsistency in mental functioning—that facilitates the emergence of disorders among some people. The high comorbidity rate of mental disorders supports such an assumption. Women with bulimia, for instance, have a significantly higher likelihood to also show signs of anorexia, alcoholism, panic-disorder, generalized anxiety disorder, phobias, and depression (Kendler et al., 1991). Many of them develop a disorder attractor more than once. This indicates, on the one hand, that people may have pre-ingrained tendencies towards certain mental disorders. On the other hand, this indicates that there may often be inconsistency tensions that are not successfully reduced by goal-oriented behaviors consistent with a motivational attractor.

Thus, normal need-tensions do not lead to the formation of motivational attractors that differentially reinforce the development of disorder attractors. Rather, it is an overall increased level of inconsistency that leads to the development of mental disorders. The reduction of this inconsistency differentially reinforces and cements the new structural pattern. An increased inconsistency level typically has its origins in conflicts whose components the individual is not or only partially aware of, so that no consciously controlled behavior is available to him or her for overcoming the conflict. This is the price one pays for avoidance, as we mentioned earlier. Consistency in consciousness is achieved through repression or dissociation in mental functioning, at the cost of overall reduced consistency (which, however, is not represented consciously).

The reduction in inconsistency tension resulting from dissociation differentially reinforces the development of mental disorders. An ever-larger portion of psychological activity is determined by the newly developed disorder attractor. The disorder attractor enslaves other mental processes and thereby achieves a higher level of consistency in mental functioning. As a result, there are two relatively consistent units in mental functioning: consciousness, which is protected from inconsistency by repression, and the disorder attractor or attractors, which automatically ensure consistency within their spheres of activity. At the same time, consciousness, the disorder attractors, and the motivational attractors are inconsistent with each other. Need satisfaction is thereby thwarted and well-being reduced, resulting eventually in illness status and need for treatment.

Thus, a short-term gain in consistency generates long-term inconsistency that leads to increased likelihood of further disorders or further stabilization of the disorder attractor. In the latter case, the disorder attractor maintains its function for the reduction of inconsistency tensions. In this case, inconsistency tension represents an essential control parameter for maintaining the disorder and should, therefore, be considered in treatment. I can imagine that such cases would not respond well to disorder-specific treatments because disorder-specific interventions require the functional autonomy of the disorder attractor as their rationale. This requirement is not always met.

These considerations suggest that psychotherapists should try to identify current patient conflicts and dissociation. Instead of explaining the development of the disorder with these conflicts, therapists should consider them as possible control parameters. If such conflicts and dissociation exist currently, they should definitely be considered as control parameters in treatment. In such cases, a purely disorder-specific intervention would yield little success and would also be questionable in regard to the treatment goal, as the therapist would tend to ignore the current motivational context for the patient's misfortune.

In my view, psychotherapy should not limit itself to eliminating disorders, but should also target human unhappiness that cannot be measured in diagnostic categories, as far as this is attainable with psychotherapeutic means. Decreasing inconsistencies in psychological functioning that interfere with a patient's basic need satisfaction can be viewed as a treatment goal in itself. In most cases, decreasing inconsistency in mental functioning will also contribute to a destabilization of the disorder attractors and remove the breeding ground for the development of further disorder attractors.

The fact that many patients simultaneously suffer from several disorders (comorbidity) indicates that there is a rich and lasting breeding ground for the development of disorders. Therefore, one should carefully assess for inconsistency producing motivational constellations in these patients and include them in treatment. This does not mean that the treatment of these patients should not be disorder-specific; it simply should not be limited to that. Patients who suffer from only one disorder and demonstrate few signs of psychological ailments otherwise would remain good candidates for largely disorder-specific interventions.

Therapy researcher: These conclusions go a little beyond those developed in our first conversation. I think it would be advantageous if we could definitely conceive of the relationship between disorder-specific and clarification-oriented interventions aiming for more than the alleviation of the actual mental disorders on the basis of a general model of the emergence of mental disorders.

Your ideas also address the conditions maintaining functionally autonomous disorder attractors. Destabilization of disorder attractors must involve influencing their current functional parameters. I think this point deserves more attention and clarification.

Disorder-Specific Therapy as an Influence on the Control Parameters of Disorder Attractors

Once developed, a disorder attractor has its own dynamic. Every time a disorder attractor is activated, a reentrant mapping occurs of the processes determined by the attractor and of other mental processes that transpire simultaneously. For instance, these include the perception of a certain environment, thoughts occurring simultaneously, or related memories and ideas. Conscious mental processes as well as those in the implicit mode of functioning are involved in such reentrant mapping. In addition, the disorder occurs under certain constraints. In the case of bulimia, the refrigerator, the kitchen, food, even the toilet or bathroom as places for vomiting, can be viewed as constraints that restrict these processes in their degrees of freedom. A person who is occupied with bulimic vomiting certainly has limited degrees of freedom in terms of his or her thought contents. At such moments the person will most likely not take pleasure in imagining a wonderful piece of art.

All of these constraints imposed by the disorder as well as internal and external conditions lead to the fact that different persons under the influence of a disorder attractor become much more similar in nature than they would otherwise be. The disorder process becomes interlocked with the constraints that eventually, in the case of a functionally autonomous attractor, also function as control parameters. The equalizing impact disorder attractors have is the basis for disorder-specific interventions. Independent of other differences in personality and life circumstances, certain processes and functional contexts are largely the same among people suffering from a particular disorder. Therefore, functionally autonomous disorder attractors may be treated with essentially the same therapeutic intervention. This forms the basis for creating disorder-specific therapy manuals.

The advantage of such manuals lies in the fact that they may contain a lot of empirically gained knowledge on the control parameters of a specific disorder and on relevant possibilities for intervention with respect to these control parameters. This knowledge transcends the individual and need not be newly elaborated by each therapist in each therapy. A therapist should possess this disorder-specific knowledge and know-how independent of the individual case.

Disorder-specific manuals are a good way to acquire this disorder-specific knowledge and know-how, and they are a great help in a case where a therapist is confronted with a disorder which she has not treated very often and for which she, therefore, has no experience-based repertoire of interventions. A therapist who has absorbed the knowledge elaborated in a manual will no longer be dependent on a manual but will actually know how to best influence the control parameters of a particular disorder.

No therapist can always be equipped with detailed current knowledge and know-how for all mental disorders as this knowledge changes far too rapidly. It is of great advantage, then, that an extensive literature on the individual mental disorders exists with practical instructions for individual cases. Today's manuals originate predominantly from behavior therapy, which may keep therapists trained in different forms of therapy from using them as aids in their practice. I find this unfortunate.

While the idea of approaching mental disorders in a disorder-specific fashion has been specifically cultivated in behavior therapy, it actually has nothing to do with the behaviorist school. In our conversations, we have derived the significance of disorder-specific interventions from theoretical considerations that have nothing to do with behavior therapy. It would be a great plus if disorder-specific knowledge could be provided to all therapists, independent of any biases towards a certain school. A project for this purpose has just been started. With the publication of a series of books—*Advances of Psychotherapy*—Schulte, Grawe, Hahlweg and Vaitl have begun the task of summarizing knowledge and know-how for every mental disorder in a small volume intended and designed to be used for quick reference in therapeutic practice.

A therapist faced with a patient suffering from a particular disorder should be equipped with up-to-date knowledge on this disorder. If she is not, she should be able to rapidly familiarize herself with such knowledge in the simplest and most efficient way. At least she should be able to update her knowledge on the disorder by the time of the next session. The patient's realization that his therapist has sound knowledge of his disorder will contribute to the induction of positive expectations for success and, thereby, to a successful treatment outcome. A series of handy volumes prepared as references specifically for clinical practice would be perfect for that purpose. Good possibilities already exist for therapists to quickly familiarize themselves with the state of knowledge on many mental disorders (Reinecker, 1994 a; Margraf, 1996; Schulte, 1996; Benjamin, 1993; Fiedler, 1995).

To provide an impression of the abundance and diversity of today's disorder-specific knowledge, table 2.5 contains an alphabetical listing that can be used as an aid in reading about the various mental disorders and problem areas when faced with a patient suffering from a particular disorder. This listing was designed by and taken from Fiedler (1997).

The listing also contains phenomena that are not mental disorders by formal definition. However, we may view all the listed disorders and problems as attractors with more or less functional autonomy.

Table 2.5:
Phenomena and disorder-specific explanation and treatment models for the most relevant mental disorders and problems.

Under the individual headings of disorders or problems listed in alphabetical order, a few relevant references for each are listed, which document current research on this disorder. This by no means claims to be an exhaustive listing, it is intended to illustrate how little it is justified today not to make systematic usage of the comprehensive disorder-specific knowledge in psychotherapy.

In conjunction with the view of mental disorders developed in this book, the references listed concern the disorder-specific control parameters of disorder attractors. The motivational control parameters specific to each individual which may also contribute to the maintenance of a disorder (see the model of efficacy components in Figure 3.4), can naturally be only vaguely ascertained from the disorder perspective as they may be very different in patients with a similar disorder. They may only be adequately accounted for by an individual case conception which systematically pays attention to such motivational control parameters (see chapters 2.34, 2.35).

Adjustment disorders (PTSDs)
Meichenbaum, D. W. (1994). *A clinical handbook/practical therapist manual for assessing and treating adults with Post-Traumatic Stress Disorder (PTSD)*. Waterloo, Ontario: Institute Press.
[see also: Post-traumatic stress disorders].

Age-related dementia (senile dementia)
Zaudig, M. (1995). *Demenz und "leichte kognitive Beeinträchtigungen" im Alter* (Dementia and "light cognitive afflictions" in old age). Bern: Huber.

Aggression and violence
Roth, L. H. (Ed.). (1987). *Clinical treatment of the violent person*. New York: Guilford.
Wong, S. E., Slama, K. M. & Liberman, R. P. (1987). Behavioral analysis and therapy for aggressive psychiatric and developmentally disabled patients. In L. H. Roth (Ed.), *Clinical treatment of the violent person* (20–53). New York: Guilford Press.
[see also: antisocial personality disorder]

Aggression and violence in schools
Hazler, R. J. (1996). Breaking the cycle of violence: *Interventions for bullying and victimization*. Bristol: PA: Taylor & Francis.
Petermann, F., Jugert, G., Tänzer, U. & Verbeck, D. (1997). *Sozialtraining in der Schule* (Social training in schools). Weinheim: Psychologie Verlags Union.

Aids
[see: HIV/Aids]

Allergies
Petermann, F. (Hrsg.). (1995). *Asthma und Allergie* (Asthma and Allergies). Verhaltensmedizinische Grundlagen und Anwendungen (Foundations and applications of behavioral medicine). Göttingen: Hogrefe.

Antisocial personality disorder
Dolan, B. & Coid, J. (1993). *Psychopathic and antisocial personality disorders. Treatment and research issues*. London: Gaskell – The Royal College of Psychiatrists.
[see also: Aggression and violence]

Anxieties, phobias, and panic disorders

Margraf, J. & Schneider, S. (1990). *Panik. Angstanfälle und ihre Behandlung* (Panic, anxiety attacks under treatment). (2.Aufl.-2.ed.). Berlin: Springer.

Reinecker, H. (1993). *Phobien* (Pobias). Göttingen: Hogrefe.

Schulte, D. (1996). *Therapieplanung* (Therapy planning). Göttingen: Hogrefe. (dort im Anhang—appendix).

[see also: social phobia]

Asthma

Petermann, F. (Hrsg.). (1995). *Asthma und Allergie. Verhaltensmedizinische Grundlagen und Anwendungen* (Asthma and Allergies, Foundations and applications of behavioral medicine). Göttingen: Hogrefe.

Attachment disorders and interaction disorders (interpersonal disorders)

Hahlweg, K. (1994). Beziehungs- und Interaktionsstörungen (Attachment disorders and interaction disorders). In H. Reinecker (Hrsg.), *Lehrbuch der Klinischen Psychologie* (Handbook of clinical psychology) (2. Aufl.-2.ed; S. 435–458). Göttingen: Hogrefe.

Attention-deficit hyperactivity disorders -ADHD

Barkley, R. A. (1990). *Attention deficit hyperactivity disorder. A handbook for diagnosis and treatment.* New York: Guilford.

Lauth, G. W. & Schlottke, P. (1993). *Training mit aufmerksamkeitsgestörten Kindern* (Training with ADHD children.) Weinheim: Psychologie Verlags Union.

Behavioral disorders in childhood

Brack, U. B. (Hrsg.). *Frühdiagnostik und Frühtherapie. Psychologische Behandlung von entwicklungs und verhaltensgestörten Kindern* (Early diagnosis and early therapy, psychological treatment of children with developmental and behavioral disorders. Weinheim: Psychologie Verlags Union.

Petermann, F. (Hrsg.). (1996). *Lehrbuch der Klinischen Kinderpsychologie* (Handbook of clinical child psychology.). Göttingen: Hogrefe.

Borderline personality disorder

Linehan, M. (1993 a). *Cognitive behavioral treatment of borderline personality disorder.* New York: Guilford.

Linehan, M. (1993 b). *Skills training manual for treating borderline personality disorder.* New York: Guilford.

Cancer

Fawzy, F. I. & Fawzy, N. W. (1994). A structured psychoeducational intervention for cancer patients. *General Hospital Psychiatry, 16,* 149–192.

Chronic diseases

Holroyd, K. A. & Creer, T. L. (Eds). (1986). *Self-management of chronic disease: Handbook of interventions and research.* New York: Academic Press.

Petermann, F., Noeker, M. & Bode, U. (1987). *Psychologie chronischer Krankheiten im Kindes- und Jugendalter* (Psychology of chronic disease in childhood and adolescence). Weinheim: Psychologie Verlags Union.

Schulz, P. & Hellhammer, D. (1992). *Psychologische Aspekte chronischer Krankheiten* (Psychological aspects of chronic disease). In H. Reinecker (Hrsg.), Lehrbuch der Klinischen Psychologie (Handbook of clinical psychology) (2. Aufl. 2.ed..; S. 565–590). Göttingen: Hogrefe.

Compulsions (Obsessive-compulsive disorders)

Reinecker, H. (1991). *Zwänge. Diagnose, Theorien und Behandlung* (Compulsions. Diagnosis, theory and treatment.). Bern:Huber.

Süllwold, L., Herrlich, J. & Volk, S. (1994). *Zwangskrankheiten. Psychobiologie, Verhaltenstherapie, Pharmakotherapie* (Compulsive disorders. Psychobiology, behavior therapy, pharmacotherapy.) . Stuttgart: Kohlhammer.

Crises and crisis intervention

Fiedler, P. (1988). Existentielle Krisen und Krisenintervention (Existential crises and crisis intervention). In G. Hörmann & F. Nestmann (Hrsg.), *Handbuch der psychosozialen Intervention* (Handbook of psychosocial intervention) (S. 114–127). Opladen: Westdeutscher Verlag.

Roberts, A. R. (1995). *Crisis intervention and time-limited cognitive treatment*. Thousand Oaks, CA: Sage.

Crohn's disease (Morbus Crohn, Colitis ulcerosa)

Wittmann, H. B., Glier, B. & Spörkel, H. (1994). Verhaltensmedizinische Intervention bei entzündlichen Darmerkrankungen (Behavior therapy for illnesses of the gastrointestinal tract) (Morbus Crohn, Colitis ulcerosa). In M. Zielke & J. Sturm (Hrsg.), *Handbuch Stationäre Verhaltenstherapie* (in Handbook of inpatient behavior therapy) (632–639). Weinheim: Psychologie Verlags Union.

Dependent personality disorder

Bornstein, R. F. (1993). *The dependent personality*. New York: Guilford.

Vogelsang, M. (1996). Ein Modell kognitiv-behavioraler Gruppentherapie bei dependenten Persönlichkeitsstörungen (A model of cognitive-behavioral group therapy for dependent personality disorders.). *Verhaltensmodifikation und Verhaltensmedizin* (Behavior modification and behavioral medicine), *17*, 233–249.

Depression

Hautzinger, M. (1997). *Depression. Psychologie affektiver Störungen* (Depression. Psychology of affective disorders). Göttingen: Hogrefe.

Herrle, J. & Kühner, Ch. (Hrsg.). (1994). *Depression bewältigen. Ein kognitiv-verhaltenstherapeutisches Gruppenprogramm nach P. M. Lewinsohn* (Mastering depression, a cognitive-behavioral therapeutic group program according to P. M. Lewinsohn). Weinheim: Psychologie Verlags Union.

Developmental disorders in childhood

Brack, U. B. (Hrsg.). (1986). *Frühdiagnostik und Frühtherapie. Psychologische Behandlung von entwicklungs- und verhaltensgestörten Kindern.* (Early diagnosis and early therapy, psychological treatment of children with developmental and behavioral disorders) Weinheim: Psychologie Verlags Union.

Petermann, F. (Hrsg.). (1996). *Lehrbuch der Klinischen Kinderpsychologie* (Handbook of clinical child psychology). Göttingen: Hogrefe.

Diabetes mellitus

Petermann, F. (Hrsg.). (1995). *Diabetes mellitus. Sozial- und verhaltensmedizinische Ansätze* (Diabetes mellitus. Social and behavioral medicine approaches). Göttingen: Hogrefe.

Disorders of impulse control

Fiedler, P. (1996). Dissoziative, vorgetäuschte und Impulskontroll-Störungen. In J. Margraf (Hrsg.), *Lehrbuch der Verhaltenstherapie* (Dissociative disorders, simulated disorders and disorders of impulse control (Band 2- Vol.2; S. 319–336). Heidelberg: Springer.

Fiedler, P. & Mundt, Ch. (1996). Dissoziative Störungen, vorgetäuschte Störungen und Störungen der Impulskontrolle (Dissociative disorders, simulated disorders and disorders of impulse control) In K. Hahlweg & A. Ehlers (Hrsg.), *Psychische Störungen und ihre Behand-lungen* (Mental disorders and their treatment) (S. 355–436). Göttingen: Hogrefe.

Dissociative disorder

Fiedler, P. (1996). Dissoziative, vorgetäuschte und Impulskontroll-Störungen (Dissociative disorders, simulated disorders and disorders of impulse control). In J. Margraf (Hrsg.), *Lehrbuch der Verhaltenstherapie* (Handbook of behavior therapy) (Band 2- Vol.2; S. 319–336). Heidelberg: Springer.

[see also: Post-traumatic stress disorders]

Drug Dependencies and addiction

Beck, A.T., Wright, F. D., Newman, C. F. & Liese, B. S. (1997). *Kognitive Therapie der Sucht* (Cognitive therapy of addiction). Weinheim: Psychologie Verlags Union.

Bühringer, G. & Küfner, H. (1996). *Drogen- und Medikamentenabhängigkeit* (Drug and medication dependency). In K. Hahlweg & A. Ehlers (Hrsg.), Psychische Störungen und ihre Behandlungen (Mental disorders and their treatment) (S. 513–588). Göttingen: Hogrefe.

Elsässer, K. (1996). *Verhaltenstherapeutische Unterstützung des Benzodiazepin-Entzugs* (Behavior therapeutic support of withdrawal from benzodiazepemes). Weinheim: Psychologie Verlags Union.

Scholz, H. (1996). *Syndrombezogene Alkoholismustherapie* (Syndrome-related therapy for alcoholism). Göttingen: Hogrefe.

Eating disorders

Gerlinghoff, M. & Backmund, H. (1995). *Therapie der Magersucht und Bulimie* (Therapy of anorexia and bulimia). Weinheim: Psychologie Verlags Union.

Jacobi, C., Thiel, A. & Paul, T. (1996). *Kognitive Verhaltenstherapie bei Anorexia und Bulimia nervosa* (Cognitive behavior therapy of anorexia and bulimia nervosa). Weinheim: Psychologie Verlags Union.

Rief, W., Stock, C. & Fichter, M. M. (1991). Das Anti-Diät-Programm als integrativer Therapiebaustein bei anorektischen, bulimischen und adipösen Patienten (The anti-diet program as an integrative therapy unit for anorexic, bulimic and obese patients). *Verhaltenstherapie,*(Behavior therapy) 1, 47–54.

[see also: Obesity]

The elderly (prevention in old age)

Erwin, K. T. (1996). *Group techniques for aging adults: Putting geriatric skills enhancement into practice.* Bristol: PA: Taylor & Francis.

Oswald, W.D. & Gunzelmann, T. (Hrsg.). (1995). *Kompetenztraining. Ein Programm für Senioren-gruppen* (Competence training. A new program for seniors). [Das SIMA-Projekt-The SIMA-project]. Göttingen: Hogrefe.

Oswald, W. D. & Rödel, G. (Hrsg.). (1995). *Gedächtnistraining. Ein Programm für Senioren* (Memory training. A program for seniors). [Das SIMA-Projekt-The SIMA-project]. Göttingen: Hogrefe.

Epilepsy

Queisser, H. R., Armstrong, H. E., Smith, W.R. & Davis, G. R. (1980). Psychoeducational skills training for individuals with epilepsy. In D. Upper & S. M. Ross (Eds.), *Behavioral group therapy* 1980 (219–234). Champaign: Research Press Company.

Factitious disorders (as a mental disorder vs. simulation)

Fiedler, P. & Mundt, Ch. (1996). Dissoziative Störungen, vorgetäuschte Störungen und Störungen der Impulskontrolle (Dissociative disorders, simulated disorders and disorders of impulse control.). In K. (Hahlweg & A. Ehlers (Hrsg.), *Psychische Störungen und ihre Behand-lungen* (Mental disorders and their treatment.). (S. 355–436). Göttingen: Hogrefe.

Fear of flying

Kinnunen, P: (1996). *Flugangst bewältigen. Informationen zur Entstehung und Behandlung für Be-troffene und Therapeuten* (Mastering fear of flying. Information on the development and treatment for patients and therapists) Weinheim: Psychologie Verlags Union.

[see also fears and phobias]

Gastrointestinal disorders

Cuntz, U., Pollmann, H. & Enck, P. (1994). Verhaltenstherapie bei Erkrankungen des Gastrointesti-naltraktes (Behavior therapy for illnesses of the gastrointestinal tract). In M. Zielke & J. Sturm (Hrsg.), *Handbuch Stationäre Verhaltenstherapie* (in Handbook of inpatient behavior therapy) (619–631). Weinheim: Psychologie Verlags Union.

HIV and AIDS

DiClemente, R. J. & Peterson, J. L. (Eds.). (1994). *Preventing AIDS: Theories and methods of behavioral interventions.* New York: Plenum Press.

Hüsler, G & Hemmerlein, G. (1996). *Leben auf Zeit. Ein Psychotherapiemanual für den Umgang mit HIV/Aids und anderen lebensbedrohlichen Krankheiten* (Life against the clock. A psychotherapy manual for dealing with HIV/Aids and other life-threatening diseases.) Bern: Huber

Learning and motivational disabilities in childhood and adolescence

Betz, D. & Breuninger, H. (1993). *Teufelskreis Lernstörungen. Theoretische Grundlagen und Standardprogramm* (The vicious cycle of learning disorders, theoretical foundations and standard programs) (3. Aufl- 3.ed.). Weinheim: Psychologie Verlags Union.

Life-threatening illnesses
Hüsler, G. & Hemmerlein, G. (1996). *Leben auf Zeit. Ein Psychotherapiemanual für den Umgang mit HIV/Aids und anderen lebensbedrohlichen Krankheiten* (Life against the clock. A psychotherapy manual for dealing with HIV/Aids and other life-threatening diseases.). Bern: Huber.

Marital and couple's problems (prevention)
Bornstein, P. H. & Bornstein, M. T. (1993). *Psychotherapie mit Ehepaaren. Ein integrativer Ansatz* (Psychotherapy with couples, an integrative approach.).Bern: Huber.

Thurmaier, F., Engl, J., Eckert, V. & Hahlweg, K. (1992). Prävention von Ehe- und Partnerschafts-störungen EPL (Ehevorbereitung: Ein Partnerschaftliches Lernprogramm) (Prevention of couple and relationship disorders (Marriage preparation: A partnership learning program). *Verhaltenstherapie*, 2 (Behavior therapy 2), 116–124.

[see also: Separation and divorce; attachment and interaction disorders].

Neurodermatitis
Stangier, U., Gieler, U., Ehlers, A. (1996). *Neurodermitis bewältigen* (Mastering neurodermatitis). Heidelberg: Springer.

Neuropsychological disorders
Kryspin-Exner, I. (1988). Klinische Neuropsychologie und Verhaltenstherapie (Clinical neuropsychology and behavior therapy). *Verhaltensmodifikation und Verhaltensmedizin* (Behavioral modification and behavioral medicine), 9, 97–118.

Wittling, W. (1990). Neuropsychologische Störungen (Neuropsychological disorders). In H. Reinecker (Hrsg.), *Lehrbuch der Klinischen Psychologie* (Handbook of clinical psychology). (2. Aufl. 2.ed.; S. 527–566). Göttingen: Hogrefe.

Obesity
LeBow, M.D. (1991). Adipositas. *Psychotherapie und Nachbehandlung von Übergewicht bei Erwachsenen* (Obesity. Psychotherapy and follow-up treatment of adult obesity). Bern: Huber.

Stunkard, A. J. & Wadden, T. A. (1993). *Obesity: Theory and therapy*. New York: Raven.

Pain
Basler, H. D. & Kröner-Herwig, B. (Hrsg.). (1995). *Psychologische Therapie bei Kopf- und Rücken-schmerzen. Ein Schmerzbewältigungsprogramm zur Gruppen- und Einzeltherapie* (Psychological therapy of headache and back pain. A program for mastering pain in individual and group therapy.). München: Quintessenz.

Mühlig, S. (1997). *Schmerz und Schmerzbehandlung bei Kindern und Jugendlichen* (Pain and pain treatment in children and adolescents.). Weinheim: Psychologie Verlags Union.

Panic disorder
[see: Anxiety and phobias]

Parkinsons
Leplow, B., Bamberger, D., Möbius, T. & Ferstl, R. (1993). Verhaltenstherapeutische Gruppenprogramme bei Parkinsonpatienten (Behavior therapy group programs for Parkinsons patients.). *Therapiewoche Neurologie und Psychiatrie*, (Therapyweek, Neurology and Psychiatry.) 7, 59–68.

Strehl, U. & Birbaumer, N. (1996). *Verhaltensmedizinische Intervention bei Morbus Parkinson* (Behavioral medicine intervention in Parkinsons disease). Weinheim: Psychologie Verlags Union.

Pathological gambling
Klepsch, R., Hand, I., Wlazlo, E., Kaunisto, E. & Friedrich, B. (1989). Pathologisches Spielen (Pathological gambling). In I.

Hand & H.-U. Wittchen (Hrsg.), *Verhaltenstherapie in der Medizin* (Behavior therapy in medicine) (313–326). Berlin: Springer.

Petry, J. (1996). *Psychotherapie des Glücksspiels* (Psychotherapy of gaming). Weinheim: Psychologie Verlags Union.

Personality disorders
Beck, A. T., Freeman, A. u. a. (1993). *Kognitive Therapie der Persönlichkeitsstörungen* (Cognitive therapy of personality disorders). Weinheim: Psychologie Verlags Union.

Fiedler, P. (1995). *Persönlichkeitsstörungen* (Personality disorders) (2. Aufl- 2 ed.). Weinheim: Psychologie Verlags Union.

Turkat, I. D. (1996). *Die Persönlichkeitsstörungen. Ein Leitfaden für die klinische Psychologie* (Personality disorders. A guideline to clinical psychology) Bern: Huber.
[see also: Borderline-personality, dependent, antisocial, avoidant-personality disorder]
Phobias
[see anxiety, social anxiety, fear of flying]
Post-traumatic stress disorder-PTSD
Meichenbaum, D. W. (1994). *A clinical handbook/practical therapist manual for assessing and treating adults with Post-Traumatic Stress Disorder (PTSD).* Waterloo, Ontario: Institute Press.
Saigh, P. A. (Hrsg.). (1995). *Postraumatische Belastungsstörungen* (Post-Traumatic Stress Disorder.) Bern: Huber.
Steil, R. & Ehlers, A. (1996). Die Posttraumatische Belastungsstörung. Eine Übersicht (Post-traumatic stress disorders. An overview) *Verhaltens-modifikation und Verhaltensmedizin* (Behavioral modification and behavioral medicine.), *17*, 169–212.
[see also sexual abuse, crises (intervention)]
Primary Hypertension
Bischoff, C. & Pein, A. v. (1994). Verhaltensmedizin der essentiellen Hypertonie (Behavioral medicine in primary hypertension). In M. Zielke & J. Sturm (Hrsg.), *Handbuch Stationäre Verhaltenstherapie* (Handbook of inpatient behavior therapy) (659–674). Weinheim: Psychologie Verlags Union.
Renal disease
Broda, M., Koch, U. & Muthny, F. A. (1989). Bedarf und Möglichkeiten der psychologischen Intervention bei Dialyse- und Nierentransplantationspatienten (Need for and possibilities of psychological interventions for dialysis and kidney transplant patients.). In I. Hand & H.-U. Wittchen (Hrsg.), *Verhaltenstherapie in der Medizin* (Behavior therapy in medicine) (262–274). Berlin: Springer-Verlag. [Adults]
Jochmus, I., Tieben-Heibert, A., Stein, L., Maiwald, G., Diekmann, L., Reichwald Klugger, E., Korn, R., Weck, K. & Schärer, K. (1982). *Psychosoziale Betreuung chronisch nierenkranker Kinder und Jugendlicher* (Psychosocial care of children in adolescence chronically affected by kidney disease). Münster/Heidelberg: Universitäts-Kinderkliniken. (Nephrologische Abteilung der Universitäts-Kinderklinik, Robert-Koch-Straße 31, 48149 Münster). [children]
Rheumatism (Polyarthritis)
Jungnitsch, G. (1992). *Schmerz- und Krankheitsbewältigung bei rheumatischen Erkrankungen. Psychologische Hilfen im Einzel- und Gruppentraining* (Mastering pain and illness of rheumatism, psychological assistance in individual and group training).München: Quintessenz.
Schizophrenia
Roder, V., Brenner, H. D., Kienzle, N. & Hodel, B. (1992). *Integriertes psychologisches Therapie-programm für schizophrene Patienten* (Integrated psychological therapy program for schizophrenic patients.). (IPT; 2. Aufl.- 2 ed.). Weihnheim: Psychologie Verlags Union.
Watzl, H. & Rist, F. (1996). Schizophrenie (Schizophrenia). In K. Hahlweg & A. Ehlers (Hrsg.), *Psychische Störungen und ihre Behandlungen* (Mental disorders and their treatment) (S. 1–154). Göttingen: Hogrefe.
Schizophrenia (family and relatives)
Fiedler, P., Niedermeier, Th. & Mundt, Ch. (1986). *Gruppenarbeit mit Angehörigen schizophrener Patienten. Materialien für die therapeutische Arbeit mit Angehörigen und Familien* (Group therapy with relatives of schizophrenic patients. Materials for therapeutic work with relatives and families.). München, Weinheim: Psychologie Verlags Union.
Hahlweg, K., Dürr, H. & Müller, U. (1995). *Familienbetreuung schizophrener Menschen. Ein verhaltenstherapeutischer Ansatz zur Rückfallprophylaxe* (Family care of schizophrenics. A behavior therapy approach for preventing relapse.). Weinheim: Psychologie Verlags Union.
Separation and divorce (prevention of divorce effects)
Haynes, J., Bastine, R., Link, G. & Mecke, A. (1993). *Scheidung ohne Verlierer* (Divorce with no losers.). München: Kösel.

Sexual abuse, rape
Calhoun, K. S. & Atkeson, B. M. (1994). *Therapie mit Opfern von Vergewaltigung. Hilfen bei der Überwindung der psychischen und sozialen Folgen* (Therapy with rape victims. Helping to overcome mental and social after-effects.). Bern: Huber.
Ecker, D., Graf, B., Mempel, S., Scheidt, B. & Tempel-Griebe, H. (1994). Diagnostische Aspekte und gruppentherapeutische Erfahrungen bei der Behandlung sexuell missbrauchter und vergewaltigter Frauen (Diagnostic aspects and group therapy experiences in the treatment of sexually abused and raped women.). In M. Zielke & J. Sturm (Hrsg.), *Handbuch Stationäre Verhaltenstherapie* (in Handbook of inpatient behavior therapy) (763–773). Weinheim: Psychologie Verlags Union.
Meichenbaum, D. W. (1994). *A clinical handbook/practical therapist manual for assessing and treating adults with Post-Traumatic Stress Disorder (PTSD)*. Waterloo, Ontario: Institute Press. [see also: PTSD]

Sexual disorders
Adams, H. E. & McAnulty (1993). Sexual disorders: The paraphilias. In P. B. Sutker & H. E. Adams (Eds.), *Comprehensive handbook of psychopathology* (2nd. ed.; 563–580). New York: Plenum Press. [Paraphilias]
Hoyndorf, S., Reinhold, M. & Christmann, F. (1995). *Behandlung sexueller Störungen. Ätiologie, Diagnostik, Therapie: Sexuelle Dysfunktionen, Missbrauch, Delinquenz.*(Treatment of sexual disorders. Etiology, diagnostics, therapy: Sexual dysfunction, abuse, delinquency.). Weinheim: Psychologie Verlags Union.
Zimmer, D. (1996). Funktionelle Sexualstörungen (Functional sexual disorders.). In K. Hahlweg & A. Ehlers (Hrsg.), *Psychische Störungen und ihre Behandlungen* (Mental disorders and their treatment.). (S. 723–798). Göttingen: Hogrefe.

Sleep disorders
Backhaus, J. & Riemann, D. (1996). *Schlafstörungen bewältigen* (Mastering sleep disorders.). Weinheim: Psychologie Verlags Union.
Riemann, D. & Backhaus, J. (1996). *Behandlung von Schlafstörungen. Ein psychologisches Gruppenprogramm* (Treatment of sleep disorders. A psychological group program.). Weinheim: Psychologie Verlags Union.

Social anxieties, avoidant-personality disorder
Reinecker, H. (1994). Soziale und spezifische Phobien (Social and specific phobias.). In H. Reinecker (Hrsg.), *Lehrbuch der Klinischen Psychologie* (Handbook of clinical psychology) (2. Aufl.- 2 ed.; S. 91–116). Göttingen: Hogrefe.
Renneberg, B. (1996). Verhaltenstherapeutische Gruppentherapie bei Patienten mit selbstunsicherer Persönlichkeitsstörung (Behavioral group therapy for patients with an avoidant-personality disorder.). In B. Schmitz, T. Fydrich & K. Limbacher (Hrsg.), *Persönlichkeitsstörungen: Diagnostik und Psychotherapie* (Personality disorders: diagnostics and psychotherapy.). Weinheim: Psychologie Verlags Union.

Somatoform disorders
Rief, W. & Hiller, W. (1992). *Somatoforme Störungen. Körperliche Symptome ohne organische Ursache* (Somatoform disorders. Physical symptoms without organic causes.). Bern: Huber.
Salkovskis, P. M. (1996). Somatoforme Störungen (Somatoform disorders). In K. Hahlweg & A. Ehlers (Hrsg.), *Psychische Störungen und ihre Behandlungen* (Mental disorders and their treatment.). (S. 308–354). Göttingen: Hogrefe.

Somatoform disorders in dentistry, oral hygiene and orthodontics
Fabinger, A. A. & Fiedler, P. (1996). Somatoforme Störungen in der Zahn-, Mund- und Kieferheilkunde: Theoretische Einordnung, verhaltenstherapeutische Perspektiven und Fallbeschreibung (Somatoform disorders in dentistry, oral hygiene and orthodontics: Theoretical classification, behavior therapy perspectives and case description.). *Verhaltensmodifikation und Verhaltensmedizin,* (Behavioral modification and behavioral medicine) *17*, 213–231.

Stuttering (dysphemia)
Fiedler, P. & Standop, R. (1994). *Stottern. Ätiologie, Diagnose, Behandlung* (Stuttering, etiology, diagnosis, treatment.) (4. Aufl.-4 ed.). Weinheim: Psychologie Verlags Union.

Suicide prevention

Freeman, A. & Reinecke, M. A. (1995). *Selbstmordgefahr? Erkennen und Behandeln: Kognitive Therapie bei suizidalem Verhalten* (In danger of suicide? Recognition and treatment: Cognitive therapy for suicidal behavior.). Bern: Huber.
[see also: Crisis intervention]

Tinnitus

Goebel, G. (Hrsg.). (1992). *Ohrgeräusche. Psychosomatische Aspekte des komplexen Tinnitus* (Hearing noises. Psychosomatic aspects of the complex Tinnitus.). München: Quintessenz.

Ulcerative colitis (Colitis ulcerosa)

Wittmann, H. B., Glier, B. & Spörkel, H. (1994). *Verhaltensmedizinische Intervention bei entzündlichen Darmerkrankungen* (Behavioral medicine intervention in infected ulcerative colitis) (Morbus Crohn, Colitis ulcerosa). In M. Zielke & J. Sturm (Hrsg.), Handbuch Stationäre Verhaltenstherapie (Handbook of inpatient behavior therapy) (632–639). Weinheim: Psychologie Verlags Union.

Therapist: Regarding your views on the benefits of therapy manuals—while I do share your opinion that such manuals are useful for many purposes, especially for acquiring disorder-specific know-how, I would also like to caution you of some dangers of such manuals. A therapist who routinely works with such disorder-specific manuals might easily overlook attractors that are not considered in these manuals but are nevertheless relevant to the patient's condition. Two patients suffering from the same disorder may not be as equal as one might assume when taking a disorder-specific perspective. Therefore, such patients should not be treated right away exclusively as suggested in a disorder-specific manual. Although every therapist working with a manual will adjust his or her interventions somewhat in response to the patient's unique features, it is still possible that certain aspects that have nothing to do with the special nature of the disorder may not be fully taken into account. For example, manual-guided therapists might neglect motivational attractors that are useful from the resource activation perspective, or interpersonal attractors that are significant for the patient's problem but are not yet included in the manuals.

In addition, even if patients receive the same diagnosis, one mental disorder does not necessarily equal another. A case of circumscribed bulimia is different from bulimia that is embedded in a complex pattern of comorbidity. For the first, a manual-guided treatment may be perfectly in order; however, this may not be ideal for the latter. For the comorbid case, one must also target the "breeding ground" of all the other disorders, and one must recognize and address the inconsistency-reducing function that the bulimia and/or other disorders still have. In such a case, a therapist will not be able to simply alleviate one disorder after the other with the aid of a therapy manual. Even in mental disorders, after all, the whole is more than the sum of its parts.

In my opinion, a manual should typically be applied only once a case conceptualization has been completed in which a disorder-transcending perspective has been assumed, much as you and I concluded at the end of our first dialogue. Nothing has changed about this conclusion as the result of our considerations here. The acknowledgment of the functional autonomy of disorder attractors does not change a thing with regard to the relevance of the other perspectives. After our second dialogue, the resource perspective, the interpersonal perspective, and the conflict perspective seem to be even more justified. However, our considerations in this conversation have given some indication as to when it might be appropriate to limit oneself to a disorder-specific treatment and when one should go beyond that. Once it is clear that we are faced with a functionally largely autonomous disorder attractor, the disorder may very well be treated using a disorder-specific manual, because this guarantees the greatest chance for effectively influencing the specific control parameters of the disorder attractors.

The view that mental disorders are independent determinants of mental functioning is by no means universally accepted in psychotherapy. According to the psychodynamic perspective, mental disorders have a close functional connection with goal-oriented mental functioning. This is why our view of mental disorders clearly differs from that of psychodynamic therapy, even though both acknowledge the essential role of conflicts and repression processes in the development of mental disorders. The fundamental difference is that, according to our conceptualization, mental disorders as attractors are thought to be largely functionally autonomous. The functional autonomy of attractors, as we have seen, has considerable consequences for conclusions regarding the treatment of such disorders. What about the functional autonomy of interpersonal attractors, the last form of attractors we recognized as important for psychotherapy?

2.52   Interpersonal Attractors

Therapist: I frequently include patients' significant others in therapy, so this question has captured my interest from the very beginning. Given my clinical experience, I have formed my own opinion about this issue already. By nature, humans are always interacting with other people, as we already discussed when we spoke about basic needs. The patient has control over the interaction patterns which develop with primary reference persons; however, they are equally strongly determined by those reference persons. In a very small child, motivational attractors tend to mirror interaction patterns with his primary reference persons rather than vice-versa. Once these interaction patterns are internalized and have grown into stable motivational attractors, the patient carries them forward into new relationships. This, however, is also true for the person's interaction partners. Neither person is able to control the interaction by himself, rather, one or several interpersonal attractors develop in the interaction between them. These are interpersonal processes that always repeat themselves in a similar way.

These regularities in interpersonal interactions become obvious particularly in a couples relationship. Although these regularities are influenced by both partner's motivational attractors (as well as jointly created situational conditions), they often have such functional autonomy that they are not voluntarily changeable by either one of partners. The interaction pattern described by Watzlawick, Beavin and Jackson (1969) as "symmetric escalation" is a perfect example: Both partners want to have the last word, and, via positive feedback, both work themselves into a never-ending exchange of words. Unilateral modification of such interpersonal attractors is so difficult because nonverbal communication behavior and pragmatic significance become such dominating control parameters. In such situations, however, the awareness of the participants is usually focused on the content of what is being said.

Interpersonal attractors are associated with the goals of both interaction partners, and, therefore, their activation is frequently accompanied by strong feelings. These attractors may be a source of continuous negative feelings, exerting a strong negative influence on well-being. Both individuals may have the desire to change the interaction but are unsuccessful because the stable attractor enslaves their interaction behavior. It may often be easier for a third party (e.g., a couples therapist) to create a relationship with both in such a way that negative interpersonal attractors are destabilized and new ones are ingrained. Couples therapy is an expression of the unique dynamics of interpersonal attractors.

The interpersonal attractors that have become established in a patient's original family may also be of therapeutic value. Because of their developmental history they are closely linked with motivational attractors. When interpersonal attractors are activated by the presence of family members in therapy, this also activates important motivational and emotional attractors in a "bottom-up" fashion. Modifying old interaction patterns simultaneously means overwriting old activation tendencies with new experiences. This overwriting applies to both parties, such that it becomes less likely for the old interpersonal attractor to slip back into its previous pattern.

2.53   The Development and Treatment of Mental Disorders From the Self-Organization Perspective

Therapy researcher: We have now developed an ensemble of four psychotherapeutically relevant types of attractors. According to our considerations, they arise from the reduction of need and inconsistency tensions. However, after their original appearance, they become functionally autonomous determinants of mental functioning. Along with other pre-existing determinants, they come to exert an effect on need and inconsistency tensions. In addition, the attractors act both as constraints and control parameters for one another. Each change at a certain point of these complex functional contexts may have effects on other processes. Given these reciprocal influences in a densely interconnected neural system, one clearly sees that the influence of an attractor on one of the control parameters not only has an impact on that one itself, but also on other mental processes. Because of the complexity of these mutual connections, it is impossible to predict precisely what kind of effect a targeted therapeutic intervention will have outside of its immediate, intended goal.

In general, the immediate impact on a certain attractor can be anticipated relatively well; for example, when an agoraphobic disorder attractor is impacted via stimulus confrontation. Yet, other processes that are triggered by such procedures are no longer under the influence of the relatively uniform disorder attractor. Instead, control is then exerted by the individual constellation of other attractors, constraints, and control parameters, which may differ quite a bit from patient to patient.

I have attempted to illustrate the complexity of these relations in a diagram (Figure 2.39).

The focus of the diagram is the experience and behavior to be understood and changed. I have differentiated between implicit and conscious experience and behavior and installed a consistency filter between the implicit and the conscious mode of functioning as already seen in Figure 2.25. Only a small portion of the entire experience and behav-

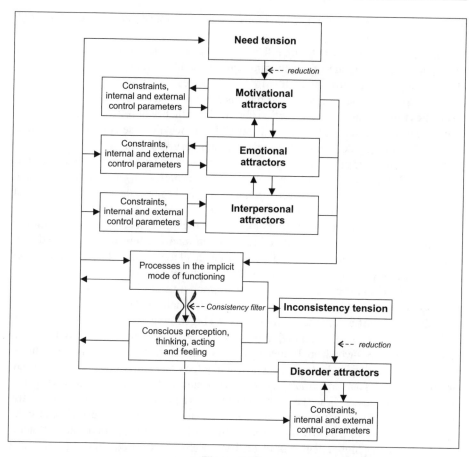

Figure 2.39:
Schematic illustration of the development of mental disorders as disorder attractors via the reduction of an inconsistency tension. Explanation in the text.

ior takes place in the conscious mode of functioning. Whatever gets into this mode of functioning has to first pass through the consistency filter.

However, consciousness is a powerful control parameter with the ability to influence all attractors. Therefore, there are directional control arrows from consciousness to all boxes symbolizing the internal and external control parameters of the attractors. Thus, consciousness is both the product of the attractors and one of their most powerful control parameters. Via this control parameter, a person can consciously change himself. A large portion of the communication between a therapist and her patient takes place on a consciousness level. The therapist can, therefore, exert an influence on the control parameters of the different attractors via the patient's consciousness. However, the content of the patient's consciousness must be compatible with his motivational attractors. If too many discrepancies are present, the content does not pass the consistency filter. This is also true for everything a therapist suggests to the patient. In addition, the change intended by the therapist must match desired perceptions by the patient; it must be consistent with his or her important motivational attractors. Otherwise, the "moving" force is lacking.

The attractors directly determine the processes occurring in the implicit mode of functioning. In this mode of functioning, simultaneously transpiring processes may also be inconsistent with one another to a certain degree. However, only those processes are possible that are permitted by existing neural activation tendencies. These tendencies function as constraints, consistent with the theory of self-organization. They limit the amount of inconsistency that is possible. As we discussed earlier, the implicit mode of functioning does allow for some contradictory behavior.

The implicit mode of functioning contains processes that are not represented in consciousness. However, not all of these processes are repressed by avoidance attractors. Most of these processes simply remain unconscious, because the conscious mode of functioning has such limited processing capacity.

The more discordant the influences exerted by the attractors are for the experience and behavior in the implicit mode of functioning, and the fewer goal-oriented processes pass the consistency filter under the influence of avoidance attractors, the greater the inconsistency tension in the system. There may be inconsistencies between processes occurring in the conscious versus the implicit mode of functioning, but it is also possible that there are inconsistencies within the implicit mode.

A high degree of inconsistency tension is the breeding ground for the development of disorder attractors. Given a high amount of inconsistency tension, natural fluctuations in the system—which are limited by the systems' current and general constraints—may be reinforced by reduction of inconsistency tension. The result is what Edelman termed selection of a neural group. A new kind of neural activation pattern forms because of positive feedback. This activation pattern enslaves a portion of psychological activity, and this results in a reduction of inconsistency tension. Tension is reduced because the mental processes (attractors) that were activated until the emergence of the new attractor were linked with a higher degree of inconsistency tension. Consequently, the influence of these old attractors decreases; a considerable portion of psychological activity is now determined by the newly established disorder attractor. For the time being, this reduces inconsistency in mental functioning. The more the newly established disorder attractor determines psychological activity, the more the system is relieved for now from inconsistency tension.

Thus, the arrows in the figure point from the "disorder attractors" box to all control parameters of the other attractors. The development of a mental disorder has an immediate impact on all other determinants of psychological activity. By the time therapists meet a person with a mental disorder, the determinants of psychological activity that have led to the development of a disorder have already changed in him.

Mental functioning has progressed further by the time a patient presents for therapy, and it remains in a continuous process of development. The inconsistency-creating constellation of motivational attractors that led to the development of the disorder may have dissolved in the meantime.

On the other hand, even after the development of a mental disorder it may be that the constellation of attractors and control parameters existing afterwards continues to produce inconsistency tensions. In this case, the disorder's relieving effect was only temporarily effective. It led to the development of a disorder attractor that now continues to exist in a functionally autonomous fashion. Continuing inconsistency tensions may then lead to the development of more disorder attractors, which leads to the phenomenon of comorbidity. The fact that comorbidity is frequent among the mental disorders suggests that the processes described here occur quite often.

In cases of such comorbidity, it would not make sense to treat all disorder attractors with disorder-specific interventions. It would require additional interventions to halt or decrease the permanent production of inconsistency tensions, which means specifically influencing avoidance and conflict attractors, given that these contribute the most to the development of inconsistencies.

However, it cannot be expected that a decrease of inconsistency tensions will make the disorder attractors that developed in the meantime disappear by themselves. Under the influence of once existing inconsistency tension, new neural activation tendencies have become established. Via reentrant mapping, they have, over time, interlocked with all other kinds of conditions and processes, in particular with the patient's other mental processes such as certain ideas, behaviors, etc. They themselves have thereby become part of the disorder.

An example would be the "negative thoughts" addressed particularly by cognitive therapies. It seems very likely to me that these thoughts have only been linked with the developing disorder attractor via reentrant mapping and were not the actual cause of the disorder. The reason for this is that the special cognitive features of depressed persons' functioning—referred to by Beck (1979) as the "cognitive triad"—can only be found during depressed states and not prior to those. Via reentrant mapping, these special cognitive features have become part of the functionally autonomous attractor, contributing to its maintenance. This places them among the internal control parameters of the attractor. Changing these negative thoughts, therefore, is an essential part in destabilizing the attractor. The more components of the functionally autonomous attractor can be destabilized, the more the attractor is destabilized overall, releasing psychological activity that may now again be determined by goals consistent with motivational attractors.

According to this view, all therapies focused on mental disorders should attempt to exert direct influence on the internal and external control parameters of the disorder attractors because they are helping to sustain the disorder. A large portion of these control parameters are in fact special features of the disorder, having become linked to it by reentrant mapping. These control parameters can best be identified by inter-individual disorder-specific research. Disorder-specific experimental research can best ascertain how these parameters can be influenced directly. Great progress has been made in this field over the last two decades, and this knowledge should definitely be utilized in the treatment of mental disorders. Thus, the disorder-specific portion of a therapy consists of the therapist attempting to influence directly the disorder-attractor via the box "internal and external control parameters," with the aim of destabilizing it. In order to do so, the appropriate neural activation patterns have to be activated and overwritten with new experiences. In our first dialogue we had referred to this as problem actuation and problem solving.

If no greater inconsistency tensions remain in the patient, the destabilization and overwriting of a disorder attractor can be considered a satisfactory therapeutic accomplishment.

If stronger inconsistency tensions remain in the patient, however, therapy should not limit itself to destabilizing one or several disorder attractor(s). Therapy would have to determine the factors that continue to produce these inconsistency tensions. The goal would be to influence these inconsistency-producing conditions, to reduce inconsistencies so they won't have to be reduced by disorder attractors. Thus, therapy becomes an alternative to the development of disorder attractors, a more constructive way of reducing inconsistency tensions.

Avoidance and conflict attractors are a fundamental source of inconsistency tensions. If there are any indications of current inconsistency tensions in a patient, therapy should focus on locating the causes and change them. An indication for persistent inconsistency tensions, for instance, would be the simultaneous coexistence of several mental disorders, a recent new development of disorders, or noticeable dissociations in the person's experience and behavior.

In case of strong, current inconsistency tensions or diagnosable mental disorders, therapy should focus on disorder-specific interventions but, even more so, on changing motivational attractors to reduce the inconsistency tensions. This would correspond to what we called intention changing or intention forming therapy in our first conversation. According to this model, it would be advisable to utilize interventions that influence both the disorder and motivational attractors, either simultaneously or sequentially. The existence of inconsistency tensions is the most important criterion for deciding whether a disorder-specific treatment or also a change in motivational attractors should be pursued.

If no disorder-specific therapy is performed, and therapy focuses only on changing the motivational attractor, the mental disorders may nonetheless improve, even if they have become functionally autonomous. One reason is that the patient may possibly influence the control parameters himself; for example, by no longer avoiding feared situations but by exposing himself to them, by changing his way of life, etc. Underlying these self-initiated changes might be changes in the constellation of motivational attractors, which might have been achieved by therapeutic clarification. These changes then lead to improved need satisfaction, a reduction in inconsistency tension and consequently to an improved emotional state. This creates motivation for new behaviors where none existed previously.

In addition, successful clarification-oriented therapy also changes patients' consciousness. New consciousness that emerges in therapy creates new potentials for conscious control in the patient. He gains understanding of what he can personally do to overcome his disorder. The combination of a changed motivational situation and a changed consciousness may become the basis for a self-initiated destabilization of the disorder attractor so that it can be overwritten with new experiences. Thus, something that is quite similar to what happens in a disorder-specific therapy occurs, except that the patient is not actively supported by the therapist's expertise in overcoming the disorder.

For many patients, however, such support can make a critical difference. Without it, destabilization of the disorder attractor may never take place. At any rate, withholding such support represents a risk at the patient's expense. Even in a disorder-specific therapy, it is ultimately the patient himself who behaves in a new fashion, exposing himself to new experiences. Thus, even purely clarification-oriented therapies may lead to the destabilization of disorder attractors. The empirical findings listed in our first conversation also point to this fact.

I see no reasonable argument for keeping the patient from disorder-specific support. The view we developed here suggests that, for the cases we discussed, interventions should be most effective if they focus on changing motivation, consciousness and on mastery-oriented, disorder-specific procedures. These interventions do not exclude one another, but supplement and intensify each other.

Naturally, there are patients in clinical practice who do not meet criteria for a specific diagnosis according to the DSM-IV or ICD-10. Those patients may also suffer intensely from their condition. Their suffering may be caused by either emotional or interpersonal attractors. Examples would be patients who are unable to control feelings of aggression or jealousy, or couples who start therapy due to relationship problems. In these cases considerations similar to those for disorder-attractors apply. On the one hand, attractors causing the suffering should be addressed directly with problem-specific interventions to account for their functional autonomy. The analysis of the control parameter of these attractors may reveal that motivational attractors are a significant internal control parameter for them. In this case, therapy should focus on changing the motivational attractors.

Therapy researcher: There seems to be an essential difference between the depiction in your Figure 2.39 and what I described in Figure 2.25, in that your figure gives greater consideration than mine to the determinants of psychological activity, with their own dynamic and influence on mental functioning. In fact, this was a specific criticism you had about my figure. The functional autonomy of attractors requires disorder-specific and problem-specific interventions. In my figure this was not sufficiently acknowledged.

For therapeutic practice, it is best to consider the context in both sketches. Figure 2.39 takes into account some aspects that are insufficiently acknowledged in Figure 2.25. On the other hand, Figure 2.25 contains contexts that are important for planning therapeutic interventions, and these are insufficiently expressed in Figure 2.39. Figure 2.25 offers a more differentiated basis, as far as the influence of motivational attractors in therapy is concerned.

Our ideas in this fourth part of our second dialogue are leading to the unanimous conclusion that the mechanism of psychotherapy ought to be conceptualized strictly with respect to the present. Regardless of whether we are dealing with disorder, emotional, interpersonal or motivational attractors, what needs to be changed are current control parameters that maintain that which needs to be changed. The inclusion of the patient's past via memories, genograms, or reports given by family members on past events may have two useful functions:

1. It may pinpoint problem aspects and control parameters that are difficult to recognize in the current cross-section, and these may presently still play an important role.
2. Memories may activate current neural activation tendencies that need to be over-written with new experiences. In doing so, it is essential that current activation tendencies are activated and overwritten, so that they exert a positive effect on the present, and not for the purpose of changing memories. Change always occurs from present to future, not from the recalled past to the present.

Psychologist: This last sentence seems such unfathomable wisdom to me as to place it at the limits of being banal, so much that it seems a good candidate for being the final word for our second dialogue.

Should we not end our conversation at this point? I think we have achieved the goal of an in-depth understanding of the mechanism of psychotherapy. If we add up the summaries presented by you at the end of the third part (chapter 2.44), and here just now in this chapter, we arrive at an understanding of the mechanism of psychotherapy which in my view, while largely congruent with the view developed in our first conversation, nonetheless goes far beyond that, by connecting our understanding of what occurs in therapy with an empirically based view of mental functioning.

I am for now rather exhausted and feel quite drained. I feel as though I just participated in a process of self-organization myself. Through synergetic feedback something new has been produced out of the possibilities that must have already existed in the three of us. However, I would not have been able to come up with what has emerged in this conversation, although I certainly have contributed to what went into this process.

Therapist: You certainly did! If any of us deserve a break, it is you. You have succeeded in thoroughly revising my previous bias against academic psychology. For the first time, I am really proud to be a psychologist. After this conversation, I have no problem with being identified with this discipline. I believe I have found a new identity in the course of this conversation. In the future I will view myself as a psychological therapist.

I am very excited about plunging into my therapeutic practice with all these new insights, to begin implementing all of this. While a lot of new content spins around in my head at the moment, I do have a wealth of new inspiration. I just have to transform this information in a way that enables me to best implement these insights into practical action. This is what I plan to work on intensively in the near future.

On the other hand, I am very interested to still meet with you for a final conversation in order to discuss the conclusions that I wish to draw from all this for my practice.

Therapy researcher: I am also interested in that. In addition, I would like to know which implications this has for therapeutic practice and training. This is something I would still like to discuss with you.

Psychologist: While this is also of interest to me, I will be more of an engaged conversational partner than a contributor. I feel there is little I can add to that discussion.

Therapist: Don't worry about that, you have contributed sufficiently to our knowledge for now. I believe this is up to me since I have been more absorbing than contributing to our discussions; I now feel able to offer my own contribution. All I need is a few months for testing the ideas that are now growing within me.

Therapy researcher: Very well, let's get together again in a few months then, whenever you feel you will have had sufficient opportunity to implement into practice the inspirations you received. We await your invitation for a third dialogue.

Third Dialogue

A Psychological Model of Therapy

Part 1:   A Theory of Psychotherapy

A Three-Component Model of How Psychotherapy Works

3.1   From Theory to Practice

Therapist: A few months have passed since our last conversation. This period has been very intense and constructive for me as I have attempted to implement in practice some of the insights from our first two dialogues.

Psychologist: I am eager to hear about this. Have you been able to use our theoretical ideas in practice? Have you changed anything based on these ideas?

Therapist: Most certainly! The greatest change is that I believe I have a better understanding about what occurs in the therapies I conduct. I have been able to answer for myself most of the questions I posed at the beginning of our first dialogue. I have a clearer conception about what happens on the patient's side, and this improved understanding is very satisfying.

  Of course, understanding the change processes in my patients has consequences for my therapeutic actions. I feel more secure in my actions, mostly because I have gained a better sense of why and how to approach patients in particular ways during different phases of therapy. I am much clearer about the change processes my patients should go through, and what I can do to facilitate this process.

Therapy researcher: This sounds very promising. It is exactly what I want to achieve with my research.

Therapist: I do not believe that either one of us would have come this far alone. Your contributions from therapy research were very helpful. I was able to apply them directly to therapeutic situations. However, I gained a deeper appreciation of the processes occurring in psychotherapy primarily by learning about the basic science perspective conveyed by our basic scientist. Our second dialogue convinced me that the therapeutic change process can be understood only if action **between** patient and therapist is somehow related to processes occurring **within** the patient. This is how we can explain why particular interpersonal processes in psychotherapy may lead to lasting changes in the patient's experience and behavior. What is required, then, is a model that explains how changes in mental functioning come about.

  I can articulate now what I often felt was missing in therapy research. Even well-established research usually documents only **that** something occurs a certain way, but not **why** it is that way. I would like to **understand why** particular effects follow when I proceed in a particular fashion. This understanding requires an appreciation of processes occurring within the patient, even if I am unable to directly observe or inquire about them. Thus, what I need is a model of mental functioning—a certain kind of psychology—that helps me understand why particular influences lead to specific effects. Psychotherapy research does not provide such a scientifically based psychology. Maybe this shortcoming contributes to practitioners' well-known dissatisfaction with therapy research.

Therapy researcher: You may be right; I had not considered this perspective before. For example, in the leading volume on psychotherapy research, the *Handbook of Psychotherapy and Behavior Change* by Bergin and Garfield (1994), almost every aspect of psychotherapy is examined empirically; yet, almost no information is provided about basic psychological research on human mental functioning.

Therapist: Exactly. Our second dialogue points to this deficit. I am convinced now that a scientifically based psychotherapy requires an empirically based model of the person. What drives people's actions? How do experience and behavior relate to one another? What are the associations between perception, thinking, feeling, wanting and action? How do mental processes develop and change, how do disturbances in these processes develop, and how can they be influenced?

I have attempted to integrate ideas from our basic scientist with earlier considerations on the mechanisms of psychotherapy. Based on this integration, I have developed a model and applied it to questions that interest me as a practitioner. This model relates processes occurring in therapy to an understanding of basic mental functioning. The model has become a great help in my work. It allows me to address therapeutic problems for which there are no prefabricated solutions. It also helps me integrate the many findings from therapy research into a coherent perspective.

I have gained greater clarity on how to conceptualize patients' mental functioning, and this understanding, in turn, allows me to draw inferences on how these processes can be influenced to facilitate therapeutic change.

Our model of mental functioning combined with my knowledge of therapeutic interventions has yielded a new model of the therapeutic process. In a way, this has created a space that allows me to move with my ideas and actions. Based on individual case conceptualizations, I can develop such a psychological space for my patients to explain their present state and behavior. In treatment planning, the dimensions of time and change are then added. Which transformations should the patient experience in this therapeutic space? In which sequence? And how can I contribute to these transformations with my interpersonal behavior and with targeted interventions?

Psychologist: This sounds very practice-oriented, and yet you mentioned that the basic science considerations I presented earlier influenced your new understanding of therapy. Could you give us an introduction to your model and show us the connection between theoretical foundations and practical conclusions?

Therapist: I will try. Let me begin by focusing on processes within the patient, given their fundamental importance. First, I will tell you what I think happens with a patient during a successful course of therapy. This leads to some natural conclusions regarding the therapist's ability to contribute to successful therapeutic outcome. Combining the patient's and therapist's perspective then yields a coherent view of the therapeutic process.

Therapy researcher: What you are announcing is a complete theory of psycho-therapy! If we have a scientifically based understanding of mental functioning and a scientifically based model of the therapeutic process, would anything still be lacking in order to have a scientific theory of psychotherapy?

Therapist: In my opinion we would still lack an understanding of how mental disorders develop and are maintained. However, our second dialogue has provided valuable ideas on this issue.

I leave it to you to decide whether my conclusions from the preceding dialogues can be called a theory. I recall your skepticism in this regard at the beginning of our first dialogue. Perhaps it is appropriate to call it a theory, given that my view is based on the empirical findings and theory both of you quoted during the first two dialogues. How else should one refer to a view based on so many scientific findings?

I personally prefer the term "model," actually. Ultimately, this is not supposed to be a purely theoretical endeavor, but a model that is useful for creating a certain reality. The practical conclusions from this model are of primary importance. The theoretical view and my conclusions together I prefer to call a model; perhaps a model for psychological therapy in the true sense of the word.

It is supposed to be a model for creating a certain reality. The point is not so much for me to gain a better understanding of psychotherapy and change my practice accordingly. Instead, the model acquires value only when others are persuaded and inspired to change their thinking and action.

It would also be useful if we came up with an idea of how psychotherapeutic service provision might look based on this model. In order to implement such a model, it would of course be required to train therapists accordingly. Thus, we should think about how therapeutic training might look based on this model .

Psychologist: This again sets up quite an agenda for us. I hope you realize that you must take the lead this time. Please do not expect any original contributions from me, as my understanding of therapeutic practice is limited. However, I will be available and involved as an interested participant.

Therapy researcher: Same here. I have thought of additional research findings that would fit nicely with what we have discussed so far, but I have not given much thought on how to implement these findings in concrete therapeutic practice. I will only contribute occasionally. You are going to have to take the lead if our third dialogue is to go beyond the two previous ones.

Therapist: I feel prepared. I suggest that I begin by talking about what happens for a patient during a successful course of psychotherapy, and what a therapist can do to facilitate these processes. This will be a theoretically based view of the therapeutic change process. We may also refer to it as a psychological theory of psychotherapy. Later, I will elaborate by developing a model of psychologically based therapeutic practice. Towards the end of this dialogue, we will eventually be able to address questions on psychotherapeutic training and care.

3.2   Improvement of Well-Being Through Positive Control Experiences

In our first conversation I mentioned the rapid improvements in well-being that are often observed in the initial phase of therapy. You had confirmed that this observation from clinical practice is supported by many therapy research findings, and you explained it as the result of a positive feedback process initiated by resource activation and the induction of improvement expectations (sections 1.2-1.5). After our second dialogue I had a much better understanding of what actually happens for the patient.

When a person seeks psychotherapy, the underlying reason is an incongruence between actual experiences and motivational schemata. The patient's suffering is a direct expression of this incongruence. Intentional schemata are the tools the individual has developed for meeting his basic needs. An incongruence between actual experiences and intentional schemata—mental suffering—means, therefore, that important basic needs are not being fulfilled. When I meet in therapy a person suffering from a mental disorder, I think it can be assumed that the person's basic needs are in some way unfulfilled.

This is obvious with respect to people's need for orientation and control (section 2.37). People seek psychotherapy only when they cannot resolve their mental difficulties on their own. On the one hand, suffering from an uncomfortable, painful disorder violates the basic need for avoiding displeasure and pain (section 2.38). On the other hand, such suffering also violates the need for control. The patient has not been successful in his efforts to end or avoid the displeasure associated with the disorder—be it panic, depression or some psychosomatic symptom. Frequently, he may neither know what to do nor what the source of the problem is. He has no control over something that is very important to him. At the beginning of therapy he finds himself in a state of loss of control.

The act of starting therapy may represent a certain reduction of this state of lost control. At the very least, starting therapy constitutes a step the patient was able to take himself in order to regain control. At the beginning of therapy, if the patient receives information about what the disorder is all about, how it can be treated, and what he can do to facilitate treatment, then these are all positive perceptions regarding his need for orientation and control. Such perceptions should be accompanied by positive feelings, such as hope and relief. Anything that promises to re-establish control is suited to improve the patient's well-being.

Control is experienced when one is able to act in accordance with one's goals. Exercising control means being active. The patient should be given opportunities at the beginning of therapy to be active in a way that is consistent with his goals and abilities, that is consistent with his positive motivational schemata. Interventions and the therapeutic context should allow the patient to act in a manner that is consistent with the intentional schemata he brings with him to therapy. In this way, his perceptions will lead to fulfillment of his need for control. The more successful the therapist is in activating existing resources within the patient, the more likely it becomes that the patient has positive perceptions that match his need for control. Resource activation leads to control experiences, and—especially for a person who is in a state of lost control—such experiences are important to regain a positive balance of need fulfillment.

Therapists can also promote early control experiences by using easily administered, mastery-oriented interventions. For instance, I can use relaxation training, allowing the patient to experience his ability to attain a more relaxed and calmer state. Then, I can instruct him to use this newly acquired skill in a targeted fashion. This also promotes the expectation that he can facilitate well-being by his own actions, even if the relaxation training itself does not have any direct effects on his disorder.

Transparency and a clear structure to the therapeutic process also have a positive impact regarding the patient's need for orientation and control. Such clarity creates space for the patient, allowing him to orient himself and be active. This promotes the person's own activity, consistent with the therapeutic goals. If the patient learns that he can contribute to therapy, he has positive control experiences.

Jerome Frank (1961, 1982) attributed the effects of therapy, in part, to the fact that the patient is given a rationale to explain and change his condition, which then leads to a procedure derived from this rationale. In his "placebo"-therapy, Fish (1973) emphasized that this rationale must be adapted to the special nature, convictions and expectations of the patient. I can understand better now why Frank's healing factors lead to improvements in well-being. They end or ease the patient's painful loss of control by creating positive expectations, which then provide some orientation. If the proposed procedures make sense to the patient, he can envision a clear path that he can take to improve his unbearable state.

There is a good likelihood, then, that at the beginning of therapy a patient will have positive perceptions regarding his need for control. These need-fulfilling perceptions should lead to subsequent improvement in well-being. Frank is right; this is true for therapy in general, not just for psychotherapy. Moreover, it holds not just for a particular form of psychotherapy. Nonetheless, the extent to which a patient actually has perceptions that fulfill his need for control depends very much on the specific intervention of the therapist. The patient will experience control primarily if he is able to act in therapy in accordance with his motivational schemata, leading to positive mastery experiences. If the therapist implements the two principles of resource activation and intention realization, then this will lead to positive perceptions regarding the patient's need for orientation and control. Positive emotions are triggered by these perceptions and lead to subsequent improvements in well-being.

Not only does this mechanism make sense to me, but it also shapes my own therapeutic actions. I should always make a point to ask myself: Do my interventions and the general therapeutic situation facilitate the patient's chances to have positive perceptions regarding his need for orientation and control? What can I do to ensure that the patient has such perceptions as often as possible? How should I arrange therapy so that the patient can act in accordance with existing schemata, making positive mastery experiences that facilitate progress towards valued goals? The concrete interventions resulting from these questions may look very different for each patient, because patients enter therapy with very different schemata. However, transparency, a clear structure, and an acknowledgment of the patient's autonomy seem advisable in all cases to promote patient control experiences.

Therapy researcher: It also makes sense to me that control experiences may be important primarily at the beginning of a therapy. Such experiences soothe the acute pain caused by disorder-related loss of control. Your comments suggest, however, that control experiences are also critical over the long-term course of therapy; in fact, you seem to suggest that positive patient experiences regarding the need for orientation and control may account for some of the overall effectiveness of successful therapy.

Therapy research discussed in our first dialogue indicates that clarification and mastery experiences account for a substantial proportion of the positive effects of psychotherapy. Gaining clarity and mastering difficulties are positive experiences with regard to the need for control. Conversely, the absence of such experiences in therapy may lead to increased feelings of helplessness and, thereby, to a worsening of the condition.

Therapist: Yes, I can well imagine that. It seems safe to assume that therapy patients experience an incongruence between actual experiences and their need for orientation and control, which contributes to diminished well-being. Control experiences are facilitated via the effective treatment components of resource activation, clarification, and mastery. These factors help diminish the problematic incongruence, which is experienced as positive by the patient. Well-being improves as the incongruence regarding the need for control is reduced.

I believe that the patient's incongruence regarding his need for control also determines when he is ready to end therapy. When the patient feels he can cope with the situation by himself, the moment has come to end therapy

Therapy researcher: This view of the processes at the beginning of therapy may help explain the findings by Howard et al. (1992) and Bieri (1996), who reported that successful therapy first yields improvements in well-being and only later improvement in symptoms. Well-being does not improve because symptoms—the actual cause for therapy—improve, but symptoms improve predominantly among patients who first experience improved well-being. If we consider the initial phase of therapy from the perspective of the need for control, then this sequence of changes makes sense.

It seems remarkable that we can make these broad statements without considering the nature of the patient's particular problem. The processes we described here are relevant for explaining the effectiveness of therapy in general, but they are not problem-specific. These dynamics likely apply to a variety of patients with a host of different problems.

Psychologist: If I follow you correctly, you attribute psychotherapeutic effectiveness, in part, to its need-fulfilling function, to the fact that therapy facilitates need-fulfilling experiences even before specific symptoms have been treated by targeted interventions.

Do you believe that improvement of well-being through need-fulfilling experiences only applies to the need for control, or are other basic needs also relevant in this respect?

Therapist: I just wanted to address this. I believe that analogous processes apply to the need for attachment and self-esteem. Let me elaborate first on the topic of interpersonal experiences in psychotherapy from an attachment perspective.

3.3 Improving Well-Being Through Positive Interpersonal Experiences

With regard to the need for attachment, things are in some ways different than with the need for control. We cannot assume that every patient's need for attachment is currently unmet. Many patients suffer because their interpersonal relationships are inadequate to meet their needs, and insecure attachment patterns have demonstrably high correlations with mental disorders (section 2.39). Therefore, improvements in the area of interpersonal relationships are often a high priority among the therapeutic goals. However, this does not apply to every case, and the therapeutic relationship should certainly not become a substitute for otherwise unsatisfactory relationships. People who feel comfortable and secure in intimate or family relationships may still need psychotherapy for other reasons.

Nevertheless, the psychotherapeutic situation appeals directly to the patient's need for attachment. According to Bowlby (1969, 1995), people are born with an innate need to seek and maintain proximity to a person who can cope better with life's challenges. Children seek comfort and protection in the attachment person. They require the attachment person primarily when a threat arises, when they feel the need for help and support. A person affected by severe illness—who has had a severe accident, or who suffers from a severe mental disorder—is in need and feels that he needs help. His need for a person who might offer comfort and help in his misery is acutely activated.

A therapist who exudes an air of competence, who conveys that she knows what must be done while at the same time giving undivided attention to the patient, will facilitate positive perceptions regarding the patient's acutely activated need for comfort and help. This is all the more true if the therapist is equipped with the qualities that characterize a good attachment figure.

Positive attachment patterns can be facilitated by a host of therapist behaviors, including attending sensitively to the patient; nonverbally reflecting his emotions; commenting what the patient reports with her facial expressions (see section 2.24); being there for the patient without dominating him; showing warmth and engagement by intonation, body posture and facial expression; giving the patient freedom and autonomy while at the same time directing and structuring when the patient needs support. According to Ainsworth's research, such behaviors characterize positive attachment patterns (section 2.39). The features characterizing a good attachment relationship are largely congruent with those constituting a good therapeutic relationship, according to therapy research (Orlinsky, Grawe & Parks, 1994). A therapist who implements the factors contributing to a good therapeutic relationship will facilitate positive perceptions regarding the patient's need for attachment.

When a child finds refuge, comfort, protection, and support by re-establishing contact with the attachment figure, he or she will return to his surroundings with renewed strength to pursue his goals. Similarly, a psychotherapy patient in a good patient-therapist relationship will be able to face his difficulties independently, with renewed strength and courage. Additionally, the patient might have received useful hints, information, or advice from the therapist. In this strengthened condition, the patient's prospects for making real, successful experiences that are consistent with his goals are much better than in his previously demoralized state. Therefore, positive experiences regarding his need for attachment in therapy will increase the likelihood of having further positive experiences outside of therapy.

In addition, a good therapeutic relationship facilitates positive control experiences on part of the patient. For the patient, the therapist's sensitive responding means that his behavior achieves effects that are consistent with his motivational schemata. A good personal relationship and a good therapeutic relationship are similar in that they simultanously offer comfort and autonomy. In such relationships, relying on help does not equal a loss of freedom or autonomy.

According to Grawe's concept of complementary relationship (Grawe, 1992; Grawe et al., 1996), the therapist ought to act in a way that allows the patient to have experiences consistent with important but unfulfilled motivational schemata. This conveys to the patient positive control experiences, and it signals him that he is being understood and accepted in his innermost concerns, instead of being evaluated negatively. This experience creates the basis for the patient's trust and confidence, assuring him that the therapeutic relationship will offer support for his innermost needs.

Therefore, a good therapeutic relationship enables the patient to have a multitude of positive experiences with regard to two activated basic needs: the need for control and the need for a consistent relationship that offers protection and support. These experiences are intensified to the degree that the patient experiences congruence regarding his most important intentional schemata. On the one hand, then, the therapist should implement some certain general principles in shaping an optimal therapeutic relationship; principles that apply to every relationship. On the other hand, she should tailor her interpersonal behavior specifically to the individual patient. This is particularly important for patients whose learning history has interfered with the acquisition of the capacity for problem-free, secure attachment. With such patients, an optimal therapeutic relationship does not emerge by itself but has to be actively and specifically shaped by the therapist's behavior.

When we are successful in creating a good therapeutic relationship, there are favorable conditions for positive changes. On the one hand, such a relationship is a foundation for jointly confronting patient problems later on in therapy. On the other hand, a good relationship in and of itself has immediate positive effects on the patient's well-being. This latter aspect is what I tried to emphasize here.

3.4 Improving Well-Being by Self-Esteem-Enhancing Experiences

Suffering from a mental disorder is a threat to one's self-esteem. Most people are embarrassed when they seek the help of a psychiatrist or psychotherapist. Being physically ill is not perceived as a personal failure, but having a mental disorder is viewed as just that. For most people, mental disorders carry profound stigma and are thus best concealed from public scrutiny.

The feeling of needing to hide something that is experienced as a personal failure or disgrace is incongruent with one's need for self-esteem. Concealing one's mental disorder for as long as possible serves to protect self-esteem. Conditions may have changed somewhat with improved knowledge on the development of mental disorders and increased societal acceptance of psychotherapy; however, not being able to cope independently with such problems—having to admit one's need of help in the face of uncontrollable experiences—is certainly incompatible with the need for self-esteem. As a therapist, then, I can safely assume that my patient's need for self-esteem is compromised and acutely activated. The psychotherapy setting itself, obviously, does not typically enhance people's self-esteem. This is where the patient must reveal his problematic sides. Admitting to problems one cannot cope with is quite the opposite of a self-esteem-enhancing experience.

The importance of resource activation for psychotherapy stems, in part, from this recognition. Giving the patient the opportunity to reveal his strengths and positive sides, and acknowledging these explicitly, creates exactly the kind of self-esteem-enhancing perceptions the patient needs as he enters therapy. In this regard, it was very validating for me to hear that social psychology has documented people's tendency to evaluate themselves more positively than is objectively justified (section 2.40). This matches my therapeutic experience. I find that it is almost impossible to overdo it when it comes to acknowledging patients' strengths and positive features, even when this sometimes exceeds realistic terms. This is always good for the patient. Such acknowledgments are congruent with his need for positive self-esteem.

This does not mean that patients always accept such self-esteem-enhancing statements; even "normal" persons do not always accept praise. According to what you said earlier, persons with low self-esteem—and especially depressed people—tend to have "realistic" or non-self-esteem-enhancing perceptions. Sometimes, they even seem to maintain low self-esteem actively (section 2.40). However, you also mentioned that this represents self-protection; protection from threats that might follow open self-esteem enhancing behavior. In situations when they do not need to acknowledge explicitly their wish for increased self-esteem, however, even depressed persons demonstrate a tendency toward self-esteem-enhancing behavior.

This matches my experiences as a therapist. When I offer positive confirmations to a patient with low self-esteem, acknowledging his positive sides, then I must take full responsibility for my statements and not expect any affirmation. Usually I conceal these remarks in peripheral commentary, so as to not turn them into a main theme. This leaves the patient the freedom not to be forced into commenting. The remarks have their self-esteem-enhancing effects without the patient's specific acknowledgment.

Focusing on the patient's resources as a theme, however, is not the only opportunity for creating self-esteem-enhancing perceptions. If I processually convey to the patient my interested engagement—that I view him as an interesting and amiable person—then he will also have meaningful self-esteem-enhancing experiences. Also, if I let him talk about a hobby or a topic in which he is the expert, this represents an activation of his resources. The patient views himself reflected in his competences. The process of resource activation counterbalances the inherent imbalance in the therapeutic relationship, where the therapist is the expert and the patient the one with the problems.

If I choose my interventions in a way that allows the patient to actively participate, then I offer him the opportunity to experience himself as capable. He then has self-esteem-enhancing experiences beyond those triggered by my praise, which can always be questioned. These experiences derive from his own perceptions. The more opportunities I provide for the patient to act consistent with his strengths and positive intentions, the more I engage in the process of activating his resources, the more the patient receives the opportunity to have self-esteem-enhancing perceptions.

Therapists who employ resource-oriented thinking and acting have many possibilities to create self-esteem-enhancing perceptions. Such perceptions are associated with positive emotions, even if the patient does not openly reveal them. These positive experiences have positive effects on the quality of the therapeutic relationship and they lead directly to improvements in well-being.

Therapist-directed resource activation leads to patients' self-esteem-enhancing perceptions. If a patient acts based on his resources, he also has positive control experiences. According to this line of reasoning, therapists' resource activation impacts well-being via patients' positive control experiences and via self-esteem-enhancing perceptions. Resource activation also has positive repercussions for the quality of the therapeutic relationship, which, in turn, has a positive impact on well-being. The therapeutic relationship is, of course, also one of the most important foundations for successful work on the patient's problems over the further course of therapy.

3.5 The First Component of Effective Psychotherapy: Inconsistency Reduction Through Resource Activation

Therapy researcher: I had interpreted the rapid improvements we discussed in our first dialogue—which are actually not so rare at the beginning of a therapy—as resulting from a positive feedback process, triggered by induction of positive improvement expectations as well as resource activation. However, I had not considered patient needs or motivational schemata. According to our second dialogue, however, these are the actual driving force of mental functioning and of change processes. I admit that this whole process seems clearer and more plausible from your perspective.

Therapist: The therapist may have two beneficial influences, for the most part: She can either act in a way that allows the patient to have positive interpersonal experiences, or she can focus specifically on activating resources that the patient brings to therapy. To simplify, I want to call both of these the **shaping of a resource activating relationship**. Activating resources leads to positive control experiences and to self-esteem-enhancing perceptions. Each positive interpersonal experience, control experience, and self-esteem-enhancing perception equals a reduction in existing incongruities between the patient's experiences and motivational schemata. This **incongruence reduction** is accompanied by improved well-being. This improvement also engenders a more positive balance of pleasure/displeasure. Thus, the result is a more complete satisfaction of all four basic needs.

For the patient, these positive effects are experienced as linked directly to the therapist. This, in turn, leads to greater confidence in the therapist and to greater openness in the therapeutic relationship. As the therapist provides opportunities for the patient to act in accordance with his goals and abilities, the patient comes to experience himself not as a passive object, but as someone who is capable of creating effects that are consistent with his goals. Confidence, openness and readiness for active participation are precisely the features that characterize the patient's contribution to a positive thera-peutic relationship (Orlinsky, Grawe & Parks, 1994; Schulte, 1996). Perceiving posi-tive patient behavior also reinforces the therapist's willingness to commit to the pa-tient. The characteristics of a good therapeutic relationship develop on both sides.

The experience of being an active part in such a relationship strengthens patients' self-esteem. Improved self confidence, well-being, and the recognition that behavior effectively leads to desired outcome, further mobilizes his positive resources. Similar to a motor that has once been started, resource activation becomes a self-perpetuating process.

With improved well-being, strengthened self-confidence, and positive efficacy ex-periences—backed up by a strong therapeutic relationship—it becomes highly likely that the patient takes steps towards independent mastery of some of his problems. For instance, he may expose himself to situations previously avoided. Or, consistent with Kuhl (1983, 1994), he may become more action-oriented, reestablishing relationships that had dried up in the past. He may take care of things he had put off until now, or he may take risks he previously avoided, trying out whether something is indeed unbear-able or merely uncomfortable. These steps are the core of therapeutic intervention in problem solving-oriented therapies, such as the self-management therapy of Kanfer, Reinecker and Schmelzer (1991). The patient can plan and perform these actions, col-laborating with the therapist as needed.

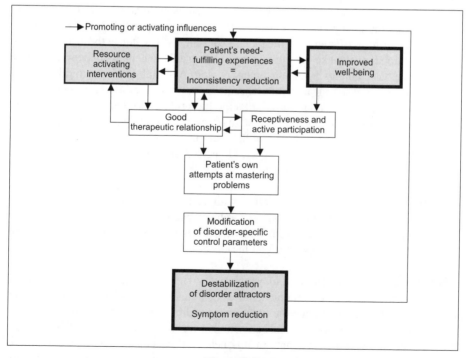

Figure 3.1:
The first effectiveness component of psychotherapy: Resource activation.

It is easily conceivable that the patient, based on his improved overall condition and confidence, himself initiates mastery experiences that are equal in effect to those he might have made in formal problem-solving therapy. Using the language of the Rubicon model, we might say that the patient's need-fulfilling experiences in therapy have so strongly increased the volitional strengths for certain intentions that they are now sufficient for successful intention realization.

If patients' mastery experiences change the control parameters of a specific disorder—for instance, weakening catastrophic anticipation in panic disorder—the result will be a destabilization of this particular disorder attractor, i.e., the reduction of a symptom, similar to what would have happened in a targeted disorder-specific therapy.

In Figure 3.1, I have attempted to graphically summarize this process, which is set in motion by resource activation but quickly becomes self-perpetuating.

What do you think of this perspective on the psychotherapeutic change process?

Psychologist: Everything you said seemed quite plausible. However, if I take a closer look at this figure now, I imagine that therapists might see it as quite a provocation. Except for a resource-oriented shaping of the therapeutic relationship, therapists need not contribute anything to this process, according to the figure. Thus, they may not need any problem-specific knowledge or skills, but only need to be resource-oriented people who have good attachment qualities.

Therapist: Not exactly. Resource activation does not mean that the patient's strengths are discussed exclusively the entire time. The patient is in therapy because of his problems, and facilitating a good relationship also means turning to the issues that relate to the patient's suffering. Therefore, the patient's problems are often at the primary focus, and the therapist must make the impression of being able to help the patient; otherwise she loses the basic quality of an attachment person. As Frank (1961) recognized years ago, the therapist must come up with a convincing rationale for the patient's problem(s) and articulate clear ideas about how to tackle the problem(s). Otherwise, the patient will not feel that he is in competent hands. In terms of facilitating patients' need-fulfillment, it is critically important here that the therapist can convince the patient and tell him what he can do and what to expect. Objective truth in the scientific sense is of secondary importance in this situation .

Psychologist: I am not fully satisfied with your response; it sort of rubs me the wrong way. This would mean that all research on specific etiologies and disorder-specific interventions would be in vain. This is not what I had in mind for the model of mental functioning I developed for you in our second dialogue.

Therapy researcher: Perhaps I may interject and mediate here? I believe your views are not really incompatible. Of course, more accurate information and advice improves the patient's chances to change the functional conditions or control parameters of his specific disorder. The experience and behavior that constitute his disorder will be changed only if the functional determinants of this behavior are changed by relevant experiences. Such experiences, however, may result even without scientifically accurate problem definitions.

Let us consider agoraphobia as an example. A therapist might say to a patient: "It is really important that you avoid any situation that might trigger your fear. Every time you experience fear in a situation, your fear will likely re-emerge. If you are unsuccessful in avoiding feared situations until we have determined the true cause of your fear, then your fear will become increasingly stronger." With such an instruction, the patient will most likely never have successful mastery experiences that would change his agoraphobic symptoms, regardless of how resource-oriented the therapist proceeds otherwise.

Alternatively, the therapist might say: "You just need to have courage; never mind your fear. Do what you want and do not let your fear get in the way; it is all a question of your strong will." In this case, we still do not have a scientifically appropriate definition of an agoraphobic problem. It would be more likely, however, that the patient, given his overall improved well-being and confidence, might expose himself to experiences that effectively influence the control parameters of the agoraphobia. This would result in a reduction of his symptoms. Thus, even on the basis of a layman's definition, effective modification experiences can occur.

Therapist: Thanks for this clarification. Of course, this is what I meant. It was certainly not my contention that a therapist needs no problem-specific knowledge. Figure 3.1 is not a complete model of the therapeutic process as I view it. However, the figure explains why successful therapeutic outcome may occur even without scientifically accurate, problem-specific knowledge.

Therapy researcher: At any rate, the functional relations illustrated in Figure 3.1 explain why layman therapists in comparative outcome studies achieve similar or almost equal therapeutic outcomes compared to professionally trained therapists. In the Vanderbilt Study (Strupp & Hadley, 1978) that is quoted time and again, the layman therapists were college professors who were selected on the basis of how popular they were among students. Such persons presumably have the traits that make a good attachment figure. In the way they shape their relationships, they are likely more resource-oriented than deficit-oriented or critical. The professional therapists in these studies were trained psychoanalysts. Psychoanalysts often tend towards deficit-oriented thinking, and—indeed—in his Vanderbilt-Studies, Strupp found that interpretations by the psychoanalytic therapists had often an undertone that could be perceived as critical by patients. Thus, the possibility exists that resource-oriented shaping was performed more competently by the layman therapists than by the professional therapists. If we consider the therapeutic process as depicted in Figure 3.1, it seems quite plausible that laymen therapists might sometimes achieve better results than professional therapists.

Placebo research and the successful outcomes achieved by layman therapists suggest that specific technical knowledge—which professional therapists have certainly to a higher degree than layman therapists—is less important than frequently assumed. One might also express this in a positive way: A relatively large portion of psychotherapeutic effectiveness is attributable to the functional relations illustrated in Figure 3.1. This portion is so large that the incremental effect of therapist-induced, problem-specific interventions may be statistically insignificant in many cases. This would also explain why we frequently do not find statistically significant differences in effectiveness when comparing different forms of therapy.

Therapist: I think there is much to say about this explanation of the "equivalence paradox" (Stiles, Shapiro & Elliott, 1986). Obviously, the lion's share of psychotherapeutic effectiveness is based on factors that are usually neither recorded nor controlled in comparative therapy studies. Whether a successful therapeutic outcome occurs depends on how much the positive feedback process we described previously can be triggered. On the one hand, this depends on the skill of the therapist in terms of utilizing the patient's potential. On the other hand, this process very much depends on patient characteristics, especially on his motivational schemata, and on the therapist's success in establishing a relationship and activating the patient's resources to trigger and maintain the positive feedback process. Especially among patients with strong avoidance schemata, the resource-oriented shaping of the relationship constitutes the most important task for the therapist. If she fails at this, the entire therapy will fail. Later I would like to address in more detail the role of patient's motivational schemata in this process.

Therapy researcher: What we summarized here is typically not considered at all or mentioned only in passing in therapy manuals that are used in comparative treatment studies, such as the NIMH study on depression (Elkin, 1994). Therapy manuals are focused on elaborating a problem definition and on targeting the problem derived from such definitions. If the therapy process is studied later, then it is done mostly for the purpose of examining the extent to which the therapist has stuck to the manual. The factors shown Figure 3.1 are rarely considered. Thus, important factors that might lead to differences in therapeutic outcome remain unacknowledged. Not surprisingly, we often observe greater unexplained variance within treatment groups than differences between treatment conditions.

This was precisely the case in the NIMH study I just cited as an example. Beck's Cognitive therapy and Klerman and Weissman's Interpersonal Therapy did not differ in their effect on the depressive symptoms. However, they were also not much more effective than a placebo condition. In this condition, placebo-medication was given in the context of clinical management, which in fact was a rather intensive form of psychological patient care by the psychiatrist who administered the medication. A positive feedback process, as conceptualized in Figure 3.1, was evidently initiated in all three conditions.

At any rate, the results of this study may hardly qualify as an evidence for the problem-specific effect of cognitive and interpersonal therapy. Nonetheless, the specific features of each therapy interacted with specific patient traits, but in a somewhat different fashion than one might have expected based on the rationales of the two therapies. Beck's cognitive therapy, which targets patients' cognitive distortions, was more effective among patients entering therapy with an already low level of cognitive distortions. Interpersonal therapy was aimed at improving patients' social adaptation, and it worked better among patients who were already better adapted when they began therapy. Thus, specific therapy characteristics interacted with specific patient resources, not deficits. Patients who entered therapy with relevant resources tended to benefit more than others. This indicates that the effects of the therapies were based largely on resource activation. This was true not only in the placebo condition, but also in the two "real" psychotherapy conditions.

Therapist: These results demonstrate something very important to me: Patient's **specific** traits interact with **specific** features of therapeutic interventions. These effects, then, are by no means unspecific. Such resource-targeted effects should be planned and generated with equal care as problem-specific, diagnosis-related interventions. I believe that this offers one of the greatest opportunities for increasing the effectiveness of psychotherapies. Given its actual importance in terms of initiating meaningful improvements, this process is given far too little attention in current theory, therapeutic practice, and training.

As a result of our conversations, I have come to the conclusion that the positive feedback process initiated by resource activation is **one of three main effective components of psychotherapy**. By effective component I mean complex processes and not single factors. One might also call them effective mechanisms. I will use these terms interchangeably. Effective **component** expresses the idea that this is a part of a larger whole. In the psychotherapeutic process, three parts or components may be distinguished, which eventually produce overall outcome. Each process contributes independently to outcome. The three processes are closely intertwined with one another and can be separated only on an analytic level. The analytic separation of these processes is useful for therapeutic practice because it enables therapists to reflect on the process of therapy and her own actions from the perspective of these components. Such reflection may facilitate therapists' capacity to control these important components in a way that maximizes the effectiveness of psychotherapy.

Thus, resource activation refers on the one hand to processes set in motion within the patient. On the other hand, it describes the therapeutic activities required to initiate and stimulate these patient processes. The initiation and continuous stimulation of what I termed resource activation is among the most important tasks for a therapist, regardless of theoretical orientation. Logically, this process comes first, because—as illustrated in Figure 3.1—it lays the groundwork for subsequent interventions. If resource activation is not set in motion at all, then there will be no positive changes in therapy. In my opinion, therapists should be trained for this task much more specifically than they presently are.

Psychologist: Now I am really curious. What are the other two components of therapy?

Therapist: My response will hardly surprise you, because it is based on ideas you elaborated in our second dialogue. However, my three effectiveness components are adaptations of your ideas to the needs of therapeutic practice. Each of the components represents a rather complex process, as we already saw in the case of the first component. In reality, of course, the three processes interact with one another. For simplicity's sake, I will first describe the components separately, and later address their interactions.

The second component is **the destabilization of disorder attractors through problem-specific interventions**. The third is the **reduction of inconsistency in mental functioning by changing motivational attractors**. I will now introduce the second component, which is conceptually linked to the ideas developed in this section.

3.6 The Second Component of Effective Psychotherapy: Destabilizing Disorder Attractors Through Problem-Specific Interventions

According to our second dialogue, mental disorders represent complex neural activation patterns with the characteristics of an attractor. Disorders consist of various perceptual, behavioral, cognitive, emotional, and physiological components that have been linked into one neural group via "reentrant mapping," according to Edelman (1987, 1995). Activation of one component triggers the activation of another one via well ingrained neural connections; positive feedback loops then lead to the full activation of the entire pattern. The different components, therefore, function as control parameters that can activate the attractor.

Let us consider agoraphobia as an example of a disorder attractor. The most important components of this attractor are cognitive ones; specifically, the response expectancy (Kirsch, 1990) that fear will arise (fear of fear), the dreadful anticipation of what will happen next (outcome-consequence-expectancy), and the negative expectation that one will be unable to cope with the fear. Another important component is avoidance behavior, and another one is the experienced feeling of fear. As discussed in our second dialogue, this feeling of fear is stored in emotional memory, which is different from the memory that stores avoidance behavior. Additional components are the physiological components of fear, the facial expression of fear, and the subliminal attention towards instead of away from anxiety stimuli (Williams et al., 1988). Each of these components functions as a control parameter that influences the likelihood of the disorder attractor's activation. Some components are activated in parallel, whereas others are sequentially activated, such that one component leads to the activation of another. Some of these components are experienced consciously, whereas others are activated in the implicit mode of functioning. These implicit components are not part of the subjective disorder experience. They can either be assessed with appropriate tools, such as measures of physiological arousal, or they may be inferred from overt indicators.

Each component of the disorder attractor can also be viewed as an attractor in its own right, with specific control parameters that influence its activation. If I want to influence a component of the agoraphobia disorder attractor—because it functions as a control parameter of the disorder attractor—then I have to first influence the control parameters that influence this particular component. For instance, the component of physiological arousal has control parameters other than, say, response expectancies. Thus, in order to destabilize a disorder attractor effectively, i.e. to disrupt the disorder's inherent dynamic, I have to first know which control parameters/components should be targeted to yield the greatest therapeutic effect. Additionally, I need to understand how these control parameters can best be influenced. Cognitive therapy approaches, for example, provide a good deal of information on how to effectively alter expectations. Therapists can use this knowledge when treating any disorders for which expectations function as important control parameters. There is no need to adopt the entire cognitive theory of the disorder, which may perhaps overemphasize the role of cognitions at the expense of other relevant aspects.

Therapy researcher: I see this very similarly. The role of expectancies or other variables as control parameters can be determined only through disorder-specific research. Theoretical developments in other areas can sometimes suggest new potential control parameters. For instance, recent studies have revealed that a patient's perceived control (Kuhl, 1994) is among the relevant control parameters for agoraphobia (Hartung, 1990; Schulte, Hartung & Wilke, 1996), at least in the context of exposure therapy. Perhaps perceived control is also a control parameter relevant for the treatment of other disorders, but this can only be determined through further research.

Exposure therapy is known to be very effective in about three out of four patients, in terms of destabilizing the agoraphobia disorder attractor. Based on such therapy results, we can conclude that exposure-based interventions effectively influence relevant agoraphobia control parameters. In particular, avoidance behavior as well as expectancy components appear to be altered effectively. However, in order to effectively influence these control parameters, the patient must first be in an action-oriented control mode. Thus, the foundation for exposure must be established first, by bringing the patient into such a control mode. This action-control mode, in turn, has its own specific components and control parameters, which must in turn be known and influenced.

Our goal must be to develop theories for both the basic pathology and treatment of individual disorders, which yield the relevant control parameters for each disorder attractor. Some control parameters may be relevant for many disorders; for instance, this may be the case for the variable action vs. state orientation. Others appear to be very disorder-specific. Eating disorders are a good example of how important it is to steer clear of generalized assumptions.

For the treatment of anorexia, it appears to be essential that control parameters are influenced that directly concern eating. In a study by Herzog, Hartmann and Falk (1996), anorexic patients were initially treated purely psychodynamically in an inpatient setting. No attempts were made to directly influence eating behavior. Only five of twenty patients fulfilled the criterion of satisfactory weight increase in this treatment. In a second phase of the study with twenty more patients, the treatment, procedures were extended. In addition to psychodynamic therapy, the psychodynamically-oriented team began to use interventions developed in behavior therapy, designed specifically to influence eating. The success rate jumped from 25% to 70%. This is very convincing evidence for how targeted, disorder-specific interventions can contribute to the effectiveness of psychotherapy and, in fact, for how useful such interventions can be in achieving satisfactory results.

In the case of bulimia, however, the situation may be different. Good results can be achieved with disorder-specific, cognitive-behavioral interventions that focus directly on modifying eating behavior and its immediate context. Equally good results were achieved in one study, however, with a procedure that exclusively targeted patients' interpersonal relationships. Fairburn and colleagues (1991) showed that bulimia problems and eating behaviors were greatly improved after 16 sessions of interpersonal therapy, which was modeled after Klerman and Weissman's conception. These improvements were as strong as those produced by a cognitive-behavioral therapy that focused predominantly on eating behavior per se. When interpreting these results, it is perhaps important to consider that in the first two sessions the interpersonally treated patients had been given an explicit rationale for why improving interpersonal relations would lead to an improvement of bulimic problems. These results suggest that it is not absolutely necessary to target the eating behavior itself in order to change the bulimia disorder attractor. Apparently, there are other control parameters that can be utilized to influence eating behavior.

We still know very little about the functional relationships that might explain such findings. The examples from the domain of eating disorders demonstrate on the one side, the disorder-specific nature of these issues, but they show us on the other side that components other than diagnostic criteria can be considered control parameters for the disorder. The disorder components themselves appear to be only one part of what can be considered control parameters of a disorder. Therefore, disorder-specific treatment may mean more than targeting exclusively the diagnostic components of a disorder.

Therapist: I see things similarly. Control parameters of a mental disorder may also include motivational attractors or a constellation of motivational attractors. In our first dialogue, for instance, we mentioned Guidano and Liotti (1983), who reported that agoraphobics frequently face a conflict between the desires for protection and for freedom/autonomy. According to our second dialogue, the inconsistency in mental functioning associated with such a conflict might facilitate the development of agoraphobia. Over time, life situations might change, and the disorder attractor might become functionally independent from its original facilitative conditions. Of course, conflicts between motivational attractors might also continue to function as control parameters for the disorder attractor. Naturally, other control parameters may not simply vanish, but, instead, another one may simply be added. All this would have to be considered in treatment; the relevant control parameters would have to be identified and influenced in order for the agoraphobic symptomatology to be destabilized.

In the case we described here, the agoraphobia would also have an intra-psychological function, in addition to its disorder-specific dynamic. This function would also need to be considered in treatment. Additionally, the patient's agoraphobia might have an interpersonal function, given that interpersonal attractors may function as control parameters for mental disorders. This interpersonal control parameter would also require therapeutic intervention, which could be achieved with problem-specific measures, such as couples or family therapy. The point would be to increase the likelihood for destabilization of the disorder attractor as much as possible.

Destabilization of the disorder attractor may be most effective if the attempt is made to influence concurrently as many relevant control parameters as possible. All disorder components according to the DSM or ICD can be considered control parameters. On the other hand, other aspects of mental functioning or the patients' life situations may be relevant parameters. Thus, on the one hand, the therapist must formulate a specific diagnosis, in order to determine which disorder is present and which specific components are manifested in the individual case. On the other hand, the therapist must clarify whether other intra-psychological or interpersonal control parameters ought to be considered. Examples of intra-psychological control parameters might be a state-oriented control mode or a motivational conflict constellation. An example of an interpersonal parameter would be if the disorder plays a functional role within a particular relationship pattern.

We can see that disorder-specific diagnosis and intervention is a complex and challenging task. The complexity is further increased if we take into consideration that comorbidity—the simultaneous existence of several disorders—is the rule rather than the exception. In 69% of cases, there is at least one other applicable diagnosis according to Axis I of the DSM (Sanderson et al., 1990). Personality disorders may further complicate the picture. Sometimes disorders do not occur simultaneously but precede one another. Almost three-quarters of all anxiety patients have experienced a depressive episode sometime prior to their anxiety disorder (Häfner & Veiel, 1986).

In light of this comorbidity, it may not be wise to view each disorder separately, as though the others did not exist. In a comprehensive treatment plan, comorbidity should be acknowledged explicitly; not simply by targeting each disorder by itself with disorder-specific measures. Such additive thinking would not account for the fact that one and the same person is experiencing all of these disorders. This is a topic I will focus on later, when we discuss the third component of psychotherapeutic change.

Overall, I regard this second component of effective psychotherapy, the destabilization of disorder attractors by altering their control parameters, as only one part—albeit an important part—of psychotherapy, even in patients who clearly suffer from a specific disorder. In my view, a therapist who focuses solely on the disorder is virtually always wrong. For a disorder-specific intervention to be effective, it is crucial that the patient is motivated to change and is open for the corrective experiences that the therapist provides. The patient must allow himself to truly have these experiences, or even to create them by his own activity, and this must occur in a context where the patient feels he is moving closer to his own goals. If psychotherapy research has demonstrated anything, then it is that the motivational context in which interventions occur is more important than the interventions themselves. Obviously, equal success can often be achieved with different interventions. Given the number of control parameters that can be targeted, and the number of options for targeting them, this is indeed plausible. However, any treatment will be unsuccessful if the motivational requirements are lacking on the patient's side. This motivational foundation also includes a trusting therapeutic relationship.

Disorder-specific interventions as I have described them here also require the first component—resource activation. Without resource activation, disorder-specific interventions will remain unsuccessful. If no relevant motivational schemata are activated, such that the required interventions are of no particular personal significance, then no therapeutic progress can be expected. This, of course, is based on the model of mental functioning we developed in the second dialogue. Changes cannot be forced against this basic principle of mental functioning, which posits that all psychological activity is oriented towards creating perceptions in accordance with activated, salient goals. Only motivational schemata that already exist in the patient and become activated in therapy may function as the motor of therapeutic change. This is why it is so important to activate the patient's motivational and other resources, by shaping a resource-oriented therapeutic relationship.

3.7   The Therapeutic Functions of Resource Activation

According to our reasoning up to this point, I see five positive therapeutic functions of resource activation:

1. The need-fulfilling effects of resource activation enhance well-being, promote the patient's self-confidence, encourage him in his attempts to solve his problems, and increase the likelihood that his coping efforts succeed.
2. The positive experiences initiated by the therapist facilitate the patient's trust, leading to a positive therapeutic relationship. This solid therapeutic relationship subsequently provides needed support for the patient. I described these two related effects earlier, as the first component of effective psychotherapy.
3. The patient's improved condition, resulting from incongruence reduction and a positive therapeutic relationship, increases his openness for further therapeutic interventions and results in increased willingness for active participation. The patient is more willing to expose himself to new experiences, even when this means forcing himself to overcome reluctance or enduring something uncomfortable.
4. Each time resources such as positive motivational schemata are activated, the neural activation patterns underlying these schemata become more deeply engrained. As these patterns become activated more easily, they are also activated more frequently and thus come to occupy more space within the patient's mental activity. The more mental functioning becomes dominated by positive motivational schemata, the less it will be influenced by avoidance and disorder attractors. The more successful the activation of resources, the more the patient actually acts in accordance with his positive goals and experiences the corresponding positive emotions. In turn, less space remains, so to speak, for problematic experience and behavior. Resource activation and destabilization of disorder attractors play into each other's hands. Destabilization of a disorder attractor creates room for resources; the activation and engraining of resources reduces space for disorders to unfold. Activating resources and simultaneously intervening on specific disorders have synergistic effects. This dual focus increases the likelihood that the patient's mental life will once again be dominated by positive motivational schemata.

Therapy researcher: This is immediately evident in the treatment of depression, where successful resource activation is almost synonymous with desired therapeutic outcome. If the patient once again acts in accordance with his positive goals, we have achieved exactly the result Lewinsohn (1974, 1976) was striving for in his theory of depression. Based on his loss-of-reinforcement hypothesis, Lewinsohn aimed to facilitate patients' ability to engage in positive activities, which the patient enjoyed or found meaningful in previous times. The therapist actively encourages or even pushes the patient to pursue such activities. This is fully consistent with the idea that positive activities strengthen relevant neural pathways, such that over time the activities become more easily activated. It seems to me that Lewinsohn's therapy approach is based primarily on what we called resource activation. It is interesting to note that his therapy appears to be as effective in the treatment of depression as Beck's cognitive therapy (see Grawe, Donati & Bernauer, 1994 pp. 466—477).

Therapist: Let me finish my list; I still owe you the fifth point:

5. Neural activation patterns that are tied to strong negative emotions can be modified or overwritten only when they have been activated. Their modification, therefore, is inevitably linked with the experience of painful emotions. Therapeutically, such problem activation is only fruitful when it leads to clarification or mastery experiences. The probability that the patient has such positive experiences is enhanced when resource activation is used to create a positive context for problem activation. By emphasizing resource activation, the therapist can aid her patient in reframing negative feelings—they are transformed from something uncomfortable and overwhelming to something that must be confronted actively in order to achieve salient goals.

Therapy researcher: This brings to mind the result of a recent study that confirms your point. In a study at the University of Bern, Smith (1997) examined two different types of therapy sessions that involved emotionally painful problem activation. One type of session might be described as fruitful and the other as unfruitful problem activation. In a fruitful problem activation session, patients had positive clarification and/ or mastery experiences, despite the painful emotions they had to endure. Unfruitful sessions were defined by the absence of such positive experiences. One criterion for evaluating the "fruitfulness" of a session was the patients' judgment immediately after each session. Fruitful and unfruitful sessions were significantly different, in that more resource activation occurred in fruitful therapy sessions. Resource activation and other process features were assessed independently from videotapes. The raters were unaware of which type of therapy session they were rating. Thus, resource activation appears to be crucial while problems are actually processed in therapy, not just during the preparation phase.

Resource activation turned out to be particularly crucial when patients had worsened between therapy sessions, when they showed up for the session in a demoralized state. Among therapists who worked predominantly with a problem-oriented focus with such demoralized patients, even worse outcome tended to be observed in the next session.

Therapist: This is consistent with Figure 3.1, which shows that resource activation has a positive effect on well-being via need satisfaction. This positive effect should be stronger among patients with more pronounced current needs. Smith's findings seem to support specifically the relations postulated in the figure. This is a case where psychotherapy research was truly on the ball! In all seriousness—according to our theoretical considerations, things should be as specified in the figure, and I am happy that this assumption, which is quite new to me, has been empirically confirmed so rapidly. After this discussion, I am almost inclined to assume that resource activation is more critical to a good therapeutic outcome than the therapist's problem-specific intervention. Appropriate problem-related interventions may be of crucial significance to alleviating mental disorders. However, one requirement for such interventions is resource activation. Frequently, resource activation alone may suffice for the patient to cope successfully with his disorder.

I think the relationship between a resource-oriented, interpersonal approach and problem-specific interventions can best be demonstrated by adding to our previous Figure

3.1 the second component of effective psychotherapy (Figure 3.2). With this modification, we might speak of a two-component model of the mechanism of psychotherapy.

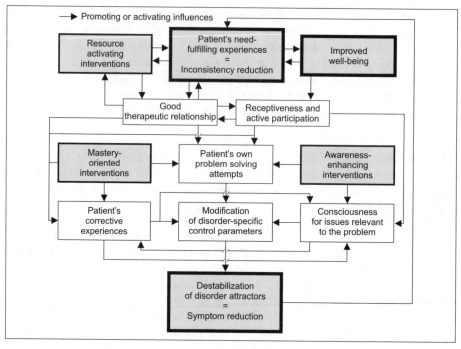

Figure 3.2:
Two-component model of the mechanism of psychotherapy.

The addition of the second component of psychotherapeutic change already makes the model more complete. I believe one might view this figure as a rather realistic depiction of what takes place during a successful behavior therapy. The newer behavior therapy models, such as Schulte's (1996) dual-therapy model, explicitly acknowledge the therapeutic relationship and motivational aspects in addition to disorder-specific interventions. Although resource activation typically receives a little less emphasis than it does here, I still think that behavior therapists like Schulte would agree for the most part with this view of therapeutic events.

I believe that behavior therapies could become even more effective if they conceptualized, acknowledged, and implemented the process of the resource-activating therapeutic relationship in the same way that they considered disorder-specific interventions. In many controlled studies these factors have been relatively neglected. Many behavior therapists seem convinced that they can increase their effectiveness primarily by improving what they already do—focusing on disorder-specific interventions. However I believe that their potential for increased effectiveness is linked to the first and the third of our three components of effective psychotherapy.

This applies at least to therapies targeting disorders that have already been well researched, for which disorder-specific approaches have already been developed. A good example, again, would be agoraphobia. Treatment effectiveness for disorders that are less well studied, on the other hand, might also be enhanced by further differentiating the second component.

Psychologist: Perhaps such concluding thoughts on the potential for psychotherapy effectiveness should be saved for later, when we have addressed all three components. I can imagine which direction you will take with the third component, given that you have not yet mentioned the clarification aspect of psychotherapy. From the first dialogue, I know that this is important to you. I am curious though, how you propose to connect this with your first two components. After all, wasn't it your goal to develop an integrated model of the therapeutic process, in which the three components function as parts of a whole?

Therapist: Indeed, this is my goal, and I suppose it is shared by all three of us. The foundations have been elaborated primarily by the two of you. From my perspective as a therapist, I am only elaborating the consequences of our first two dialogues. I am interested in a model of the therapeutic change process that is useful for my clinical practice. Naturally, I would like to include everything that proved to be important in our first two dialogues. The third component appears to be inevitable in that respect. This component is primarily concerned with the clarifying function of psychotherapy. My understanding of clarification from the first dialogue has been broadened quite a bit in the course of the second dialogue. The third component is indispensable not only for understanding the process of therapeutic clarification, but also for understanding mental disorders in general and the tasks that follow from this for psychotherapy. Without this third component, the image I have of an optimal psychotherapy would remain quite incomplete.

Psychologist: Well then, let's not lose any time. How do you conceptualize this third component?

Therapist: Actually, I suggest that we arrive at a joint conceptualization through our discussions. I know that both of you must regard Figure 3.2 as an incomplete view of the psychotherapeutic process, especially after what you said in the first two dialogues. It would be rather strange for me to introduce a view here that you, in fact, developed earlier.

3.8 The Third Component of Effective Psychotherapy: Inconsistency ReductionThrough Modification of Motivational Schemata

Therapy researcher: Let me begin by stating that I fully endorse the two-component model illustrated in Figure 3.2. It has a high explanatory value for the many established effects of psychotherapy, and it may serve as a good prescriptive model for actual clinical work. However, this model of psychotherapy neglects one area of therapeutic intervention, the effectiveness of which has been documented beyond a doubt. This is why this model fails to be truly exhaustive.

I am referring here to the possibilities offered by clarification-oriented therapies, such as client-centered therapy, the process-experiential approach by Greenberg, Rice and Elliott (1993), and psychodynamic therapies, as far as evidence exists for their effectiveness (see Sloane et al., 1975, for instance). The established symptom-reducing effect of such therapies cannot be explained by interventions targeting components of specific disorder attractors. Nevertheless, relevant control parameters of the disorder attractor are obviously effectively being influenced. This effect may be explained, in part, by the first component of psychotherapeutic change, illustrated in Figure 3.1. Resource activation leads to improvements in well-being, which then facilitates the patient's own attempts at problem-solving. These attempts may lead to mastery experiences and influence the disorder's control parameters.

However, the question is, why should such patient-initiated coping be as effective as intensive expert interventions? Attributing the effect of clarification-oriented therapies entirely to the first component of psychotherapeutic change would automatically render the significance of the second questionable. Within our model, this would be a contradiction.

An alternative explanation would be that these therapies destabilize the disorder attractor by influencing control parameters other than those targeted by symptom-oriented interventions. They destabilize the disorder attractors in a manner different from symptom-centered therapies. Grawe, Donati and Bernauer (1994, pp. 718—731) presented findings from different studies suggesting that different therapies achieve quantitatively similar effects in qualitatively different ways. They influence different patient characteristics. Their effects are achieved not only in a different manner, but also in different persons. The effects of different therapies differ qualitatively from one another if one considers the entire spectrum of possible therapeutic effects and the correlation patterns of changes for different treatment conditions. Establishing such qualitative differences, however, requires rather subtle, sophisticated methods for measurement and analysis. Such differential effects tend to be obscured in mean values of symptomatic improvement.

Clarification-oriented therapies may lead to symptom changes by influencing these other control parameters. However, these parameters may differ among patients. This is why it is difficult to document uniform relations via correlational analyses at the group level of analysis. It also seems entirely possible that a disorder attractor might have control parameters that are unique to only one individual patient. A certain motivational constellation may function as a control parameter for the symptoms of one patient, but not for another. Some patients may have characteristics functioning as control parameters that play an entirely different role in another patient. Such idiosyncratic control parameters, however, cannot be detected with traditional, disorder-specific group-based research methods. That is, if groups of patients with the same DSM/ICD disorder are studied regarding their common features, only those control parameters will be detected that are common to all patients or at least for a sufficiently large segment of the group.

If we take seriously the possibility that idiosyncratic, person-specific control parameters exist—and I see no reason for why they shouldn't—then it might also be possible that disorders can be influenced via these parameters. Naturally, such person-specific interventions would not apply equally at the level of an entire treatment group. I attribute the symptom-reducing effects of clarification-oriented therapies, in part, to their ability to identify and alter these idiosyncratic control parameters.

3.9   Inconsistency Reduction Via Motivational Clarification

Therapist: I completely agree with that. In my opinion, it is important to recognize that the patient's disorder occupies only one part of his mental activity. This part is embedded in the context of his remaining mental activity. The other mental processes might be related in a number of possible ways to disorder-related processes. They might be largely independent, and, thus, not particularly relevant for the disorder. They may also have been triggered by the disorder. They may constitute preconditions for the processes constituting the disorder, in the sense that they are related to the development of the disorder. Further, they may function as current control parameters for the disorder. If such processes play a functional role in sustaining the disorder for most people affected by that particular disorder (e.g., response expectancies among agoraphobics), then they will most likely be identified in disorder-specific research and thus become amenable to targeted interventions.

However, if such processes are idiosyncratic or specific to only one person, then they will inevitably by missed by group-level research. Those parts of mental activity that are not directly controlled by a disorder attractor are influenced primarily by the person's motivational schemata. Therefore, primary candidates for a person's individual disorder control parameters are specific constellations of his or her motivational schemata. This circumstance also explains their individuality. The motivational schemata people form over the course of their lives differ greatly from person to person, and individual constellations of such schemata are even more idiosyncratic.

Motivational schemata determine a person's actions and experiences. They also determine the content of his consciousness. Consciousness represents the most powerful control parameter for people's actions. If a person were consciously aware of the function played by a motivational schema or schema constellation, in terms of creating or sustaining his disorder, then one might expect that this person would consciously change his (schema-related) actions, thereby positively influencing his disorder. At least this might be expected in the context of therapeutic support, where the two processes of psychotherapeutic change we discussed earlier are already present.

However, the patient may be unaware of the function of his motivational schemata for his disorder, or even of the schemata themselves. Their activity may take place in the implicit mode of functioning (sections 2.12-2.15). Thus, motivational schemata can impact the patient's experience and behavior without any conscious representation of these processes. His reaction tendencies may be stored in implicit memory, not in conceptual memory. In that case, he would not be able to consciously access or influence these processes. Such processes may be triggered bottom-up, but they cannot be controlled top-down, as we have seen in our second dialogue.

Thus, one precondition for the controllability of these processes is that they become represented in consciousness. For this to occur, two conditions must be fulfilled simultaneously: First, the processes must be activated in the implicit mode of functioning, and second, the patient's attention must be focused on these activated processes.

Directing attention is also determined by motivational schemata (section 2.41). Only contents that are consistent with already present contents will be accepted into consciousness. In our second dialogue we referred to this process as the inconsistency filter. Avoidance schemata may trigger a systematic redirection of attention, away from processes that have been activated "bottom-up." This resistance to facing what has been avoided may be overcome in two ways: First, through a strong conscious intention to face the situation, even if it is painful; in other words, through a strong intention to want to understand what has thus far appeared incomprehensible. In order for this to happen, appropriate intentional schemata must be activated. Second, overcoming this resistance can be facilitated by another person (a therapist, for instance) who helps to consciously redirect attention to areas it would rather avoid, areas from which implicit processes would normally redirect attention. This difficult process requires a trusting relationship with the helper or therapist.

If both conditions are combined in therapy, there is a good chance that new contents of consciousness will emerge, representing processes that before were implicit and difficult to integrate. Because the old contents of consciousness were controlled by motivational schemata that were incompatible with the newly formed content, this process leads to the accommodation of these former schemata. Therefore, the formation of new conscious content for formerly implicit processes, which had been actively excluded from consciousness, is accompanied by a change in the structure of motivational schemata. Forming new neural connections against the inhibiting influence of already extant connections also impacts the very neural networks from which the inhibiting influence originated. This process would be called reciprocal accommodation by Piaget (1976).

Thus, the formation of new conscious content in the psychotherapeutic clarification process has two consequences:

- It creates the foundation for formerly implicit processes to become consciously controllable. If these processes function as individual control parameters for a disorder attractor, then the patient gains conscious control over them, which has positive implications for the destabilization of the disorder attractor.
- It leads to reciprocal accommodation of motivational schemata that previously exerted an avoidant influence on mental activity. If these motivational schemata previously functioned as control parameters for the disorder attractor, then this parameter is thereby effectively influenced, which contributes to the destabilization of the disorder attractor. At the same time, the diminishing influence of avoidance schemata creates space for the pursuit of intentional schemata, which might lead to better need fulfillment.

3.10   Inconsistency Reduction Via Corrective Experiences

Therapy researcher: Successful therapeutic clarification seems to have a third positive effect. Gaining clarity is in itself a need-fulfilling experience. It satisfies the need for orientation and control. This need is already addressed when the patient gains a new understanding, but it is fulfilled even more potently when the patient experiences that, based on his new awareness, his actions can achieve new effects that are consistent with his goals.

However, as significant as clarification experiences may be for explaining the effects of psychotherapy, it appears to me that they are not the only way to bring about inconsistency reduction. After all, the impact of motivational avoidance schemata is expressed not only in the avoidance of awareness (we might also say, repression), but also in people's other actions. A person might avoid exposure to certain situations because he fears they might somehow violate his needs. He may do this consciously or non-consciously, and he may or may not be aware of his fears. His fears and the related avoidance behavior typically result directly from past experiences, but they may also be acquired vicariously by identification and social learning (modeling). These fears correspond to certain neural activation patterns.

Avoidance behaviors have the effect of perpetuating these fear-related activation patterns because they prevent the overwriting of the patterns with new experiences. Avoidance behavior that corresponds to real contingencies in the environment is of course adaptive. However, persons who have developed avoidance patterns, either through past experiences or vicarious learning, will usually no longer test whether the contingencies of the current life situation still require the avoidance. In fact, if the current life situation offered the potential for positive experiences, then the avoidance would prevent the person from even perceiving such options for happiness, such opportunities for pursuing positive motivational schemata. The intentional schemata become blocked in their development by avoidance schemata. They may only be partially activated and then are immediately inhibited by the activity of an avoidance schema. Because of the dominance of the avoidance schema, no corrective experiences occur. The person does not learn that current life conditions might actually permit more positive life experiences. His positive intentional schemata are no longer translated into action; they are expressed merely in the form of wishes. For the person to make progress in this respect, his intentional schema would have to be activated to such a degree that he can actually have experiences consistent with his goals. Corrective experiences require the activation of an intentional schema beyond the threshold at which the avoidance schema dominated previously.

Thus, each corrective experience is in a sense the result of a risky test. In order for the patient to expose himself to the risk of renewed (psychological) injury, other schemata must be activated simultaneously; schemata for which the test has great importance. Resource activation is important in this respect because it has the potential to activate such positive motivational schemata. Positive corrective experiences occur primarily when positive resources are activated in tandem with problematic activation patterns. I referred earlier to the relevant findings by Smith (1997) (see chapter 3.7). These findings appear plausible as well from the perspective we've taken here.

Corrective experiences do not require conscious awareness. They may also occur in the implicit mode of functioning. The main requirement is that relevant activation patterns are activated. An example for how corrective experiences can occur in the implicit mode of functioning are relationship tests, as described by Sampson and Weiss (1986). After initial positive attachment experiences with the therapist, the patient may perhaps take the risk of revealing more of his innermost wishes. At this stage, however, protection strategies (avoidance schemata) and corresponding concerns are activated, so that his behavior is not fully consistent with his wish. If the therapist responds in line with the patient's concerns, then his avoidance strategies are reinforced. If the therapist responds are in line with the patient's wish, then a corrective experience may occur. In this latter case, the activation pattern linked with the intentional schema of the wish is reinforced differentially, consistent with Edelman's (1987) views of neural group formation. The corresponding neural connections become better engrained, the activation pattern is triggered more easily, or it becomes more easily activated spontaneously. In similar situations in the future, the approach component is now activated more strongly, whereas the avoidance component is activated less strongly. The patient may be more likely to recognize similar situations in the future as opportunities to pursue a wish, and he begins to act more generally in line with his wishes rather than his fears.

Corrective experiences of this implicit kind are based on bottom-up activation of the relevant schemata. As we have seen in our second dialogue, such activations are tied closely to specific perceptual conditions (section 2.13-2.15); they do not generalize easily. However, it would be desirable if the patient could transfer corrective experiences to other people and situations. Such transfer would be facilitated if the patient developed an explicit awareness of the corrective experience process. Roth (1995) relates awareness in general to the formation of new neural connections. Even if this is not true in a strict sense, it still seems likely that awareness facilitates learning and the application of learned material to new situations. Therefore, it is wise for a therapist to not only ensure that she passes a relationship test, so that corrective experiences may occur, but also to ensure that the patient develops an explicit awareness of the entire process.

Thus, the beneficial effect of corrective experiences in therapy is greater to the degree that the patient develops an awareness for what is happening in session or when he is consciously aware of having these corrective experiences.

This appears to happen quite often in therapy. Changes in motivational schemata do not always happen via clarification. That is only the case when both the awareness of the schema itself and of the avoidance tendency were being avoided. With many difficulties, however, the patient is very well aware of what he is avoiding and why. This is true for social phobias, for instance. A blushing phobic knows that he avoids situations in which he feels he might blush. He also knows that he avoids these situations because he experiences blushing as an embarrassment. The personal meaning of embarrassment is typically quite salient for him and may easily be explicated in therapy.

When a therapist uses social skills training, so that the patient increasingly risks exposure to public scrutiny and thereby experiences situations that were previously avoided, then this is often done with the explicit awareness of changing motivational schemata through corrective experiences. Such conscious work on motivational schemata, aimed at strengthening the activity of intentional schemata and weakening avoidance schemata, has been shown to be very effective, according to studies on social skills training of. In fact, social skills training is one of the most effective therapeutic procedures of all (see Grawe, Donati & Bernauer, 1994, pp. 275—308).

Thus, inconsistency reduction of motivational schemata is not synonymous with therapeutic clarification work. Targeted mastery experiences may modify motivational schemata as effectively as control parameters of disorder attractors.

Therefore, our third process of psychotherapeutic effectiveness, "inconsistency reduction through changing motivational schemata" may be facilitated in different ways:
– By inducing clarification experiences through therapeutic clarification work;
– By consciously inducing mastery experiences, which weaken avoidance schemata and strengthen intentional schemata;

– By corrective experiences in the implicit mode of functioning, which weaken unconscious fears and promote need-fulfilling behavior.

We distinguished in our first dialogue between clarification-oriented and mastery-oriented therapies. From the perspective of our three-component model of the mechanism of psychotherapy we could also distinguish therapeutic procedures in terms of the particular points at which they facilitate therapeutic changes. Some therapies attempt to impact disorder-specific control parameters of disorder attractors, whereas others target individual motivational control parameters. This difference corresponds approximately to that between symptom-oriented and conflict-oriented therapies. According to our model, these two possibilities for influencing mental disorders complement each other. They are derived from one and the same model of mental functioning and are not incompatible. According to our model, mental disorders may be reduced more effectively the more their relevant control parameters are changed. Included here are control parameters of the disorder pattern itself and those that have played a role in the disorder's developmental history and have maintained or possibly gained a functional role for maintaining the disorder later in life.

Both clarification and mastery experiences play a crucial role in both processes. The person who has gained some understanding about a control parameter of his disorder has a better chance for successfully influencing his disorder, compared to a person lacking such knowledge. However, the neural activation patterns representing the relevant control parameters of a disorder attractor are replaced with new activation tendencies only through real experiences. Both clarification and mastery experiences may play a role in symptom-centered therapies. For the modification of motivational attractors or schemata as well, an understanding about their control parameters is a positive factor for the targeted induction of mastery experiences, which clear the path for a stronger activation of intentional schemata and thereby lead to better need-fulfillment. Most remarkable here is that the lack of clarity about the control parameter is not simply caused by a deficit in knowledge but is a product of active avoidance. Clarity may be created only through therapeutically guided work on awareness against the active force of avoidance. This resistance to the transformation from the implicit to the conscious mode of functioning is caused by precisely the avoidance schema which is to be changed.

This transformation from the implicit to the conscious mode of functioning has fascinated therapists to such a degree that they often missed the fact that there is only a gradual difference between conscious avoidance and the avoidance of consciousness. Avoidance of consciousness concerns not only external behavior but also one's own cognitions. It is a more pronounced and generalized avoidance than the avoidance of certain situations and behaviors. If a patient not only consciously avoids but also unconsciously represses, then this reflects a particularly pronounced and engrained avoidance pattern. In this case the avoidance cannot be discussed directly with the patient. Instead, one must first create a basis for addressing the avoidance by making this pattern conscious and explicit. If this is achieved, then the avoidance schema is already weakened substantially.

Psychotherapeutic clarification differentiates itself from other methods that change motivational schemata in that the weakening of avoidance schemata is accompanied by a switch in the psychological mode of functioning. The goal, however, is ultimately the same, to attain stronger activation, realization, and development of positive intentional schemata while at the same time restraining the activity of avoidance schemata. From my perspective, it would seem illogical to limit therapeutic work to facilitating new awareness or consciousness. This would be akin to stopping halfway through a task. After all, a person who has recognized that he is avoiding might nevertheless continue to avoid situations and behaviors that would lead to need-fulfilling experiences. Therefore, changing motivational schemata should not end with clarification; the patient may still require the therapist's support to overcome situation-specific avoidance.

Thus, our third process of psychotherapeutic change includes both clarification and successful coping/mastery experiences. Characterizing this process as simply clarification would be insufficient. Clarification may or may not play an important role in this process. To attain enduring changes of motivational schemata, there must be changes in actual situation-specific behavior. Facilitating the required experiences may be the center of this mechanism as much as the facilitation of new insight or consciousness.

On the one hand, the third effective component of psychotherapy—modification of inconsistency-creating motivational schemata—has a purpose in and of itself. It facilitates better need-fulfillment. On the other hand, this process may have a symptom-reducing effect, when it changes motivational schemata that functioned as control parameters of a disorder attractor.

The third effectiveness component of psychotherapy is the most complex of the three, because the issue is essentially one of changing conflict schemata that have op-

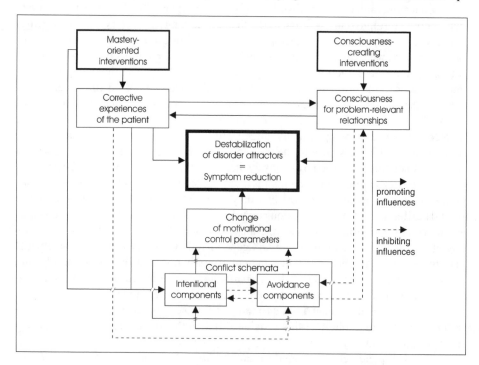

Figure 3.3:
The third component of psychotherapeutic change: Modification of motivational control parameters through mastery-oriented and clarification-oriented interventions.

posing goal components. If we want to illustrate the functional relationships in form of a flow chart, as we have with the first two components, then it is important to consider both promoting/stimulating and inhibiting influences. These influences flow from the avoidance components.

Despite this increasing complexity, I have tried to illustrate the functional relationships of the third component in the form of a flow chart (Figure 3.3).

The focus of the third component of psychotherapeutic change involves the modification of conflict schemata and their functional relations. The lower portion of the figure depicts the conflict schema with its intentional and avoidance components. We can see that the avoidance component is embedded in mental functioning with inhibiting connections, and this is primarily what creates the increased complexity.

If the intentional component of a conflict schema becomes activated, the avoidance component will also become subsequently activated, thus inhibiting the intentional component. Both components hinder each other in their activity, resulting in a discordant tension. When this discordance or internal inconsistency becomes elevated excessively, then mental functioning is no longer controlled by clear motivational structural patterns. This results in fluctuations at a high level of tension, facilitating the development of new structural patterns that are not organized around satisfying needs. We conceptualized mental disorders as such emergent structural patterns.

Three negative influences are associated with the avoidance component of a conflict schema:

- It can prevent the patient from exposing himself to situations that might facilitate corrective experiences.
- It can prevent the patient from developing insight into the functional relationships that might enable him to voluntarily change them.
- It can prevent a change of the motivational control parameters of a disorder attractor. Thus, the avoidance component has a critical role in terms of sustaining the disorder.

The activity of the avoidance component may be inhibited by two influences. First, the patient may force himself to be exposed to situations that have the potential for corrective experiences. The patient can initiate such exposure experiences himself, or they can be facilitated by coping-oriented therapeutic interventions. These experiences would be congruent with the intentional component, which would activate and strengthen it at the expense of the avoidance component.

The second possibility for inhibiting the avoidance component is the creation of awareness for problem-relevant relationships, either through insight-facilitating, clarification-oriented interventions, or through the patient's own efforts. Having gained such insight, the patient can then employ his capacities more consciously, controlling his actions in the service of intentional rather than avoidance components.

Thus, both the patient and therapist can contribute to changing the conflicted motivational constellations that sustain the disorder. Such changes can be achieved via coping-oriented or insight-facilitating/clarification-oriented interventions. If such changes occur, then the disorder attractor will be destabilized.

Additionally—and simultaneously—the disorder attractor may be destabilized through influences that target its specific control parameters. These influences are illustrated in the upper part of Figure 3.3. They were part of the second component and have already been addressed. They have been included here to emphasize that a therapist essentially has four options for problem-focused interventions:

- The therapist can use **coping/mastery-oriented** interventions to impact **disorder-specific control parameters**.
- He or she can use **coping/mastery-oriented** interventions to achieve a change in **motivational constellations**.
- He or she can facilitate **insight** in the patient for relevant **disorder-specific relationships,** which will enable him to voluntarily control his problematic behavior.
- He or she can use clarification-oriented interventions that cause the patient to develop **insight** for the **motivational determinants** of his experience and behavior, which will enable him to act in a reflective and controlled manner in the pursuit of need-fulfillment.

In addition to these four problem-focused interventions there are, of course, the resource-oriented interventions, which are part of the first component of psychotherapeutic change.

3.11 Inconsistency as a Breeding Ground and Control Parameter of Mental Disorders

Psychologist: Prior to explaining the figure, you said that the modification of motivational schemata did not just serve to influence the individual control parameters of disorder attractors, but was also a purpose in itself. I find this intriguing. If the issue in psychotherapy were really only the destabilization of disorder attractors, then Figure 3.3 might imply that the ultimate purpose of therapy is the reduction of particular symptoms. While this may be an important goal, I wonder about its position in a broader context. Why must the patient be relieved of his disorder? Does the disorder prevent him from happiness by causing severe suffering and interfering with the fulfillment of basic needs? In referring to a disorder as an illness, don't we suggest that it prevents him from fulfilling his basic needs? If inability to fulfill his social role is the criterion for the definition of an illness, don't we say the same, only in different words? In fact, social roles, such as parenthood, partnership, work, etc., are nothing other than the socially sanctioned ways for the fulfillment of basic human needs.

Without a doubt, mental illness limits a person's chances for happiness or the fulfillment of his basic needs. According to our second dialogue, this applies in two ways:

- The disorder itself is incongruent with his basic needs, as explicated in your discussion of the first component.
- Non-fulfillment of basic human needs is the breeding ground for mental disorders. Mental disorders emerge from normal mental functioning. A person who is neither hurt nor encumbered in his basic needs will not develop any major mental disorder. Incongruence between experience and basic needs is the breeding ground upon which mental disorders develop as new attractors of mental functioning (see Section 2.51). Such incongruence can develop when mental processes inhibit or interfere with one another, such that order patterns that facilitate need-fulfillment do not emerge. In-

congruence can also result from actual traumatic experiences, as is the case with post traumatic stress disorders.

Therefore, the ultimate goal of psychotherapy is to increase consistency in mental functioning. **Mental functioning is consistent to the extent that actual experiences are congruent with intentional schemata, and to the extent that motivational schemata are concordant with one another**. Mental disorders are both products and producers of incongruence and discordance in mental functioning.

Successful treatment by means of the first two components of psychotherapeutic change may reduce the capacity of the mental disorder to produce inconsistency, without impacting the inconsistency that produced or sustains the disorder. As a scientist, I am not really satisfied with a theory of psychotherapy that merely explains what sustains mental disorders but not how they form. As a basic psychologist I am not just interested in technical solutions to problems. I am also interested in the general phenomenon of mental disorders, particularly their etiology.

Therapist: It is not only you who thinks this way. Why do you think psychoanalysis continues to compete successfully with academic psychology? Psychoanalysis delivers answers to the "why" questions, and this makes it attractive for many therapists. Therapists want to understand mental disorders, including the reasons for their existence and their etiology. You said yourself that the need for orientation and control is basic to all humans. Thus, we as mental health professionals share this need. I want to be able to exert control over mental disorders, both by treating them effectively and by understanding them.

Your conception of mental disorders as disorder-attractors made excellent sense to me. However, acknowledging a disorder's intrinsic dynamic does not mean we should ignore its relations to other aspects of mental functioning. After all, it is quite possible that the conditions that originally facilitated the emergence of the disorder continue to persist. In fact, these conditions might have developed further since the disorder's first emergence, and these changes may not be of a positive kind. This persistent context is important to consider, even if the disorder has over time developed a separate, intrinsic dynamic.

According to our second dialogue, mental disorders develop at a time when inconsistency in mental functioning is increased. Which particular kind of disorder develops is influenced by preexisting, genetically and epigenetically acquired vulnerabilities as well as current situational control parameters. Such vulnerabilities will develop into disorder attractors only under conditions of increased inconsistency.

Internal inconsistencies are produced when motivational schemata are in conflict with one another. This is facilitated to the degree that avoidance schemata inhibit intentional schemata. If certain perceptions, memories, or thoughts trigger the simultaneous activation of intentional and avoidance schemata, then stimulating and inhibiting forces are in simultaneous opposition to one another. Neither the intentional nor the avoidance schema becomes the dominating structural pattern that clearly determines momentary psychological activity. This reciprocal blockade leads to a mounting tension, which we have referred to as discordance. In this scenario, mental functioning remains in a tense, ambiguous, non-orderly state. In this condition of tension, of fluctuations between competing structural patterns, new structural patterns may emerge quite easily. In our second dialogue we assumed that such conditions facilitate the development of disorder attractors. They have the capacity to increase the structural order in such a mental functioning in situations marked by the lack of a clear dominance of consistent motivational attractors. This process explains the differential reinforcement of the new, disorder-related neural group, to use Edelman's (1987) terms.

The inconsistency must be present for a sufficiently long period in order for the new attractor to become established as a distinct neural group. The motivational constellation that produced the discordance initially becomes a part of the new activation pattern. Thus, the disorder attractor can be activated via the activation of this motivational constellation. Indeed, the motivational constellation functions as a control parameter of the disorder attractor.

In our second dialogue we discussed that discordance in mental functioning is avoided by the principle that two incompatible intentions cannot be represented simultaneously in consciousness. Avoidance schemata that are involved in a mental conflict may direct attention away from the processes involved in the conflict, such that the very components of the conflict are no longer represented in consciousness. The processes linked to the conflict thus transpire in the implicit mode of functioning, whereas consciousness is occupied by other contents. The result is a dissociation of processes in the conscious versus implicit modes of functioning. The person's understanding of his experience and behavior is systematically distorted, because he is literally unaware of the true determinants of his mental functioning in these situations. Thus, his conscious mental activity is no longer an effective control parameter for the motivational attractors involved in the conflict. The person is unable to employ conscious reflection and control for resolving his conflict. Even after a disorder attractor has become established, the conflict continues to function as a control parameter for the disorder attractor. The conflict may activate symptoms and lead to further inconsistencies in mental functioning. This, in turn, may facilitate the development of additional disorder attractors. The activation potentials developed in the context of the first disorder attractor then function as constraints in the formation of the next disorder attractor. These processes may help explain the phenomenon of comorbidity, which is so frequently encountered in research and clinical practice.

3.12   Inconsistency and Comorbidity

Therapy researcher: Comorbidity is indeed an important but still neglected topic in psychotherapy research. By and large, therapy research has not recognized the implications of these comorbidity findings, although the topic has become a major focus in psychopathology research (Maser & Cloninger, 1990). Disorder-related theories that are based on various therapeutic approaches remain uninfluenced by this comorbidity research (Cloninger et al., 1990). Accordingly, conceptualizations of therapeutic intervention have not considered this topic explicitly. In this respect, therapy research remains at at the preceding developmental stage, which was concerned with the identification and diagnosis of the various disorders. Not too long ago, patients in therapy studies were rather insufficiently characterized as neurotics or psychosomatics, for example. Justifiably, this was generally viewed as unsatisfactory, because it was often unclear for whom specifically the findings applied (Kiesler, 1966).

Progress in the diagnostic systems has now enabled us to make reasonably reliable and informative diagnoses. Currently, the ICD-10 or DSM-IV are used for this purpose. This has led to a shift in research, such that homogenous groups of patients with the same disorder are now typically being treated. This way, one can at least conclude that results apply to patients with particular, specified disorders.

Therapy research proceeds analogously. Increasingly, treatment procedures are specified and documented in therapy manuals. This makes intuitive sense: The idea is to find specific matches between certain disorders and treatment procedures, which then informs empirically based case conceptualization and treatment planning.

This research strategy, however, is based on a very questionable premise. It is rare that a psychotherapy patient can be diagnosed with only one specific disorder. In reality, most patients suffer from more than one diagnosable disorder (Cloninger et al., 1990). Other patients may not even reach the number of criteria required for a specific diagnosis. They may not receive any diagnosis, despite the fact that they suffer tremendously.

Therefore, the results of therapy studies that focus on diagnostically homogeneous patient groups apply for only a small segment of all patients with that disorder; that is, they apply for patients who have only that particular disorder. It cannot be assumed, for instance, that results applying for patients with pure agoraphobia generalize to those with comorbid depression, personality disorders, or addiction problems. In fact, it is obvious that treatment procedures would have to be adjusted based on these comorbid disorders. Treatment for a depressed agoraphobic is different from that for a non-depressed agoraphobic. Exposure therapy would be indicated for the latter patient, whereas this could not be performed with the first patient, given her depressed state. However, her depression also could not be treated with conventional treatment designed for comorbidity-free depression. For instance, if one followed Lewinsohn's (1974, 1976) recommendations, encouraging the patient to pursue activities that she previously enjoyed, then one would soon reach severe limits imposed by the agoraphobic immobility.

Generally, the question is whether symptoms co-occurring with other symptoms can be conceptualized and treated regardless of their comorbidity context. In this regard, it is important to recall that the precise demarcations between disorder categories are superimposed on the person by the diagnostician, based on patients' easily recognizable surface characteristics. It seems unlikely that the functional relationships in patients' mental activity would be demarcated in a correspondingly neat pattern. This seems all the more unlikely given that such functional relationships are explicitly excluded from disorder definitions.

Even among persons who suffer from several comorbid disorders, we can assume that each disorder attractor has a distinct intrinsic dynamic, which must be taken into account in treatment. However, it seems likely that mono-symptomatic and comorbid disorder attractors have, at least in part, different control parameters that must be addressed in treatment. This would mean that non-comorbid and comorbid disorders must be approached differently. However, therapy research has not yielded clear evidence for this. In fact, despite the issue's obvious significance for therapeutic practice, therapy research has hardly even begun to tackle the problem.

Let me explain the problem of comorbidity with an example. For a change, I will discuss a disorder other than agoraphobia, one that currently has a much lower success rate in treatment than agoraphobia.

Somatoform disorders is a relatively new diagnostic category, introduced as recently as the DSM-III. Somatization refers to the development of somatic symptoms without organic cause and without actual physical evidence. In this sense, they are distinguished from the classical psychosomatic disorders, such as asthma, neurodermatitis, or chronic infectious intestinal diseases. Before they were defined with precision in ICD and DSM, different terms were used for them, which one still encounters today: functional disorders, psycho-physical exhaustion, psycho-vegetative lability, vegetative dystonia, nervous exhaustion syndrome, neurasthenia, somatized depression and many more. In some cases only individual symptoms or syndromes are emphasized, such as globus hystericus, premenstrual syndrome, chronic gastrointestinal diseases, or heart anxiety syndrome. Multiple somatization disorder with at least four individual symptoms in men, and six individual symptoms in women, occurs in 5-11% of the general population (Swartz et al., 1990; Smith, 1991). Women are 5-10 times more frequently affected than men. Thus, this is a quantitatively relevant disorder which also generates huge costs. These patients continue to see physicians over and over again because they are extremely concerned about their health and are frustrated that the doctors continue to confirm that they are physically healthy. They produce increases of 14 times the outpatient and 16 times the inpatient costs, as compared to the general population (Smith, Monson & Ray, 1986). The proportion of patients with somatization disorders in physicians' offices is considerably higher than that in the general population. Weiffenbach et al. (1995) found that 32% of 400 patients in general family practices around the area of the German city of Mainz had a mental or somatoform disorder. Patients with somatization disorder experience tremendous pressure from their suffering and are severely affected in their occupational, family, and social environments.

I am quoting these numbers to show that my example does not refer to a peripheral disorder but to one of the clinically relevant and common disorders. This is a disorder with frequently changing symptoms and a distinct tendency to become chronic. Symptoms typically occur prior to age thirty and persist from then on. Among a sample of patients with somatization disorder, Smith, Monson and Ray (1986) found a mean symptom duration of thirty years. According to studies by Craig et al. (1993) as well as Speckens et al. (1996), spontaneous remissions are particularly rare in somatization disorders.

It is the rule rather than the exception that somatization disorder occurs along with other mental disorders. There is a considerable extent of comorbidity. Table 3.1 lists the frequency with which somatization disorders occur with other disorders. This information is taken from different studies (Brown, Golding & Smith, 1990; Golding, Smith & Kashner, 1991; Rief et al., 1992).

Psychologist: This is a rather great extent of comorbidity. If the numbers in this table are reliable, this would actually mean that, on average, a patient with somatization disorder has almost four additional diagnoses.

I do not know much about therapeutic practice, but such an extent of comorbidity must pose considerable problems for therapy. For instance, how does a therapist know which disorder to target first?

Table 3.1:
Comorbidity of somatization disorders with other mental disorders. The percentages indicate how high a portion of patients with somatization disorders simultaneously have one of the other mental disorders.

Axis I Disorders	Axis II Disorders
Major depression 65%	Personality disorders overall 61%
Dysthymic disorder 30%	Two or more personality disorders 37%
Generalized anxiety disorder 33-54%	Avoidant personality disorder 27%
Panic disorder 20-34%	Paranoid personality disorders 21%
Phobias 31-40%	Compulsive personality disorder 17%
Obsessive-compulsive disorder 16-23%	Schizotypal personality disorder 15%
Alcohol dependency 16-26%	Histrionic personality disorder 11%
Schizophrenia 10-12%	Borderline personality disorder 11%
Drug and medication dependency 5-9%	Dependent personality disorder 9%
Eating disorders 4%	Narcissistic personality disorder 3%
	Schizoid personality disorder 3%

Therapist: This is indeed a great problem in practice; yet, so many formal diagnoses are hardly ever made for one patient. The patient will typically emphasize certain symptoms, and as long as no standardized diagnostic interview is performed, the possibility that he may also meet criteria for other diagnoses is easily missed. However, among patients with somatoform disorders, the results of comorbidity research correspond well to clinical experience. These patients often have all sorts of other disorders so that without a guiding case conceptualization, one could easily flounder.

Therapy researcher: Perhaps later we can discuss in greater detail the problems related to the phenomenon of comorbidity in the context of therapeutic practice. I have selected this example primarily because I want to illustrate some fundamental considerations regarding the development and treatment of mental disorders.

Without a doubt the extent of comorbidity for somatization disorder is quite large. This is why I chose it as an example. However, we do find comorbidity for every mental disorder, not just somatization disorder.

It would be tremendously useful to assemble all extant findings in this area in a "comorbidity matrix." I am thinking of matrix similar to a correlation matrix. Every disorder would be cross-referenced with the others and the percentage of commonality would be listed in the appropriate cell of the matrix. Then, we could see at a glance the frequency with which certain disorders occur along with other ones, and certain patterns might be evident from such a matrix. In such a comorbidity matrix, the conditional probabilities for disorder x, or the existence of y, might be listed in the upper part, and the lower part would contain the reverse conditional probability. For example, it is more likely that a patient with an anxiety disorder suffers additionally from depression rather than the reverse (Cloninger et al., 1990). Such a listing would allow us to ascertain which disorders are a more solitary occurrence and which are more likely to occur in a comorbidity pattern, as does somatization disorder.

Persons with multiple disorders are evidently characterized by psychological conditions that favor the formation of mental disorders. It would seem unwise to ignore such conditions in psychotherapeutic treatment, because they might represent the most important control parameters for the disorders.

What kind of psychological conditions might these be? According to our theoretical considerations, they should be conditions that make it difficult to fulfill basic needs. Indeed there is evidence suggesting that such conditions exist frequently among persons with somatization disorders. A study by Swartz et al. (1987) suggests that 60% of such persons belong to the lowest social strata. Even more have a poor education. They are significantly less frequently married than the average population, and even if they are married, their relationship often falls short of meeting their interpersonal needs. According to a study by Smith, Monson and Ray (1986), 63% of patients with somatization disorder had considerable marital problems, many were unemployed or disabled, and 32% of them had previous suicide attempts.

For these persons, all four basic needs are poorly satisfied. Low education, unemployment, and poverty are obviously detrimental to the needs for control and self-esteem. Both the need for attachment and the need to experience pleasure are evidently not well satisfied among these persons either. The high rate of attempted suicides speaks for itself. All these detrimental conditions have more of a long-term nature and can be changed only with great difficulty.

Also, the high prevalence of personality disorders among these persons speaks for itself. Personality disorders are defined by the **long-term** presence of disturbances in experience and behavior. A person's personality is primarily determined by his motivational schemata. Among those with personality **disorders,** a persistent constellation of motivational schemata has formed that, on the one hand, is excessively focused on avoiding potentially need-fulfilling experiences, and on the other hand, is poorly adjusted to the person's social environment and is directed inflexibly towards fulfilling a very limited range of needs (Young, 1994). Accordingly, adequate satisfaction of basic needs does not occur; otherwise we would not speak of personality **disorders**. Personality disorders are defined by an incongruence between the person's experiences and his actual wishes.

This inconsistency arises largely because a person's motivational schemata are not in agreement with one another. The inconsistency is sustained continuously by a discordance of motivational schemata. This is not a passing discordance created by particular life situations, vanishing again once the situation changes, but these are self-perpetuating inconsistent constellations.

Such lasting inconsistencies in mental function, based in a self-perpetuating constellation of motivational schemata, are an unrelenting breeding ground for the development of mental disorders. As these conditions continue to exist even after the emergence of a disorder attractor, they remain a part of the newly formed activation pattern underlying the phenomenology of the disorder. They remain control parameters for the respective disorder. Yet it is a control parameter that is not a component of the disorder itself, but one that already existed and will continue to exist independently of the disorder. This parameter, however, is bound to the newly developing neural assembly as the disorder emerges. It is an individual control parameter of the disorder, a parameter that is intertwined with the individual schema structure of the affected person.

When we are faced with a patient suffering from multiple comorbid disorders, we can assume the likely presence of a continuous breeding ground for the development of mental disorders. We can also assume that a specific constellation of motivational schemata constitutes one of the individual control parameters for his various disorders.

As a consequence, therapy for such patients should be aimed primarily at changing the inconsistency-creating motivational schemata, which comprise the continuous breeding ground for the development of new mental disorders and the control parameters for already existing ones. This does not mean that therapy should avoid targeting other disorder-specific control parameters. Both approaches together can best help to destabilize the disorder attractors, whereas influencing only disorder-specific control parameters might not suffice in many cases.

Empirical findings on the treatment of somatization disorder tend to agree with this conclusion. Inpatient, disorder-specific, cognitive-behavioral therapy of a large sample of patients with somatization disorder yielded pre-post effect sizes for changing the somatization problem of .40, on average (Rief & Hiller, 1998). Such a low level of effectiveness in cognitive behavioral therapy is remarkable in a negative sense. Behavior therapy usually produces effect sizes of approximately 1.20 or above, across different samples (Grawe, Donati & Bernauer, 1994). In the same meta-analysis, an average effect size of .36 was documented for control groups. Therefore, current interventions that aim to destabilize the disorder attractor "somatization" by targeting directly the components of this disorder attractor have proven to be remarkably ineffective.

Given my previous considerations, this appears plausible. It might be useful to focus treatment for these patients on the individual control parameters of the disorder, that means, above all else, one ought to target the individual constellations of motivational schemata, with the aim of lowering the high inconsistency level that, based on current findings, seems to exist among these patients.

Results of a study by Sachse (1997) suggest that this approach might be more effective than a purely disorder-specific intervention. This study involved patients with ulcerative colitis, not patients with somatization disorders. The treatment was based on the conception of goal-oriented client-centered-therapy (Sachse, 1992, 1996), which we mentioned several times previously. Thus, the treatment plan was not symptom-oriented, but instead focused on changing motivational schemata. This was a directive, clarification-oriented therapy, tailored specifically for the motivational characteristics of this patient group, but not for their physical symptoms.

The outcome of this clarification-oriented procedure reached an average effect size of 1.3 across different measures. The effect size for decreases of psychosomatic symptoms even reached 1.7 (Sachse, 1997). These effect sizes approach those found for cognitive-behavioral interventions in anxiety disorders. For patients with psychosomatic disorders, they are remarkably high.

We cannot directly compare the effect sizes from Rief and Hiller with those from Sachse because of differences in the types of patients treated and in measuring methods. However, the effect sizes reported by Sachse suggest that for some disorders, one can achieve better effects by influencing motivational schemata as individual control parameters, compared to purely disorder-specific treatment. In the study by Sachse, the emphasis in therapy was on the third component of our three-component model of psychotherapeutic change, whereas the emphasis in Rief's study was on the second component. The combined use of both components might lead to even greater success.

3.13   Disorder-Focused Versus Motivation-Focused Interventions

Therapist: It makes sense to me that the mental functioning of patients with a high degree of comorbidity must be characterized by the presence of a mental "breeding ground" that facilitates the development of disorders. Also, it seems reasonable to assume that this breeding ground is based on a constellation of motivational schemata that creates mental inconsistencies. However, wouldn't it be possible for a conflict constellation that has led to the formation of a disorder attractor to ease up again, without the aid of therapy? In fact, conflicts are not purely intra-psychological matters; they are associated with particular life situations. If life situations change in a way that reduces the conflict, or if the person's experiences lead to a strengthening of intentional schemata and a weakening of avoidance schemata, then one might expect lasting reductions of discordance, even without therapeutic interventions. The disorder attractor may persist in such a situation because it might have developed its own intrinsic dynamic, but the original motivational constellation would no longer function as a control parameter. In such cases, motivation-changing therapy might not help much, whereas a therapy that follows our two-component model might very well help.

Conversely, a therapy following the two-component model may not suffice when an increased inconsistency based in motivational conflicts continues to exist, and when the original conflict constellation continues to function as a control parameter for the disorder attractor(s). In that case, the goal would be to facilitate a permanent change in the conflict constellation, by weakening avoidance schemata and strengthening intentional schemata. If avoidance schemata have led to a lack of awareness for the conflict components, then therapeutic clarification as described earlier would also be required.

Therapy researcher: Based on these considerations, signs of increased inconsistency in mental functioning are the most important criterion for deciding whether to pursue a disorder-focused or a motivation-changing therapy. For instance, pronounced comorbidity might signal permanently elevated inconsistency. However, it would be preferable if one could pinpoint the degree of inconsistency directly. I would like to introduce a method for such inconsistency assessment later in the dialogue (section 3.25).

Patients diagnosed with an Axis I disorder should do quite well in a therapy that follows the two-component model, but only as long as they have a low level of mental inconsistency. By contrast, patients with a disorder and an elevated level of inconsistency should benefit more from therapy that utilizes the first and third change components. However, the best form of therapy for these patients would be one that attempts to implement all three components of psychotherapeutic change.

Thus, our change component model suggests some clinically relevant predictions that can be examined empirically. This would also be a chance to examine the accuracy of the assumptions our model is based on. I think it is entirely possible to design a study in which the interaction of these treatment conditions is examined. The components 1 and 2 vs. 1 and 3 vs. 1 and 2 and 3 would be examined in interaction with the variable "inconsistency level." However, such a study would require that the level of mental inconsistency can be measured reliably. I do believe that such assessment would be possible, but I do not want to interrupt our thoughts right now with such methodological considerations.

Therapist: I am extremely curious about the findings of such a study, but do you really think it is possible to separate the three mechanisms in practice? Shouldn't we expect that these processes often occur simultaneously in psychotherapy and that they blend to the point of becoming indistinguishable in their effects?

Psychologist: This is an important question, not only regarding experimental design but also more generally. After all, you emphasized earlier that the change **components** were parts of a whole. I remember you also said that these processes could be separated only on an analytic level. What do you think about this now? How can we conceptualize the interrelationships among these processes?

3.14 The Interplay of the Three Change Components in Therapeutic Practice

Therapist: We have seen already that each of the three processes is in itself complex. This complexity is all the more apparent when we consider the entire therapeutic process, where almost everything is interdependent. Fortunately, this process is not completely elusive. Although its content is complex, it can be disentangled and articulated. In Figure 3.4 I have attempted to do exactly this.

Because of the multitude of important relationships, the figure appears complex at first glance. However, all these interconnections are already known from our previous discussions, and we can easily establish order from a number of perspectives.

Two types of reciprocal influences in mental functioning can be distinguished: activating and inhibiting influences. This is consistent with our view of mental functions as neural activation patterns that have the ability to activate or inhibit each other. The activating, promoting influences are depicted here as solid lines, whereas the inhibiting influences are dashed lines.

First of all, the figure shows our three component processes, "**resource activation**" (top part), "**destabilizing of disorder attractors**" (middle part) and "**changing motivational schemata**" (lower part). In addition, the three main forms of therapeutic interventions—resource activating interventions, coping/mastery-oriented interventions, and insight-facilitating interventions—are highlighted by their gray shading.

Each of these interventions has an immediate effect on the patient as well as several indirect effects, which are conveyed via feedback loops in the mental and therapeutic processes.

The therapist's **resource-activating interventions** lead directly to the patient's need-satisfying experiences; specifically, they address his need for orientation and control, his need for attachment, and his need for self-esteem. In turn, all this enhances well-being, which corresponds to his need for avoiding displeasure. These positive, need-satisfying effects facilitate the patient's receptiveness for therapeutic interventions and

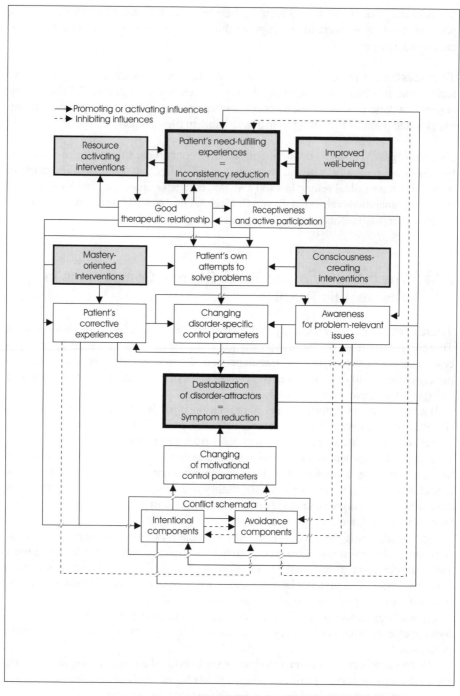

Figure 3.4:
Three-component model of the change mechanism of psychotherapy

promote active participation in therapy. The positive effects of resource-activating interventions are also experienced as validating by the therapist, thereby strengthening a positive therapeutic relationship on both sides.

The patient's positive experiences in therapy and his improved well-being encourage him to become active in independent problem-solving. The success of the patient's own attempts at problem-solving can be nurtured in several ways. For example, the therapist might provide relevant information about the patient's disorder and how best to approach it. Also, initial therapist-induced mastery experiences might be transferred by the patient to real-life situations.

The patient's self-initiated problem-solving attempts may impact relevant control parameters of his disorder(s), which may lead to a destabilization of a disorder attractor and therefore to symptomatic improvement. This is the first component process, which we termed resource activation.

The therapist's resource-activating interventions can also have the side-effect of activating the third component process. Resource activation entails the activation of positive motivational schemata. Frequent activation means that these schemata will become better ingrained and thus gain greater influence on overall psychological activity. This is essentially positive. In the service of activated intentional schemata, the patient may expose himself to experiences that were previously avoided. This, in turn, may lead to real mastery experiences. Additionally, influenced by his intentional schemata, he may be ready to direct awareness towards areas that have previously been avoided. Thereby, he may gain new insight or consciousness for problem-relevant issues. Both of these processes may contribute to the destabilization of disorder attractors and to improved well-being. These positive effects would still be considered part of the resource-activating process.

However, the activation of positive intentions (or the use of coping/mastery-oriented interventions) may simultaneously activate the avoidance component of a conflict schema. This is depicted at the bottom of the figure. Through resource activation, the positive wish component of a conflict schema may be activated, which then activates the avoidance component. In turn, the avoidance component exerts an inhibitory influence on the activity of the partially activated intentional component. Intentional and avoidance activation patterns are activated simultaneously and inhibit one another, leading to an increased conflict tension and, therefore, to an increased level of inconsistency.

If the activated conflict functions as a control parameter for a disorder attractor, then symptoms may intensify when a positive intention is activated. This may also happen if the avoidance component of a conflict schema is activated by mastery-oriented or insight-facilitating interventions. If the conflict is targeted successfully in therapy, then this worsening of symptoms should be temporary and should be followed by lasting improvement. However, if the conflict is ignored because the therapist is not attuned to these processes, then resource-activating, mastery-oriented, and insight-facilitating interventions may lead to a worsening of symptoms. Again, the cause would be the non-deliberate activation of an avoidance component associated with a conflict schema.

Such unintentional activation of avoidance components would also manifest in therapy in ways other than worsening of symptoms. That is, one might expect an increase in resistance to therapeutic interventions. A therapist who monitors this possibility can respond sensitively, either by temporarily reducing the activation of conflict components, or by specifically targeting the conflict itself.

Thus, resource activation does not come without the risk of undesired side-effects. These may be manifest, for instance, in the form of intensified relationship tests. Avoidance strategies may be activated so strongly that the resultant behavior becomes destructive and difficult to manage in therapy.

On the other hand, the activation of avoidance components may be employed in a very systematic fashion. For instance, the patient's awareness could be directed towards the activated avoidance processes, resulting in the formation of new awareness for the conflicted processes. This newly created consciousness may become a powerful control parameter for previously unconscious processes. In turn, this process may lead to a decrease in overall mental inconsistency, to better need-satisfaction, and to the destabilization of the disorder attractor. Thus, we have arrived at the third component process.

This process illustrated in the bottom part of Figure 3.4 refers to the permanent modification of motivational schemata. If a schema is to be changed, it must first be activated. The activity of conflict schemata may be inhibited or weakened both by positive mastery experiences and by facilitation of insight or consciousness for them. This allows the intentional component to gain more influence on psychological activity and to develop further in the course of transactions that are now no longer being avoided. This stronger activity of the intentional component leads directly to better need fulfillment and to positive feedback processes (see process 1).

Activating conflict schemata can also have a positive impact on symptom course. The more the activity of the intentional components outweighs that of the avoidance components, the greater the reduction of conflict tension. Thus, the inconsistency level can be reduced. If the conflict has functioned as a control parameter for a disorder attractor, then this conflict reduction will lead to a reduction in symptoms. In addition, the level of inconsistency is permanently reduced, which makes the development of more disorder attractors less and less likely. From the patient's perspective, the core of this third process is the decreased activity of avoidance schemata and the strengthening of positive intentions. The therapist can promote this by coping/mastery-oriented as well as insight-facilitating interventions.

This change requires that the relevant activation tendencies are in fact activated and exert an influence on mental functioning. Ensuring that this requirement is met is an integral part of all therapeutic interventions, be it resource-activating, mastery-oriented, or insight-facilitating interventions. Often, relevant schemata will be activated on their own; if this is not the case, however, they may need to be activated by targeted interventions.

All the positive therapeutic effects associated with this third process influence in turn the first process of resource activation, enhancing its positive effects of need-fulfillment, symptom-reduction, and enhancement of well-being.

It is entirely possible that this third process of change, along with the first, will achieve such positive effects on symptoms and well-being that the treatment goals are already achieved. This is primarily likely when the changed motivational schemata originally functioned as control parameters of the disorder attractors.

If this is not the case—if symptoms are sustained primarily by control parameters associated with the disorder's intrinsic dynamic—then the first two processes can serve at least to destabilize the disorder attractor. In this case, such destabilization would also represent the most important therapeutic goal.

Even when internal inconsistency is broadly elevated, the combination of the first two processes can lead to a destabilization of disorder attractors and thereby to symptom reduction. However, the discrepancies with their negative impacts on mental functioning will most likely remain, limiting the likelihood of a good therapeutic outcome. Need fulfillment remains compromised and the continued elevated inconsistency entails the risk that more disorders might develop. In addition, the largely unchanged conflicted motivational schemata may influence disorder attractors so strongly that intervening on disorder-specific control parameters alone is insufficient.

Therapy researcher: This might be one of the main reasons explaining that in about 25% of the cases there is no satisfactory therapeutic outcome in otherwise successful disorder-specific therapies, such as exposure therapy with agoraphobic patients. These may be patients for whom motivational conflict constellations function as important symptom-maintaining factors. In these cases, a combination of all three processes or of the first and third processes would be more promising.

In our first dialogue I already mentioned a study by Teusch (1995) that partially confirms this assumption. This is a comparative therapy study of patients with agoraphobia and panic disorders. A clarification-oriented, client-centered therapy, which might be considered a combination of processes 1 and 3, was compared with a procedure that included the addition of exposure therapy, which is commonly used to treat this disorder. Unfortunately, the study did not include any treatment condition implementing only a disorder-specific procedure. Otherwise, one could view this study already as an example of the experimental design I sketched out earlier, in which the goal would be to compare a combination of processes 1 and 3 with a combination of 1 and 2 as well as a combination of 1, 2, and 3.

The results of the study are already interesting as they stand. The combination of processes 1 and 3 proved to be surprisingly successful for this disorder. This suggests that conflicting motivational schemata play a significant role as control parameters of the disorder in a segment of the patients. This confirms findings by Grawe's study (1976), which I also mentioned in our first dialogue. In this study, a clarification-oriented, client-centered therapy was as effective as a symptom-oriented behavior therapy in terms of reducing phobic symptoms. Interestingly, different patients tended to benefit from the two forms of therapy. Given our considerations, this should be expected. In the context of our three-component model the forms of treatment compared by Grawe could be viewed as combinations of 1 and 2 as well as 1 and 3. Overall, the combination of 1 and 2 had a slight advantage, but the combination of 1 and 3 proved to be surprisingly effective.

The study by Teusch confirmed the beneficial effects of processes 1 and 2 in a very similar patient group. As we anticipated, though, the combination of all three processes proved to be the most effective. However, this superior effectiveness was observed only immediately after therapy termination. According to a follow-up evaluation the patients treated with combinations 1 and 3 later demonstrated equally positive effects as those treated with all three components. The reason was that these patients continued to improve, even after termination of treatment. The observation that a combination of processes 1 and 3 may lead to delayed positive effects is confirmed by two more comparative therapy studies that examined clarification-oriented, client-centered therapies. In the studies by Grawe (1976) as well as Grawe, Caspar and Ambühl (1990 b), patients treated with client-centered therapy demonstrated remarkably strong and positive changes for some features, such as internal control expectations and self-image over the follow-up period. It seems logical that a change in motivational schemata may lead to positive effects later on, because the decrease of the avoidance schemata's influence opens the path for the further development of positive motivational schemata, and these positive effects will manifest themselves, in part, only after termination of therapy. The destabilization of disorder attractors through disorder-specific interventions, however, has immediate positive effects, and these positive results are already observable during therapy.

The results reported by Teusch generally confirm our model's prediction that the use of all three therapeutic change components can be more effective than the use of only two. We also ought to note that the studies reviewed here did not consider the moderator variable we deemed crucial in terms of predicting the effectiveness of disorder-specific and motivation-changing interventions. According to our model, therapeutic effectiveness could be enhanced even more if the level and kind of patients' mental inconsistency were integrated explicitly in case conceptualization and treatment planning.

At any rate, our earlier considerations regarding the role of motivational constellations as control parameters of mental disorders are certainly relevant for explaining the symptom-reducing effects of components 1 and 3, which have already been documented in several studies. Apparently, the opportunities to impact mental disorders via such control parameters are greater than the currently dominating cognitive-behavioral models would suggest. These intervention-related findings, in turn, can and should inform basic conceptual models of these mental disorders. The model we explicated here, which regards motivational conflicts as a breeding ground and control parameter of mental disorders, is better suited to explain extant findings than models exclusively focused on disorder-specific control parameters.

Psychologist: I feel that I've now understood the mechanism of psychotherapy, at least more so than before our conversations. Therefore, I am very content with the outcome of our discussions. On the other hand, I am not the one who has to perform therapy.

How do you feel about this, given that you are the one who has to actually work with such a model? Is this model helpful for therapeutic practice?

3.15   The Value of the Component Model for Therapeutic Practice

Therapist: I use the model as a framework for reflecting on my therapeutic practice. It is useful primarily because it helps me conceptualize all the interventions I already use in practice. The model helps me to estimate the relative value of different interventions and to accurately anticipate the effects of therapeutic actions. When desired effects do not occur, the model can also help me figure out the reasons for such failure.

However, the model is too abstract in many ways for my work with individual patients. It tells me that I should activate the patient's resources, but it does not suggest which specific resources should be activated in individual cases. It tells me under which conditions disorder-specific, mastery-oriented interventions make sense, but it says nothing about which specific interventions are helpful in each case. It tells me that under certain circumstances it may be important to pay attention to motivational conflicts, but it does not say any thing about the kinds of conflicts in each particular case.

It would be useful to have a method for formulating case conceptions based on this model. The model does suggest which factors I ought to consider in case conceptualization and therapy planning. After our detailed discussions, the many factors contributing to this model may seem self-evident, but in the context of current psychotherapy, this is by no means the case.

My experience suggests that what we referred to as resource activation is typically implemented inadequately in therapeutic practice. Most therapists either work with components 1 and 2 or 1 and 3, but few attempt to utilize all three components, as the model suggests. The model distinguishes disorder-specific and motivational control parameters and relates these factors to one another. The complementary relationship between these parameters is inconsistent with currently dominating psychotherapeutic theorizing. Many therapists—and especially those from a conflict-theoretical background—may have difficulties conceptualizing mental disorders as disorder attractors with their own intrinsic dynamic. Other therapists may be unaccustomed to the distinction between two modes of mental functioning and to the concepts of discordance and incongruence and their functional role in mental life. Furthermore, the model's emphasis on basic needs—especially on these four particular basic needs—distinguishes it clearly from other therapy models.

Given the current stage of psychotherapeutic theorizing, then, the model's assumptions and its implications for therapeutic practice are by no means self-evident. The fact that these ideas seem plausible or even self-evident to us at this point is a consequence of the foundation we've laid in our first two dialogues.

A necessary further step would be to make the model more tangible by formulating a guide for case conceptualization and treatment planning. Naturally, I would be the one most interested in such a guide, but I do think that articulating this might still be a bit premature. I think that our first two dialogues have implications for explaining psychotherapeutic phenomena beyond those we discussed in our three-component model.

Our first two dialogues suggest that we adopt certain perspectives on mental functioning and psychotherapy. For instance, in our third dialogue we paid scant attention to patients' interpersonal relations, even though our earlier discussion showed that they are very important for need-fulfillment.

I think that the three-component model does not explicate all the possible perspectives suggested by our earlier discussions. Our three-component model focused on principles explaining the mechanisms and effects of psychotherapy. However, as a therapist, I must consider even more factors if I want to explain the multitude of therapeutic phenomena and truly utilize the ideas we developed earlier.

I have thought long and hard about all the perspectives that might help explain the mechanism of psychotherapy. My conclusion is that five dimensions with two perspectives each are needed to classify and relate to each other the multitude of phenomena occurring in psychotherapy. These ideas have yielded a coherent system of psychotherapeutic phenomena. The dimensions and perspectives in this model can be combined in a number of ways. Each combination corresponds to a certain psychotherapeutic phenomenon, which, according to this model, can be viewed as functionally equivalent. The large number of possible perspective combinations corresponds to the multitude of therapeutic phenomena. The system that accounts for the combinations organizes this multitude into a uniform whole, within which one can gain some orientation.

Psychologist: We are quite curious to find out more. Let's hear the details on these intriguing dimensions and perspectives.

Systematizing the Mechanism of Psychotherapy

3.16   Dimensions and Perspectives of Psychotherapy

Therapist: Figure 3.5 provides an overview of the dimensions and perspectives my system of therapy is based upon.

Let me give you a brief description of the dimensions and perspectives listed in the figure and demonstrate to you what can be accomplished with that system.

We are already well acquainted with the **evaluation dimension** and its **problem perspective** and **resource perspective**. We discussed this dimension several times in each of our dialogues. Each part of therapy and mental functioning can be viewed from the problem or the resource perspective. Depending on the perspective one takes, a very different picture results with different therapeutic implications. These views complement rather than contradict each other. They point to different therapeutic options that may be pursued simultaneously or sequentially.

In the **system dimension** I distinguish between an **intra-personal** or intra-psychological versus an **interpersonal** perspective. The intra-personal perspective refers to the patient's mental functioning. When I assume this perspective as a therapist then I reflect on the processes transpiring within the patient. I focus on within-patient processes that I want to activate or inhibit, and I contemplate how I might understand and change the patient's mental functioning. In assuming this perspective, I am thinking in terms of activation tendencies and activation patterns. Which activation patterns are activated; how can I overwrite extant activation tendencies with new experiences? For instance, if I think about a disorder attractor, a motivational schema, incongruence or discordance, then I have taken an intra-psychological perspective. At the same time I am also assuming a problem perspective. Thus, I am pursuing a **combination of perspectives**.

Psychotherapeutic phenomena always correspond to a combination of perspectives. They are positioned simultaneously on all five dimensions. The system allows us to

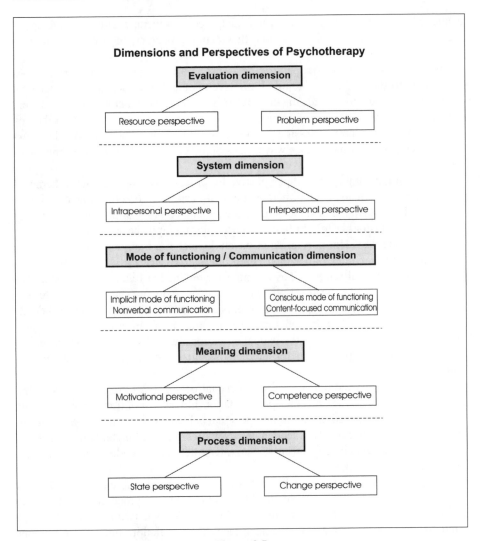

Figure 3.5:
Dimensions and perspectives of psychotherapy.

arrange psychotherapeutic phenomena in a five-dimensional space. Combinations of perspectives are coordinates in this five-dimensional space. I can assign a position to each therapy phenomenon by specifying five corresponding coordinates. In each dimension, two values correspond to the two possible perspectives. According to this system, each psychotherapeutic phenomenon can be defined by a combination of five perspectives.

I will later use examples to illustrate how this model works. For now, let me continue to briefly introduce each of these dimensions and perspectives.

The second perspective within the system dimension is the **interpersonal perspective**. Psychotherapeutic processes are by definition of an interpersonal nature. All therapeutic settings—individual therapy, group therapy, couples therapy, and family therapy—are interpersonal. When thinking about therapeutic processes, the interpersonal perspective is indispensable.

However, the interpersonal perspective—just as the intrapersonal perspective—is not limited to the setting of therapy. Intra-psychological processes and interpersonal relationships occurring outside the therapy are at least of equal therapeutic relevance. I haven't introduced a separate dimension for the distinction between "within therapy sessions vs. outside therapy sessions" to keep the system clear and manageable. However, a therapist must naturally always focus on processes both inside and outside of therapy.

In assuming the interpersonal perspective for processes occurring within therapy, I am focusing specifically on the therapeutic relationship. In directing my attention to events outside of therapy, I am focusing on the patient's relationships with other important persons in his or her life. In family and couples therapy, these two foci overlap.

It is especially evident that the intra-psychological and interpersonal perspectives complement one another rather than being alternatives. Everything that affects the patient's interpersonal relations has meaning for his mental functioning. This makes immediate sense for his need for attachment and self-esteem. The patient's interpersonal relations function as important control parameters for his motivational schemata and, frequently, for disorder attractors. On the other hand, intra-psychological processes have a direct impact on the patient's relationships. His motivational schemata are important control parameters for interpersonal attractors or recurring interpersonal patterns.

Both the intra-psychological and interpersonal perspectives are assumed simultaneously when we consider the concepts of relationship tests or of transference. Certain activation tendencies lead to certain interpersonal behaviors. Certain interpersonal patterns activate certain activation tendencies. New interpersonal patterns overwrite existing activation tendencies, and newly ingrained activation tendencies lead to new interpersonal patterns.

The third dimension concerns the mode of functioning or communication. **Mode of functioning** refers to intra-psychological functioning. Mental processes may transpire in the **implicit** or in the **conscious** mode of functioning. The two processes function simultaneously, not alternatively. We have seen that the relations and transformations between the two modes of functioning of psychological activity are highly relevant for therapy. Thus, a therapist should regularly assume both perspectives on mental functioning.

The communication mode does not refer to intra-psychological events but to the interaction between therapist and patient. In speaking of a **communication mode** I assume the interpersonal perspective; in speaking of the mode of functioning, the intra-psychological perspective. Regarding the communication mode we can make a distinction analogous to the one we made for the intra-psychological mode of functioning. The analog or nonverbal communication mode corresponds to the implicit mode of functioning; the content-related or digital communication aspect corresponds to the conscious mode of functioning.

The **meaning dimension** engenders two perspectives that complement each other; the **motivational** and the **competence** perspective. All processes in mental functioning may be viewed in terms of their function for the individual's goals or needs. The same processes may also be regarded in terms of "being able or not being able to;" that is to say, in terms of the ability or competence aspect.

This distinction also makes sense for interpersonal processes. I can ask whether a problem behavior fulfills a certain function for the system or for individual participants. This would be the motivational aspect. The same processes, however, can also be conceptualized as an inability to behave in a different fashion.

If I am dealing with a couple that continuously argues, I could ask what it is that drives each of the partners to behave in such a way towards the other. However, I could also view their argument as a communication and problem solving deficit. I can interpret the behavior in one way or the other by assuming the motivational or the potential perspective. The meaning that I attribute to the behavior flows from these different assumptions. From the motivational perspective, I would lean towards a clarification-oriented intervention, whereas from the potential perspective, I might favor coping/mastery-oriented interventions.

Behaviorally oriented forms of couples therapy often favor the competence perspective, whereas insight-oriented forms of couples therapy tend to favor the motivational perspective. Evidently, it is possible to destabilize interpersonal attractors both via motivational and via potential control parameters. You reported on a study by Snyder and Wills (1989), in which both forms of intervention were about equally effective in the short term, with slight advantages for the mastery-oriented intervention, but over the long-term, the clarification-oriented intervention clearly proved to be superior (Snyder, Wills & Grady-Fletcher, 1991). Findings like these show that both perspectives yield rich possibilities for intervention, with each having its own merits and disadvantages. As we heard earlier when we discussed the study by Teusch (1995), the same logic applies for the destabilization of disorder attractors.

The second therapeutic process within our three-component model focuses predominantly on the competence perspective. By contrast, the third of these processes focuses primarily on the motivational perspective. Both perspectives yield different but complementary starting points for therapeutic interventions. From the intra-psychological perspective, the goal is the destabilization of disorder attractors and motivational attractors; from the interpersonal perspective, the goal is destabilization of interpersonal attractors. Even if the goal is destabilization of intra-psychological attractors, is may still be indicated to assume the interpersonal perspective because interpersonal relationships may function as control parameters for intra-psychological attractors. The same applies in the reverse.

The **process dimension** can be divided into a **state perspective** and a **change perspective**. The state perspective corresponds to defining a problem, whereas the change perspective corresponds to problem-solving. This resembles the two traditional facets of the problem-solving paradigm. In terms of the therapist's tasks, these two perspectives correspond to the diagnosis and intervention.

The state perspective also entails the process of activating an extant activation tendency. From the therapist's point of view, activating an extant activation tendency may already represent an intervention. The process of change from an intra-psychological perspective means overwriting existing activation tendencies with new experiences. Thus, the current state is being transformed.

Identifying a problematic interpersonal pattern, for instance, would be a combination of interpersonal, problem, and state perspectives. The destabilization of an interpersonal attractor would be a combination of interpersonal, problem, and change perspectives. From the content perspective and the therapist perspective, identifying a problem would correspond to the state perspective. However, from the perspective of the patient's mental functioning, the formation of new awareness would mean changing existing activation tendencies.

Thus, under the process aspect a state is being activated, whereas from a content perspective, a state is being identified. From the content perspective, however, the therapist's activation of a state by the therapist constitutes an intervention. For instance, he or she may activate a resource or identify a problem.

Within the process dimension, then, the two perspectives yield different meanings, depending on whether one focuses on the therapist's work or on the patient's mental functioning. For the therapist's work, the two perspectives of the process dimension can be defined as identifying/defining/diagnosing and intervening. In this context, intervening also includes activating the patient's states. For the patient, the state perspective refers to the activation of extant activation tendencies, whereas the change perspective refers to the transformation of one state into another.

3.17   Applying the System to Individual Therapies

Psychologist: Your examples show that more than one perspective is typically needed to adequately conceptualize a segment of therapy. Your system requires thinking in terms of perspective combinations.

Therapist: This is exactly how this system is meant to work. It should guide you towards a multi-dimensional way of thinking and prevent you from ignoring potentially important perspectives of psychotherapy. By helping the therapist to view a case from all perspectives, the system ensures that all therapeutic possibilities are considered and pursued as indicated.

Therapy researcher: I suspect that the multitude of possible perspective combinations allows us to conceptualize a multitude of therapeutic constellations. However, I'd like to see if we could apply the system to a few concrete examples now, just to evaluate how useful the system really is. If it really covers the majority of effectiveness-related therapy aspects, then the system should be well-suited for practice as well as for research purposes.

Therapist: I can imagine that it would be. This would require the development of a therapeutic process measure based upon this system. That's a task I find quite intriguing. However, what's most important to me is that therapists and those who train them learn to think in perspectives. Not everybody needs to be an expert in all the interventions resulting from the perspective combinations. However, every therapist should be able to assume all perspectives and to apply them to particular cases. I think that such a system can also be helpful as a framework for therapy training and supervision. The system could be useful for reflecting upon sessions that have already occurred and for planning therapeutic procedures in the future.

The process of reflecting on a therapeutic event may begin at any point in the system that seems relevant to the problem at hand. From this starting point, one may sequentially assume all other perspectives. The combination of perspectives is attained automatically because the relevant phenomena can be located on all five dimensions. Assuming all perspectives counteracts one's natural tendency to ignore certain potentially relevant aspects. By taking one particular perspective, it's possible to mentally combine that one with all other perspectives. This process will typically suggest certain combinations that are especially relevant for one's goal or question. Once this combination has been identified, one can elaborate on it and adapt it for the particular therapeutic goal.

I would like to illustrate this principle with a clinical example. Let us imagine a therapist performing exposure therapy with an agoraphobic patient. They have been together in a crowded place downtown for a while now, which the patient has avoided for years. The therapist intends to reduce the anxiety symptoms with an empirically supported intervention, exposure therapy.

Let us first consider how well this situation is suited to facilitate the therapist's primary goal: the destabilization of the agoraphobic disorder attractor. This leads us to focus on the second mechanism of our component model of psychotherapeutic change. According to our system, we assume the problem perspective. In this situation, an intra-psychological disorder attractor is activated in the conscious mode of functioning. This conscious activation is an advantage because it facilitates the ingraining of new activation tendencies and promotes generalization to other situations. In the conscious mode of functioning, the patient is able to employ his conscious planning and control capacities. Consciousness is the most powerful control parameter for voluntary behavior. It enables the therapist and the patient to communicate openly about the important aspects of the situation.

The patient experiences her fears at full intensity and is completely aware of them. In the state dimension, a problem-related activation pattern is fully activated. This activation is necessary in order for the activation pattern to be overwritten with new experiences. From the perspective of therapeutic work, the activation of the problematic activation patterns is considered the first part of an intervention.

The competence perspective is primarily relevant for the transformation of the activated state. Previous activation tendencies are to be overwritten by mastery experiences. The exposure is intended to facilitate the formation of new activation patterns. Thereby, new activation tendencies are to be ingrained that exert an inhibiting influence on tendencies related to the disorder—the avoidance, the fear, the negative expectations, and the concomitant cognitions.

The patient's active enduring in the fear-triggering situation should change many disorder-specific control parameters. In fact, if the patient stays in the situation long enough, new activation patterns may be activated and ingrained. The exposure inhibits and weakens the previous avoidance pattern. The cognitions "I will be able to do it, I can overcome my fear, I will not give in" accompany the exposure and come to replace previous catastrophizing thoughts. The reduction of fear weakens old thoughts and promotes positive response and self-efficacy expectations. These are all positive effects that are related to the competence aspect. After this exposure, the patient has gained confidence to perform actions she previously couldn't pursue.

The more often these new activation patterns are activated, the better they are ingrained and is capable of inhibiting old ones. In fact, it is necessary that the exposure is repeated as much as possible. The patient is to enter each new exposure with somewhat changed activation tendencies until the new ones are eventually so well ingrained that they are much more easily activated than the old tendencies.

These considerations demonstrate that this therapeutic intervention/situation has a high potential to be effective.

What I described here with our five-dimensional system and the terminology of our model corresponds to the second component of the change model we discussed earlier. This model and the system are compatible and complement one another. By using both in my clinical case conceptualization, I minimize the probability of ignoring important aspects of therapy.

However, both the change component model and the system involving the combinations of perspectives suggest that I consider even more questions, mainly regarding the resource perspective.

If I look at the same situation from the resource perspective, the question arises which interpersonal resources are activated. An interpersonal resource, for instance, might be activated if the patient's spouse supports her during the exposure, as would be the case in a so-called "spouse-aided exposure therapy." But this is not the case in our example.

The therapeutic relationship could also be considered an interpersonal resource. The interpersonal processes between the therapist and the patient may be viewed from the resource perspective. Does this relationship show the characteristics of a good therapeutic relationship? The content of the therapeutic discourse as well as the nonverbal communication between therapist and patient should be examined accordingly. As mentioned in our second dialogue, nonverbal behavior influences primarily the patient's implicit mode of functioning.

I might notice that the nonverbal exchange between patient and therapist lacks the qualities of a positive attachment relationship. While the therapist provides helpful instructions at the content level, she may not be fully devoted nonverbally, perhaps with too little focus in her facial expression on the patient's experience at the moment. Perhaps the therapist is not responding to the patient's searching looks and demonstrates a lack of engagement in the way she relates to him overall. Perhaps the therapist does not convey a sense of confidence and appears insecure at times. Thus, the patient has little perceived support and does not feel safe and secure. At the level of the implicit mode of functioning, the patient has perceptions that are incongruent with her activated need for attachment.

In this situation, the patient may go along on a superficial level, but the exposure may simply reflect compliance with the therapist's instructions rather than being self-initiated or intrinsically motivated. Motivational resources may neither be activated nor does the therapist make any attempts in this direction. The patient may misunderstand some of the instructions or implement them in a way other than what was intended. The therapist may expect more responsibility and control from the patient than she is able to manifest in this situation. The therapist has little understanding for the patient's behavior and request for help. He regards the patient's signs of dependency not as a motivational and potential resource for coping but as a problem behavior that should be ignored.

Overall, the resource perspective may lead to the conclusion that the patient's problematic activation patterns are strongly activated, whereas positive motivational schemata are not activated simultaneously. Also, the therapist appears to make no efforts to activate motivational schemata with suitable measures. He has obviously neglected this while preparing the patient for the exposure therapy. According to the study by Smith (1997) you mentioned earlier, this would be an example of an "unfruitful problem activation." While an important problem of the patient is activated, the therapist has done little to set the mechanism of resource activation in motion. Thus, the patient is unable to overwrite her problematic activation patterns with positive mastery experiences. Therefore, it is very unlikely that a successful destabilization of the disorder attractor will take place, even though the requirements for the second mechanism actually appeared to be fulfilled.

Our example demonstrates how even appropriate disorder-specific treatment may fail. From the perspective of our system, the reason for this failure is that the first component of psychotherapeutic change, which is the most important basis for therapeutic success, has not been pursued successfully. As soon as we assume a resource perspective, several weaknesses in the intervention are revealed.

Such therapeutic failures can be avoided if a therapist self-critically considers the various perspectives or perspective-combinations. The system suggests points at which the therapist can change the therapy's direction. In our example, such points would primarily concern the neglected resource-oriented shaping of the therapeutic relationship.

Psychologist: However, the therapist might also have favored the competence perspective at the expense of the resource as well as the problem perspective. Conceivably, motivational constellations function as control parameters of the patient's symptoms. The therapist would miss this if he neglected to consider the symptoms from the motivational perspective. Such failure to employ our model's third effectiveness component might also explain the unsatisfactory outcome of the exposure therapy.

Therapist: Indeed, I had not considered this aspect. Such motivational problems would require a different approach. The therapist would have to identify problem-relevant motivational schemata and try to activate them. He would have to facilitate the activation of patterns that inhibit previous activation patterns and ingrain new neural connections. Possible interventions would be confrontation, fostering new insight, or consciousness by directing attention, interpretations, deepening the processing level of patient's self-experience, etc., or even influencing motivational schemata directly, for instance, by social skills training.

3.18 Applying the System to Phenomena in Psychotherapy

Therapy researcher: I now understand better what you mean by "perspective combinations." Actually, it seems quite natural to think in terms of combinations of perspectives. Most of the terms we use to communicate about psychotherapeutic phenomena already imply a combination of perspectives, even though this is not typically acknowledged explicitly. For instance, a transference interpretation could be regarded as a content-related (communication dimension) intervention (change dimension) regarding an interpersonal (system dimension) problem (evaluation dimension) that is activated in the implicit mode of functioning (mode of functioning and state perspective). The process of transference itself includes both an intra-psychological and an interpersonal aspect.

Indeed, it should be possible to categorize the terms of different therapy schools with this system. This would remove them from their school-specific context without losing their functional significance for the mechanism of psychotherapy.

Therapist: Yes, this is exactly my idea. We can use this system to discuss psychotherapeutic phenomena without having to adopt entire school-specific realms of ideas. I believe that each therapy school emphasizes certain phenomena of psychotherapy at the expense of others. Such exclusion of some phenomena is not necessary. Our system allows us to focus on all possible therapeutic conceptualizations without excluding any. This enables therapists to consider the whole range of therapeutic possibilities in their work, applying ideas developed within the various therapy schools without having to adopt their entire way of thinking.

We have already seen that the system is compatible with the previously elaborated process model of psychotherapy. It is also compatible with the view of mental functioning that we developed in our second round of discussions. For instance, in the case example we just reviewed, I have adopted a number of the previously developed ideas, and the change component model is based on the same foundations as well. If we combine the view of mental functioning developed in our second dialogue, the change component model, and this system, we possess a theoretical foundation of psycho-

| | | Intrapersonal Perspective | | | | Interpersonal Perspective | | | |
| | | Motivational | | Competence | | Motivational | | Competence | |
		State	Change	State	Change	State	Change	State	Change
Problem perspective	Implicit mode of functioning	1	2	5	6	9	10	13	14
	Conscious mode of functioning	3	4	7	8	11	12	15	16
Resource perspective	Implicit mode of functioning	17	18	21	22	25	26	29	30
	Conscious mode of functioning	19	20	23	24	27	28	31	32

Figure 3.6:
System of combinations of perspectives in the form of a 32-field matrix.

therapy, the range of which transcends the individual therapy schools. Furthermore, this foundation is more consistent with current psychotherapy and psychology research, given that it was derived from research described in our first two dialogues. I believe that this provides us with a theoretical foundation for a psychotherapy that is not oriented towards any particular therapy school.

Therapy researcher: I would like to try this out. We should be able to capture the processes referred to by different therapy schools with the system's new terminology. This should enable us to detach therapeutic processes from particular therapy school terminology and integrate them into a uniform view. We want to integrate the processes emphasized by the different therapy schools rather than their ideas or terminology.

Therapist: Yes, this should be possible. Let's give it a try using at least a few examples. We can elaborate $2^5 = 32$ combinations of perspectives based on our system with terms that are currently used in psychotherapy, and we can then work the different topics into our theoretical explanatory framework.

The system can be presented in the form of a matrix having 32 fields with each field corresponding to a combination of perspectives. In Figure 3.6 I have gone ahead and presented such a 32-field matrix leaving the individual fields empty.

One could now fill these fields with content, perhaps with an everyday language description of therapeutic events for instance. However, we could also use the terminology of the various therapy schools for describing these events.

These same events could also be described using the terminology we developed here. Thus, we can express the same issues in different terms. The terms we developed in the course of our discussions are suited to describe the phenomena in all 32 fields. The language used by the individual therapy schools in each case would only be suited for some of the fields. One advantage of the terminology we developed is that it can be used to communicate across the entire field of change-relevant psychotherapeutic aspects.

Psychologist: Have you already given this a try? I imagine this to be a tough job. That would almost be a dictionary! The individual terms of the various therapy schools would be distributed across the entire fields and next to them would be the translation, so to speak, into the terminology we developed.

Therapist: I do believe this would be manageable. But for our dialogue such a lexical endeavor would certainly be rather tiring, and this is something I would like to spare us. However, I could at least give you an example of how I imagine one sub-area of the matrix would appear. For instance, we could divide the entire matrix into four equal parts with eight fields each. This yields four sub-matrices; namely, one each for the:
– intrapsychological problem perspective,
– interpersonal problem perspective,
– intrapsychological resource perspective,
– interpersonal resource perspective.

I could go ahead and follow the system field by field and try to fill the fields with topics, at least for one of these sub-matrices. I think the matrix for the intra-psychological problem perspective would be the most productive.

3.19   Psychotherapy From the Intrapersonal Perspective

For the intra-psychological problem perspective in table 3.2 I have filled in these eight fields with commonly used terms from psychotherapy. I will briefly explain these terms and delineate how they can be viewed from the theoretical position we have developed here.

Field 1

Let us first consider field one. We are looking at processes occurring within the person in the **implicit mode of functioning**, and we view them under the **motivational perspective**. Here, we find mostly concepts from psychoanalysis. What is referred to as **unconscious wishes** and **fears** by psychodynamic conceptions corresponds in our model to the goal components of motivational schemata that influence psychological activity in the implicit mode of functioning. The goal components have an influence only when they are activated bottom-up. They cannot be activated or controlled top-down by consciousness.

The activation tendencies representing the motivational schemata need not be concordant with one another. Intentional and avoidance schemata may inhibit each other. Depending on the strength or ingraining of the activation tendency of the avoidance schemata, the need satisfaction through the intentional schemata may be blocked. The result is an incongruence between experiences and needs as well as an inconsistency tension. This situation corresponds to what the psychodynamic model terms **unconscious conflict**.

Motivational schemata whose activity has so far not been at the center of conscious attention are active in the implicit mode of functioning. The activation tendencies underlying them are stored in implicit memory. They are not part of conceptual memory and, therefore, will not become contents of the consciousness as long as they do not become the object of conscious attention.

The fundamental principle of mental functioning is a striving for consistency. Whatever is not concordant with the contents of consciousness is not allowed to enter into consciousness because this would create discordance. Just like everything else in mental functioning, the content of consciousness is determined by motivational schemata. Attention is being directed according to the fundamental principle of mental functioning, which seeks to avoid incongruence and discordance. Whatever is inconsistent with the content of consciousness is also inconsistent with the motivational schemata determining this content. In the service of these schemata, attention is directed away from inconsistency-creating perceptions, memories, and thoughts. Attention does not focus on discordant motivational schemata in the implicit mode of functioning. Instead, psychological activity is actively concentrated on avoiding conscious awareness of such processes.

This motivated activity aimed at inconsistency avoidance corresponds to what Freud termed **repression**. The formation of new consciousness for processes in the implicit mode of functioning corresponds to the ingraining of new neural connections. Repression is the active inhibition of activation patterns that might lead to the ingraining of new activation patterns accompanied by awareness. If at all, such new activation ten-

Table 3.2:

Eight-field matrix containing the combinations of perspectives for the intrapersonal perspective. The individual fields contain the phenomena and the terms used by the various therapeutic approaches.

		State	**Intervention/change**
		1	**2**
Motivational perspective	Implicit Mode of Functioning	- unconscious wishes and fears - unconscious conflicts - repression - resistance - defense mechanisms - symptom substitution - self-ideal discrepancy - inferiority complex	- corrective emotional experience - uncovering therapy - insight - working through - confrontation - interpretation - clarification - focusing - process-experience approach - self-exploration
		3	**4**
	Conscious Mode of Functioning	- reinforcement - avoidance behavior - conscious fears - expectations - irrational ideas - dysfunctional cognitions - volition	- token economies - reinforcement schedules - Socratic dialogue - reality tests - reframing - paradoxical interventions - role playing - self-commitment - therapy preparation
		5	**6**
Competence perspective	Implicit Mode of Functioning	- attention disorders - processing styles - deficit in coping mechanisms - deficit in emotion regulation - encoding and decoding abilities for expression - stress reactions - conditioned body reactions - attachment style	- deficit-specific training procedures - relaxation and meditation procedures - biofeedback
		7	**8**
	Conscious Mode of Functioning	- social inhibitions - conscious deficits such as inability for self-control with bulimia and gambling, etc. - inability to control response behavior such as in sleeping disorders, anxiety and depression	- assertiveness training - disorder-specific interventions such as exposure therapy, self-control experiences, stimulus control

dencies can only be ingrained against the **resistance of repression**. This would require that attention, directed by another sufficiently strong, activated intentional schema, focuses on the inconsistency-creating processes.

Developing consciousness for previously unconscious processes entails establishing and ingraining new neural connections. If such activating and ingraining of new activation patterns is actively inhibited by extant avoidance activation patterns, we speak of repression. If attention is directed towards incongruence-creating or discordance-creating contents, negative emotions arise. Therefore, working on new consciousness for perceptions that have previously been avoided typically activates negative emotions as well as avoidance strategies and creates a **resistance** against the process of becoming conscious.

A pre-attentive pre-selection determines the direction in which conscious attention is directed. Pre-selection occurs in the service of motivational schemata. It occurs in the implicit mode of functioning. For recurrent events, automated processes form over time in the implicit mode of functioning. Such processes are strongly ingrained activation tendencies that have the function of protecting the individual from inconsistencies. We have referred to these automated protection mechanisms as the inconsistency filter. We can also call them consistency safeguards. These mechanisms serve to protect the individual from overly strong inconsistencies that may affect his ability to function. Thus, they have a positive internal adaptation function for the individual. Repression would be such a consistency-ensuring mechanism.

Such **consistency-ensuring mechanisms** may be viewed as a form of intrapsychological **coping**. They have a largely positive function for the individual as long as they do not jeopardize external adaptation; that is, as long as they do not undermine the effective pursuit of personal goals. If they do so, they may themselves become a problem. An awareness may be formed even for these automatically occurring consistency-securing mechanisms by directing attention towards them in the moment when they are activated. From a therapeutic perspective, this is only necessary when such a safety mechanism impacts those experiences and behaviors that prevent the individual from relating to his environment in a way that satisfies his needs. The term **defense mechanisms** as used in psychoanalysis refers to such processes but conceptualizes them differently.

If the individual's consistency safeguards are no longer adequate for preventing too high of a degree in inconsistency, mental activity moves into a state of instability which favors the formation of mental disorders as a new structural pattern.

We have already discussed the emergence of mental disorders as a new pattern of mental activity, and it need not be repeated here. Our ideas differ from those of psychoanalysis and lead to different therapeutic consequences. The differences between our view and the psychoanalytic view may be demonstrated with the help of the psychoanalytic concept of **symptom substitution**. According to our model, there is no reason to assume such an idea. In viewing mental disorders as disorder attractors, the disorders may very well be reduced such that their intrinsic dynamic is disrupted by exerting a direct influence on the disorder's components. This destabilizes the disorder attractor, and there is no connection between this destabilization and the emergence of other possible disorders.

Therapy researcher: From an empirical point of view there is no reason to assume such symptom substitution. A great many case histories have demonstrated that improvements achieved by symptom-oriented interventions are usually of lasting duration, and it would actually be akin to denial to continue holding on to the idea of symptom substitution.

Therapist: An entirely different story concerns the well-substantiated fact of comorbidity. One and the same person may develop several disorders over the course of his life, oftentimes even within a relatively short time frame. This can be explained, according to our view, by an increased inconsistency level that functions as a lasting extant breeding ground for mental disorders. However, destabilizing a disorder attractor tends to reduce inconsistency in mental functioning. Following a successful disorder-specific treatment, the likelihood for other disorders to develop is lowered rather than raised.

According to our view, lasting mental conflicts can be one source among many contributing to the emergence of mental disorders. Consistently conflicted motivational schemata may interact with certain life situations to favor the production of new structural patterns in the form of mental disorders. A therapy that successfully modifies this conflicted motivational constellation, therefore, reduces the likelihood that more mental disorders will appear.

The topics listed in Field 1 show that problematic intrapsychological states and processes for which the patient lacks awareness were conceptualized in the most differentiated fashion by psychoanalysis. However, we also find relevant concepts in other types of therapies, such as Rogers' self-ideal discrepancy, Adler's inferiority complex as well as Berne's life-script, which are all constructs that view intra-psychological problems from a motivational perspective. According to these views, therapy consists primarily of creating a consciousness for the processes described by this terminology, for instance, through a process of self-exploration, as Rogers does.

In therapy approaches that do not distinguish between conscious and unconscious processes, it is sometimes difficult to classify constructs as implicit versus conscious. This is true, for instance, for Ellis' and Beck's irrational beliefs or dysfunctional cognitions. Based on our considerations, such constructs typically influence mental activity in the implicit mode of functioning; however, they are defined in such behavioral terms that it is easy to link them to the conscious mode of functioning.

Field 2

Let us now turn to Field 2. It contains the therapeutic interventions that produce changes in the states or processes listed in Field 1. Alexander's (1946) term **corrective emotional experience** fits nicely in this context. Motivational schemata can change when people's perceptions are incongruent with their schemata. The activation patterns related to such perceptions are incongruent with extant activation tendencies. When incongruent perceptions are activated with sufficient strength, they overwrite extant activation tendencies. New neural connections form, and new activation tendencies are ingrained. This is the process Piaget (1976) termed accommodation of schemata.

If this process involves important motivational schemata, then the corrective experiences are accompanied inevitably by strong negative emotions. Indeed, such incongruities are typically accompanied by emotions (section 2.21). An experience that is incongruent with an avoidance schema may, however, simultaneously be consistent with previously unfulfilled wishes; that is, these perceptions may be congruent with previously unfulfilled goal components of positive motivational schemata and, therefore, be accompanied by positive emotions. Thus, corrective experiences are frequently associated with mixed feelings. Early in the process, negative emotions dominate, but with increasing deactivation of the avoidance schema, positive emotions eventually prevail.

Corrective emotional experiences may occur in the implicit mode of functioning, as is the case in relationship tests. However, such experiences are often accompanied by increased attention. This leads to a transformation from the implicit to the conscious mode of functioning. New consciousness emerges for the processes determined by the motivational schemata. This produces changed schemata. This process of consciousness formation is often referred to as **uncovering therapy**. This term does not fit very well with our view. According to our model of mental functioning, the process of consciousness formation creates something new rather than uncover something that already exists. Psychoanalytic terminology suggests that therapy lifts a cover from the unconscious that was created by repression, thereby rendering this content accessible through **insight**. Our model maintains that new neural connections are activated and ingrained that change motivational schemata and are linked to the quality of consciousness.

The psychoanalytical term of "**working through**" is a better description. In this process, more and more experiences are assimilated to newly forming contents in conceptual memory. The new schema is being differentiated. This differentiation is a process of ingraining of new neural connections. The schema may be activated by all kinds of perceptions, thoughts, and memories. Over time, the schema may be activated with increasing ease and via top-down processes. That is, the schema can eventually be activated voluntarily in the conscious mode of functioning. As mentioned earlier, establishing and ingraining new neural connections is accompanied by negative or mixed feelings. It does not happen automatically but requires active effort. Thus, the term of "work" really applies quite well.

How can attention be directed towards processes determined by motivational schemata in the implicit mode of functioning? One possibility is that the therapist confronts the patient with aspects of his behavior and experiences that are determined by these schemata in the moment. **Confrontation** is one of many possibilities for directing of attention in this way.

Another tool for directing attention is **interpretation**, which can be used to guide the patient's attention towards aspects of his experience and behavior for which he had previously not formed self-awareness. However, a requirement for the transformation from the implicit to the conscious mode is that the processes the interpretation refers to are activated at that particular moment in the implicit mode of functioning. Interpreting something that the patient reports at that moment—something that is already part of conceptual memory—is directing attention to contents not to process. New cognitive connections may then perhaps be formed among extant content, and the patient may use these new connections later for new thoughts evolving in therapy. However, this does not change motivational schemata. A change of motivational schemata would require the process of activating these schemata.

Content-oriented interpretations may aid the patient to expose himself later on to corrective experiences; however, such interpretations do function as corrective experience in themselves. Unfortunately, such interpretations may sometimes have no therapeutic effect whatsoever. They rearrange extant cognitive contents without having any effect on experience and behavior. On the process level, they may even have a negative effect; for instance, when the patient perceives the interpretation as a personal criticism or attack.

Interpretations about processes that occur in the present, however, contribute directly to the modification of activated schemata. However, such interpretations fulfill their attention-directing function only if the patient comprehends what the therapist intends. Thus, interpretations should not be too "deep." One way for the therapist to guide the patient's attention is through statements that deepen the processing level of patient's **self-exploration**, as described by Sachse (1992). These interpretations should follow closely what the patient says and help explicate meaning that is already implicitly contained in his statements. In addition, they should refer to activated motivational schemata (which Sachse refers to as affective schemata).

Additional examples of interventions used to direct the patient's attention to implicit processes are **focusing** (Gendlin, 1978) or the process-experiential techniques approach described by Greenberg, Rice, and Elliott (1993), which we already discussed numerous times. However, these interventions often refer to interpersonal processes and may, therefore, also be placed in the interpersonal problem perspective.

Field 3

In Field 3 we find mainly cognitive behavioral constructs. Although classical behavior theory viewed the person as a "black box," and behavior therapy refrained from making statements about intra-psychological processes, positive and negative **reinforcement**, two main constructs of classical behavior therapy, nonetheless fit with the intrapersonal perspective. Reinforcement moves or motivates behavior. The relevant behavior occurs more frequently following reinforcement. According to Skinner (1969), reinforcement refers to operant behavior, by which he means voluntarily controllable behavior. Operant behavior can be attributed to the conscious mode of functioning even if it may occur automatically and without conscious attention.

According to our view, behavior is focused on creating perceptions congruent with activated goals. These goals are a means for satisfying basic needs. Neural activation patterns that lead to need fulfillment become more and more strongly linked as a neural group, consistent with Edelman's model (1987). Although Edelman calls this process reinforcement, he means something entirely different than what Skinner meant. Neural activation patterns that repeatedly lead to need satisfaction are increasingly well ingrained and may be activated more and more easily. We have referred to such activation tendencies as motivational schemata.

When a motivational schema is activated, goals and the means for their realization are also activated. Reinforcement—i.e. the ingraining of motivational schemata—requires the schema's activation. The occurrence of goal-congruent perceptions ingrains the respective activation tendency and simultaneously represents need satisfaction. The better the current need satisfaction, the more the behavior will be determined by other, currently less-well satisfied needs. The behavior reinforced before will then become less intrinsic or will be shown less frequently. At the same time, the respective activation tendencies are ingrained even better so that the behavior can be activated even more easily in the future; namely, as soon as the need is no longer deactivated.

Reinforcement of problematic behavior can thus have the undesirable effect of increasing the frequency of this behavior and facilitating the ease with which the behavior is activated. This undesirable consequence occurs even though the intensity of the problem behavior may diminish temporarily, given the temporary need fulfillment associated with the behavior. These considerations suggest that one of the most effective ways for reducing problem behavior might be to find other ways of satisfying the needs. That is, need fulfillment should not be contingent upon the problem behavior. By finding alternative—less problematic—avenues for need fulfillment, the need becomes deactivated, and the problem behavior diminishes. This is the basis, for example, of the principle of complementary relationship formation (Grawe, 1992, 1995b; Grawe et al., 1996). By facilitating patient perceptions that are congruent with the patient's activated motivational schema, the therapist can effectively deactivate the schema and thereby prevent the problem behavior from interfering with therapy. Once this is accomplished, the therapist and patient can work together on identifying more appropriate ways of satisfying the patient's basic needs.

According to our view, fostering patients' need-fulfillment by facilitating perceptions that are congruent with activated motivational schemata is one of the most important interventions a therapist can use. It is an excellent way for reducing problematic behavior. This way, resource activation may reduce the problem behavior without having to target it directly.

Thus, the fact that behavior usually occurs more frequently following reinforcement may be explained very well by our view. Our theoretical conception, however, goes beyond that by specifically reflecting the function behavior has for the individual's needs. While this leads to therapeutic options that appear to be in direct opposition to assumptions of behavior theory, they are, nonetheless, empirically substantiated.

Avoidance behavior that is perpetuated by negative reinforcement is also a main construct of behavior therapy. In our view, avoidance behavior is determined by an avoidance schema that is focused on protecting one of the basic needs. Each avoidance schema has a corresponding but underdeveloped intentional schema. This intentional schema is focused on the satisfaction of the need, but it is typically underdeveloped and weakly ingrained because the avoidance schema inhibits its activation. If avoidance is too dominant, the positive wish component of the intentional schema may not be recognizable as it is not expressed in experience and behavior. Thus, it may appear as though there were no conflict between an approach and an avoidance tendency. In principle, however, every avoidance schema is associated with a conflict between avoidance and intention.

If the avoidance happens consciously, it is associated with certain **fears** related to the violation of a need. Fears correspond to expected reactions or consequences. **Expectations** are a main construct of cognitive behavior therapy approaches (Bandura,

1969; Kirsch, 1990). They correspond to easily activated neural activation tendencies that influence experience and behavior in both the implicit and conscious mode of functioning. According to expectancy-value theories, their influence is moderated by the meaning the expectations have for the individual's motivational schemata.

Irrational beliefs and **dysfunctional cognitions,** according to cognitive therapy approaches, often include an expectation and a value component. In our conception, they are not the actual determinants of the experience and behavior but are themselves determined by motivational schemata. Given our ideas in the second dialogue, cognitions have three functions:

- They are partially accurate reflections of the given reality.
- They are partially goal directed, evaluative interpretations of reality determined motivational schemata, thereby influencing the emotions.
- They have a function for the control of voluntary behavior.

The terms "irrational" and "dysfunctional" refer to the interpretive portion of cognitions. This portion is to be changed due to the influence it has on behavior and emotions. Cognitive therapy techniques seek to increase the reality share of cognitions. This happens, for instance, via "Socratic dialogue" or via targeted reality tests. They also seek to change the interpretive portion, such that certain situations are placed in the context of intentional schemata instead of in the previous context determined by avoidance schemata. This, for instance, happens through reframing. The activation of motivational schemata different from the currently activated ones is the most important way in which **paradoxical interventions** achieve their effects. Through activation of these schemata in the implicit mode of functioning the therapeutic situation takes on an entirely different meaning for the patient than it had on the content level of communication.

Another approach for changing cognitions is by starting with emotions and behavior. By activating behavior or emotions not in agreement with the cognitions, the cognitions may be weakened. The activation of emotions and behaviors that are inconsistent with the cognitions may be attempted via behavior tests or **role plays**. In addition, one may try to influence experience and behavior by using resource activation, an influence that is inconsistent with negative emotions.

Cognitions themselves may be viewed as attractors with certain control parameters. Therapeutic interventions begin with these control parameters. The cognitions themselves are among the control parameters of emotions and behavior. They may also be control parameters of disorder attractors. By influencing the control parameters of cognitions and thereby changing them, the therapist alters an important control parameter for problematic behavior.

Cognitive therapists have recognized that their therapies tend to be more effective when they include real behavior. This is how they have become cognitive behavior therapists. Increasing the effectiveness of pure behavior therapy by including cognitions and the effectiveness of pure cognitive therapy by including environment-related behavior may be well explained by our theoretical conception. Cognitions, emotions, and behavior are mutual control parameters for one another. The more control parameters are influenced therapeutically, the faster a problematic attractor can be destabilized.

A current development of CBT is the explicit inclusion of **volition** in psychotherapy. This also applies primarily to the realm of cognitive behavior therapies, such as the self-management approach by Kanfer, Reinecker, and Schmelzer (1991) or Kuhl's concept of action-orientation (Kuhl, 1994), applied to the therapy process by Schulte and his associates (Hartung, 1990; Schulte et al., 1996). In memory research, the storage of plans and intentions is viewed as a separate form of memory (Goschke, 1996 a). If we regard intentions and plans as neural activation tendencies then it seems obvious that these must be activated repeatedly and associated with as many triggers as possible so that they can exert as large an influence as possible on mental functioning. For this to happen it is an advantage if they can be connected with motivational schemata that already have a very well ingrained activation tendency. The capability of activation patterns that underlie such plans and intentions can be easily activated, resulting in a high volitional strength for a behavior which is consciously controlled in line with certain goals. The formation of strong intentions is, for instance, a crucial step in the preparation for exposure therapy in which the volitional strength for exposing oneself to unwanted experience must be matched against strong avoidance tendencies.

Field 4

I have already addressed the types of therapeutic interventions listed in Field 4 when I spoke about the states and processes to which they are applied, so I will move on directly to the next field.

Psychologist: May I interrupt you for a second? I find it very interesting how you use the perspectives of our theoretical system to illuminate the different terms of psychotherapy, clearly demonstrating how much the notion of unconscious processes, or the lack thereof, differentiates psychodynamic therapies from cognitive behavior therapies. The relevant differences in the theoretical assumptions do indeed have far-reaching consequences for our therapeutic considerations and actions.

However, if you continue this way, we will be sitting here for a very long time. You just moved through four of thirty-two fields. Does it really make sense to continue the application of this system in such detail? Could we not limit ourselves to a few examples and a few remarks for each field? In case questions arise at particular points, we can always ask for some expanded commentary.

Therapist: I truly did not realize how long this was taking. It is still new and stimulating for me to view the entire therapeutic world I have lived in for such a long time from a uniform perspective. Our ideas place the separate worlds of psychodynamic and cognitive behavior therapies in a perspective which, while explaining what divides them, simultaneously transforms separation into a relationship in which both can complement one another. Such a complementary relationship is so far away from today's therapeutic reality, yet it appears so obvious!

For me, this produces a concrete vision for my own therapeutic practice, but this vision naturally still needs to be complemented by the 28 fields we haven't yet discussed. I will take your concerns to heart and will comment only briefly on each field.

Field 5

Fields 5-8 refer to intrapsychological problems and their alteration from the **competence perspective**. Field 5 contains problem aspects for which the individual himself lacks awareness because they concern information processing in the **implicit mode of functioning**.

Therapy researcher: Perhaps you should let me discuss this field for a change, because it appears to me we are speaking about phenomena which I, as a therapy researcher, have more contact with than a practicing therapist has. The features of mental functioning belonging to Field 5 have received little attention in classical psychotherapy until recently. No knowledge was available about the function of information processing features as control parameters for mental problems and disorders. Our knowledge about the functional meaning of these potential aspects of mental functioning is based on experimental research.

One example are the **attention disorders** among schizophrenics. Another example would be what Williams et al. (1988) reported as the **pre-attentive focus** of persons with anxiety disorders towards fear-triggering stimuli, whereas such stimuli are avoided by normal persons on the implicit level of functioning. Still another example would be various processing styles such as the experience vs. behavior related processing style distinguished by Beutler and Clarkin (1990). Problematic coping mechanisms may contribute to the formation of mental problems, as can peculiarities of emotion regulation (Horowitz et al., 1996). Problematic encoding and decoding abilities for emotional expression are correlated with mental disorders, as we have seen in our second dialogue (sections 2.24-2.26). Stress reactions that are not consciously perceived by the individual but can be documented on the physiological level may be components and control parameters of mental and physical disorders. Illness-promoting bodily reactions may form through classical conditioning without any awareness on the person's part.

Such aspects of implicit information processing may also be possible causes for both the formation and the perpetuation of mental and physical disorders. In our terminology, they are both constraints for the development of and control parameters for the perpetuation of disorder attractors. Our knowledge about the functional relevance of characteristics of psychological functioning to be attributed to this field is currently increasing. Relevant studies are mostly performed in neuropsychology and behavioral medicine. The progress in these areas may cause the landscape of psychotherapy to change a great deal in the coming decades. Due to this research we may one day begin to understand why one person develops a particular disorder whereas a second person, under seemingly similar conditions, develops a different disorder. To the degree that it will be possible to influence these determinants, the possibilities for disorder-specific treatment will also once again clearly improve.

Considering these variables in diagnosis requires hypothesis-driven studies with highly specialized methods. It is the therapist's responsibility as an expert to consider all these variables of the implicit mode of functioning. The patient relies on the therapist to have the specialized knowledge and responsibly for making the right decisions. This will have an effect on the therapist-patient relationship.

Not all characteristics and states in this field, however, are beyond the realm of traditional psychotherapy. For instance, behavior summarized by the term "attachment style" is largely regulated in the implicit mode of functioning and may be viewed from the competence aspect. Motivational factors clearly play a role in the development of attachment styles. However, once insecure attachment styles have formed, it makes sense to conceptualize such difficulties to trustfully enter into relationships as an inability, not just as a particular motivational constellation. Concepts such as attachment style may be conceptualized as intra-psychological as well as interpersonal.

Field 6

Deficit-specific training procedures are used primarily as therapeutic interventions for these deficits and unfavorable mechanisms of information processing. Less specific relaxation techniques, hypnosis, or meditation may also be useful in the treatment of certain functional aspects of the autonomic nervous system. Biofeedback may also be effective in treating certain aspects of psychophysiological functioning.

The development of such specific procedures requires disorder-specific and deficit-specific experimental research. As far as such deficits that are not represented in the conscious mode of functioning are concerned, therapeutic practice will always have to rely on disorder-specific research. This will have an impact on practicing therapists' self-image and their relationship to research. In the near future a therapist will not be able to afford to maintain a distant relationship to empirical research or he will find that he has failed in his chosen profession.

Therapist: Such prognoses will not be well received by all therapists. This would require a considerable change in identity. Perhaps we can return to this later and discuss more in detail what an optimal psychosocial care will demand of future psychotherapists. I think for now we should continue with the discussion of the remaining fields for the intra-personal problem perspective, as I am now reaching Field 7.

Field 7

This field is about deficits and competencies that the patient is consciously aware of. Social inhibitions would be an example. The patient experiences such inhibitions as a "being afraid of doing something," as an inherent inability. This does not mean that the same behavior couldn't be conceptualized as a motivational constellation; for instance, as resulting from the activity of an avoidance schema or a motivational conflict constellation. Such a constellation could function as a control parameter of the social inhibition. The patient may not be aware of such motivational control parameters even if he is aware of his inhibitions. The motivational constellation may influence his behavior in the implicit mode of functioning.

To target such motivational control parameters a therapist would need to use motivation-changing procedures. However, the motivational perspective should always be complemented by the competence perspective. There is empirical evidence that social inhibitions should also be viewed as a deficit in ability and be treated accordingly. Such competence training is among the most effective therapeutic procedures (Grawe, Donati & Bernauer, 1994). Empirically, viewing such problems as deficits and approaching them with training programs has yielded positive results.

However, not all patients with social inhibitions respond positively to such training procedures. Very good therapeutic outcomes were achieved in only about half of the patients (Wedel & Grawe, 1980). In some of the patients who experienced no improvement, motivational control parameters might have been responsible for sustaining the symptoms. Given our discussions, such cases would require that all three change components be pursued, not just the first two. The problem should be viewed under the motivational and the capability aspect.

A similar approach should also be taken for other problems to be viewed and treated under the competence aspect. Examples would be the inability for self control in bulimia or gambling, or the inability to control response reactions such as sleep disorders, anxieties, depressions etc. These problems can be effectively treated with disorder-specific interventions under the capability aspect.

For all the disorders I mentioned, there are patients who do not respond well to this form of treatment. Again, for some of them, as just explained for social inhibitions, motivational control parameters might be responsible for sustaining the problems.

It is therefore advisable to systematically consider this possibility, at least for patients who show signs of such motivational control parameters. We already discussed this earlier in this dialogue (section 3.13). Comorbidity and an increased level of inconsistency would represent possible indications that the problem should be treated not just under the competence but also under the motivational aspect.

Field 8

All therapeutic interventions that result from a conception of problems as competency deficits are considered problem-specific and disorder-specific measures. In our second dialogue (section 2.51) we already considered a list by Fiedler (1997) that contains references on possible problem-specific interventions for a multitude of disorders and problems. This list would fill Fields 7 and 8 with many more examples than are needed here.

Psychologist: I am getting a clear idea now how one can place—with the help of your system—seemingly separate phenomena and concepts of psychotherapy into a holistic context so they do not exclude but complement one another. I see no reason why this should not apply similarly for the interpersonal perspective and the resource perspective. However, what interests me the most right now is how you want to combine these different possibilities in practice. Since you had indicated your desire to introduce a case to us, would this perhaps be the right time?

Therapist: Yes, I believe we are now ready for this, but before doing so I would like to offer some brief commentary on the interpersonal and resource perspective. The intra-psychological problem perspective strongly dominates in psychotherapy, receiving the most attention, and these two other perspectives remain rather neglected. We should not make the same mistake.

Therapy researcher: I do not think there is much danger of that. The resource perspective has, in fact, taken on just such significance in our ideas. You have made the process of resource activation the main foundation for successful psychotherapy in your change component model. Perhaps the interpersonal perspective has not been acknowledged sufficiently so far. While I would like for you to explain this perspective a bit more, I do not find it necessary for you to do this as systematically as you did for the intra-personal problem perspective.

3.20   Psychotherapy From the Interpersonal Perspective

Therapist: In psychotherapy we are confronted with people who suffer. When a couple comes to therapy because of relationship problems, it is still the individual persons who suffer from that relationship. Suffering is a state of mental functioning. Therefore, the intra-psychological perspective is indispensable for psychotherapy even if the problems are of an interpersonal nature. Suffering consists of certain neural activation patterns and exists always in the context of an individual's mental functioning.

A person's intra-psychological functioning is fundamentally related to other people. It is motivated by basic human needs, and these are only fulfilled in the interpersonal context. A human being needs other human beings as existentially as air for breathing.

This particular need is the immediate focus of the need for attachment. The feeling of self-esteem includes explicit and implicit social comparisons. Even control experiences largely occur in interpersonal contexts. In fact, the majority of experiences regarding human pleasure and displeasure occur in interpersonal contexts.

Thus, interpersonal relatedness is an integral part of motivational schemata. Grawe (1986) referred to these schemata as relationship schemata. Motivational schemata aim to get the individual into a certain transactional relation with his environment, and the other individuals are by far the most important part of this environment, especially those who have become important persons of reference over the course of his life.

Thus, people's motivational schemata develop in the context of important relationships. A certain sequence of activation patterns in the intra-psychological perspective corresponds to certain relationship patterns in the interpersonal perspective. Whether I speak of motivational schemata or interpersonal patterns depends on my perspective. Interpersonal processes and intra-psychological processes are linked with one another. Changes in a person's motivational schemata also bring about changes in the person's interpersonal patterns, and vice-versa. Changing interaction patterns, therefore, is one of the most important means for changing motivational schemata.

However, interaction patterns cannot be reduced to the individual's intra-psychological processes. There is more than one person involved in a relationship. The emergent interaction pattern is linked with both individuals' motivational schemata. The relationship that results is never determined solely by a single person. If the relationship is to be of any duration, both sides must have an interpersonal pattern enabling sufficiently congruent perceptions. The participants' motivational schemata create a room for possibilities within which the interaction patterns may unfold; they do not determine them entirely.

We may conceive interaction patterns as interpersonal attractors with their own intrinsic dynamic. They may not be reduced to intra-personal motivational constellations nor to situational conditions. They develop from a specific constellation of conditions that includes both external circumstances and motivational tendencies and related competences (motivational schemata) as important control parameters. Following their formation, relationships may develop their own dynamic similar to that which we conceptualized for disorder attractors. Interpersonal attractors may be changed via their control parameters. Situational conditions do not directly impact the interaction patterns, but have an effect via influencing the participant's mental functioning. For that functioning, the interaction patterns themselves represent important control parameters. Thus, the modification of interpersonal attractors influences the motivational schemata of the participants.

A person's past and present interaction patterns are, therefore, of utmost importance if one wants to comprehend his or her mental functioning. Motivational schemata and interaction patterns relate to one another like key and keyhole. Interaction patterns are the arena in which a person's most important problems manifest themselves, and they are simultaneously the most important resource for the satisfaction of his needs. Therefore, they merit the highest of attention from the therapist.

Relationships are not just important for understanding mental functioning but also for changing it. Psychotherapy essentially takes place in interaction patterns. This alone makes the interpersonal perspective indispensable for psychotherapy. The interaction patterns a patient enters into do not just yield important insight about his motivational schemata, but they are also the lever by which to change the schemata.

Relationships in therapy may and should be viewed both under the problem and the resource aspects. Additionally, it is useful to distinguish them in terms of whether the interactions are happening only on a process level or whether they are also represented in the participant's consciousness, and whether what is happening on a process level is congruent with the content addressed in therapy.

The notion of **transference** is particularly well suited to demonstrate the close intertwining of intra-psychological and interpersonal processes. Transference means that neural activation tendencies ingrained in the first years of life under the influence of the attachment need towards the earliest persons of reference are activated in the implicit mode of functioning during the therapeutic interaction, influencing the patient's experience and behavior towards the therapist. They are activated bottom-up in the therapeutic relationship, which offers the chance to develop an awareness for these early developed motivational schemata by directing the patient's attention to what he does, feels, and thinks towards the therapist.

Fears and avoidance reactions may also be among these transference reactions towards the therapist. This is most likely happening if the patient has had negative experiences as a small child with his primary attachment figures with respect to his basic needs, and if the therapist or situation sufficiently resembles these early childhood experiences such that the previously ingrained activation tendencies are activated. If this occurs, there is a good chance the patient will have different experiences with the therapist, which may help to overwrite the old activation tendencies with new experiences, ingraining new activation tendencies. We already decided that such establishing and generalizing of new activation tendencies is specifically promoted by a transformation into the conscious mode of functioning.

From that point of view, the psychoanalytic transference concept agrees with our model of mental functioning. Important as this perspective regarding the interactional processes in psychotherapy may be in some cases, it is, however, as important to have an awareness that it is only one of many possible perspectives on interactions. It is more an intra-psychological than an interpersonal perspective on a genuinely interpersonal event, and it views the therapeutic relationship unilaterally under the problem perspective. Viewing the interactions between patient and therapist only under this perspective does not really account for its multitude of implications.

From an interpersonal perspective the term **counter-transference** assumes a one-sided view of interactional processes. The therapist is as much an actor in the relationship as the patient is. Which motivational schemata he activates in the patient and what kind of interaction pattern develops is at least as much determined by how he approaches the patient as it is by the patient's transference tendencies. The therapeutic relationship is above all else a real relationship.

According to our model of therapeutic change, the therapeutic relationship is clearly more significant under the aspect of resource activation than under transference. If the therapist does not succeed in shaping the relationship such that the patient's positive resources are activated, the entire therapy will fail. On the other hand, therapeutic transference work is only one of many techniques for bringing about changes in the patient's problematic motivational schemata.

Additionally, from an interpersonal perspective, the therapeutic relationship is only one of many real relationships the patient has, and definitely not the most important among these. The interpersonal perspective assumes a **supra-individual perspective**. If interpersonal relationships play a functional role in the patient's intra-psychological suffering, then from an interpersonal perspective, these are the current real relationships. All environmental influences, including the interpersonal ones, impact mental functioning via existing activation tendencies, but these activation tendencies are not the only influences on the meanings that the interpersonal processes have for the patient. It is also the real nature of the processes themselves that establish the meanings they have for the patient. And from an interpersonal perspective, there are many more ways to influence the real nature of interaction processes than there are for the patient's intrapsychological processes.

The intrapersonal perspective opens more possibilities for intervention than when one primarily assumes the intrapersonal perspective or merely supplements it with the therapeutic relationship. Among the various approaches, it was mostly the systemic approach that emphasized and elaborated just how important the meaning of a person's real relationships is under the problem and resource aspect. According to our theoretical view, a person's real relationships are of utmost significance for his present need satisfaction and, therefore, for his well-being. Consequently, a therapist has to always get an exact picture of the nature of a patient's real relationships if she wants to understand his life situation. In many cases, the goal of a therapy is to improve these real relationships in order for the patient's basic needs to be better satisfied.

If one wants to improve the real relationships, limiting oneself solely to influencing the patient is not very wise. This would not account for the independent dynamics of relationships and the impacts of those control parameters on the relationships that the patient cannot control. From an interpersonal perspective, the therapist, therefore, will frequently arrive at the conclusion that including the patient's real persons of reference in therapy under the problem and resource aspect would be desirable. Such chances are almost always overlooked if the therapist does not systematically include the interpersonal perspective in his or her work, which involves more than just focusing on what is happening between patient and therapist. Currently, the interpersonal perspective is strongly tied to a certain therapeutic approach, namely the system-oriented. A psychotherapy that is not marked by the boundaries between the schools of therapy should enable all therapists to assume both the intra-personal and the interpersonal perspective, and to utilize the resulting therapeutic possibilities necessary for each case.

Part 2:   Psychological Therapy in Practice

Case Conceptualization and Treatment Planning

3.21   From the Intake Interview to Case Conceptualization and Treatment Planning

Psychologist: A therapist using this system can employ a wide range of therapeutic maneuvers. However, wouldn't this multitude of perspectives be confusing rather than helpful for a practitioner? With so many pressures to make quick decisions and take action, would any therapist really be able to consider all these factors?

Therapist: This is not how the system is intended to work. A therapist ought to be trained to assume all perspectives, to ensure that no potential intervention will be neglected. However, it is impossible, of course, to focus on all perspectives at the same time. I explained the system's various individual fields to show that it isn't necessary to switch from one theoretical system to another if one wants to account for the multitude of therapeutic phenomena.

The various perspectives can all be derived from a coherent theoretical foundation. The more skilled a therapist is in terms of thinking in these categories or the more she has internalized these ideas, the easier she will find its application to all sorts of problems. Which perspectives are especially relevant will depend on the specific problem. When therapist and patient work together on a particular problem, different perspectives may be required at different stages over the course of treatment, and the most important task is to assess what the patient's most urgent problems are and how they should be treated.

Let me illustrate the conclusions arising from our change component model and our system with a problem that is frequently encountered by therapists. I am referring to the situation where the patient is seen for the initial intake interview; that is, before anyone has even decided whether therapy is necessary or what kind of therapy would be needed.

Essentially, we are talking about two separate therapeutic tasks: **case conceptualization** and **treatment planning**.

It is natural that a therapist initially assumes the problem perspective to determine whether psychotherapy is even indicated. Which problems are we dealing with? This question is posed from the intra-personal and interpersonal perspectives.

From the intra-personal problem perspective, the therapist may ask whether one or several disorders are present, according to Axes I and II of the DSM-IV or the ICD. Do the patient's problems meet the criteria for specific mental, personality or developmental disorders?

Are other problems present that do not match these categories, such as incongruities and discordances among patients' motivational schemata? Incongruities may result from a problematic life situation that must be resolved immediately, or they may reflect a long-term problematic constellation of motivational schemata that produces self-perpetuating inconsistencies.

Next, the therapist must ask: Which of these problems is the patient aware of and for which ones does he lack insight? Problems the patient is already aware of may be treated with coping or mastery-oriented procedures. If the patient lacks adequate awareness for certain problems, the most urgent task for the therapist is to facilitate insight or awareness for this problem. Thus, therapy should be clarification-oriented.

Further, the therapist should think about the patient's motivation for treatment. Which of the problems is the patient motivated to work on, and which not? What the therapist identifies as the problem may not be consistent with the patient's agenda.

With regard to a patient's motivation for therapy, the therapist must switch to the resource perspective. Are positive motivational schemata activated such that treatment of particular problems would lead to perceptions consistent with patient goals? It only makes sense to proceed with components 2 and 3 if these requirements are met. Otherwise, one would need to assess if relevant resources could be activated—via therapy or in some other way—to create the conditions for successful therapeutic work. If this cannot be achieved, then no psychotherapy is indicated.

The intra-personal problem perspective should be complemented by the interpersonal perspective. This perspective is assumed naturally when patients begin therapy by reporting problems with partners or family. However, when patients do not define their problems as interpersonal, it is important for the therapist to actively assume the interpersonal perspective and evaluate the patient's life from this angle. Illness as it is commonly conceived in the community or in the health care system involves an individual-focused perspective. As I argued earlier, this perspective is indeed indispensable. Yet, the great significance of interpersonal relationships for a person's physical and mental well-being is so frequently taken for granted that it may often be neglected.

Therefore, the therapist's goal must be to gather information about the patient's important interpersonal relationships during the initial clarification phase. Questioning the patient may be one suitable approach, but more will be learned about these relationships by including significant others in these first meetings. The chance for the therapist to observe these interactions and obtain information from different sides is important, because the patient may have no conscious awareness of existing interpersonal problems. Most people are not aware of whether they are part of a coalition, live in a family with diffuse borders, or are in a symmetric interaction pattern with their partner.

Interaction patterns can be a problem in themselves because the persons involved suffer from the interactions. They may also be a problem because they play a functional role for the patient's intrapsychological problems. The intake interview focuses initially on figuring out whether interpersonal problems play a role at all and whether they need to be considered for case conceptualization and treatment planning.

A systematic analysis of the problematic situation from the interpersonal perspective in a pre-therapy intake interview is critical for selecting an appropriate therapeutic setting. When interpersonal relationships play a significant role in the overall problem, it is generally advisable to create situations with actual interactions between the persons involved in therapy that allow the therapist to intervene and overwrite the patients' neural activation patterns with new experiences, thereby ingraining new activation tendencies.

Even the dyadic setting of individual therapy is suited for activating and overwriting problematic activation patterns with corrective experiences. However, individual therapy is inherently limited in this respect. For instance, a young, charming female therapist would not elicit the same interaction patterns that the patient tends to create in response to fatherly authority figures. For correcting such interaction patterns, family therapy or group therapy might be preferable, or it might be advisable to refer the patient to a therapist who is a better candidate for such "transference."

Selecting a setting is critically important for the question of which therapeutic options will be available in therapy later on. This is one of the most crucial decisions in therapy overall. In current systems of psychotherapeutic care this important decision is very often *de facto* predetermined by the therapist the patient sees first. In most instances the patient is treated within the setting preferred by that particular therapist. In outpatient therapy, the setting tends to be individual therapy, unless the practitioner is a couples- or a family therapist.

Most therapists favor individual therapy, which explains its popularity. This setting is usually consistent with the patient's expectation of opening up to only one therapist, not to several persons. It is much easier for the therapist to meet this expectation than to suggest a different setting and convince the patient of its benefits. Furthermore, the individual therapy setting is the one most easily created and controllable by the therapist. Getting family members and partners to participate in therapy is in many instances not easy and represents quite a therapeutic challenge. It may not be possible to create *ad hoc* an adequate group setting for a single patient; the therapy group has to already exist and its composition must be suitable for this specific patient. Also, a multiple-person setting requires solving many more complex logistical problems, regarding, for instance, the schedule.

Given these additional difficulties, one can easily see how it is that most therapists favor individual therapy. Even the simple fact that in an individual setting the therapist can devote the most individual attention to the patient and thus facilitate a positive relationship argues in favor of this setting.

All these advantages, however, do not change the fact that a person's relationships with other people are of utmost significance for his well-being, both in a positive and negative sense. Therefore, a setting that includes significant others can have a therapeutic potential that cannot be matched by individual therapy.

This applies as well for the resource aspect. With respect to the need for attachment, the patient's significant others, such as parents, siblings, partners, children, and close friends, are his most important resources. This remains true even when significant others are involved in creating or sustaining the problems that led to therapy. A therapist who does nothing but "problematize" the patient's most important relationships remains blind to the fact that these relationships also have an indispensable positive function in the patient's life. One goal of therapy should be to strengthen the positive function of these relationships for the patient. On the one hand, this can be accomplished by working on problems in the relationship that undermine its positive functions. In a much more direct way, however, the therapist can try to activate these relationships with respect to their function as a positive resource for the patient. Thus, including significant others in therapy is considered an important therapeutic tool, primarily under the resource aspect.

At the very least, the inclusion of significant others is recommended for the purpose of gathering information during the initial diagnostic phase. This will yield a much more detailed picture of the patient's life than could be obtained by the patient's verbal report alone. Even though significant others ought to be routinely included during the initial diagnostic phase, it is not always necessary that they be included in the actual course of therapy.

The various therapeutic settings are not mutually exclusive. They may be combined with each other to make use of their strengths and to compensate for their weaknesses. Therapy can start with one particular setting and then switch to a different one, entirely or temporarily. An extremely inhibited, distrustful patient may first be treated in an individual setting, one that enables the therapist—via a resource-oriented approach to shaping the therapeutic relationship—to prepare the patient for more stressful thera-peutic interventions, such as those that occur in a multiple-person setting. Then the patient may be additionally—or eventually even solely—treated in a group setting which usually offers a much greater chance to work on his generalized inhibitions. Individual, couple, or family sessions may alternate depending on what the emphasis is in therapy at any given time.

We know from experience, however, that the groundwork for any setting other than that of individual therapy has to be laid right at the beginning. As early as in pre-therapy assessment, both therapist and patient should jointly develop a perspective on the problem that entails the desirability or necessity for including significant others in the therapy, provided that the therapist views this as potentially indicated. The "pre-scription" and justification of the treatment setting is a very important part of the over-all treatment plan suggested by the therapist at the end of the clarification process. If this suggestion does not already expressly contain convincing justifications for the desired treatment setting as part of an overall therapeutic rationale, it might be very difficult to implement a different setting later on.

The intake assessment eventually leads to ideas about a treatment plan that is spe-cifically tailored for the patient. The most important aspects to be considered for a preliminary tailored case conceptualization are summarized in Table 3.3. It is designed such that it could theoretically be used by the practitioner as an "intake assessment sheet" which will aid in determining what might be the best therapy to offer a given patient.

Therapy researcher: Indeed, we seem to have arrived at the topic of therapeutic practice. If I understand you correctly, then you think this worksheet is a logical, prac-tical consequence of the system we have just introduced. I can follow you on this. On the other hand, it seems that you view the ideas the therapist has while filling out this worksheet to be the final result of an intake assessment. Yet you have told us very little about the intake assessment process itself. How does this relate to the actual therapy? Who performs this, if not the therapist who does the therapy? How long does such a intake assessment last, how is it structured? I do not have any concrete ideas about all this yet.

Table 3.3:
Intake assessment sheet for structuring suggestions for a patient-tailored treatment plan following the intake assessment.

Intake Assessment Sheet

A. Problems to be treated

1. Axis I disorders

- -

2. Axis II disorders

- -

3. Problematic life situations

- -

4. Inconsistency-producing constellations of motivational schemata

- -

5. Problematic interaction patterns

- -

6. Additional problems

B. Therapeutic approach

Which problems require a **mastery-oriented**, which a **clarification-oriented** approach? More than one type of intervention may be rated when it appears that a combination of both approaches is indicated.

Problem 1:

	coping/mastery-oriented	0	1	2	3	4
	clarification-oriented	0	1	2	3	4

Problem 2:

	coping/mastery-oriented	0	1	2	3	4
	clarification-oriented	0	1	2	3	4

Problem 3:

	coping/mastery-oriented	0	1	2	3	4
	clarification-oriented	0	1	2	3	4

Problem 4:

	coping/mastery-oriented	0	1	2	3	4
	clarification-oriented	0	1	2	3	4

Problem 5:

	coping/mastery-oriented	0	1	2	3	4
	clarification-oriented	0	1	2	3	4

What appears to be the optimal combination of **clarification-oriented** and **mastery-oriented** interventions with particular regard to temporal order ?

C. Therapeutic setting

Under the aspect of **resource activation** and **problem treatment**, which therapy settings are favored? When multiple settings are considered rank them in order.

	Resource activation	Problem treatment
Individual therapy		
Group therapy		
Couples therapy		
Family therapy		

Which **setting** or **combinations of settings** appear best indicated under all the considered perspectives? With combinations of settings, place in temporal order.

Which important **significant others** should be included in therapy if possible?

D. Notes about the therapist characteristics
(Gender, age, additional favorable or contra-indicated characteristics)

E. Notes on the therapeutic relationship
(complementary relationship, expected relationship tests)

F. Notes on patient's primary motivations for therapy

G. Treatment planning

What treatment combination appears most appropriate for this patient?

Therapist: So far I have addressed very little of that since I wanted to first explain the purpose of this intake assessment. If you have no more questions about the criteria for the preliminary case conceptualization that is developed in the course of the intake assessment, I can then move on to the process itself. If there is anything you do not understand, please feel free to ask. You see, I have become so accustomed to this procedure that I may fail to give a detailed commentary on each step. Basically, I have practiced this form of intake assessment and case conceptualization so many times in the past months that it has become my second nature. I cannot even imagine my practice functioning in any other way.

3.22   The Intake Assessment Procedure

Any patient-tailored treatment plan requires a pre-therapy assessment into exactly what such a plan should look like for a particular patient. Therapy can begin only after the case conceptualization has been accomplished. The intake assessment should not be conceived of as therapy yet and should not be portrayed as such to the patient.

In practice, the intake assessment should be clearly distinguished from therapy, regarding its goals, its procedure, the patient's and therapist's expectations, and even with regard to the facility in which the intake assessment is performed. The patient is to be expressly told that his actual therapy has not yet begun, but that he is undergoing a thorough examination prior to therapy, the goal of which is to determine the therapy best suited for him. It would be explained that this examination requires an intensive

interview with him and—pending his agreement—with especially important significant others. He would be asked to fill out a number of questionnaires in which he is to
specify his problems in more detail than would be possible in the limited consultation
time available. The questionnaires completed between the interviews would be analyzed immediately, providing more information to the therapist to determine the best
therapy. In the final stage of this intake assessment, a group of experienced therapists
would decide on the best therapy for the patient in a special "case conceptualization
and treatment planning meeting." The interviewer would discuss the treatment plan
with the patient in a final consultation, and the patient would then have time to reflect
on this. Once the patient has decided to participate in therapy, the interviewer would
put him into contact with a therapist specifically qualified for this treatment. This therapist
would not be the interviewer who performed the intake assessment.

The actual procedure happens exactly as described above. I have illustrated this in
the form of a flow chart in Figure 3.7.

Therapy researcher: This procedure appears ideal for inducing positive improvement expectations. One should actually expect that such an intake assessment itself
already has some therapeutic effects.

Therapist: According to my experiences, this is indeed the case. In general, patients
like such an intake assessment. Patients experience the time and effort invested in find-

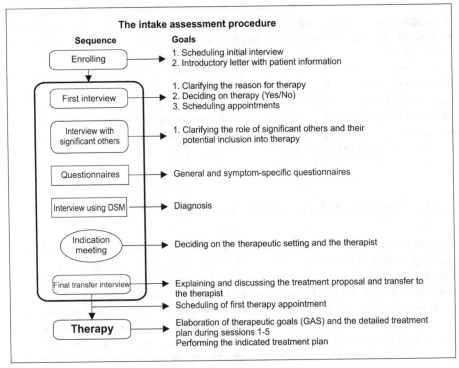

Figure 3.7:
Process flow chart of the intake assessment.

ing out the best therapy for them as a very special kind of care. Finally, someone out there really cares thoroughly about all their complaints and ailments. The interviewer's questions about certain diagnostic and differential-diagnostic criteria give the patient the impression that his disorder is being handled by an expert. The intake assessment is structured clearly and transparently for the patient. He experiences the interviewer as someone who knows exactly what he or she does and why. Test results and profiles (see Figure 3.13 and the following pages in section 3.26) can also be used in talking with the patient to facilitate an impression of professional competence.

The patient's impression that he receives special care and competence is in fact accurate. In a situation where such a thorough assessment and case conceptualization is performed, he is truly in good hands. The likelihood for him to be treated with the correct therapy is greatly increased compared to the situation where he would receive treatment based on just any therapist's opinion and preference. Thus, the interviewer justifiably radiates confidence; she does everything to make sure this patient receives effective help.

The therapist she recommends is one who is highly competent for this therapy, since this was the main criterion for her choice. For the therapist who eventually carries out the treatment, this entire procedure yields numerous advantages for a good start:

– She starts out with an bonus in trust because she was introduced by a colleague as "the" specialist for this therapy.
– She is dealing with a patient in whom improvement expectations were already induced and who has been instructed about what to expect from this therapy. The patient is aware of what this particular therapy entails and has decided to participate.
– She can convey competence and trust, since she is actually competent for the type of therapy the patient will receive.
– Unlike a therapist consulted directly by a patient, she has a head start in knowledge. Not only is information received from the interviewer about the patient's most important problems , but recommendations as to how to shape the therapeutic relationship are also available. Without having had any prior communication with the patient, she is nevertheless able to relate to the patient in a way that is optimal with respect to various aspects, such as resource activation, the shaping of a complementary relationship, and she is prepared for potential relationship tests. She can thus avoid establishing interaction patterns that would be disadvantageous over the course of therapy.

The intake interviewer, therefore, lays the foundation for the practicing therapist, and it is the patient who benefits mostly from that.

I have discussed my intake procedure with many therapists time and again, and many have responded that this intake assessment, with all the time and effort involved, may indeed be an imposition on the patient. While this may be the case for many therapists, mostly because this procedure deviates from their common practice, the patients themselves may experience it quite differently. In fact, their experience is that the extent of care and effort devoted to the assessment and case conceptualization matches the extent of their suffering.

Apart from that, only therapists react that way who have not experienced just how much more convenient it is to perform a well-prepared therapy. It is quite a bit easier to do the therapy with all these advantages.

Therapy researcher: According to all this, the intake interview would already have very positive effects in terms of realizing the first change component of our model, regardless of whether the case conceptualization is accurate. Assuming that a carefully established case conceptualization facilitates the likelihood that the patient receives the therapy best suited for his needs, the second and third component should also be much better implemented than would be the case without this kind of intake assessment. Therefore, it is to be expected that therapies preceded by an appropriate intake assessment are much more effective than commonly performed therapies. By commonly performed therapies I mean those in which a patient is treated by the therapist he initially saw for his problem, undergoing the kind of treatment that is typical for that therapist's approach.

Therapist: While I am unable to really report any established empirical evidence for that, I am convinced that such an intake assessment procedure alone would already be a very effective tool for increasing the average quality of psychotherapies and their outcomes beyond the extent realized today.

Of course, for the most part the outcome depends on how well therapy is performed and how well the therapeutic techniques objectively match the patient's problems. In my view, even within the therapies themselves, there is still considerable room to improve efficacy, but what is most important is laying the proper groundwork for therapy by choosing the correct setting.

Particularly for case conceptualization it is important to take a systematic look at the entire spectrum of therapeutic possibilities. Regarding the available therapeutic scope, the change component model and the system introduced here can prevent one from having the kind of narrow vision that results from the traditional boundaries among the therapy schools. Thinking in terms of this system allows combining all therapeutic possibilities into a tailored therapy, regardless of which therapy school they may have been developed in. The procedure, having proved effective for a certain purpose, must be separated from its original theoretical rationale. There is no loss here, because obviously the procedure, and not the rationale, yields the therapeutic effect. As long as they are effective, the procedures are given a specific place within our theoretical view, and their future application is no longer derived from their original rationale but from this new theoretical conception. This conception allows the entire spectrum of therapeutic possibilities to be accounted for. All those procedures that have proven effective but have not yet found a place in our system should be viewed as suggestions for revisions or extensions of this system.

Therapy researcher: Your idea for every psychotherapy to be preceded by a broad systematic intake assessment, carefully conducted case conceptualization, and treatment planning would produce considerable changes in the therapeutic care system as it is currently practiced. I doubt whether appropriate therapeutic structures for such a tailored form of care are presently available.

Therapist: I have some ideas about that as well. I do believe that the care systems would have to change in order to exhaust all the potentials of effective psychotherapy. Furthermore, we would have to have therapists who are trained accordingly and are able to perform these tailored therapies in a manner that is consistent with the treatment plans. But I do not wish to discuss care and training at this point, as I would first like to talk a little more about how these tailored therapies may look like and how they can be implemented.

Therapy Planning and Practice

3.23 Developing a Tailored Treatment Plan

Patient-tailored therapy requires a treatment plan that is individually tailored for a particular patient (or particular couple or family). When therapy has been preceded by an intake assessment, and a case conceptualization has been formulated, then a general framework is already established, which will guide subsequent treatment decisions. However, even in this scenario, a specified treatment plan or therapy plan would still have to be articulated. If no intake assessment has been conducted at this point, then the therapist must initially pursue the same questions that could have been asked in an intake assessment. It may not be necessary in each case to formulate a detailed case conceptualization, but a few strategic decisions must certainly be made. For instance, one must decide what the best therapy setting might be for a particular patient. Once the proper setting has been selected, the therapist must decide how exactly to proceed; that is, she will have to come up with a concrete treatment plan.

I have designed a therapy planning sheet that I use for my own therapies, similar to the one introduced to you in Table 3.3. It contains crucial questions for the therapist in developing her treatment plan and leaves space for handwritten notes. Of course, the answers can also be typed into a computer to save space. See Table 3.4 for this therapy planning sheet.

The worksheet is not suited as perfectly for couples or family therapies. The questions pertaining to the setting need to be formulated more specifically in such instances. They must relate more to the system level, without losing sight, of course, of the individual patient. There is no need at this point to elaborate on each and every detail of therapeutic practice. In general, however, all these considerations about therapy planning also apply to therapies that occur in a multiple-person setting. My following notes refer primarily to the kind of therapy focused on an individual patient's suffering.

In planning a procedure the therapist must ask and answer the following questions from the perspectives we have developed here:

1. Which **resources** can be **activated** and how?

Consistent with our system the therapist must focus on the patient's **individual** resources and those within his **interpersonal** environment. Including other persons in therapy requires specifying not only the individual's resources but also those of the other persons and those at the super-individual system level. What is described in the following for the single patient generally applies for the couple or family as well.

Table 3.4:
Work sheet for developing an individual treatment plan according to the change component
model.

Therapy Planning Work Sheet

1. Which *resources* can be activated and how?

Resources: *How to activate them?*

---

2. Which *disorders* are to be worked on and how?

2.1 Disorder 1:   Which components?   How to proceed?

- -

2.2 Disorder 2:   Which components?   How to proceed?

- -

2.3 Disorder 3:   Which components?   How to proceed?

---

3. Which *interaction patterns* are to be worked on and how?

*3.1 Interaction
pattern 1:*   Describe the concrete sequence   Where and how is this
                 of the problematic interactions   sequence to be changed?
                 step-by-step

---

*3.2 Interaction
pattern 2:*   Describe the concrete sequence   Where and how is this
                 of the problematic interactions   sequence to be changed?
                 step-by-step

---

*3.3 Interaction
pattern 3:*   Describe the concrete sequence   Where and how is this
                 of the problematic interactions   sequence to be changed?
                 step-by-step

4. Which *motivational schemata* are to be activated and how?

*4.1 Schemata the patient is **aware** of:*

Avoidance schemata,   Schema   How to activate them?
to be weakened   Which corrective experiences?

Intentional Schemata   Schema   How to activate them?
to be strengthened: Which corrective experiences?

4.2 **Conflict schemata** for which there is little or no **awareness**:
Conflict schema 1:   Avoidance component   How to activate?
                                                How to direct attention to them?
                                              Which corrective experiences?

| | Intentional component | How to activate?
How to direct attention to it?
Which corrective experiences? |

- -

| Conflict schema 2: | Avoidance component | How to activate?
How to direct attention to it?
Which corrective experiences? |

- -

| | Intentional component | How to activate?
How to direct attention to it?
Which corrective experiences? |

- -

| Conflict schema 3: | Avoidance component | How to activate?
How to direct attention to it?
Which corrective experiences? |

- -

| | Intentional component | How to activate?
How to direct attention to it?
Which corrective experiences? |

5. Relationship shaping

5.1 Shaping a complementary relationship

Content	Process
Which statements/ formulations?	How to behave nonverbally?

- -

5.2 Which **relationship tests** are to be expected?

Test 1:

Patient's side	Therapist's side
Behavior:	How should the therapist behave?
Wishes:	How should the therapist not behave?
Fears:	

- -

Test 2:

Patient's side	Therapist's side
Behavior:	How should the therapist behave?
Wishes:	How should the therapist not behave?
Fears:	

- -

Test 3:

Patient's side	Therapist's side
Behavior:	How should the therapist behave?
Wishes:	How should the therapist not behave?
Fears:	

6. Motivation for the therapy

For which *goals* and *procedures* is the patient most *motivated*, consistent with his existing motivational schemata?

7. Concrete treatment plan

Which goals should be worked on with which interventions and in what order?

The patient's **motivational tendencies** and **abilities** are his individual resources and both may be used for therapy.

As for the question about **how** to activate the resources, it is important to figure out which of these should be activated by addressing the respective **content** and which should be activated on a **process** level. Process-activation means giving the patient the chance to behave and represent himself in accordance with certain tendencies and abilities without this being openly addressed. Activation by openly addressing the content involves explicit references by the therapist to the patient's tendencies and abilities. Very often the therapist can combine both forms of activation.

2. Which **disorders** (according to Axis I of the DSM) are to be targeted with disorder-specific interventions?

All these questions must be decided for each disorder. Disorder attractors may be destabilized through directly targeting each of their individual components. The goal is to specify the predominant disorder components and control parameters (for instance, specific cognitions, expectations, avoidance behavior). One must also determine how each of these components is to be influenced.

At this point, the therapist may want to consult disorder-specific treatment manuals in which the most important components and control parameters of a disorder are listed, along with a description of how they can be influenced. For this purpose, I would recommend the "Manuals for Therapeutic Practice" that have been developed specifically for the various mental disorders. These appear in the series *Progress in Psychotherapy* published by Schulte, Grawe, Hahlweg and Vaitl. Examples include: Rief and Hiller (1998) on somatoform disorders and hypochondria, Hahlweg and Dose (1998) on schizophrenia, Hautzinger (1998) on depression, or Schneider and Margraf (1998) on panic and agoraphobia. The information in these manuals is restricted solely to what a therapist needs to know for immediate diagnosis and intervention when faced with one of these disorders, and that information is further limited solely to the disorder-specific aspect of treatment. Such literature cannot replace a patient-tailored treatment planning, but it does facilitate the disorder-specific portion.

Usually **Axis II disorders** (personality and developmental disorders) cannot be treated with prescribed disorder-specific interventions. Disorder-specific interventions such as dialectical behavior therapy by Linehan (1987) for borderline-personality disorder, for example, are complex treatment programs that actually include all therapy components.

Such complex disorders should, therefore, be deconstructed into their components for therapy planning. For instance, according to Benjamin (1993), the individual personality disorders may be characterized by certain interaction patterns that are, in turn, linked to a specific constellation of motivational schemata (Young, 1994). As a rule, therapy planning for patients with personality or developmental disorders should, therefore not, be handled by checking question 2 for the disorders, but by checking questions 3 (for interaction patterns) and 4 (for motivational schemata).

3. Which **interaction patterns** should be changed?

The interaction patterns need to be specified as accurately as possible by a prototypical course of interaction: For instance, one interaction partner behaves in this way, the other responds in that way, and so on.

In planning how to change the course of an interaction it is important to distinguish how the interaction pattern should be **activated on a process level** and how one should **intervene** to bring about a **specific change**.

For the question of how the problematic interaction may be processually activated, the setting is especially important. It may be an advantage, for instance, to include significant others in therapy. Therefore, the question of the setting should be given careful consideration when deciding how to change interaction patterns.

Various concepts, such as coalition formation, triangulation, diffuse borders, symmetric escalation, collusion, etc., have been developed for these problematic types of interactions occurring in established interpersonal systems. Heuristically, such concepts may be used for defining the problem; however, they need to be specified in terms of the individual person so it is clear what and who specifically is meant. The manner in which these interactions are to be changed should be specified only after specifying the sequence of these interactions on a behavioral level.

Patients' motivational schemata (i.e. motives and abilities, or deficits in ability) as well as situational circumstances can be considered as control parameters for interpersonal attractors. The important question is whether or not the participants (i.e., patients or significant others) have conscious awareness of the functional roles of these control parameters. If so, mastery-oriented interventions are indicated, and if not, awareness-creating interventions would be preferable. The best intervention will typically be a combination of the two.

4. Which **motivational schemata** are to be changed?

An unfavorable constellation of motivational schemata may itself be the main problem to be addressed in therapy, as is the case in personality disorders. Even if he does not meet the criteria for a certain diagnostic category, the patient's constellation of motivational schemata—in interaction with his present situation—may lead to a high level of suffering because his basic needs are insufficiently satisfied.

In addition, an inconsistency-creating constellation of motivational schemata may also function as a control parameter for a particular mental disorder, and beyond that, it may serve as a lasting breeding ground for the development of additional disorders. That is particularly likely when a high level of comorbidity already exists.

Those are three good reasons why it is important to check whether specific motivational schemata need be changed in therapy. Motivational schemata cannot be observed directly. They must be inferred, which is particularly true for conflict schemata. The patient often has no awareness especially for those. Hence, altering motivational schemata is important primarily among patients who lack awareness for what it is that they should actually change. In these cases, a clarification-oriented, awareness-creating procedure is needed. The therapist should at least be aware of what it is that the patient avoids most, since it is her task to process-activate the relevant conflict or avoidance schema, directing the patient's attention to the processes that determine his experience and behavior at that moment.

If the patient is aware of his avoidant behavior, a mastery-oriented procedure is indicated. The avoidance schema must be process-activated for corrective experiences to take place. In case of a conflict schema, corrective experiences are achieved by weakening the avoidance component of the schema and reinforcing (i.e. ingraining) the wish component.

Thus, a therapist attempting to specify which motivational schemata ought to be changed needs to determine whether the patient has awareness for the activities of these schemata. If that is the case, she must further determine which mastery experiences might weaken the avoidance component and which intentional components should be strengthened, and how this can be accomplished.

If no conscious awareness exists for the schema, this means that this schema controls the patient's experience and behavior via the implicit mode of functioning. The therapist then needs to establish how the schema may be process-activated bottom-up, and which techniques to apply to direct the patient's attention to the activity of the schema and to keep it there so the patient can develop consciousness for it. Greenberg, Rice and Elliott (1993) have described techniques that could be useful for this.

5. How should one **shape the relationship**? Based on our previous discussions this question requires a resource and a problem perspective.

From the resource perspective we need to address the question of complementary relationship-shaping. Complementary relationship-shaping aims to provide the patient with need-fulfilling perceptions, thereby facilitating the process of resource activation, which, at least in our conception, underlies every successful therapy. One requirement for planning complementary relationship-shaping is that the therapist gets some idea of the most important motivational schemata and of the intentional components of the conflict schemata. If the therapist behaves in a fashion complementary to the patient's latent wishes, then she enables the patient to have need-fulfilling perceptions that he would otherwise not have.

I have already discussed the goals the therapist needs to behave complimentarily towards; namely, the intentional schema components. The therapist ought to develop a concrete plan for implementing the complementary relationship. The **therapeutic procedures** to be applied are also part of this. These should be selected and designed to enable the patient to participate actively in a manner that is consistent with extant goals and abilities. If one is working with a patient with a very pronounced autonomy schema, steps must be taken to ensure that he is informed about the various options, which will allow him to participate or codetermine every step and let him be in charge as much as possible. Active instruction would be given only upon his expressed request or approval. Planning should include what the therapist explicitly wants to realize as well as what she wants to avoid.

The plan should also specify how the therapist wants to relate **nonverbally** to the patient. Some examples would be: Not responding to the patient's dismissive tone, but taking everything as seriously as the content suggests. Or: Leaning forward towards the patient with an open body posture, not distancing oneself, looking at him often and in a friendly way, smiling, when the patient behaves condescendingly or makes disparaging statements.

For the concrete implementation of the complementary relationship, it is crucial that the therapist has developed a clear understanding with **words/expressions/sentences/images** she should use as often as possible in her communication with the patient which make the patient feel good regarding his most important goals and wishes; what agrees with his goals and values, and what is it that confirms them? It is useful to devise a list of remarks that would represent perceptions corresponding to the patient's goals. Formulating such remarks may lead to a more precise conceptualization of how the patient would like to see himself reflected in his interpersonal environment.

Later, when the actual therapy is performed, this list is very helpful and should be consulted time and again as a preparation for the individual therapy sessions. The art of complementary relationship-shaping includes using these expressions, words, sentences, and images incidentally slipped, even when commenting on a completely different subject. Remarks that are intended to effect a specific change such as: requests, suggestions, interpretations or confrontations, for example, can be introduced with a subordinate clause referring to one of the patient's important positive goals. This way the therapist's interventions can be placed in the context of the patient's own goals, even if the interventions themselves might very well initially evoke uncomfortable feelings. Creating such a context may increase the patient's receptiveness for interventions intended to cause change, contributing directly to making these interventions more effective. Additionally, these remarks slipped in on the side may, irrespective of the interventions otherwise, also repeatedly lead to self-esteem-increasing perceptions with positive effects for how he experiences the therapy sessions.

The question of expected **relationship tests** arises from the **problem perspective**. I mentioned earlier that the therapist may also activate conflicted wishes and fears with her complementary relationship behavior and that it is important for her to behave in a manner consistent with the wishes and not with the fears, so the patient can make corrective emotional experiences. However, such relationship tests may be provoked not solely by the therapist's complementary strategy but also by an interpersonal situation in itself. It is to be expected that the patient brings his most important motivational schemata into the interpersonal situation of therapy, and quite probably this also applies to his conflict schemata. The relationship with the therapist can activate wishes that are linked to a conflict schema. Thus, activating such wishes may simultaneously activate the fear that the wish will not be attained. As the patient strives to create perceptions consistent with this wishes but simultaneously aims to prevent potential disappointment, the therapist is practically invited to act in a way that confirms the patient's fears.

Interaction patterns and conflict schemata should therefore be considered when formulating which relationship tests might be expected from the patient. Often more than one possible relationship test can be defined. For each relationship test, four components should be specified:
- The **behavior** that might be displayed by the patient,
- the **wish** driving this behavior,
- the **fear** of how the therapist might react and,
- the desired **behavior by the therapist** that might lead to a positive corrective experience in the patient and the behavior the therapist should actively avoid.

Specification of these components prepares the therapist for the early detection of these relationship tests, thus preventing the situation where she is suddenly in the position of having to develop an idea on the spot about how to react in the best interest of the patient.

6. Which **therapeutic goals** does the patient seem most **motivated** for at the moment?

Which positive motivational schemata are especially strongly activated in the patient's present life situation? Therapy goals that allow perceptions congruent with these positive motivational schemata should be targeted first. The same applies for the choice of techniques employed to achieve these goals. This essentially means determining the procedures for which the patient tends to have the highest motivation and the best abilities.

7. Which goals should be targeted and given what priority, and in which **temporal order**, **format** and **therapeutic setting**?

Our three-component model of the mechanism of psychotherapy offers some guidelines on this. Top priority must be to get the process of resource activation going. If this is not successful, treatment has little chance to succeed. The patient must have need-fulfilling experiences. Shaping a resource-oriented relationship can promote this, as can the therapist aiding the patient in making initial mastery experiences.

Thus, along with resource activation, the therapist may start with any interventions that promise the most success, the majority of which are the well tested, disorder-specific interventions. Priority may be given to these because mental disorders cause the strongest immediate suffering. According to the three-phase model of Howard and colleagues (1992), following an initial increase in feelings of well-being—which we would ascribe to the process of resource activation—most likely the symptoms of the mental disorder(s) will improve first. In addition to the first change component, this would indicate that during the first therapeutic phase the therapist employs mostly the second change component, which is more about mastery-oriented and disorder-specific interventions than about those that create awareness and change motivations.

There are also patients who come to therapy with a clarification-oriented motivation, who primarily want to have a better understanding of what is going on with them. In a situation where the need for orientation and comprehension is especially strongly activated, starting with awareness-facilitation rather than with mastery-oriented interventions is recommended. These spontaneously active schemata should be considered from the resource aspect so their spontaneous activity can be utilized for therapy.

Therefore, when formulating the temporal sequence of the treatment plan, therapy goals, and specific interventions, therapists should be guided by the resource- rather than the problem perspective.

Therapy researcher: As you comment on therapy planning, it becomes clear to me that any therapist wanting to implement such a patient-tailored therapy must have quite a rich repertoire of therapeutic interventions. This includes being competent to shape a resource-oriented relationship with very different persons, being able to perform disorder-specific interventions for the various mental disorders, being able to activate avoidance schemata, being able to facilitate mastery experiences to change motivational schemata, and being able to employ awareness-creating interventions, such as attention focusing, confrontations, interpretations, clarification-oriented conversation, and much more.

I am aware that we simply have to presume such competence rather than making it the subject of our conversation. After all, we are not reinventing the wheel here. What I really want to know is how would you imagine a therapist should acquire this kind of competence? I would like to discuss some questions about the therapist's training later.

There is another urgent question we should not put off. According to your concept of therapy planning, motivational schemata play a very special role both under the resource and under the problem aspect. Yet, you simply presume that we have knowledge of these schemata. One important point remains undisclosed. I would like to know how the therapist becomes familiar with these motivational schemata, especially since the avoidance schemata are rather difficult to recognize, as you pointed out. It is exactly the avoidance schemata that play a crucial role in therapy planning from the problem perspective. In our theoretical concept, for example, discordance between motivational schemata also plays an important role and you have, for instance, referred to levels of inconsistency. My question is: How can schemata and inconsistencies be ascertained somewhat reliably so they may be included in therapy planning? You must have some ideas about that because otherwise you would not have been able to ascribe such an important role to these constructs.

3.24 Schema Analysis

Therapist: Of course, you are absolutely right. Leaving this point out so far has allowed me to give you an overview on the entire planning of therapy. Patient-tailored therapy planning in the manner just introduced is impossible without both a schema- and a consistency analysis. The constellation of motivational schemata plays such an important role in our theoretical conception—first for the understanding of mental disorders, second for an explanation of the mechanism of psychotherapy, and third for the actual therapy planning—that it must be fully grasped in order to draw practical conclusions from it, which has been our declared goal.

How can motivational schemata and their possible inconsistency-creating constellation be operationalized or grasped with a reasonable amount of therapeutic effort?

Grawe's work group has been devoted to exactly this question for over twenty years. My response to your question will therefore refer mostly to procedures developed by this group.

About twenty years ago, Grawe conceptualized a method for measuring what we refer to as motivational schemata. At that time, this was known as "vertical behavior analysis" (Grawe & Dziewas, 1978; Grawe, 1980 b, 1982; Caspar & Grawe, 1982). Beginning with the patient's interpersonal behavior, the method was used to infer his most important "interaction plans." The method presumes that the patient employs his interpersonal behavior, particularly his nonverbal behavior, to achieve certain interpersonal goals. It does not assume conscious pursuit of these plans by the patient. Plans may be pursued both in the implicit and in the conscious mode of functioning. In this respect, the concept of "plan" and the concept of motivational schema are identical. The theoretical basis for this plan concept, which marked the turn from behaviorism to cognitive psychology, was laid down by Miller, Galanter and Pribram (1960).

In a second phase, vertical behavior analysis was methodically and conceptually developed into "plan analysis" by Caspar and Grawe, who is an associate of Grawe (Grawe & Caspar, 1984; Caspar, 1989). In its advanced form, this method of deriving a plan from observable behavior is described in detail in Caspar (1996). Elaborating in detail on the method itself would lead me too far afield. It suffices to say that it is well tested in clinical practice and is applied by many cognitive behavior therapists. The outcome of a plan analysis is an individual hierarchical structure of the patient's most important approach and avoidance plans. Such a plan structure basically gives us some insight into the goal components of the patient's most important motivational schemata.

In a third phase, Grawe (1986) substituted the plan construct with the schema construct originally developed by Piaget (1976) and Neisser (1974). The reason for this change was that the schema construct was better suited to conceptualize change processes. Thus, the plan analysis explains the patient's current experience and behavior but it was not well suited for conceptualizing changes. Piaget, however, was primarily concerned with developmental processes, and he developed not only the schema construct but also the dialectical processes of assimilation and accommodation. Grawe's schema-theoretical conception of the therapeutic change process (Grawe, 1986, 1987, 1988) exceeded plan analysis by emphasizing change process rather than the analysis of experience and behavior. Nonetheless, plan analysis remained an important instrument of schema-theoretical based case conceptualization.

Grawe and associates further developed plan analysis into schema analysis (Grawe et al., 1996) to facilitate schema-theoretical case conceptualizations. In schema analysis, "negative emotional schemata"—those that are oriented towards the avoidance of negative emotions—play an important role. The avoided negative emotions, according to this model, stem from the violation of positive wishes or intentional schemata. Thus, by including both approach and avoidance processes, schema analysis emphasized conflicted motivations. In this model, the activity of the intentional or approach component was thought to be blocked or inhibited by the dominant avoidance component. However, instead of vanishing completely, the intentional component was thought to continue to exist and influence experience and behavior in the form of indirectly expressed or non-conscious wishes.

This maps on quite nicely to the conceptualization of conflict schemata you developed in the second dialogue. According to your model, avoidance schemata that aim to avoid violations of basic needs are often balanced by weaker or latent wish components. If we encounter an avoidance schema, then, we should also look for such a hidden wish component. Clearly, conflicts receive more attention in schema-analytical case conceptualizations than originally in plan analysis.

Another modification is that schema-analysis pays greater attention than plan analysis to processes in the patient's social network. Thus, schema-analysis assumes much more of an interpersonal perspective than does plan analysis. Similar to the concept of interpersonal attractors, relationships are attributed their own super-individual dynamic.

I do not wish to discuss the various components of schema-analytic case conception in any greater depth. Detailed written instruction (Grawe et al., 1996) and an example of a case analysis (Heiniger et al., 1996) are available. This method is being applied routinely in clinical practice for some years now, and it is the basis of therapy planning according to Grawe's concept of a general psychotherapy. I will introduce a case example for this later, which will make clear exactly which therapeutic consequences result from schema-analytical case conceptualizations.

Therapy researcher: I would welcome that. However, I still do not fully comprehend how a therapist gets a handle on the patient's motivational schemata. Is the therapist supposed to proceed purely non-deductively every time, inferring from the patient's behaviors which goals they might serve? Isn't this rather inefficient? You state that the method has long been applied in clinical practice, but by now wouldn't we have more extensive experiences regarding which constellations of intentional and avoidance schemata occur most often in clinical practice? Somehow it should be possible to benefit from all these experiences.

Therapist: Grawe and the members of his group were proceeding in exactly this way. Today, schema analyses are based on the experiences gained from those previously performed. One associate of Grawe's, Grosse Holtforth, extracted all of the goal components of intentional and avoidance schemata deduced by the therapists from 77 schema analyses documented at the Psychotherapy Center of the University of Bern, where plan and schema analysis were developed. These goal components were supplemented by another 48 components from Ford's (1992) goal taxonomy, so that all potentially relevant goals were truly represented. After correcting minor deviations in language, there were a total of 279 intentional and 138 avoidance goal components. Each of these approach and avoidance goals was written on a small card and passed out to 30 therapists of different theoretical orientations who were asked to arrange the schemata according to categories they were allowed to develop on their own.

The similarity values resulting from these ratings were entered into a hierarchical cluster analysis. Based on these results, a goal taxonomy was constructed for the intentional and for the avoidance goal schemata. This taxonomy includes 14 broad classes for approach goals and 9 for avoidance goals, with each goal class having 3-4 more specific sub-goals. The goals are listed in Table 3.5. It is important to note that these goals are not theoretically derived but deduced from actual clinical work.

Table 3.5:

The empirically derived goal taxonomy for clinically relevant approach and avoidance goals by Grosse Holtforth and Grawe. The goals are broad goal categories with 3-4 sub-goals each. These sub-goals are formulated into items that are presented to both patient and therapist for assessment.

Taxonomy of Approach and Avoidance Goals	
Approach Goals	Avoidance Goals
Intimacy / Attachment	Loneliness / Separation
Affiliation / Sociability	Deprecation / Derogation
Altruism	Humiliation / Embarrassment
Help	Accusations / Criticism
Recognition / Approval	Dependency / Autonomy-loss
Status / Admiration	Hostility / Aggression
Autonomy	Vulnerability / Loss of control
Performance	Helplessness
Control	Failure
Education / Understanding	
Spirituality / Meaning	
Variety / Excitement	
Self-confidence	
Self-reward	

The sub-goals were reformulated into commonly understood items such as "being tender with somebody," "having control of myself," "sticking to the rules," etc. These items were the basis for the construction of a questionnaire with eventually 114 items. The questionnaire is available in two forms, one for the self-assessment of the patient, and one for an assessment of patient's goals by the therapist.

The questionnaire is also available in a computerized version, with the items appearing on screen and being easily answerable with just a mouse click. The computer then produces two profiles of the patient's most important goals; one for intentional and one for avoidance goals. There is a highly significant difference between psychotherapy patients and non-patients, in that patients clearly endorsed more avoidance goals. Interestingly enough, though, the patients also rated intentional goals lower, but still significantly higher than non-patients. It would seem that in psychotherapy patients approach and avoidance goals are both more salient than is the case for non-patients.

The therapist independently assesses the patient on the same items. This way, the therapist attains a profile of the patient's most important goals from her own perspective. The differences in self-assessment and external assessment are of specific interest because they provide insight as to what the therapist might have neglected in her view of the patient, or they may yield some information on schemata that are not represented in the patient's consciousness but are expressed in his behavior.

On the basis of these profiles and a final integration of all available information, the therapist determines what the patient's most important intentional schemata likely are. For the conflict schemata, the avoidance components are described first, followed by the more or less latent wish components. By definition, these wish components are not necessarily openly observable but can only be inferred.

Based on the goal component, every important schema is further elaborated with the aid of the computer. Computer templates or frames, in Minsky's (1975) terms, are used, in which fields appear that can be filled in by the therapist for each individual patient.

Such a frame contains the following components (fields) for **intentional schema,** which the therapist is supposed to provide detailed information on:

Frame for an intentional schema
- **Definition** of the intentional schema:
- **Goal component** of the schema: definition of the goal, need or wish. Prototypical perceptions, situations, or events in line with this goal are helpful for making the goal component more tangible:
- **Action component:** Plans and behaviors used by the patient to attain the goal:
- Examples of **cognitions** accompanying the schema's activity:
- **Emotions** accompanying the activity of the schema:
- Examples of **situations** in which the schema is activated:

A conflict schema requires more components to be elaborated:

> **Frame for a conflict schema**
> - **Definition** of the conflict schema (choose a term best suited for this particular patient):
> - **Avoidance goal component:** Which transactions with the environment are avoided? Which emotions are associated with these transactions, i.e. which emotions are avoided?
> - **Wish component:** Which latent wish can be inferred, the violation of which would result in the avoided emotions? By definition it must be wishes which the patient is not very well able to satisfy in his present life situation:
> - **Cognitions** accompanying the schema's activity, such as fears, irrational beliefs, rationalizations, negative fantasies:
> - **Emotions** actually experienced, accompanying the activity of the avoidance schema (not the avoided emotions, but the emotions experienced while in the process of avoiding):
> - **Avoidance plans/strategies and avoidant behavior:**
> - **Approach behavior in line with the wish component:** are there any noticeable attempts of the patient to satisfy the original wish? Which behaviors, which plans can be interpreted as an attempt to do so?
> - **Situations:** In which situations is this schema activated? Which situations are actively avoided by the patient, which domains does he therefore exclude from his life ? Which kinds of situations will most easily bring out the avoided emotions?
> - **Developmental conditions:** information on the conditions under which the conflict   schema developed over the course of the patient's life history (for example family constellations, traumatic events):

To give you a more concrete idea of how a completed frame of a schemata may appear as part of a schema analysis, Table 3.6 illustrates an example for an elaborated intentional schema, Table 3.7 for a conflict schema.

Table 3.6:
Example of an elaborated intentional schema (IS)

IS 1

Definition: Support and trust among family and friends.

Transactions (goal) to be established: reliable relationships.

Plans: Do everything for your loved ones, keep the family together, promote coherence, establish your own family, mediate between those that are close.

Behavior: Does a lot for the parents, spends a lot of time with the parents, helps friends whenever he can, mediates between family and friends that do not come along, plans a family, takes his girlfriend's opinion into consideration, puts off his own wishes in favor of the perspective to live together with his girlfriend in the future.

Cognitions: I am happy when the most important people around me come along well; I would like to repay my parents somehow for my happy youth; family means sticking together and jointly overcoming problems; I would like to be there if someone needs me; I would like to have people that are there for me if I need them.

Emotions: Happiness, love, well-being, security.

Situations: Interactions with close persons.

Table 3.7:
Example of an elaborated conflict schema (CS)

CS 1

Definition: Avoid defeats.

Avoided transactions (goal): Failing.

Avoided emotions: Shame, disappointment, anger.

Accompanying emotions: Insecurity, fear.

Plans: Do not give up; make an all out effort; do not accept rejections; avoid test situations.

Behavior: Makes an all out effort to achieve his goals; reflects intensively about his problems; goes through training in an insurance company after failure in business school; still courts his ex-wife after separation; needs several attempts to start therapy; postpones exams; is unable to study properly due to thinking about his ex-wife.

Cognitions: I should actually manage all this myself; I have lost; I am powerless; I am disappointed about myself that I am unable to manage this on my own; I have to perform better no matter what happens; turbulent feelings lead to a lack of achievement; people in psychotherapy are weak.

Positive wish: acknowledgment and esteem by significant others.

Approach behavior: Continues with this behavior until no longer able.

Situations: Apprenticeship, relations to those persons.

Development: Father was very successful in his occupation, partial association of esteem and occupational achievement; observational learning; apprentices dropping out from their training are considered failures, drop out from business school.

The therapist will have quite a tangible understanding of the most important determinants controlling the patient's mental functioning following such an elaboration of each important schema.

A therapist familiar with this particular form of computer-assisted schema analysis requires about an hour to get to this point. However, an assessment and analysis of the inconsistency in mental functioning is still needed.

3.25 Consistency Analysis

According to our model, the incongruence between needs and actual experiences and the discordance of motivational schemata may serve as a breeding ground for mental disorders. Further, we reasoned that individual control parameters may form the basis for the disorders' tenacious nature. Testing this assumption requires that inconsistency in mental functioning be reliably and validly assessed. Clinical consequences for this assumption can only be drawn when a therapist is sure that there is an increased inconsistency level in a patient, and when the therapist knows which schemata are involved in the inconsistency.

These considerations have led to even further advancement of schema analysis by Grosse Holtforth and Grawe. The schemata elaborated in the procedure we just described become the subject of another computer-assisted analysis aimed at quantifying the total inconsistency in mental functioning and localizing its sources.

To determine the extent of the incongruences, therapist and patient independently assess whether the patient is currently able to realize his most important goals. This procedure yields an overall incongruence level and a localization of the specific sources of incongruence. Schemata that most urgently require change are thus localized.

Incongruities or external inconsistencies are largely based on discordances or internal inconsistencies between motivational schemata. Thus, the next step of the consistency analysis is focused on a more detailed analysis of the internal inconsistency in mental functioning.

In this analysis, a therapist and patient separately rate the compatibility or incompatibility of previously identified schemata. This is done in the format of triadic comparisons. A computer program for conflict measurement developed by Lauterbach (1996) and adapted for this purpose is used to accomplish this. The goal components that are most important for the individual's schemata become elements of these triadic comparisons. Each goal is assessed for its incompatibility with each other goal in an indirect form. The computer program calculates a total index for the extent of inconsistency among the various elements from the total number of triadic comparisons. This index then corresponds to what we refer to as the inconsistency level in mental functioning; something we consider to be very important for therapeutic decisions. Additional conflict values are also computed, pinpointing in greater detail the sources of discordance and giving us more specific information about the kinds of conflicts. Finally, the computer program comes up with the schemata that contribute the most to the discordance.

The consistency analysis yields concrete information for the therapist about whether, and at which points, motivation-changing interventions make sense. It creates an operationalized, empirical foundation for therapeutic decision-making with respect to the third of our three change components of successful psychotherapy. For me, this is a first step towards the goal of establishing a reliably operationalized and testable basis for motivation-changing interventions, similar to that which exists for disorder-specific interventions.

Therapy researcher: Because this method appears suitable for research as well as for therapeutic practice, it achieves much of what I said was necessary in our first conversation (section 1.26): the empirical measurement of motivational conflicts and their inclusion into research questions. I wonder why you didn't mention this method earlier. This is exactly what I had requested, and I never heard a word about these developments.

Therapist: I have only recently learned about the development of schema analysis into consistency analysis; this information has not even been published yet. I heard about it incidentally and attempted to get more detailed information. Then I had the opportunity to try this out on my computer and was rather impressed by both the clinical relevance and the multitude of results produced by the consistency analysis. I have not even been able to report everything here because I did not fully understand precisely how this works. With this method, it is even possible to obtain quantitative information about the consciousness level of the patient's individual conflicts. What I have yet to understand though is how the method computes this, but this will be published very soon, and when that happens, you will probably immediately understand this, as you are more familiar with such methods.

Just the fact that something like that has been developed is a bright spot on the horizon. In the past we always had to switch to a different ideology when dealing with conflicts rather than specific disorders. I hope that these days will soon be behind us; in fact, I no regard such work as utopian.

Psychologist: I have been quiet for a while now, not because I am disinterested, but rather because I have little to contribute. However, I now have a request. While all that you said makes sense to me, I still have difficulty imagining how therapy would be conducted on a concrete level, according to your model. Could you maybe take some concrete examples from your practice and explain how such a procedure might work, or is this all still up in the air?

Therapist: As I said already: This is already reality for me, and not just for me; others have also performed therapies consistent with our theoretical view. Case reports have even been published already. Grawe's concept of a general psychotherapy is probably closest to our view here. The Psychotherapy Center of the University of Bern, where Grawe and his associates developed his clinical concepts has been performing therapies for years that may not quite correspond to our ideas, but that approximate them somewhat. Let us perhaps turn to one of these well-documented, published cases and reflect on it from our theoretical perspective. I have brought such a case report because I expected that we may need it.

If you are interested, let me introduce this case to you. It was published by the authors, who were also the therapists. We may interrupt occasionally to think about what is happening from our point of view. The case concerns a patient with a severe compulsion to wash his hands, and the authors are Ambühl and Heiniger (1997). I will read to you directly from the report.

3.26   Case Example for a Psychological Therapy

"1. Introduction

In this article we describe and discuss the therapy of a 23-year-old patient with a severe compulsion for washing. For a better understanding of this therapy we first describe the procedure commonly used for adult outpatient treatment at the Psychotherapy Center of the University of Bern.

2. Intake assessment

Prior to psychotherapy, a thorough intake assessment is conducted to clarify the nature of the problems. The purpose of this intake assessment is to derive a patient-tailored and problem-specific case conceptualization and treatment plan. This includes deciding on a suitable therapy setting as well as the question of which problems require clarification and problem solving. The decision about the best therapy setting depends on the question of which setting allows for the best actuation of extant problems, and which setting allows for the best activation of resources. In this case, the intake assessment consisted of the following steps:

- *A first meeting, including the entire family (father, mother, son) at the patient's request);*
- *A one-on-one conversation with the patient giving a detailed picture of the nature of his problems;*
- *A diagnostic test with the patient using a battery of standard measures as well as the Hamburg Compulsion Inventory as a disorder-specific measurement instrument;*
- *A behavioral observation of the patient on location, at his home;*
- *Discussing the treatment plan with a team of therapists;*
- *Discussing the treatment plan with the patient and his parents."*

Therapy researcher: This is almost exactly like the intake procedure you introduced earlier as a model (Figure 3.7, section 3.22).

Therapist: There are other institutions that work somewhat similarly, and although there are not so many, this example shows that such a pre-therapy intake procedure can be integrated in routine practice. In my own practice I have found it to be rather handy.
Continuing:

"2.1 Scheduling

The patient calls to schedule an appointment for his first meeting. At the end of the conversation he asks whether it is OK to bring along his parents; the therapist agrees. A few days prior to the first meeting the therapist receives a letter from the patient's father including a report by another therapist as well as a brief patient history written by the patient's parents. The letter reveals that their son was unable to continue his studies due to the severe compulsion, which now requires more intensive treatment. In addition, the letter contains a number of questions regarding the most recent findings on curing compulsive disorders and regarding possibilities for inpatient treatment in psychosomatic clinics. The father's letter concludes with the sentence: 'We appreciate your advice regarding how we could make some progress in treating this obsessive-compulsive neurosis.'

The enclosed report from the other therapist contains a brief patient history, diagnostic considerations, a list of the different psychotherapies previously begun by the patient along with the therapist's concomitant request: '...that this young and nice person be helped in the best way possible.'

2.2 Current life situation and problems

For eight years the 23-year-old patient has been suffering from a severe washing compulsion. Therapy is presently required because he is barely able to leave the house at this point, he goes through daily washing rituals of differing intensity and duration, and his parents are terrorized by his compulsive behaviors, enormously limiting their mobility. The entire family has reached their limits emotionally, wild arguments between parents and son are common, it seems to be only a question of time until the system crashes through a violent act. The parents are fed up with their son's problems and are no longer willing to accept the limitations imposed by his problems. They want to put an end to this and are therefore intensively looking for possibilities for inpatient care within a German speaking area.

2.3 Social and Clinical History

The patient grew up as an only child with his parents. The pregnancy was complicated and the mother was unable to have any more children, although she would have liked another one. A suction bell was used in the birth, and shortly thereafter the patient contracted hepatitis, although no blood transfusion was necessary. According to the mother, as a small child her son was already very precise, even fussy and pedantic. Early on he already showed an interest in technology, his hobby is model trains. His parents always noticed two sides in him: On the one hand, the technical interests; on the other, a very tactful and sensitive nature; they say that he was never a simple child but had always asked question upon question.

From the age of four on, the patient suffered from severe hay fever allergies, which led to his contacts with other children being possible almost exclusively at home. Because of the pollen he often had to wear a mask to go to school and was unable to play outside. For this reason he was considered odd and was already socially isolated at that time. In addition, he periodically suffered from asthma attacks, which later subsided. He was under the constant supervision of a physician. His parents maintained a diary of his allergies and about how he responded to treatments. Eventually, a successful desensitization treatment was performed so that the patient was free of allergies by the age of 15.

Around that time he began to wash the sleeves of his clothing as well as his school bag, and he also took very long showers. In school the patient was teased because of his small stature. He was at the mercy of others, ridiculed and unable to defend himself very well. Because he was at the top of his class and a teachers' favorite, his popularity among his peers was rather low and he was thereby predestined for the role of scapegoat. He was regularly abused by some of his classmates, who from thereon played a main role in his anxiety fantasies. During his time in school, the patient took judo to become tougher. He had little contact with peers, his parents treated him more like a partner than a child from early on. He had a very good relationship with his grandmother, with whom he visited often on his vacations. She died when the patient was 16.

During his years at high school the patient was again assaulted and abused—this time by different classmates. It was then that his washing compulsion worsened again. He completed his studies and successfully graduated from school at the age of twenty and then completed a four-month long military service without any major problems.

Following high school the patient enrolled in university, where he once again encountered his former classmates. These encounters worsened his compulsion to the point that he lacked the time to attend university and missed his exams. He switched to a different university in a different part of the country, hoping he would feel more comfortable there, with less chance of encountering any former classmates. The patient spent one year there. Although his compulsion decreased somewhat, his rituals still required too much time for him to successfully complete his studies. His social isolation became more extreme and he was no longer able to keep his studio clean, which remained in a state of chaos most of the time because it was flooded with water due to his extensive washing rituals. Finally, his family decided that the patient should take a one-year break from university, in order to use this time to reduce his symptoms and correct the 'basic problems' underlying them.

2.4 Previous Therapy Attempts

The patient already had several attempts at various therapies. At the age of 17, he saw a psychiatrist and underwent a behaviorally-oriented treatment, which produced a slight reduction in the compulsive symptomatology, although according to both parents and patient, the basic underlying problem remained unresolved. Next, a family therapist was consulted who tried—unsuccessfully—to come to solutions together with the family. At the same time, the patient was directed to try judo to physically loosen him up and toughen him. After graduation, right when he began attending university, the patient began psychoanalytic treatment, which he discontinued a half year later due to the lack of a trusting relationship with this therapist. Afterwards he saw the above mentioned therapist who reportedly, over a period of six months, treated him with 'analytically-oriented client-centered therapy, supplemented by behavioral and Gestalt approaches.' Due to illness, this therapist was forced to prematurely discontinue her patient's therapy and transferred him to a colleague.

At the time of enrollment, the patient already had five attempts at therapy behind him, none of which produced the desired effect: a decrease in or elimination of the compulsive disorder. On the contrary, the washing compulsion continuously worsened so that at the time of the intake interview the parents were convinced that only inpatient therapy might help."

Psychologist: No wonder the psychotherapeutic profession doesn't enjoy the best reputation in the public eye and among health insurance companies. Considering that such a young man already has attempted five unsuccessful therapies, clearly this does not show psychotherapies in the most favorable light. After all, this patient—by undergoing behavior therapy, psychoanalysis, family therapy, and more eclectic therapies—had already "scoured" the most significant therapies around, while being even worse off than ever after these five treatments. Now I am really eager to see how a therapy which you claim comes fairly close to our theoretical conception actually looked like for this particular patient and how effective it was.

Therapist: Most likely, this patient is not an atypical example of the odyssey many patients take through the system of therapy schools. How should a patient be able to find out the treatment best suited for him? It all boils down to a trial and error approach. Yet all this can be prevented if all therapies are preceded by an integrative case conceptualization and treatment planning process.

This example demonstrates that the problem of case conceptualization can most likely not be solved by formulating a differential conceptualization from each of the existing schools of therapy, considering that at some point the patient tried almost all the forms of treatment available. Every one proved to be insufficient in its effect. Maybe the reason is that each form of therapy, in the way it separates itself from the other therapies, does not fully account for the patient, whose self is not demarcated by the same boundaries as those existing between the various schools of therapy. My concept of a patient-tailored conceptualization does not point anyone towards a certain thera-peutic direction; it completely refrains from any demarcations between therapy schools. The aim is to compose a new, optimally tailored treatment plan based on all the ingre-dients available for a given patient, not to choose an "off-the-rack" therapy, but a cus-tom-made suit tailored to fit each patient.

"2.5 Description of the symptoms at the beginning of therapy

At the time of the intake interview the patient is living back in his parents' home in a small urban community. He rises in the early afternoon and one of his parents prepares a full meal for him. All of his attention is directed at avoiding any contact with anything that could possibly be associated with his former classmates who had previously ha-rassed him at the two schools. He walks very slowly in small steps through the few rooms of the house that he is still able to walk through. While doing so he is completely concentrated on avoiding getting too close to the wall or something 'dangerous.' Even the parents are not allowed to come too near him. He sits only on certain chairs cov-ered with white cloth. The patient abandoned his original room a few years ago think-ing that he could thus keep it clean from (imaginary) dirt. He moved into the guest room. Even his model train set, which is worth a small fortune, he wanted to keep absolutely clean. It has been piled into boxes that sit in the chaotic basement in which he has not set foot in years.

Although the patient is meticulously focused on avoiding all 'dangerous' and 'fear-eliciting' objects or situations, he is nonetheless never certain whether he may or may not have come into contact with the dirt of these former classmates, and the more likely this assumption appears to him, the more he must do something to reduce this fear. The only thing that helps him is to wash himself intensively. He does this daily and exten-sively in the kitchen, often in front of his parents while they are having dinner. In earlier times he washed in his parents' bathroom until they finally succeeded in driving him out of there. Since then he washes himself in the kitchen: With a piece of soap he foams lather for approximately 15 minutes to foam the entire counter and front side of the sink. Then he washes his hands and forearms, proceeding to his head and hair. In the course of this

Figure 3.8:
Psychopathological condition of the patient before (pretest) and after therapy (posttest) measured with the symptom checklist SCL-90R

The zero line close to the left edge indicates the mean-value of a non-clinical normal popula-tion. The gray, uninterrupted line, with the gray-shaded area indicates the mean value of a clinical reference group of psychotherapy patients with a standard deviation at top and bottom. The patient's condition is illustrated against this background. In this patient, for instance, one can see that his phobic fear is even stronger than in the average clinical reference group. Fol-lowing therapy his condition more approaches that of the non-clinical normal population.

Illustrations of the outcome and process quality of therapies, such as in this and the following figures, are produced by a computer program called "Figuration Analysis" developed at the Psychotherapy Center in Bern. The program can be used for a routine process and outcome evaluation in therapeutic practice. It can produce "figurations" such as this and the following figures for tests and questionnaires of any kind. A description of the program and its various possibilities can be found in Grawe and Baltensperger (1998). Additional information on func-tions, application and ordering of the program: Professor K. Grawe, Institute of Psychology, Muesmattstrasse 45, CH-3009 Bern, email: klaus.grawe@psy.unibe.ch.

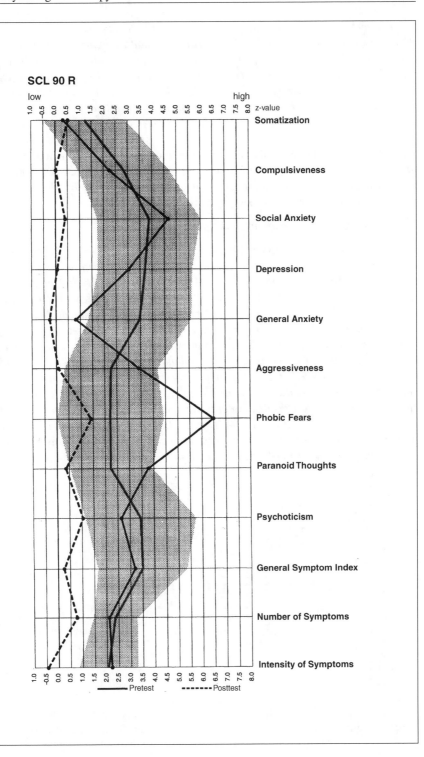

process, the patient 'sheds' himself by taking off his wet clothes and dropping them to the soaking wet floor until he finally, sometime around two in the morning, stands there entirely naked and, in his eyes, so clean that he may now go to his 'clean' bed, falling into a 12-hour long deep sleep out of exhaustion. The father, who rises first, has to clean the two kitchen sinks, dry the floor, and carry the wet clothes to the laundry room in a way strictly regimented by his son. At the end of this kitchen cleaning procedure the father unwraps a new piece of soap and angrily throws it into the soap dish."

Psychologist: I believe this very nicely demonstrates how a mental disorder can unfold its own dynamic and come to control more and more processes. This patient's compulsion has indeed become a structural pattern ruling family life. In this instance it would truly seem accurate to speak of a disorder attractor.

"2.6 Test diagnostic description of the pre-therapy state

For the test diagnostic assessment we used the standard battery of tests commonly used at the Psychotherapy Center in Bern, consisting of the Symptom Checklist SCL 90-R, the Social Anxiety Questionnaire (CSAQ), the Emotionality Inventory (EMI), the Control Belief Inventory, the Inventory of Interpersonal Problems IIP, a Self-concept Questionnaire (SCQ) rated by the patient and by a significant other, the Impact Message Inventory IMI; the Family Questionnaire FAQ, and in addition as a disorder-specific measure, the Hamburg Compulsion Inventory HCI. Except for the last, all test results are illustrated as figurations in which the individual patient is depicted in comparison with all patients treated at the psychotherapy center. The zero line indicates the mean value of the normal population (for more details see Grawe & Braun, 1994). We will not elaborate on all the test results, but only comment on the most noteworthy of these.

In the symptom checklist SCL 90-R (Figure 3.8) what strikes one first is the strongly pronounced phobic fear. This is not surprising considering how many situations and objects the patient constantly avoids due to his fear of coming into contact with dirt.

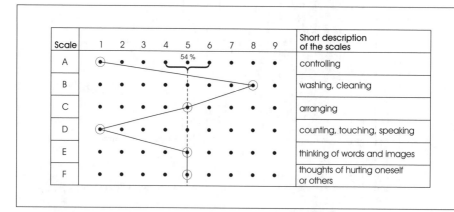

Figure 3.9:
Pretest patient profile in the Hamburg Compulsion Inventory (HCI). The HCI differentiates between different forms of compulsive disorders. The profile indicates that the patient's compulsiveness is largely limited to the compulsion for washing.

Also the noticeably strong social anxieties, vulnerability and self-consciousness in contact with others is easily explained by his interpersonal experiences. What is surprising, however, is his relatively low value on the compulsion scale which must be probably explained by the fact that the patient, except for his strong compulsion to wash, has few other compulsions and in particular no control compulsions.

This assumption is confirmed by the values in the HCI (Figure 3.9). In this inventory the patient reaches an extreme value in the area 'washing, cleaning,' whereas he has no problems at all on the scales A ('controlling') and D ('counting, touching, speaking'). In the areas C ('arranging'), E ('thinking of words, images, thought chains, thoughts prior to action') and F ('thoughts of hurting oneself and others') he is in the average range of those patients with compulsive disorders.

The EMI (Figure 3.10) clearly shows the patient's exhausted state which may be seen as a consequence of the long, intensive washing rituals. Also visible, albeit less clearly, is the aggressive mood that may have something to do with the serious arguments he has with his parents.

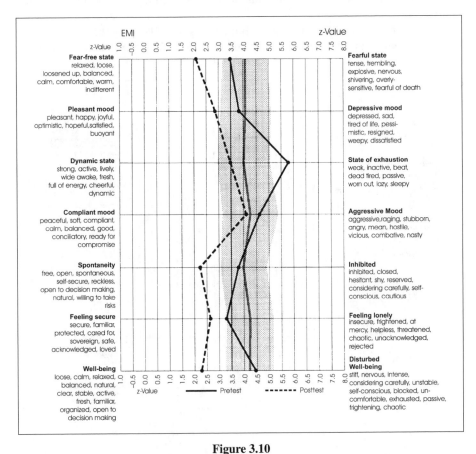

Figure 3.10
Patient's test profiles in the Emotionality Inventory (EMI). Please see Figure 3.8 for more details as these figures are similarly constructed.

The Social Anxiety Questionnaire (Figure 3.11) reveals that the patient has difficulties in his contact with others, in showing affection and he appears rather shy, inhibited, and self-conscious. Apart from that, he seems to be capable of asserting himself.

Psychologist: This is an enormous amount of time and effort invested in testing, which is apparently routinely done. Is that really feasible in therapeutic practice?

Therapy researcher: I also used to think that something of that magnitude was only possible in research projects, but I now know better. Evidently almost all patients see the point of such a thorough psychological assessment when it is presented to them as part of efforts to determine the best therapy for them. If the intake interviewer uses all these tests to formulate the case conceptualization, then it is easy to convince the patient that all this information is necessary.

I find discussing the test results with the patients also very important. You have shown us some nice figures that are also easily understood by the patients. Just a few years ago it used to take quite some time to analyze such tests and to produce such figures.

The "figuration analysis" (Grawe & Baltensperger, 1998) program enables us to have such figures in no time. These figures you showed us were obviously created

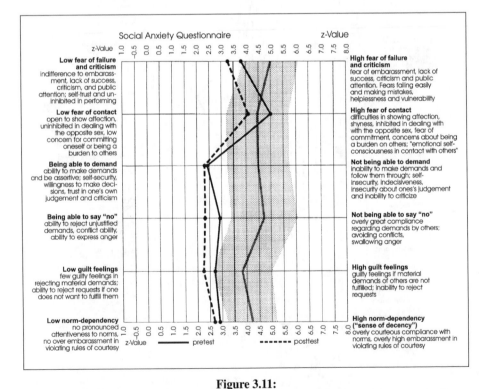

Figure 3.11:
Patient's test profiles in the Social Anxiety Questionnaire. See Figure 3.8 for more details as these figures are similarly constructed.

using this program, and at first I did not believe my eyes. This program makes it possible to virtually solve all analysis and illustration problems from relatively simple problems of quality control in therapies through highly complex problems such as those arising in research projects. Even entirely new tests, or those recently developed can be analyzed using this program. Such tools make it seem more realistic to routinely evaluate the process and outcome for all therapies in normal practice.

Therapist: I can confirm that, and now that I have worked with this program for a while I must say that the computer really does make something possible that had been unthinkable until now. Every time I look at all the nice graphics it produces for my ongoing therapies, which I can use to visualize the course of therapies, I am really pleased. As a practitioner, I truly think that it should become routine for every therapist to measure the pre- and post-therapy condition of a patient using a standard assessment battery, with measures individually selected for the patient.

Regularly gathering information with a therapy session report to be completed by the patient after each therapy session would be even more useful for the therapist. It would provide some insight regarding how the patient experiences the process of therapy. Figure 3.12 illustrates the progress of a patient in therapy. This demonstrates how the patient experiences the therapeutic relationship, whether progress is made, what kind of progress, how stressful the therapy sessions are for him, and how satisfied he is with therapy overall. These session reports may alert the therapist early on if therapy is not going well. Based on such knowledge, the therapist could then make relevant changes.

I think seeing on paper in black and white exactly what positive progress I am effecting in the patient serves to make me a much more self-assured practitioner. Yet if the results occasionally start to look less than satisfactory, there is also a chance to reevaluate the therapy plan. I see only advantages in such measurements today, whereas previously I was rather skeptical about such methods.

"3. Case Conceptualization and treatment planning

3.1 Intra- and interpersonal functions of the problem

In conceptualizing this case and formulating a psychotherapeutic treatment plan, we find it important, with respect to the compulsive symptoms, to consider Hand's (1992) differentiation between intra-individual and interactional functions.

*The intra-individual or **intrapersonal function** of the symptoms results from the question of what function the patient's washing compulsion serves regarding the regulation of his experience and behavior. A look at the patient's history makes it clear that at the intra-individual level, the washing compulsion serves to reduce his fear of having been infected by the dirt of certain classmates. This fear of getting dirty, however, is linked to avoided emotions such as anger, helplessness, humiliation, subjugation, etc. This is to say that as long as the patient is occupied with the fear of his potential contamination and the washing to reduce this fear, he is successfully able to avoid a surge of the original, negative emotions. In terms of schema theory (Grawe, Grawe-Gerber, Heiniger, Ambühl & Caspar, 1996), this compulsion is viewed as an intensive expression of a negative emotional schema's activity. The activity of the schema is focused on protecting the patient from experiencing the aversive emotions described above."*

Psychologist: In our model, I think we would probably conceptualize the compulsive symptoms differently, not as a motivational schema, but rather as a disorder attractor which has formed under specific motivational conditions. The individual dynamic this disorder has developed is obvious. Our model suggests that at the time the disorder attractor first formed there must have been an inconsistency tension lasting over a longer period. For a long time, the patient must have had experiences that were very incongruent with his need for self-esteem. These perceptions were likely associated with feelings of having no control over the humiliations he suffered from his classmates. Obviously he was not able to reduce these incongruities by exerting control over their source. The violations of his needs for control and self-enhancement were accompanied by feelings of humiliation and sheer powerlessness on the one hand and anger on the other. The emerging compulsive rituals gave him at least some sense of control and made structured mental activity possible at a time when no clear motivational structural patterns could be established. To use Edelman's (1987) terms, these rituals became differentially reinforced through reductions in inconsistency tension and bounds together in an increasingly well ingrained pattern of mental activity. These pattern became increasingly easily activated by more and more trigger points within the neural network, for instance by situational conditions, but also by emotions that had become part of these tightly connected activation tendencies. Emotions, external and internal inconsistencies, and situations that actually had nothing to do with the original experiences became possible triggers for eliciting the compulsive rituals. Strong tensions or emotions that were elicited by current life experiences led to strong activation of the pattern underlying the compulsive rituals.

Thus, it is not the conflicts originally responsible for the current symptoms that are activating pre-ingrained activation tendencies, but it is the tensions resulting from current motivational constellations. This means that the disorder attractor must be destabilized by affecting the patient's current control parameters, and new activation tendencies must be ingrained, not just for the external situations associated with the compulsive rituals, but also as reactions to tension-eliciting conditions and emotional states. Each newly developed possibility for reducing motivational tensions and regulating negative emotions that in some way differs from compulsive rituals will further reduce the danger of the compulsive disorder attractor becoming activated by the tensions.

Figure 3.12:
The therapy process from the patient's perspective.
The curves depicted are based on the patient's evaluation of therapy sessions, assessed via a patient therapy session report directly following each session. The gray line with the gray shadowed area represents the mean of all patients treated at the Psychotherapy Center in Bern with one standard deviation to the top and bottom. The patient is represented by the solid black line against this background. Session 16 was the exposure at home when there was no session report for the patient, and this is why at this point the curve is interrupted, just like at session 34. From session 50 on the gray shaded area is absent as background due to there being an insufficient number of patients treated for a sufficient length of time to serve as reference group.
Of special note is the course of the scale "progress outside of therapy." Such progress does not occur for the patient until session 50 and later. It follows the patient beginning his studies once again and making mastery experiences in real social situations (see also Figure 3.16). His emotional involvement within the sessions simultaneously decreases at that time. The focus of change has switched to the area outside of therapy.

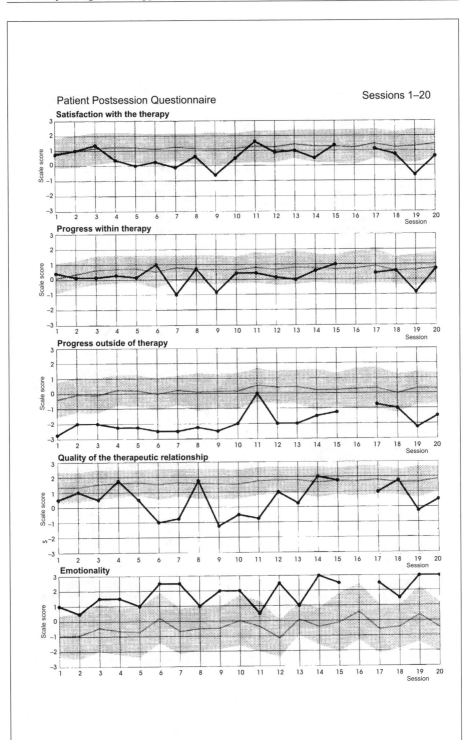

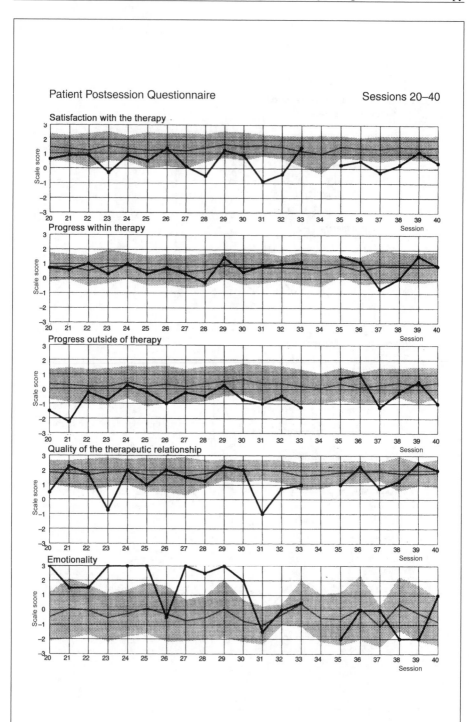

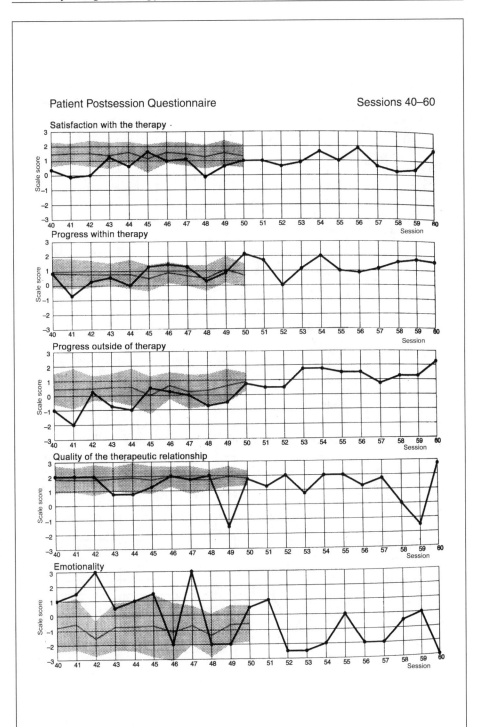

Patient Postsession Questionnaire   Sessions 40–60

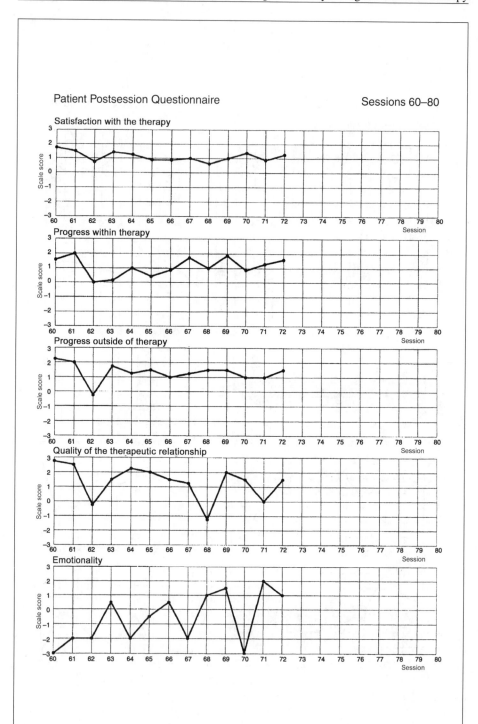

Thus, if one fully activates the disorder attractor by "contaminating" the patient, i.e. exposing him to the compulsively avoided dirt, it should be expected that not only a very strong urge for performing the compulsive rituals develops but that the emotions associated with the activation pattern also become activated. In the past these emotions were regulated by the compulsive rituals. If this possibility is removed by preventing the patient from exercising the compulsive rituals, it can be expected that these emotions become strongly activated.

Therapist: As we will hear in a moment, this is exactly what happens, but first let me continue with the case report:

"To give a description of the interpersonal functions of the washing compulsion it makes sense to first describe the family characteristics and typical interaction patterns. The family system appears to have:
- *No clear and binding rules. For example, there is neither a set time for lunch nor is it clearly regulated who is responsible for which tasks in the household. Such questions are discussed over and over again in endless conversations.*
- *No clear boundaries between parents and son. For instance, the rule is that there are no secrets from one another; the parents are also proud to have treated their son as a "partner" rather than a child from early on. Even the division of rooms in the house is unstructured: The father's office is in the family's living room, the laundry yet to be ironed is in the son's former room, the father's shirts in the son's present room, etc.*
- *No respect for the family member's personal integrity. For example, it is understood that the parents can enter the son's room at any time without knocking on the door.*
- *No adequate forms of communication. Nobody listens to the other, everybody talks loudly over one another.*
- *No possibilities for constructive problem solving. For instance, it seems impossible to come to a joint decision about whether or not the answering machine be on or off during lunch.*
The patient achieves the following with his compulsions:
- *An aggressive control of the parents by subjugating them under his compulsion; i.e. this way he can bring a little order into the otherwise chaotic household.*
- *Maintaining a certain distance, enforcing a certain personal space; thereby gaining a bit of respect for his personal integrity.*
- *Securing his parents' affection as his most important attachment figures because it is obvious that in his condition he is dependent on the affection and support of others."*

Psychologist: We see here how useful the concept of structural pattern or attractors is; it can be applied to both family interactions and neural or mental functioning. The familial interactions of this particular family obviously lacked some clear structural patterns. This increases the danger for the emergence of dysfunctional structural patterns, such as escalating arguments between parents and son. Because no familial structural patterns exist that would complement the family's needs, negative emotions such as anger or helplessness are elicited repeatedly in both the parents and the patient. These emotions have the capacity to trigger the activation pattern of the compulsion rituals. Because this introduces a particular order into family interactions in that situation, this activation pattern is not just intra-psychologically but also interpersonally reinforced.

Therapist: To return to the case report:

"In summary, we can say that this washing compulsion has very complex functions in the patient's experience and behavior. While at the intra-individual level it mainly serves the controlling of fear and the avoidance of experiencing painful feelings, at the interpersonal level it helps the patient to maintain his personal space and to simultaneously ensure the affection of his parents. Yet this last goal is exactly what seems increasingly jeopardized since his parents more and more frequently, and more vehemently threaten to put the patient into a hospital.

3.2 Conclusions for therapy planning

*Our team established the case conceptualization based on information gathered over the course of the entire pre-therapy intake process. Based on the initial understanding of this case, the disorder-specific aspect of the washing compulsion became the focus of our considerations, since its modification was considered the most important therapeutic goal from both the patient's and the parents' perspectives. We are also sure that the treatment of the washing compulsion should have first priority in light of the patient's and the family's life being completely controlled and constrained by it. Regarding the change factors in the model of general psychotherapy (cf. Grawe, 1995), this meant that therapy had to focus first on **problem solving**, i.e. the alleviation of the compulsion. The symptom-oriented procedure of in-vivo exposure with response prevention was chosen as the best treatment procedure. This required that the patient expose himself by his own free will to a situation in which most likely compulsive fears would emerge, but at the same time, as agreed upon with the therapist, he had to refrain from exercising his control behavior (of washing). If the patient agreed to such a procedure it could then be expected that he would be confronted with his avoided emotions, making it possible for them to be targeted from the perspective of therapeutic **clarification**. Viewed in this way then, even from the perspective of **problem activation**, in-vivo exposure with response prevention appeared to be the optimal approach.*

*We had the following considerations on the **resource aspect**: In light of the explosive family situation, the in-vivo exposure might best be pursued in an individual setting, as long as the therapist is successful in creating a trusting relationship with the patient and is able to negotiate a therapeutic contract with him. The patient's parents were viewed as an important resource for supporting him emotionally and with other assistance after the exposure, so he would not relapse immediately into his washing compulsion.*

As a result of this commonly shared understanding we suggested the following therapeutic treatment to the family:

1. Alleviation of the washing compulsion utilizing the method of in-vivo exposure with response prevention: This portion of treatment was to be pursued primarily in an individual setting, but also including the parents as the patient's most important resource according to the model 'clinic at home.' They had to be in charge of sup-

porting and controlling the patient following the accomplished exposure. A day 'X' was planned on which the patient was to be brought into contact with all those objects at home that he had avoided for years. This plan also included prevention of the washing ritual after the exposure.

2. *Family sessions to improve communication among the family members to agree on clear and binding regulations according to the quid-pro-quo principle to negotiate rights and responsibilities in living together, to set boundaries, to promote respecting personal integrity, as well as supporting the family in solving joint problems.*

3. *The patient's social competence and his problems with social contact were to be treated in a group setting.*
   Both patient and parents agreed to this treatment plan."

Therapy researcher: If we compare this treatment plan with our three-component model, it becomes obvious that the first point targets the second change component—destabilization of the disorder attractor. Specifically, this goal is to be accomplished by influencing the attractor components with coping/mastery-oriented interventions.

From points two and three we expect a positive effect on the motivational control parameters of the compulsive symptoms. The improved structure of family interactions would give the patient more congruent perceptions regarding his motivational schemata. This would have positive effects consistent with our first change component, leading in particular to control experiences and to improved well-being. The patient's emotional state seems, in turn, to be one of the control parameters of his compulsive symptoms so that a positive influence on the symptoms can be exerted by the first change component.

Point three includes mastery-oriented interventions to change motivational schemata that determine the patient's behavior in social interactions. This might also decrease negative emotions that constitute control parameters of the symptoms. Points two and three seem to be relevant not just for possible positive effects on the disorder; the effects have value in and of themselves because they improve the patient's need satisfaction.

What I miss in this treatment plan are strategies to facilitate an optimal therapeutic relationship as well as interventions relevant for resource activation under the intrapsychological aspect. We also lack ideas about which aspects of his problems the patient has an awareness for and which not. It seems that the distinction between the implicit and the conscious mode of functioning played no role for these authors.

Some definite ideas on the patient's motivational schemata that are indeed highly relevant for the questions just addressed are also lacking, and I am sort of surprised by that. In fact, I believe you said earlier that schema analysis was routinely used in Grawe's work group, and this case report comes from them, correct?

Therapist: Yes, when I first read this I did not realize that. I do believe the authors thoroughly considered the patient's motivational schemata. A lot of what was reported later when therapy was performed suggested that they did give some thought to this, but a schema analysis is actually missing from this report. Perhaps the authors have not included it for lack of space, but when the therapy was performed no consistency analysis existed yet, not even in Grawe's work group, as it was developed later.

"4. Therapeutic procedures and the course of therapy

4.1 Therapeutic contract

A goal attainment scaling (GAS, Kiresuk & Lund, 1979) was conducted with the patient at the beginning of therapy, in which the three main problems to be treated in therapy were defined. From the patient's perspective, the status quo at the beginning of therapy, the optimal goal-status to be reached in therapy, as well as the condition of a possible worsening for each of these three problems were formulated. The patient defined his compulsion for cleaning and washing as his first problem (Fig. 3.13), his professional career—interrupted at that time—(Fig. 3.14) as his second, and his lack of social relations (Fig. 3.15) as his third problem.

4.2 Treatment of symptoms

4.2.1 Preparing the in-vivo exposure with response prevention

The first fifteen sessions focused mainly on creating a trusting therapeutic relationship as a foundation for the difficult change process. In addition, a detailed problem and goal analysis was developed. The patient was thoroughly prepared for 'day X' on which we would bring him into contact with all those objects at home which for many years he had avoided touching. At the same time, we tried to calm down the family's emotional climate in family sessions, introducing simple rules of communication, preparing the parents for their important task related to the in-vivo exposure, and creating a climate of mutual respect and willingness to cooperate. The following therapeutic activities took place:

From the very beginning an important therapeutic goal was the shaping of a trusting therapeutic relationship for the patient and his parents, which was achieved in different ways: absolute respect for the patient's boundaries and the limits set (out of fear of contamination, for instance, the patient avoided handshakes when greeting us, which was something we accepted in the phase prior to in-vivo exposure); installing of hope of getting effective help by demonstrating professional competence; including the parents as resources; commitment and reliability of the therapist as a model for other reliable relationships; transparency in the therapeutic procedures (compare also Hoffmann, 1994)."

Therapy researcher: I think it would have been useful to mention here the patient's positive motivational schemata, which would have facilitated the planning of therapeutic relationship shaping. It seems to me that the therapists assume the existence of a strong intentional schema that is continuously activated. That is, they seem to assume that the patient has a very strong desire to have control over what happens with him. The therapists behave specifically in a manner that is complimentary to this schema. One should, therefore, assume that they were clearly aware of its importance even if the case report does not contain any explicit schema analysis.

In addition, the case report makes it clear that the therapists were aware of the significance of the first of our three change components. They prepare the disorder-specific intervention extremely carefully by first creating positive conditions for that. The points listed all agree very well with our ideas on realizing the first change component.

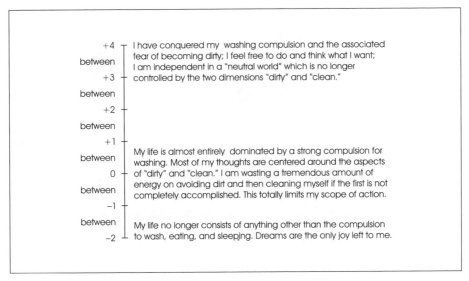

Figure 3.13:

Result of the goal attainment scaling (GAS) for the most important problem as stated by the patient (Problem No.1).

The GAS was worked out by therapist and patient together over the initial therapy sessions. The current problem state equals zero and the ideally sought goal condition as well as the ultimate potential worsening of the problem were formulated. On the one hand, the GAS may be viewed as a kind of therapeutic contract. It defines what should be accomplished in therapy. On the other hand it may be used to measure change in the patient at different times over the course of and at the end of therapy with the condition he has attained in that time assessed on the scale from -2 to +4. Such assessments of change are depicted in Figure 3.16.

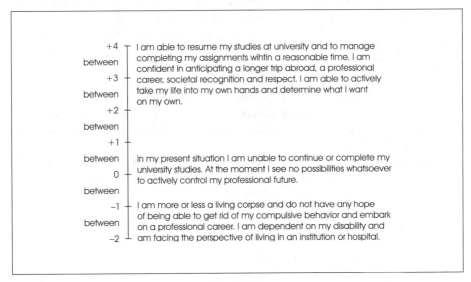

Figure 3.14:

Goal Attainment Scale for problem No. 2, for explanation see Figure 3.13.

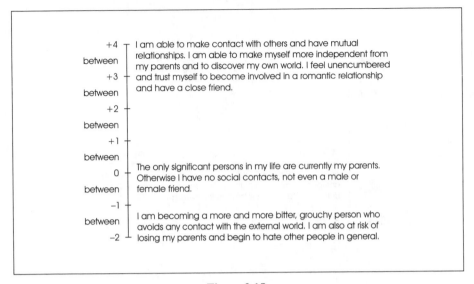

Figure 3.15:
Goal Attainment Scale for problem No. 3, for explanation see Figure 3.13.

Therapist: *"Over a period of four weeks the patient wrote out a detailed wash proto-col detailing the daily wash times, the intensity of the compulsive rituals on a scale of 1-7, what triggered the washing as well as the behavior, thoughts and emotions after washing. All in all, the patient engaged in washing for 91 hours over these 28 days, on average 3 hours 15 minutes/day with peak values of up to 8 hours per day.*

The patient came up with a first list of 'dangerous' situations and objects both inside and outside of the house and ranked them according to the degree to which they elic-ited his fear. The patient also listed objects that did not elicit fear but represented something like a last refuge of security. These objects were not to be touched, however, and they would thereby remain 'clean' for him. Included among these were his model train as well as the bed in his original room. The list of 'dangerous' objects within the house was then further detailed by the patient in a second step and eventually con-tained 61 objects ranging from coat rack to a shoelace."

I think this is a brilliantly detailed analysis of the disorder-specific components and control parameter that might be possible starting points for the destabilization of the disorder attractor.

"In a letter the therapist informed the patient and his parents about the own dy-namic of the washing compulsion and the therapeutic interventions necessary to treat this compulsion. The following five treatment steps were listed:

1. 'De-sanctifying' the house,

2. treating and eliminating or alleviating the washing compulsion,

3. developing a 'normal' washing behavior,

4. stimulus confrontation with situations and objects outside the house,

5. coming to terms with difficult events in the past.

Finally, suitable measures were established for supporting the patient in the diffi-cult times immediately following the abandoning of the washing compulsion. This in-

volved the parents turning off the main water line in the house before retiring to bed and locking the door in front of it. Furthermore, at the patient's request, the parents agreed to never leaving him alone during the two months following the exposure."

These clear instructions satisfy the need for orientation and control in all the participants, especially for the patient, who, regarding his control schema, is assured that he does not have to be faced with something unexpected and uncontrollable. It seems to me that the preparation of the actual disorder-specific interventions in this case was rather ideal.

"4.2.2 Carrying out the exposure with response prevention: 'Day X'

After all these preparations two of us went to the patient's home on 'day X' and carried out a four-hour-long exposure in the course of which he was instructed to touch all of the feared objects in the house and become contaminated with the imaginary dirt. What happened was a sort of 'de-sanctifying' of the house. This was aimed at getting the patient to experience the emotions which had long been avoided due to the compulsive behavior, and additionally, give him the certainty that the feared consequences of becoming infected by the dirt would not materialize.

What we had expected based on our considerations actually came true from the very beginning. These interventions elicited a condition of high affective excitement in the patient, i.e. the in-vivo confrontation with 'dirty' objects led directly and immediately to the expected emotions. At the point when the exposure culminated, everything that had caused the patient his 'innermost pain' burst out of him. From deep within him came an almost animal-like cry that after a time changed into weeping and wailing about all the pain and humiliations he endured at the hands of his classmates. This response definitely confirmed our hypothesis that the compulsion represented a form of the patient's coping with the psychological humiliations during his school years and mainly served to cut off the stressful emotions associated with these from the rest of what he experienced."

Psychologist: In this situation it appears to me that a complex neural activation pattern with strong emotional memory components had been activated bottom-up. The activity of this neural pattern had likely been blocked until then by the activation pattern related to the compulsive rituals. This activation obviously happens consciously, which promotes the establishment of new neural connections. The patient makes corrective experiences that help to ingrain new neural connections. He experiences that he is able to endure strong negative emotions and that he doesn't have to avoid the emotion-triggering memories and perceptions. Further, he experiences that there are other ways for regulating these emotions, apart from his usual avoidance and compulsive behavior. All this happens in a very resource-oriented context. What we have here is a "fruitful problem activation," as we have previously referred to it.

Therapist: *"As discussed with the patient, the parents took over the agreed upon tasks aimed at preventing the compulsive washing behavior following the in-vivo exposure: Control of washing and showering times; turning off the main water valve overnight; never leaving the patient alone and giving him a lot of affection and support etc. As agreed, the patient called the therapist daily in the first days following the exposure to briefly report on how he was doing."*

Psychologist: These are all interventions aimed at a better ingraining of the new neural activation tendencies that have been established in the exposure. By their frequent activation, the new activation tendencies rather than the compulsive rituals may be strengthened over time.

Therapist: *"During the following three months, the patient participated in two-hour-long individual sessions at short intervals (two sessions per week) with the following emphases: teaching him norms for normal washing behavior; planning and implementing the patient's move back to his room and bed; step-by-step exposure to objects and situations outside the house; an imaginary confrontation with former school-mates; preparations for resuming his university studies, and relocation to his studio at the university."*

Psychologist: All these seem to be very resource activating and mastery-oriented interventions with the potential for need-fulfilling experiences. Everything is focused on activating positive activation patterns—we may refer to them as resources—as frequently and as strongly as possible. The more this is done, the less space remains for activation of the problematic activation tendencies, whose activation manifests itself in the compulsive rituals.

Therapist: *"4.3 Working on the family's problems*

Family sessions were held once a month, and the arranging of mutual commitments between the family members regarding the respecting of boundaries, the guaranteeing of personal integrity as well as rights and responsibilities in family life was mainly attempted during these sessions. After some time, the patient became really angry when his father continued to enter his room without knocking on the door despite clear agreements. This led to the parents coming to the family sessions one time without their son as the patient stubbornly refused to come along stating that his parents evidently needed the therapy more than he did. Another goal was the finding of constructive problem solutions to everyday problems in lieu of endless fighting.

4.4 Contact problems/social competence

Three months after the home-based exposure the patient received a place in group therapy led by Barbara Heiniger and a colleague. This was the first time in a while that the patient had contact with persons other than his parents and therapists. There were obvious deficits in his social competencies and in his ability to relate to others. But the patient felt accepted by the group rather quickly and turned out to be an interested listener. He received feedback from others in the group about certain problematic behaviors, experiencing at the same time that he was accepted and respected."

Therapy researcher: The patient's reaction to the group setting showed that the resource strengthening and the mastery-oriented interventions chosen by the therapists turned out to be the right thing for the motivational schemata determining his general social behavior. The patient seems to respond rather positively to mastery experiences, which again points to his need for control, which had been compromised so severely before.

Therapist: *"Unfortunately, the patient was able to participate in a total of only seven group sessions because he then resumed his studies in a different part of the country. He therefore switched to individual sessions, which took place at longer intervals. The washing compulsion was no longer a problem, and these sessions focused more on the patient who wanted to reflect on what he could do in life, how he could establish contact with others, what personal things he could tell others, how he could build friendships with others, and how to prepare for his final exams at the end of his first year of school, etc. Within that one year there were approximately 12 individual, randomly scheduled sessions."*

Therapy researcher: This all seems to underline again just how urgent it was that the patient be assisted in attaining experiences which would satisfy his evidently strong needs for orientation and control. The positive effects of the therapy seem to be largely due to the patient's positive experiences regarding his need for control. His dysfunctional efforts to take control—his compulsive rituals—were replaced by a socially adequate control behavior allowing him to effectively satisfacty his needs.

Therapist: *"5. Therapeutic outcome*

The overall therapy lasted for 69 sessions over a period of 2 years. These consisted of 51 individual, 10 family, 7 group sessions, and a 4-hour in-vivo exposure at the home of the patient.

5.1 Measurement of therapy outcome

The patient's main problems concerned the compulsion for cleaning and washing, his professional career, and his social relations. Following every 10 therapy sessions, the patient rated the level he felt he was at for each of these three problems between -2 and +4 with respect to the initial state of 0 at the start of therapy (Figure 3.16).

After ten sessions the problem of his washing compulsion had gotten even worse. As for his professional career, nothing had changed and his social relations showed a slight improvement—presumably due to the newly added relationship to the therapist. As of session 20, the problem of his washing compulsion showed sudden improvement, which can be ascribed to the successful in-vivo exposure with response prevention. At the end of therapy the patient reported that he had almost completely conquered the compulsion for washing and his associated fear of becoming contaminated.

The positive change of problems 2 and 3 occurred rather late in therapy. It was not until after session 60 that the patient assessed his progress regarding his professional career as positively as the progress made with problem 1 following session 20. The reason for this may be that he only resumed his studies after session 50. His social contacts did not really change until after he resumed his studies, although the patient thought he was able to make contacts with other people much earlier. All in all, the GAS shows a very positive development."

Therapy researcher: These developments demonstrate the importance of process-activation. The patient was able to have corrective experiences only after the relevant schemata had been activated on a process-level.

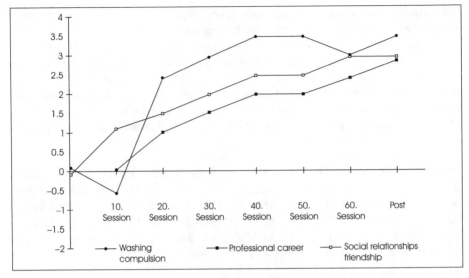

Figure 3.16:
Changes of the most important three problems in the course of therapy. The curves are based on the patient's self-rating on the goal attainment scales illustrated in Figures 3.13-3.15. The assessments were done every ten therapy sessions.

Therapist: *"5.2 Pre/post comparison*

The pre/post comparison in the other measurements partially shows striking changes, with the most dramatic change visible in the profile of the HCI—Hamburg Compulsion Inventory (Fig. 3.17, for comparison see the pre-measurement of the HCI in Fig. 3.9). All values are in the lower-normal area, the washing compulsion has completely dis-

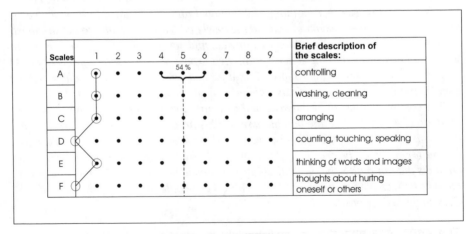

Figure 3.17:
Patient's test profile immediately following completion of therapy (posttest).
For comparison see the patient's profile in the pretest in Figure 3.9.

appeared and there are even improvements in a scale the values of which were, at the time of pre-measurement, already in the lower normal area (scale D).

All other psychopathological symptoms also improved markedly. In the SCL-90R the values after treatment lie within the range of the normal population (see Fig. 3.8).

The EMI (see Fig. 3.10) illustrates very clearly the patient's positively changed well-being, predominantly his exhaustion, which has developed towards a rather dynamic state. The least change was in the scale 'aggressive mood,' which might be interpreted as the patient now being in a phase of transition and awakening, during which a healthy portion of aggression might benefit rather than harm him.

The social anxiety questionnaire had shown the patient as relatively non-disturbed even prior to therapy. Here the most marked improvement was a clear decrease of fear of contact.

All in all, post-measurement describes a picture of an undisturbed, healthy young man!

5.3 Life situation of the patient and his parents following the end of therapy

By the time therapy was completed the patient's life situation had in many ways completely changed as compared to the situation prior to therapy two years ago: The patient is living in a studio near the university. The washing compulsion is no longer an issue for him; if asked about it he describes this compulsion as something he has left far behind, remembering it only vaguely. He is a very busy student who takes the demands of his studies very seriously and is persistent in pursuing his goals. He is perceived as a competent fellow student and is often asked for advice in technical matters, something he visibly enjoys. He is part of a social network at the university and periodically socializes with close fellow students.

The patient's relationship to his parents has greatly changed and is less tense. Due to his demanding schedule he rarely visits his parents, which can be interpreted as a sign of a positively developing detachment from home. The patient's parents are very pleased with their son's development and are confident that the washing compulsion is now consigned to the past. The parent's relationship has become noticeably less tense as a result of the reduction of the stress related to their son's condition. At the end of therapy there are no indications suggesting that the patient's symptoms had any important function for the parent's relationship.

6. Concluding remarks

We are aware that such a successful treatment of a young patient with a severe, chronic compulsion for washing is the exception rather than the rule, but in our view, this is exactly why it is important to investigate why this therapy was so successful. Certainly there are a number of factors involved, which we would like to summarize again from our perspective: Careful considerations and the implementation of a trusting therapeutic relationship, without a doubt, is an essential condition for therapeutic success. All of this was accomplished first by the strict acceptance of the boundaries set by the patient and second by a structured and competently executed therapy plan which gave both the patient and his parents assurance and confidence. Also very important was that despite his massive, dominating problems, the patient was still treated as an adult 'partner' by us. The fact that the patient had the feeling of being guided and

*of actively participating allowed him more and more to agree to a therapeutic inter-
vention aimed at confronting him with previously avoided negative emotions. The professional implementation of the in-vivo exposure at the patient's home in the presence
of his parents turned out to be a very potent method of intervention. The immediate
effects of this method went far beyond a habituation of the fears. Rather, during this
exposure the patient experienced painful emotions which had a cathartic effect on the
one hand, and brought him into contact with his underlying traumatic experiences and
the associated emotions on the other. This opened the possibility for him to process his
emotions, something his compulsive behavior prevented for years by serving as a protective mechanism.*

*Finally, therapeutic success is also essentially based on the fact that we made sure
to include the patient's parents as an important resource from the beginning (avoiding
attributions of blame), which we were successful in managing very well with the model
of 'clinic at home,' i.e. energetic and obligated support by the parents following the
exposure."*

Psychologist: Congratulations go to the therapists and certainly to the patient and his
parents for this successful therapy. What was achieved should definitely not be taken for
granted, as is obvious when considering the five previous unsuccessful treatments. If
psychotherapies were always prepared, planned, and implemented as carefully as this
one was, then maybe psychotherapy would enjoy a better reputation than it does.

This case report has even more positive things to offer. There is nothing in this
report we could not describe and explain using the concepts we have developed here.
In fact, I now understand what you meant at the beginning of this conversation about
this theoretical view opening up a room that allows you to move around confidently in
thought and action. Although I am not confident to conduct therapy myself—I lack the
necessary practical skills—I now believe I understand what takes place in a therapy.
This is something that prior to our dialogues I was unsure about.

Therapy researcher: The connection of an intrapersonal and an interpersonal perspective as well as the connection of a resource and a problem perspective in this case
was most convincing for me. None of these perspectives should have been missed.
Perhaps the previously attempted therapies failed due to their lacking one or more of
these perspectives. Since this therapy was so successful it is useless to ask whether a
more explicit consideration of the distinction between implicit and explicit mode of
functioning or better elaborated schema- and consistency analysis would perhaps have
brought even better results. Of course, this does not mean this question might not be
important in a different case.

When considering this therapy from the perspective of our change component model,
clearly all three change components were very effectively realized. The first change
component—resource activation—was used by the therapists in a very targeted fashion. Immediately following the in-vivo exposure, the very strong reaction of the symptoms demonstrates the importance of the second change component—destabilization
of disorder attractors by disorder specific interventions. It appears to me, however, that
the realization of the third change component was a major factor in this case. New
positive motivational structural patterns were systematically formed and better ingrained,

allowing the patient to better satisfy his needs for self-enhancement and improved orientation and control. The violation of these two basic needs seems to have brought about the strong inconsistency tension in this patient, which was originally responsible for the formation of the disorder attractor and also for its maintenance. This therapy systematically promoted the formation of positive intentional schemata for the satisfaction of these two needs and also supported these schemata by creating schema-facilitative external conditions. Establishing clear structural patterns in family interactions contributed to a decrease in inconsistency, something that the structural pattern "compulsive washing" had tried to accomplish in a dysfunctional fashion. Because positive intra-psychological and interpersonal structural patterns were established, the patient's mental activity was increasingly determined by need-satisfying motivational and interpersonal attractors. The disorder attractor thereby lost its function to "structure" inconsistent mental functioning, but was replaced by better, i.e. more need-satisfying, structural patterns. Most likely this would not have been possible if its disorder-specific individual dynamic had not been interrupted by this massive disorder-specific intervention.

I have not encountered anything in this case that could not be conceived and explained with the aid of our concepts. This is very reassuring, but as a researcher I also always tend to have my doubts. Could it be that you selected a case that is a particularly good fit to our ideas? As far as I remember you claimed that your system would cover the entire range of phenomena in psychotherapy which would then imply that even different therapies such as couple or family therapies could be conceptualized with these concepts in a similar fashion. I do not think that just this one case really proves this.

Therapist: My intention was not really to prove anything with this case but to demonstrate using a concrete example of how a therapy might look like when it is implemented according to principles of our psychological therapy model, and this particular case report was perfect for that. The fact that it actually reflects all of our ideas could not be foreseen.

A collection of cases with illustrative material about how to pursue a psychological therapy consistent with our concepts would certainly be helpful. But this is a future task, one that can only be accomplished after having enough such case reports available. The cases I have approached using these principles have yet to be completed. I will gladly take this as encouragement to publish such a collection of cases at some point. Case descriptions have highly persuasive effects on my colleagues in therapeutic practice even if they do not prove anything, strictly speaking.

Psychologist: This case is sufficient for me since we must keep our time constraints in mind. This third dialogue has taken longer than expected, and it is time to think about bringing it to a close. Are there things you still wish to address or is it time to begin to sum things up?

Therapy researcher: I feel one more important topic remains: therapist training. If there is ever to be wide-scale implementation of a psychological therapy as we conceive it, then it can only be accomplished through the education and training of therapists. It makes no sense to train therapists first in a certain school of therapy and then "cure" them from their dysfunctional "therapy-school thinking." It appears much more useful to train therapists right away with the goal of utilizing all therapeutic possibilities on the basis of a uniform theoretical view. I ask you: Is there a possibility to train therapists right from the beginning to be psychological therapists the way we have conceived it, or must they first be trained in the ways of one particular school in order to be able to develop beyond that at a later point?

Psychotherapy Training and Service Provision

3.27   On the Identity of Psychological Therapists

Therapist: I am not a fan of the popular opinion that therapists should be trained in one particular form of therapy before adding other elements to their repertoire. This situation would be similar to training a skier initially in an outdated style before teaching him current skiing techniques. He will never quite get rid of the old movements; they will always prevent him from becoming as good as other skiers who do not carry this dead weight of well ingrained but sub-optimal neural activation patterns.

Some people remain so attached to thinking in terms of therapy schools that they are unable to imagine a psychotherapy without distinct schools. You will see that even our psychological therapy will be compartmentalized by these people and pigeon-holed as one particular therapy school. Once internalized, it is not easy to shake off this traditional way of thinking.

Even psychotherapists develop neural activation patterns that over time become self-perpetuating. These old activation patterns would have to be activated repeatedly while the person has new perceptions that are inconsistent with the old patterns. Through that process, the old activation patterns might eventually be overwritten with new thought patterns. This process is not much different from changing the patient's strongly ingrained schemata. However, because therapists typically don't "suffer" from their allegiance to a particular therapy school, they also typically have little motivation to change their old thinking styles. This is why once the old patterns have been well ingrained, the chances for developing new activation tendencies (and new possibilities for perceiving and thinking) are slim. Therapists who were asked in their training to make their school of therapy a part of their personal identity and life philosophy are the most handicapped in this respect. For some of them, everything they learned during their training becomes an irrefutable truth instead of a professional tool for problem solving. A powerful, self-perpetuating attractor has formed here, one that can be activated practically through any aspect of human experience.

The goal of psychotherapy training should not be the formation of such a self-perpetuating thought system. On the contrary: From the very beginning of their training, psychotherapists ought to be encouraged to be curious, to develop a willingness to change, and a tendency to doubt the old and seemingly self-evident. Moreover, their instructors must serve as role models, and what therapists demand of their patients (namely, to abandon old patterns and try out something new and unknown), therapists and instructors must likewise demand of themselves. If any ideology is to be taught to therapists in training, then let it be that "the better is the enemy of the good." A consistent effort for knowledge, progress, and improved quality should be what motivates the mind of the psychotherapist, not the mindless exercise of traditional but outdated rituals.

This also holds true for future psychotherapists. By nature, psychological therapy cannot be defined by any definitive content or subject matter. In fact, its content is defined by the relevant level of knowledge of basic psychology, neuroscience, therapy research as well as clinical psychological and psychiatric research, and knowledge essentially involves change. What we have described here as a rationale for psychological therapy will be outdated tomorrow. We need not be embarrassed about that as this is the difference between science and faith.

Psychotherapists should learn to the best of their ability the best of what is available today while remaining fully aware that something better might come along tomorrow, and they should be ready and willing to learn and then make use of new material when it appears on the scene. In fact, an effort to surmount the good in favor of the better should be made consistently. I see this flexible and evolutionary process (and not any definitive content) as the core of a scientific psychotherapy.

This certainly does not mean that I wish to distance myself from the ideas we discussed and developed earlier. Those ideas currently represent great progress and will be very constructive for my work. However, I need not stick to these ideas for the rest of my life. They will be replaced by better ideas. Perhaps I will be too inflexible one day to open myself to better things, but let this be my own personal limitation. Things will and should go on without me.

Knowing that I will form new activation tendencies tomorrow should not prevent me from ingraining those that are adequate for today to the best of my ability. I need easily elicited activation tendencies that are well suited to my present situation in order to be effective in my actions. Therefore, the potent structural patterns needed for professional actions should be maximally ingrained by every aspiring therapist, and these structural patterns should match the present state of our scientific knowledge. Even our private activity is determined by such structural patterns, and the more clearly our activity is focused on certain goals aimed at satisfying our needs, the better our well-being.

The objective tasks in psychotherapy correspond to private needs. That is, the more our activity in our work as therapists is determined by objectively formed structural patterns that are suited to effectively fulfill the tasks we are faced with, the better we do our jobs and the more satisfied we can be.

What might be the nature of these structural patterns, which are objectively suited to fulfill our tasks as psychotherapists? Previously, we identified them by their goal components for motivational schemata. For our professional activity, the goals can be located in the effects we achieve with our patients. On the part of the therapist, these goals correspond to the therapist's competences.

Which competences should a psychotherapist have in order to best fulfill his tasks? What statements can we make based on our theoretical view of psychotherapy?

3.28   What Makes a Good Therapist?

I will not attempt to give an exhaustive list here of everything a therapist should know and be able to do, but will limit myself to the specific competences necessary, based on our theoretical view. Because the training of therapists is of such great importance to us, let me formulate these competences in the form of educational/ training goals. There are seven important skills a therapist should acquire in the course of his or her training:

1. Therapists should learn to perceive, think, and act in a **resource-oriented** fashion.

Traditionally, psychotherapy has always been focused on problem-oriented perception, thinking, and action. There can be no doubt that this is very important, because ultimately making improvements to someone's problems is the issue. What we want to emphasize in our theoretical considerations is the need to switch from the problem perspective to the resource perspective. Without the activation of positive resources that the patient already brings into therapy, nothing positive can be achieved in therapy. The more a therapist succeeds in activating resources in the patient, the more she mobilizes the patient's power for self-healing. We have already discussed this positive feedback process initiated by resource activation (sections 3.5 and 3.7).

Resource-oriented perception, thinking, and action are primary factors in realizing the first change component of our three-component model of the mechanism of psychotherapy. Realizing this change component immediately leads to positive therapeutic effects such as improved well-being and an increased likelihood for independent problem solving. In addition, it is this realization that creates the foundation for working on problems in a more effective and targeted fashion, regardless of whether that is with mastery-oriented or clarification-oriented interventions.

Thus, therapists must learn to get a complete picture of the motivational tendencies, the abilities, and the interpersonal resources that can be utilized for therapy, and these resources must be activated as often and as intensively as possible if their utility is to be maximized.

Resource-oriented perception and thinking is above all a matter of attitude. Therapists must develop a differentiated understanding about what kind of resources there are in a patient, and they should learn how to identify a patient's resources as fast and efficiently as possible in each case. This would require a well developed method of resource analysis, which if practiced during training could teach therapists what kinds of resources are to be considered. However, I do not know of any existing method of resource analysis. This would definitely be an area where someone might make a name for himself.

The therapist must first acquire a well-detailed picture of a patient's resources and he or she can then think about which of these resources can be process-activated, in what way, and which ones should be addressed. Therapists in training should have the chance to actually practice these ideas and resource-oriented handling of patients and significant others as much as possible. Supervision of the therapist's own cases later should also focus specifically on this aspect. This all has nothing whatsoever to do with a certain therapeutic direction or method. Whatever preferences therapists have regarding their methods, the significance of resource activation applies for all therapies and all therapists alike. Each and every therapy would benefit from the therapist having good skills in resource activation.

Unfortunately, resource-oriented perceiving, thinking, and acting are not taught in any therapy training I know of to the degree that would be adequate to our theoretical considerations. There seems to be great potential for psychotherapy to make improvements in this area, and if all therapists were to learn to take advantage of all the possibilities of resource activation, we would probably see a greatly improved efficacy in the average therapy. I believe this is a change that would be one of the easiest to implement in producing a generalized improvement in the effectiveness of psychotherapies.

However, we must ask why this aspect receives so little emphasis in therapy training. Most therapists would certainly have no objection to a resource-oriented procedure. Presumably, this can be attributed primarily to the various therapeutic approaches defining themselves in terms of how they view and approach mental problems. Their self-definition is based on assuming a problem perspective, which is therefore the focus of the particular training. The self-definition of the various forms of therapy does not include resource activation, which is why this aspect is not particularly emphasized. This is where the chance lies for a new common approach. No school's individual identity is threatened by the concept of resource activation, and paying more attention to this particular aspect will bring all schools closer together. If more attention was paid to resource activation, given the significance it has for the therapeutic outcome, then the focus would be more on the features they share rather than those that distinguish and separate them, perhaps turning the present detached relationship into a complementary one.

The resource perspective contains great integrative potential for psychotherapy, especially when psychotherapists learn to perceive, think, and act in a resource-oriented fashion right at the outset of their training.

2. Therapists should learn to perceive, think, and act in a **process-oriented** fashion.

This recommendation is based on the distinction between the implicit and the explicit mode of functioning in mental activity, which corresponds to the distinction between verbal and analog/nonverbal communication at the level of interpersonal communication.

Anything that transpires in therapy has a particular semantic meaning that is represented in the consciousness of the participants. Normally, conscious attention is directed at the verbal content being exchanged; however, there are a large number of processes concurrently transpiring in the implicit mode of functioning. These processes are also motivated: they have meanings for the patient's motivational schemata, are accompanied by emotions, elicit physical reactions, etc. To a large extent, these implicit processes determine the nonverbal behavior. These processes may play quite a significant role for the formation and maintenance of mental disorders as well as for the patient's problematic interaction with his environment.

To comprehend these meanings, the therapist must perceive and think in a process-oriented manner. The therapist follows **what** the patient says and does from a content perspective and follows **how** it is said and the patient behaves from a process perspective, while also reflecting on **why** he does that. The process perspective is always focused on what is happening in the moment. Which function does the momentary activity have with respect to the patient's motivational schemata? Which goals determine what is actually happening at the moment? Of course, these are primarily the goals activated in the explicit mode of functioning, which the patient knows himself or which may be relatively obvious. However, these can also be goals activated in the implicit mode of functioning, and those are often more therapeutically relevant.

For instance, the patient may talk about an argument at his workplace, and this report may give the therapist important information about how the patient shapes his relationships. While doing so, the patient presents himself in a certain way to the therapist. The fact that he specifically chooses this situation, how he describes it, and how he nonverbally relates to the therapist may all be determined by goals that reside outside of his consciousness. The therapist cannot obtain any information on these goals directly from the patient but must infer them from behavior and context.

What kind of situations the patient creates, how he influences them and how he reacts to situations brought on by others is largely determined by motivational schemata that are not consciously represented as intentions right at that particular moment. These situations entail bottom-up activated activation tendencies stored in the implicit memory. At the same time there are also always activation tendencies processually activated in the conceptual memory that codetermine what the patient says and does and what the particular content of his consciousness is. These can be activated and controlled top-down.

Because consciousness is such an important control parameter for experience and behavior, the content-related communication fed by conceptual memory plays a major role in psychotherapy. However, if a person experiences a large portion of his experience and behavior as something that is not determined by conscious goals—which is oftentimes the case for psychotherapy patients—it is likely that this behavior is determined by non-conscious goals in the implicit mode of functioning. A psychotherapist gains access to these implicit processes and meanings by learning to actively direct his or her attention away from processes fed by the conceptual memory—the consciously articulated contents—and instead turn to the bottom-up activated processes that occur in the implicit mode of functioning. Indeed, among the most important decoding skills a therapist must learn are the ability to not attend to the content and instead turn to nonverbal communication and pragmatic meanings (Watzlawick, Beavin & Jackson, 1967).

Therapists should also learn to encode on this implicit level; they should learn to consciously control their nonverbal behavior and the pragmatic semantic aspect of their speech in order to achieve therapeutically desired effects on the implicit level of functioning. This ability allows therapists to respond to patients' already activated schemata or to activate these schemata in a bottom-up fashion.

Earlier we encountered the concept of the relationship test. Recognizing such tests requires the ability to consciously perceive meanings that the patient expresses on only an implicit level. To pass these relationship tests, the therapist must be able to encode her own behavior on the level of these implicit meanings.

Another example would be the complementary shaping of the therapeutic relationship. The therapist decodes what the patient means in the implicit mode of functioning with respect to activated motivational schemata and then behaves in a complementary fashion to these implicit meanings.

On the level of implicit meanings, however, the therapist may also behave towards the patient's schemata in a specifically incongruent fashion in order to activate and/or to overwrite them with new experiences. Very often this goes hand in hand with the patient directing his attention—by himself or with the help of the therapist—to the incongruities and their underlying processes. These are the therapeutically fruitful moments in which the patient may form a new consciousness for the determinants of his own experience and behavior. The therapist should be ahead of the patient in her awareness for these meanings so she is to be able to offer active support in such a situation.

Process-oriented perception, thinking, and action requires the ability to both decode and encode at the level of implicit meanings. Neither of these abilities can be assumed to exist among aspiring therapists; they have to be acquired through systematic training and education.

Therapy researcher: You have touched on the topic of implicit **relationship regulation**. Although this is an important aspect of a person's mental activity, it is not the only one running in the implicit mode of functioning. Another aspect is the **intra-psychological regulation** under the aspect of avoiding incongruence and discordance. If incongruence and discordance are not successfully avoided with effective behavior in the environment, other activation tendencies might become activated that serve this intra-psychological regulation. Certain perceptions, memories, or ideas might not be permitted into consciousness to prevent incongruence and discordance from becoming too high. By definition, the individual would not be aware of these processes.

Because incongruities are always accompanied by negative emotions, these kinds of processes are also referred to as mechanisms of emotion regulation (Horowitz, Znoj & Stinson, 1996; Horowitz & Znoj, in press; Znoj et al., in press a). These processes can take on the form of active coping or avoiding. Such coping efforts function to ensure consistency, but their function can only be inferred or theoretically assumed; it is not directly observable. By contrast, the relationship between emotion and overt behavior is amenable to direct empirical study. Thus, the concept of emotional regulation is closer to empirical research.

Empirical research is just now in the process of developing measures for such processes (Znoj et al., in press b). The diagnostic value of such measures lies in their potential to alert the therapist to potential incongruences or discordances that need to be regulated in treatment. This measurement prompts the therapist to wonder which motivational schemata these discordances correspond to, which then enables her to derive consistency-increasing therapeutic interventions.

Mechanisms for securing consistency should be considered skills. It is easy to imagine a course of therapy that consists primarily of training better mechanisms for securing consistency. The improved ability to secure consistency should reduce the risk of persistently elevated inconsistency tensions, which might function as breeding ground and control parameters of mental disorders. Research has not yet identified specific consistency-enhancing interventions that could be included in an empirically-based therapeutic training program. I just wanted to bring up this training aspect because it naturally followed from our process-activation and process-oriented considerations. Perhaps this domain offers some potential for further advancements in psychotherapy.

At the present time, however, I do not think that such consistency-enhancing interventions ought to be a mandatory component of therapy training.

Therapist: It is certainly too early for that, and therapists have enough to learn already! Therapy trainees should not be burdened with issues that have yet to be conceptually and methodically refined. There is still a great deal of research and testing to be done before the intra-psychological regulation of consistency will find equal recognition among other important parts of the training.

The significance of a process orientation, however, goes far beyond that which we have discussed so far. We had stated that mental processes can only be changed if they are activated on a process level. This is true for explicit as well as implicit processes. In order to facilitate change, then, the therapist has to continuously perceive, think, and act in a process-oriented fashion. If effective change is to occur, the patient's resources must be activated on a process level; we already discussed this previously. However, the activation patterns that need to be changed must also be activated. Change can mean that new activation tendencies are ingrained, that already existing activation tendencies become better ingrained, or that problematic activation tendencies are inhibited. But even if the goal is the inhibition of problematic activation patterns, these patterns must first be process-activated. Only if activation patterns are activated on a process-level can inhibiting influences be active and effective. This process can then change synaptic transmission potentials. The new and inconsistent activation patterns must be activated as often as possible in order to ingrain new activation tendencies as strongly as possible. The more easily they are activated, the earlier and more effectively they will inhibit previously existing problematic activation tendencies.

Activation tendencies that are stored in conceptual memory can be process-activated top down from consciousness; for instance, by talking about them. However, if the activation tendencies are stored in implicit or emotional memory, then a bottom-up perceptual activation is required. This can best be done by creating as many realistic eliciting stimuli as possible. Creating family scenarios, staging psycho-dramatic scenes, Gestalt therapy exercises, guided fantasies, hypnosis, exposure to real situations, etc. are suitable for that purpose.

Activation of implicit activation tendencies, though, is only a first step. New activation patterns must then be activated to change the existing connection between perceptual conditions and implicit and emotional responses. Only if these new, inconsistent activation patterns have been activated in similar perceptual conditions will corrective experiences result. In this process, new activation tendencies become ingrained, and the content of the implicit memory is being changed. This process often happens with the patient's awareness so that this new content is simultaneously accepted into conceptual memory. The new activation patterns are occurring on a conscious level, which brings them closer to voluntary control.

Therapeutic approaches that limit themselves to the content being discussed in therapy underestimate the significance of the implicit mode of functioning for mental problems. Such content-focused approaches limit therapists to the contents of the conceptual memory in their search for the causes of and solutions to the problems. The range of this quest is extended considerably by process-oriented perception, thinking, and action. This ability to extend one's own range for discovering and solving the problems by including the implicit mode of functioning is one of the most significant professional qualifications that a therapist can bring to the therapeutic process. It is essential that this skill be acquired by the therapist in the course of training.

Process-oriented thinking is especially important for events in therapy that take place on the relationship level, which leads me to the next training goal:

3. Therapists should become **relationship experts**.

A person's happiness and unhappiness largely manifests itself in his interpersonal relationships. Whether his basic needs are satisfied depends largely on the quality of interpersonal relationships. This is why the interpersonal perspective is of utmost significance for psychotherapy. We have already discussed this in detail (sections 2.26, 2.39 and 3.20).

Relationships should be viewed from both the resource and the problem perspective. This is true for the therapeutic relationship as well as for the patient's other relationships outside of therapy. I have already explained the significance of the resource perspective so it will suffice here to point to the importance of creating a resource-oriented therapeutic relationship and including significant others as resources. All our considerations suggest that the ability to shape a resource-oriented therapeutic relationship should be at the core of every therapist's training.

Therapists should also become experts for relationship problems and learn to recognize, define, and solve interpersonal problems. There are different system-specific problem constellations for different interpersonal systems. In the course of their training, therapists should acquire the most important concepts for these different interpersonal systems , such as:

- for the therapeutic relationship, the concept of relationship test, transference, and counter-transference; in more neutral "therapy-school-independent" terms: the activation of problematic interaction patterns in the therapeutic relationship;
- for couple relationships, concepts such as symmetric escalation (Watzlawick, Beavin & Jackson, 1969), collusion (Willi, 1975), power exerting, communication skills, etc.;
- for family relationships, concepts such as coalition, triangulation, boundaries, etc.;
- for groups, in particular the concept of group cohesion (Yalom, 1974).

In saying that the therapist should be taught such concepts, I am referring to concepts in the sense of super signs (Caspar & Grawe, 1996). In contrast to global signs, super signs include an elaborated range of perceptual, thought, and action potentials. In other words, therapists in training should learn concrete diagnostic and therapeutic know-how pertaining to each of these concepts. The therapist may utilize knowledge developed in any of the individual areas for this purpose.

Therapy researcher: I also think a common reference system should be taught to therapists who learn to perceive, think, and act from an interpersonal perspective. The "interpersonal circumplex model," which dates back to Leary (1957), is particularly suited because it allows us to specify the areas in which the person has interpersonal problems. The Inventory of Interpersonal Problems (Horowitz, Strauss & Kordy, 1994) is a patient self-assessment instrument that has been well tested. Even those interaction patterns going on in the implicit mode of functioning may be specified with this model.

The *"Structural Analysis of Social Behavior"* by Benjamin (1974, 1993) is the best method for this purpose. Benjamin's method makes it possible for us to match interaction processes to certain areas of the interpersonal circle. Although this coding method was originally developed for research purposes, and it is too complex for routine application in therapeutic practice, therapists may still be trained to think using this system, albeit with compromising some of its precision and reliability. The system allows us to specify interpersonal problems in a fashion similar to the way mental problems can be categorized using the ICD or the DSM, with similar advantageous gains in understanding and knowledge. Benjamin (1993) even suggests that personality disorders should generally be specified and diagnosed on this interpersonal level. My opinion is that therapists should routinely be taught this system for interpersonal processes. In fact, this should be as routine as they are now being taught diagnostic systems for mental disorders.

Given the importance of attachment styles for psychotherapy (see section 2.39), it seems appropriate that in the course of their training aspiring therapists also familiarize themselves with the measures for the various kinds of attachment styles, such as the Adult Attachment Interview. Therapists need not always perform their own interview, but they can process the information obtained from the patient accordingly. The attachment style gives the therapist important information about the patient's interpersonal possibilities and limitations. For example, therapists might learn from such attachment measures about patient interaction patterns that can probably not be changed in the short term and should, therefore, be included in long-term treatment planning.

An extensive amount of knowledge has accumulated in recent years about problem-relevant aspects of interpersonal relationships. Given that psychotherapy focuses to a large degree on interpersonal relationships, therapists should certainly be experts in this area. The interpersonal perspective is multifaceted and will remain relevant for therapists throughout their professional lives. It makes sense, then, to expose aspiring therapists right at the beginning of their training to the domain of interpersonal knowledge. Based on such a knowledge foundation, therapists' own experience will then help elaborate and differentiate their interpersonal expertise.

4. Therapists should become **experts on disorders**.

It almost goes without saying that therapists should have an abundant and differentiated knowledge of specific disorders. This applies to all aspects of mental disorders— their etiology, epidemiology, diagnosis, and, of course, especially the possibilities to treat them. Knowledge of disorders includes a scientifically based understanding of how mental disorders develop and how they interact with other mental functions. We have developed exactly such an understanding in our dialogues.

Disorder-relevant knowledge also includes in-depth knowledge of individual mental disorders. Specifically, therapists ought to know a good deal about the intrinsic dynamics of individual disorders. Which disorder components and control parameters ought to be targeted in treatment to effectively destabilize a particular disorder? This knowledge is potentially unlimited and currently develops at such a fast pace that no single therapist could remain up-to-date at all times. The ever increasing knowledge of the various disorders ought to be distilled by experts for the demands of therapeutic practice. For example, you offered earlier an extensive reference list that includes current information on the various mental disorders (Table 2.5, section 2.51). Even more useful for therapeutic practice are the previously mentioned *Advances of Psychotherapy* by Schulte, Grawe, Hahlweg and Vaitl, which include treatment manuals for individual mental disorders.

In the course of their training, therapists should acquire a solid foundation of knowledge and disorder-specific know-how for the most common mental disorders. Additionally, therapists should know how to obtain knowledge and training for the treatment of rare disorders, which they may not encounter frequently in their practice.

Disorder-specific knowledge is often taught in behavior therapy training seminars, which typically last from two to several days. Such courses should be a mandatory part of all psychotherapists' training. It does not make sense that the entire body of knowledge on the various mental disorders should be inextricably linked to one specific school of therapy. The second change component in our process model can only be professionally actualized by a therapist who is familiar with the specific components and control parameters of the individual disorders and who is versatile in using the right tool to effectively influence them.

Disorder-specific training seminars for therapists should also be offered regularly in the form of advanced or continuing education. It is clearly insufficient to obtain this knowledge at only one time at the beginning of one's career, given the rapid pace of advancements in this area. One must remain updated throughout one's working career.

5. Therapists should become **experts on the motivational dynamic** of mental functioning.

Mental disorders do not develop in a psychological vacuum. They form in the context of a certain mental constellation and continue to exist afterwards in a certain mental context. In the way they form and are maintained, they are interconnected with other mental functions. This functioning is motivated. It is determined by the patient's motivational schemata in interaction with his life situation.

Motivational schemata play a crucial role for all three change components of psychotherapy. The process of resource activation works by allowing the patient to have need-fulfilling experiences. The person has developed motivational schemata as a means for satisfying his basic needs, and the therapist should have the best knowledge possible of his patients' motivational schemata in order to allow the patient to have experiences that are congruent with his motivational schemata.

The essence of the third change component is the immediate change of motivational schemata (sections 3.8-3.11) with the aim of increasing congruence and concordance. The focus should not necessarily be on modifying individual schemata but on changing constellations of inconsistency-creating schemata. Thus, the therapist should understand the interplay of the different motivational schemata, or, in short: of the schema dynamic. Motivational constellations may play an important role as control parameters of a disorder attractor in terms of the second change component. According to our conceptualization, motivational schemata are therefore key to understanding the mechanism of psychotherapy. Their role in therapy training should thus be important.

The term "schema-dynamic" is more specific than the expression "psycho-dynamic," which is why I prefer it. It has the additional advantage of being "therapy school neutral." Historically, the term "psychodynamic" has been so closely tied to a particular form of therapy that it would be detrimental to our plan to detach certain ideas from certain therapy school concepts. However, this does not change the fact that up to now it was mostly psychodynamically-oriented therapists who concerned themselves with the motivational dynamics of mental functioning. I think this should change. All psychotherapists should concern themselves with the motivational dynamics of mental functioning just as much as they must familiarize themselves with disorder-specific knowledge or should become experts on relationships.

A lot of the ideas developed in psychoanalysis do not really fit that well into our view of mental functioning. Were we to assume these ideas, we would lose the reach of our view because certain approaches to psychotherapy that have proven very useful agree very little with the psychoanalytic model. Other psychodynamic concepts, however, can be very easily combined with our model. In certain areas, psychodynamic concepts may be heuristically fruitful for the analysis and conception of the motivational dynamic of mental functioning. Similarly, some concepts of system-oriented therapies may be very helpful for the interpersonal perspective. This is essentially a question of empirical and conceptual compatibility.

Inconsistency of mental functioning with its two manifestations of incongruence and discordance is a central construct of our theoretical conception. Inconsistency is primarily a motivational construct. The analysis and modification of mental functioning under the perspective of incongruence and discordance is the core of our theoretical conception. Any therapist who ignores or fails to understand the dynamic of mental functioning will never be able to fully exhaust the real potential of psychotherapy. Thus concepts and methods for the analysis and modification of motivational functioning should therefore be the nucleus of every therapist's training.

6. A therapist should be able to perform both **mastery and clarification-oriented** interventions.

Both mastery and clarification are part of the design and logic behind our three-component change model. While the second component may be realized primarily via mastery-oriented interventions, the third one may be realized primarily via consciousness-facilitating or clarification-oriented interventions. The therapist must be able to apply both interventions to fully exhaust the potential offered by psychotherapy. In planning interventions, the therapist should be able to assume both a motivational and an ability perspective and be knowledgeable about the relevant consequences.

The repertoire of existing mastery-oriented and clarification-oriented interventions is quite large, and the range of therapeutic interventions accordingly abundant. Of course, a young therapist in training does not need to immediately learn all the interventions that exist. But a person in training should at least learn to be versatile in a solid and basic repertoire of clarification- and mastery-oriented procedures. This repertoire can be extended over the course of a career, so the therapist may increase his or her flexibility in using these interventions.

7. Therapists should learn to use the possibilities of **different interpersonal settings**.

In the previous sections on case conceptualization and therapy planning, we discussed the benefits of a patient-tailored case conceptualization for different therapy settings and combinations of settings. These benefits only deliver their full potential if a therapist knows the specific advantages and limitations of the various settings and is skilled in performing therapies in different settings.

Generally young therapists may acquire these skills by being given opportunities to practice in different settings throughout their training and by receiving both instruction and supervision. Most training focuses almost exclusively on individual therapy. However, if therapists work only in the individual therapeutic setting for too long, they easily develop a certain reservation towards a multiple-person setting due to their insecurity in that milieu.

Thus, therapists should be exposed to a variety of settings early in their training, including couples therapy, family therapy, and group therapy. They need to be part of a supervision group led by therapists who are familiar with these settings. The earlier therapists learn to work with these different settings, the earlier they will be able to consider the specific potentials they have for case conceptualization and therapy planning.

Unless therapists have practical experiences with different interpersonal settings, they will never fully develop the ability to assume the interpersonal perspective and to use all these different possibilities.

Therapy researcher: I completely agree with you on this particular training goal. The widespread preference for individual therapy cannot be substantiated by the findings of psychotherapy research. This preference can only be explained by the fact that therapists can more easily create and control this setting, as opposed to a multiple-person setting. Once therapists have begun to frequently work in different settings as well, they usually learn to appreciate their potentials rather quickly and usually have no problems creating the necessary structure for those. I fully agree with you that the right norms should be set in training by having aspiring therapists work in settings other than individual therapy.

Psychologist: The professional profile of a psychological therapist drawn by you here seems quite different from the present goals of therapy training. We usually only find a portion of the training goals you mentioned there. It is rather satisfying to see that the training goals listed by you are a direct result of the theoretical view we have hammered out here. This indicates to me that this was not a purely academic exercise but that real, practical conclusions can be drawn from our theoretical considerations.

I participated in this dialogue because I had assumed that basic psychology does indeed have something to contribute to psychotherapy. As a basic scientist I find that especially reassuring. Looking back, I see that without the basic science issues I introduced, the therapeutic conceptualization you introduced in our third dialogue would not have been possible.

Therapy researcher: I can happily confirm that. Without the psychological foundation you laid in our second dialogue, we would never have gotten as far as we are now. Just looking at therapy research alone would not have led us to the same conclusions.

Yes, I also see your seven training goals as a logical consequence of our theoretical model, but I also think that we should add two additional goals. These are in fact implicitly included in the original seven, but for the sake of clarity they should probably still be teased out and further elaborated. Let me try to supplement your list by distinguishing these two additional points:

8. Therapists should learn to base their interventions and the explanation for them on a **case understanding**.

According to our model, psychological therapists do not blindly apply prefabricated methods. Based on our view, therapists also do not arrive at case conceptualizations by simply pulling open a drawer and selecting a manual for their particular patient. Such simplistic methods are unrealistic because too many perspectives need to be considered simultaneously. If we limited ourselves solely to the disorder perspective, perhaps, we might view therapy a systematic application of methods. However, we have seen that the patient's resources are sometimes more relevant for treatment planning than are the patient's disorders. Moreover, we shouldn't forget in this context the functional significance of the interpersonal perspective and the patient's motivational schemata.

What distinguishes our understanding of case conceptualization and treatment planning is that all perspectives are systematically considered. This multi-perspective orientation is what makes truly patient-tailored therapy possible. The seven skills you outlined here are very important for such a patient-tailored therapy, but they must be coordinated with an individualized case conceptualization. The ability to work out a holistic or integrated view of an individual case is what is missing from your list. The therapist may learn during training to assume the various perspectives that are contained in your seven skills. However, the therapist must still learn how to summarize and integrate the findings from all these perspectives to arrive at a promising treatment plan.

Your profile of the qualifications required of psychological therapists, therefore, implies a specific kind of case conceptualization. A therapist should be able to develop such case conceptualizations for her patients, which then yields a basis for the efficient application of the various skills.

Earlier we discussed how psychological case conceptualizations and therapy plans might look. I just wanted to remind you here that the ability to develop such case conceptualizations and therapy plans should be thought of as a separate training goal. After all, people are not born with these abilities, they must be taught and practiced.

In a psychotherapy that focuses on the patient rather than on methods, therapy planning is always based on a psychological case understanding. The therapist's actions are based on an understanding of the functional contexts, which results from having internalized all that I have listed. Naturally, the need to have more than just a single perspective does not end with the case conceptualization and therapy plan. This multi-perspective orientation is also needed for the actual conduct of therapy, which leads us directly to training goal nine:

9. Therapists should learn to perceive, think, and act **multi-dimensionally**.

The system you introduced earlier includes ten perspectives for conceptualizing psychotherapy (see Figure 3.5, section 3.16). Naturally, the system allows for an even greater number of perspective combinations.

Any segment of a therapy session can look different depending on which perspective or combination of perspectives one takes. Let us assume a patient complains about not being able to sleep at night. In describing this situation, one assumes a certain perspective pertaining to the events in therapy. Content-wise (communication dimension) one focuses on a state (change dimension) under the intra-personal (system dimension) problem perspective (evaluation dimension), namely under the aspect of non-ability (meaning dimension). In the therapist's mind, one of these perspectives may predominate, whereas the others are assumed implicitly, without conscious awareness. Thus, for the therapist, the meanings of therapeutic events flow from implicit decisions that have already been made.

This same situation could also have been viewed under the process aspect: How does the patient relate to the therapist in that moment; which motives determine his behavior? Which of the patient's resources are presently activated?

These two different views can suggest very different interventions. It is important, then, to consider which combination of perspectives a therapist selects. This important choice should not be left to implicit processes for which the therapist lacks awareness.

Therefore, a major goal in training should be for therapists to learn to switch back and forth consciously between different perspectives. When a therapist assumes a certain combination of perspectives and then responds based on the meaning suggested by that combination, she should be aware that this meaning was actively chosen by her, and she should not lose sight of the fact that the current situation might also be viewed from a different combination of perspectives, which may have resulted in other interpretations and actions.

A therapist should learn to not let her behavior be guided by implicit, but rather by explicit and conscious decisions. This requires the ability to view the therapeutic situation from rapidly changing and different perspectives and perspective combinations.

Learning and practicing to assume different perspectives to view therapeutic events can be compared to learning how to read. The perspectives correspond to letters, their combinations to words. The more often the combination of perspectives is assumed, the more easily the corresponding activation patterns are activated. Assuming certain combinations of perspectives will eventually occur without the feeling of conscious effort and—just like reading—may become largely automatic. At this advanced level of competence, a therapist is able to switch back and forth effortlessly, making conscious decisions about the meanings she prefers at a given moment.

That kind of advanced training requires intensive practice. For therapists to learn to perform therapies that are consistent with our model they must receive intensive training in assuming different perspectives. I think supervision is indispensable in this context. A supervisor initially serves as a model for flexible switching between different perspectives and may instruct the aspiring therapist to follow his or her lead. By applying in supervision the perspectives to different therapeutic situations, the perspectives will gradually develop into richly developed "super signs," to which more and more experiences can be assimilated.

Thus, according to our model, supervision should not reflect the supervisor's personal thought system which the supervised trainee adapts to over time, but should refer to a psychologically based system. For didactic reasons, this process should occur on an explicit level over a longer period of time, until the supervisor and the supervisee are able to communicate about therapeutic events without having to mention the system's categories each time.

A therapist who has attained such an advanced level is far better able to account simultaneously for the many aspects of therapeutic events. For instance, disorder-specific interventions can be performed while simultaneously paying attention to shaping the therapeutic relationship, while simultaneously working on a problem and proceeding in a resource-oriented fashion and discussing topics with the patient, while simultaneously paying attention to what is currently activated on the process level, etc.

Multi-dimensional perceiving, thinking, and acting is a desired therapeutic skill that is closely associated with our view of therapy. Therefore, the development of this ability should be a high-priority training goal for psychological therapists. A great portion of psychotherapy training, the way we have conceived it here, should consist of specifically practicing information processing, partially as an alternative and partially as a supplement to practical methods. Caspar (1997) advocates such a conception of therapist training. His research on intuitive and conscious information processing among therapists may help improve empirically based therapy training in this manner.

Therapist: Those were two important additions to my seven points. It makes sense to me that these skills have to be regarded as explicit training goals, which need to be implemented with specific measures.

Psychologist: We have now clarified the goals that should be part of the training of psychological therapists, but can these goals be achieved? Can such a training be realized considering the present state of development in psychotherapy?

Therapist: I do not think this is an all-or-nothing question. One would have to work towards these goals in cooperation with the existing training institutions. Those training programs could also be evaluated to see which goals they meet and where they fall short, and the relevant adjustments could then be implemented. What is needed is primarily a willingness to move beyond present training structures and break new ground.

It would make little sense for us to design a specific curriculum for such training programs, considering all the different local conditions, regulations, legal frameworks, instructors, etc. The path toward psychological therapy training would clearly look different in different locations and institutions. Some programs would have to go further than others, given that some already consider many of the perspectives specified in our system.

The nine goals listed here can probably only be approximated; not reached to perfection. In other words, I cannot imagine that a training program—not matter how good—could not be further improved. As I said earlier: The better is the enemy of the good. Very good programs are available in psychotherapy today, but that is not to say they could not be improved. Conceptually, the program closest to our vision of a non-therapy-school oriented training for psychological therapists is perhaps the post-graduate program at the University of Bern. Even that program, however, could be improved from the perspective of our model.

It would be surprising if any training programs were already fully consistent with the ideas we developed. This would imply the existence of similar theoretical conceptions, and we would certainly have encountered these already if they did indeed exist. Realistically, it will take a while until psychological therapy as we conceive it can be realized on a broader level, but therapists who see things as we do could immediately begin to gradually approximate this goal. Some may find it fascinating that there is so much room for improvement. For instance, I began to modify my own practice directly after our second dialogue. I now derive great joy from my work, although my practice clearly represents only an approximation of the ideas suggested by our model.

There are many things I cannot change alone because the existing structures in our health care system make this very difficult. This is one last point I would like to discuss with you: What would an optimal system for therapeutic care look like, based on our ideas? If we don't develop a concrete vision first, we cannot expect that things would ever change in this respect.

Therapy researcher: This would also interest me, but I think we should make this our last topic, as our time for discussion is winding down, and we should move towards action. I have picked up numerous ideas for my research, and I assume that you too have many ideas for your practice from our third dialogue.

3.29 Psychological Therapy in the Healthcare System

Therapist: Correct, but unfortunately I am unable to implement some of these all alone. As an individual therapist I am part of a care system that dictates the structure of my own work, and very little can be changed about that. It already begins with the conditions for payment.

In an effort to achieve a certain quality control in psychotherapy, different states have instituted regulations that recognize certain therapy methods but not others. If a therapist wisely sticks to one of these recognized methods, he or she gets paid, otherwise not. In reality, however, these regulations do not reflect empirically documented efficacy but rather result from complex political disputes.

These regulations, which should of course serve to ensure quality, now have come to prevent the practice of therapies that are actually effective. According to current therapy research and our theoretical considerations, truly effective therapies would combine a variety of interventions that have been shown to lead to successful therapeutic outcome. However, the guardians of the recognized "brand name therapies" watch to see that their brand is not being watered down. Such experts are often the ones who decide which therapies are eligible for reimbursement and which ones aren't.

Psychological therapy as we conceive it would have no chance of being financed by health insurance in some countries. Actually, health insurance companies ought to pay for the most efficacious and cost-effective therapies in the interest of those they insure. Our patient-tailored therapies would certainly fulfill such criteria better than other therapies because they take advantage of a greater range of possibilities than do more traditional forms of therapy. In our model, psychological therapy is free to employ any methods that fit for the individualized case conceptualization; yet, health insurance companies stick to the established system, which defines the sacred (accepted and eligible for reimbursement) and the profane (not accepted and eligible), because they fear otherwise uncontrollably escalating costs.

These irrational conditions can only change if payment providers (e.g., insurances, government agencies) begin to judge therapies based on their actual effectiveness rather than their adherence to a particular brand-name. We currently have reliable and economic methods for recording the process and outcome of psychotherapies (Howard et al., 1996; Grawe & Braun, 1994; Grawe & Baltensperger, 1998). If there are high expectations for quality in therapist training, and if only those therapists who have completed such a training receive finances; if each therapy had to routinely undergo an assessment of process and outcome quality, and if only therapists were financed who volunteered to undergo such quality control, and for whom an average good quality of the therapies was documented, then fears of a cost explosion would be unfounded. It has been documented that good therapies contribute to reduced costs and that alternative options are often more costly (Baltensperger, 1993).

Clearly, then, how a patient is treated should be decided based on the professional assessment of therapists, and they can use all possibilities for that. Quality assurance of therapies is guaranteed by making therapists go through a sophisticated training process and continuously subjecting their therapies to quality control. On average, this would lead to a marked improvement in the quality of psychotherapies because the intervention possibilities available would be much better utilized.

This would give therapists real motivation to make sure their therapies are in fact of the highest quality. It would also serve as effective motivation to keep oneself abreast of the most recent developments by participating in continuing education. A certain competition among therapists would also develop, which would decidedly be in the patients' interest. Consequently, we would need to turn away from the old model of a method-oriented therapy. Instead, we would introduce a patient- and success-oriented system.

Beyond that, an additional effective means for improving and assuring quality would be a systematic introduction of pre-therapy intake assessments and structured case conceptualization and treatment planning methods. These aspects were discussed earlier (sections 3.21 and 3.22). Thus, you already have a good idea of what such an intake assessment involves in terms of process and effort.

In the future, therapists who limit themselves to a particular therapy method should only treat patients who have been assigned to them after a comprehensive evaluation somewhere else. This evaluation would have yielded a case conceptualization and tailored treatment plan that is consistent with the particular form of therapy they practice. Accordingly, method-specific therapies would not take place in the setting where a patient is first seen because it would be too great a risk that the person may not receive the best therapy.

Every psychotherapy should be preceded by a therapy-school-transcending comprehensive evaluation, the goal of which would be a patient-tailored case conceptualization and treatment plan. It would be ideal if there were facilities just for that purpose, where therapies themselves were not conducted, but where the specialty was purely on evaluations and recommendations to therapists. Such evaluation facilities would have to be recognized by the health care system, and precautions would have to be taken so that recommendations are made exclusively based on professional assessments and not based on the assessor's preference, socioeconomic class, or other irrelevant factors.

Even these evaluation facilities would have to be subject to quality control. This would be easy to do, given that the process and outcome of the recommended therapies would be measured regularly. Thus, whether these facilities really recommend the most efficient therapies would be monitored, which would also allow the quality of the recommended therapies to be compared with those recommended by other facilities. Institutions performing these evaluations would themselves be under a certain pressure to succeed, and this would also be in our patients' interest and therefore justified.

Pre-therapy evaluations and conceptualizations would probably be somewhat more costly, but more money would be saved by not spending it on a multitude of unsuccessful therapy attempts. Primary caregivers such as family doctors would probably more readily send patients who might benefit from psychotherapy to a specialist trained in evaluation, and the patient would come back with a report and some feedback. The overall result would be that more patients would have earlier access to suitable psychotherapy. Not only would that be an ethical goal, but from an economic point of view, it would be the most advantageous way of dealing with mental disorders.

It would be beneficial to have such evaluation specialists even if psychotherapy otherwise remained method-specific. This way, the risk for unsuccessful treatment would still be reduced because of a reduced chance of inappropriate case conceptualization and treatment plans. A major improvement in average quality, however, would only be achieved by performing a truly patient-tailored therapy, which would follow the intake evaluation, conceptualization, and treatment planning. Only then we really exhaust what this kind of psychological therapy has to offer.

Therapists in private practice would be limited, however, in their ability to offer truly patient-tailored forms of therapy. Certainly, it would be difficult for them to optimally utilize different setting combinations, group therapy, or other complex but potentially needed interventions. Given the obvious constraints of individual practice, few such therapists would be able to immediately offer the right kind of group whenever a patient might benefit from it. If the patient needs group therapy, however, it should be generally possible to refer him to an appropriate setting. If treatment requires two or more settings, then it should be routinely possible to coordinate between the different therapists or to arrange that one therapist conduct the treatment in the different settings.

Psychological therapies could be implemented even more effectively in settings where multiple therapists with different emphases and skills work together. This would provide opportunities for professional communication, consultation, and collegial supervision. In a setting where different therapists work together in collaboration, it would be less likely that therapists drift to exclusively using their preferred interventions.

Therapy researcher: I see another opportunity for enhancing therapeutic effectiveness in the development of specialized therapist emphases and competencies. Our empirical knowledge base of the various mental disorders grows and changes at a rapid pace. It is already quite difficult for a therapist to remain up-to-date on all the disorders, and it will only become more difficult in the future.

Therefore, it might be advisable for therapists to specialize in certain disorders. I do not mean that they ought to limit themselves to the disorder perspective. Indeed, they should make every attempt to regularly utilize the first and third component of our model and to use all relevant therapeutic settings. However, when it comes to our second change component—the destabilization of disorder attractors—it would make sense for therapists to specialize in certain disorders and to attend continuing education courses throughout their career to regularly update their knowledge. Thus, for example, there would be psychological therapists specialized in the treatment of depression.

Disorder characteristics are relatively easy to recognize, so it would be easy to match patients with therapists who specialize in the treatment of their disorder. Thus, therapy-school-oriented patient-therapist matching would be replaced by disorder-oriented matching. After the patient is matched with a specialist for his disorder, an initial case conceptualization and treatment plan would be formulated, as described before. This additional step would ensure that the disorder perspective does not come to dominate and is not reintroduced again "through the backdoor." After all, there is always the possibility that the disorder will not be treated directly because of a generally high inconsistency level. From the therapist's perspective, it might make sense to target the inconsistency before focusing on the disorder itself. This type of specialization would ensure that therapists have complete and specific knowledge of patients with certain disorders.

As a possible alternative to your model, in which evaluation facilities are the primary places for patients to go, a patient might first see a specialist for particular disorders who then performs the initial evaluation and treatment planning. It might be best, though, to combine both models. My suggestion would require that primary caregivers be able to adequately diagnose mental disorders, which seems rather unrealistic. The problem of comorbidity still remains. For patients with several disorders, the question would be: For which disorder should the patient see a specialist first ?

This points to the benefits of performing evaluations first in specialized facilities, which then direct the patient to therapist who specialize in the particular disorders that have been identified. This specialist therapist should also consider any other aspects that have been included in the case conceptualization and treatment plan, not just the disorder-relevant ones.

I assume that disorder-specific knowledge will continue to grow fast and that it will be increasingly difficult to train therapists in a way that they acquire all the latest skills for all disorders. It will be even more difficult for all therapists to maintain updated knowledge throughout their entire careers. This is another reason for why it would be a great relief if therapists could specialize on certain disorders.

The changes we envisioned could potentially significantly improve the quality of psychotherapy. To review, these changes include:
– replacing method-orientation with a patient- and a success-orientation,
– introducing routine quality control,
– introducing independent pre-therapy evaluations,
– facilitating disorder-oriented specialization while maintaining the fundamental principles of psychological therapy as we conceive it

Indeed, these changes might produce a considerable leap in the quality of psychotherapy. This might sound utopian, but at least it is a pragmatic, tenable utopia because all the proposed steps could be realized at the present time.

Psychologist: Such a utopian vision is a good conclusion for our dialogues. Our conversations have boosted my knowledge in a way I had not anticipated. Perhaps our common vision of a psychological therapy that goes beyond therapy schools will materialize faster than both of you expect. The better is not just the enemy of the good but also of the not so good. Your ideas make it plain to me that so many things in psychotherapy must change, and if this is truly the case, many other therapists will also see this as you do. When we assume a resource-oriented perspective, the prospects for psychological therapy do not look so bad. After all, many resources are available—they simply have to be activated.

Our conversations have obviously activated resources in us that have gone beyond that which we originally thought possible. This led to the development of a concept that none of us knew before: The concept of psychological therapy. Psychological therapy must now be "process activated," but that is not solely our responsibility.

Therapy researcher: A good concluding remark. I have nothing to add to that.

Therapist: Nor do I. But I do have another question for you to ponder on your way home: What do a trilogy, our change-component model, and Anton Bruckner's symphonies all have in common?

Epilogue

epilogue

Epilogue

Development occurs in phases of differentiation and integration (Werner, 1948). Psychotherapy has gone through a long phase of differentiation, producing a large number of therapy concepts and methods. This multiplicity of ideas and perspectives has advanced to a point of being dysfunctional. It no longer benefits those it was intended to serve but gets in the way of patients' receiving the best possible treatment. The current level of differentiation calls for integration.

There has long been a movement towards integration in psychotherapy, ranging from technical eclecticism (Beutler, 1986; Garfield, 1992; Lazarus, 1992) to the theoretical integration of existing approaches (Dollard & Miller, 1950; Wachtel, 1977; Stricker & Gold, 1993). Although I prefer these efforts over a therapy-school-oriented psychotherapy, I have my doubts on whether the combination of insufficiently explanatory concepts can yield a more solid foundation from which psychotherapy can advance beyond its current level. By combining inadequate older elements, one fails to address directly the limited explanatory power of such previous approaches. The deficits adopted and carried along in that manner become dead ballast on the route towards progress in psychotherapy.

Psychotherapy needs new theoretical approaches in order to productively utilize its current level of differentiation. Among such new approaches are those that introduce a new order to arrange the various therapeutic phenomena. One such approach, for instance, is the "transtheoretical phase model" by Prochaska, Norcross and DiClemente (1994). This model focuses on the different phases of the change process; in doing so, it assumes a perspective that has been neglected by many other approaches. Models like these do not claim to provide comprehensive explanations. They are not based on the entire body of empirical knowledge in the field of psychotherapy but instead place aspects of current knowledge into a new context.

However, some new theoretical explanatory approaches do exist that attempt to incorporate the broad spectrum of current empirical psychotherapy knowledge. These approaches include, for instance, the Generic Model of Psychotherapy by Orlinsky and Howard (1986; Orlinsky, Grawe & Parks, 1994) and my concept of a General Psychotherapy (Grawe, Donati & Bernauer, 1994; Grawe, 1994, 1995, 1997). These models differ from the previously mentioned approaches either by the breadth of their approach or by their affinity for empiricism. They represent comprehensive attempts to explain and integrate empirical knowledge in psychotherapy; their point of reference is the entire body of current empirical therapy research.

With this book I have taken a considerable step beyond previous attempts at integration. For my frame of reference I have selected findings not just from psychotherapy research but also—and predominantly—from basic empirical psychology. I have attempted to explain empirically documented effects of psychotherapy by drawing from empirically based basic science models of mental functioning.

Because of the close relationship of these constructs with basic scientific psychology, I am no longer speaking of **General Psychotherapy** but instead of **Psychological Therapy**. This is not meant to imply, though, that I distance myself from the idea of a general psychotherapy. To me, general psychotherapy stands for the attempt to utilize the entire range of methods developed in psychotherapy for the benefit of the individual patient. Thus, general psychotherapy is a therapy that is no longer hampered by artificial internal boundaries.

If we are to utilize the full breadth of psychotherapy, though, we also need a broad theoretical basis, with a range that exceeds previous individual therapeutic approaches. I have tried to formulate such a theoretical basis in this book. At the same time, I believe this to be an ongoing and incomplete process. The dialogue begun here ought to be continued. For instance, in a new discussion, our therapist might invite a personality psychologist and a psychopathologist. Undoubtedly, they would introduce new aspects and further advance the dialogue.

A personality psychologist, for instance, would place more emphasis on individual differences between patients. What can differential psychology or personality psychology contribute to patient case conceptualization and treatment planning? What hints can such fields offer us about how we should approach certain individual differences in treatment, with respect to both constraints and resources?

Involving a psychopathologist would probably introduce a stronger disorder-specific component into the dialogue. The general disorder-transcendent ideas developed by our three participants in this book might be tied more systematically to existing disorder-specific knowledge. I have been able to show only hints of that here, especially for agoraphobia. This topic remains a great task for the future.

I am confident that the theoretical framework described in this book leaves sufficient space for future differentiations. I have attempted a large integrative step. A new theoretical foundation should not integrate but replace previous foundations. A new process of differentiation can and must begin on the basis of this new theoretical foundation. Many differentiations could already be made on the basis of extant knowledge. I have not embarked upon this here because it would have overloaded my plan and also exceeded my own expertise, but there are others who are qualified to take on such a task.

Further differentiations will certainly emerge from future research. Such new knowledge will further inform the ideas and concepts I introduced in this book. As I have stated before, psychological therapy is not a finished product; it always remains subject to revision and refinement. It remains in a continuous state of evolution because of its close ties to empirical research in basic psychology, psychotherapy, and clinical psychology/psychiatry. Adding the *Logos* to psycho-therapy marks the scientific character of the endeavor. This should help to protect against any therapy-school-like encrustation. Indeed, psychological therapy as I envision it must always remain open to future advances in knowledge.

References

Abramson, L. Y., Metalsky, G. I. & Alloy, L. B. (1989). Hopelessness depression. A theory-based subtype of depression. *Psychological Review, 96,* 358–372.

Abramson, L. Y., Seligman, M. E. & Teasdale, J. D. (1978). Learned helplessness in humans: Critique and reformulation. *Journal of Abnormal Psychology, 87,* 49–74.

Adam, K. S. (1994). Suicidal Behavior and attachment. In M. B. Berling & W.H. Sperman (Eds.), *Attachment in adults – clinical and developmental perspectives.* New York: Guilford.

Adams, H. E. & McAnulty, S. (1993). Sexual disorders: The paraphilias. In P. B. Sutker & H. E. Adams (Eds.), *Comprehensive handbook of psychopathology* (2nd ed., pp. 563–580). New York: Plenum Press.

Adler, A. (1920). *Praxis und Theorie der Individualtherapie.* [Practice and theory of individual therapy] München: Bergmann.

Adler, A. (1927). *Studie über Minderwertigkeit von Organen.* [Study of the inferior nature of organs] München: Bergmann.

Ainsworth, M. D. (1982). Attachment retrospect and prospect. In C. M. Parkes & J. Stephenson-Hinde (Eds.), *The place of attachment in human behaviour.* London: Tavistock.

Ainsworth, M. D., Blehar, M. C., Waters, E. & Wall, S. (1978). *Patterns of attachment: A psychological study of the strange situation.* New York: Erlbaum.

Alexander, F. (1950). *Psychosomatic medicine. Its principles and application.* London: Allen & Unwin.

Alexander, F. & French, T. M. (1946). *Psychoanalytic therapy. Principles and applications.* New York: Wiley.

Allport, G. W. (1937). *Personality: A psychological interpretation.* New York: Holt.

Allport, G. W. (1943). The ego in contemporary psychology. *Psychological Review, 50,* 451–478.

Ambühl, H. (1991). Die Aufnahmebereitschaft des Klienten als zentrales Bindeglied zwischen therapeutischer Tätigkeit und Therapieerfolg. [The client's openness as a central link between therapeutic intervention and outcome] In D. Schulte (Ed.), *Therapeutische Entscheidungen* (pp. 71–88). Göttingen: Hogrefe.

Ambühl, H. (1992). Die therapeutische Beziehungsgestaltung unter dem Gesichtspunkt der Konflikt-dynamik. [Shaping the therapeutic relationship seen from the perspective of conflict dynamics] In J. Margraf & J. C. Brengelmann (Eds.), *Die Therapeut-Patient-Beziehung in der Verhaltenstherapie* (pp. 245–264). München: Gerhard Röttger.

Ambühl, H. & Heiniger, B. (1997). Psychotherapie bei einem Patienten mit Waschzwang. Ein kontrollierter Einzelfall. [Psychotherapy with an ablutomania patient. A single controlled case] *Verhaltenstherapie und psychosoziale Praxis, 29,* 175–196.

Anchin, J. C. & Kiesler, D. J. (Eds.). (1982). *Handbook of interpersonal psychotherapy.* New York: Pergamon Press.

Arbeitskreis OPD (Eds.). (1996). *Operationalisierte psychodynamische Diagnostik. Grundlagen und Manual.* [Operationalized psychodynamic diagnostics. Foundations and manual] Bern: Huber.

Atkinson, J. W. (1957). Motivational determinants of risk taking behavior. *Psychological Review, 64,* 359–372.

Atkinson, J. W. & Birch, D. A. (1970). *A dynamic theory of action.* New York: Wiley.

Atkinson, R. C. & Shiffrin, R. M. (1968). Human memory: A proposed system and its control processes. In K. Spence (Ed.), *The psychology of learning and motivation* (pp. 89–195). New York: Academic Press.

Baade, F.-W., Borck, J., Koebe, S. & Zumvenne, G. (1982). *Theorien und Methoden der Verhaltenstherapie. Eine Einführung.* [Theories and methods of behavior therapy. An introduction] Tübingen: DGVT.

Backhaus, J. & Riemann, D. (1996). *Schlafstörungen bewältigen.* [Mastering sleep disorders] Weinheim: Psychologie Verlags Union.

Baddeley, A. D. (1990). *Human memory. Theory and practice.* Boston: Allyn & Bacon.

Baltensperger, C. (1993). *Der gesellschaftliche Nutzen von Psychotherapie.* [The social value of psychotherapy] Unpublished dissertation. Bern: Institut für Psychologie der Universität.

Bandura, A. (1977 a). Self-efficacy: Toward a unifying theory of behavior change. *Psychologica Review, 84,* 191–215.

Bandura, A. (1977 b). *Social learning theory.* Englewood Cliffs, NJ: Prentice Hall.

Bandura, A. (1982). Self-efficacy mechanism in human agency. *American Psychologist, 37,* 122–147.

Bandura, A. (1989). Human agency in social cognitive theory. *American Psychologist, 44,* 1175–1184.

Bänninger-Huber, E. (1992). Prototypical affective microsequences in psychotherapeutic interaction. *Psychotherapy Research, 4 (2),* 291–306.

Bänninger-Huber, E. & Steiner, F. (1986). *FACS in psychotherapy research.* Berichte aus der Abteilung Klinische Psychologie. [FACS in psychotherapy research. Reports from the department of clinical psychology] Zürich: Psychologisches Institut der Universität.

Barkley, R. A. (1990). *Attention deficit hyperactivity disorder. A handbook for diagnosis and treatment.* New York: Guilford.

Barron, J. W., Eagle, M. N. & Wolitzky, D. L. (Eds.). (1992). *Interface of psychoanalysis and psychology.* Washington, DC: APA.

Bartlett, F. C. (1932). *Remembering: A study in experimental and social psychology.* Cambridge: Cambridge University Press.

Bartling, G., Echelmeyer, L., Engberding, M. & Krause, R. (1992). *Problemanalyse im psychotherapeutischen Prozess.* [Problem analysis in the psychotherapeutic process] Stuttgart: Kohlhammer.

Basler, H. D. & Kröner-Herwig, B. (Eds.) (1995). *Psychologische Therapie bei Kopf- und Rücken-schmerzen. Ein Schmerzbewältigungsprogramm zur Gruppen- und Einzeltherapie.* [Psychological therapy for headache and backache. A pain management program in group and individual therapy] München: Quintessenz.

Bateson, G., Jackson, D. D., Haley, J. & Weakland, J. (1956). Toward a theory of schizophrenia. *Behavioral Science (1),* 251–254.

Baumeister, R. F. (1991). *Meanings of life.* New York: Guilford.

Baumeister, R. F. (1993). *Self-esteem: The puzzle of low self-regard.* New York: Plenum Press.

Beck, A. T. (1967). *Depression: Clinical, experimental, and theoretical aspects.* New York: Haper & Row.

Beck, A. T. (1976). *Cognitve therapy and the emotional disorders.* New York: International Universities Press.

Beck, A. T., Freeman, A., et al. (1993). *Kognitive Therapie der Persönlichkeitsstörungen.* [Cognitive therapy of personality disorders] Weinheim: Psychologie Verlags Union.

Beck, A. T., Rush, J. A., Shaw, B. F. & Emery, G. (1979). *Cognitive therapy of depression.* New York: Guilford Press.

Beck, A. T., Wright, F. D., Newman, C. F. & Liese, B. S. (1997). *Kognitive Therapie der Sucht.* [Cognitive therapy of addiction] Weinheim: Psychologie Verlags Union.

Becker, E. (1971). *The birth and death of meaning.* New York: Macmillan.

Becker, P. (1995). *Seelische Gesundheit und Verhaltenskontrolle.* [Mental health and behavior control] Göttingen: Hogrefe.

Beier, E. G. (1966). *The silent language of psychotherapy. Social reinforcement of unconscious processes.* Chicago: Aldine.

Benjamin, L. S. (1974). Structural analysis of social behavior. *Psychological Review, 81,* 392–425.

Benjamin, L. S. (1993). *Interpersonal diagnosis and treatment of personality disorders.* New York: Guilford.

Benoit, D. & Parker, K. C. (1994). Stability and transmission of attachment across three generations. *Child Develoment, 65,* 1444–1456.

Berger Bertschinger, A. (1993) *Empirische Untersuchung von Familientherapie.* [Empirical investigation of family therapy] Upublished Master's thesis. Institut für Psychologie der Universität Bern.

Bergin, A. E. & Garfield, S. L. (1994). *Handbook of psychotherapy and behavior change (4th ed.).* New York: Wiley.

Berman, W.H. & Sperling, M. B. (1994). The structure and fuction of adult attachment. In M. B. Sperling & W. H. Berman (Eds.), *Attachment in adults.* New York: Guilford.

Berne, E. (1967). *Spiele der Erwachsenen.* [Adult's games] Reinbek: Rowohlt.

Betz, D. & Breuninger, H. (1993). *Teufelskreis Lernstörungen. Theoretische Grundlagen und Standardprogramm.* [The vicious cycle of learning disorders. Theoretical foundations and standard program] (3rd ed.) Weinheim: Psychologie Verlags Union.

Beutler, L. (1986). Systematic eclectic psychotherapy. In J. C. Norcross (Ed.), *Handbook of eclectic psychotherapy* (pp. 94–131). New York: Brunner/Mazel.

Beutler, L. E. & Clarkin, J. F. (1990). *Systematic treatment selection – Toward targeted therapeutic interventions.* New York: Brunner/Mazel.

Beutler, L. E. & Consoli, A. J. (1992). Systematic eclectic psychotherapy. In J. C. Norcross & M. R. Goldfried (Eds.), *Handbook of psychotherapy integration* (pp. 264–299). New York: Basic Books.

Beutler, L. E., Mohr, D. C., Grawe, K., Engle, D. & MacDonald, R. (1991). Looking for differential treatment effects: Cross-cultural predictors of differential psychotherapy efficacy. *Journal of Psychotherapy Integration, 1,* 121–141.

Bieri, E. (1996). *Das Drei-Phasen-Modell therapeutischer Veränderungen.* [The three-phase-model of therapeutic change] Unpublished Master's thesis. Universität Bern: Institut für Psychologie.

Biermann-Ratjen E. M. & Eckert, J. (1985). *Stationäre Gruppenpsychotherapie: Prozesse, Effekte, Vergleiche.* [Inpatient group psychotherapy: Process, effects, comparisons] Berlin: Springer.

Biermann-Ratjen, E., Eckert, J. & Schwartz, H. J. (1979). *Gesprächspsychotherapie: Verändern durch Verstehen.* [Client-centered psychotherapy: Change through understanding] Stuttgart: Kohlhammer.

Birbaumer, N. & Schmidt, R. F. (1996). *Biologische Psychologie* [Biological psychology] (2nd ed.). Berlin: Springer.

Bischoff, C. & Pein, A. von (1994). Verhaltensmedizin der essentiellen Hypertonie. [Behavioral medicine of essential hypertension] In M. Zielke & J. Sturm (Eds.), *Handbuch stationäre Verhaltenstherapie* (pp. 659–674). Weinheim: Psychologie Verlags Union.

Blanck, P. D., Buck, R. & Rosenthal, R. (1986). General introduction: Nonverbal communication in the clinical context. In R. Buck P. D. Blanck & R. Rosenthal (Eds.), *Nonverbal communication in the clinical context* (pp. 1–6). University Park and London: Pennsylvania State University Press.

Blanck, P. D., Rosenthal, R. & Vannicelli, M. (1986). Talking to and about patients: The therapist's tone of voice. In P. D. Blanck, R. Buck & R. Rosenthal (Eds.), *Nonverbal communication in the clinical context.* University Park and London: The Pennsylvania State University Press.

Blatt, S. J. (1990). Interpersonal relatedness and self-definition: Two personlity configurations and their implication for psychopathology and psychotherapy. In J. L. Singer (Eds.), *Repression and dissociation* (pp. 299–336). Chicago: The University of Chicago Press.

Bohus, M. (1996). Zur Funktion von Verhaltensanalysen bei der Therapie von Borderline-Persönlichkeitsstörungen. [The function of behavioral analyses in the therapy of borderline personality disorders] In F. M. Caspar (Ed.), *Psychotherapeutische Problemanalyse.*Tübingen: dgvt-Verlag .

Bohus, M. & Berger, M. (1992). Der Beitrag biologisch-psychiatrischer Befunde zum Verständnis depressiver Erkrankungen. [Biological-psychiatric findings and their contribution to understanding depressive illness] *Zeitschrift für Klinische Psychologie, 21 (2),* 156–171.

Bonanno, G. A. & Singer, J. L. (1990). Repressive personality style: Theoretical and method-ological implications for health and pathology. In J. L. Singer (Ed.), *Repression and disso-ciation* (pp. 435–470). Chicago: The University of Chicago Press.

Bonanno, G. A. & Singer, J. L. (1993). Controlling one's stream of thought through perceptual and reflective processing. In D. M. Wegner & J. W. Pennebaker (Eds.), *Handbook of mental control* (pp. 149–170). Englewood Cliffs, NJ: Prentice Hall.

Borkovec, T. D. & Nau, S. D. (1972). Credibility of analogue therapy rationales. *Journal of Behavior Therapy and Experimental Psychiatry, 3,* 257–260.

Bornstein, R. F. (1993). *The dependent personality.* New York: Guilford.

Bornstein, P. H. & Bornstein, M. T. (1993). *Psychotherapie mit Ehepaaren. Ein integrativer Ansatz.* [Psychotherapy with married couples. An integrative approach] Bern: Huber.

Borod, J. C., Koff, E. & Buck, R. (1986). The neuropsychology of facial expression: Data from normal and brain-damaged adults. In P. D. Blanck, R. Buck & R. Rosenthal (Eds.), *Nonver-bal communication in the clinical context.* University Park and London: The Pennsylvania State University Press.

Bowen, M. (1972). On the differentiation of self. In J. Framo (Eds.), *Family interaction: A dialogue between family researchers and family therapists* (pp. 111–173). New York: Springer.

Bowen, M. (1976). Theory in the practice of psychotherapy. In P. Guerin (Ed.), *Family therapy: Theory and practice* (pp. 42–90). New York: Gardner Press.

Bowen, M. (1978). *Family therapy in clinical practice.* New York: Jason Aronson.

Bower, G. H. (1990). Awareness, the unconscious, and repression: An experimental psychologist's perspective. In J. L. Singer (Ed.), *Repression and dissociation* (pp. 209–232). Chicago: The University of Chicago Press.

Bowers, T. G. & Clum, G. A. (1988). Relative contribution of specific and nonspecific treatment effects: Meta-analysis of placebo-controlled behavior therapy research. *Psychological Bul-letin, 103,* 315–323.

Bowlby, J. (1969). *Attachment and loss. Vol. 1: Attachment.* New York: Basic Books.

Bowlby, J. (1973). *Attachment and loss. Vol. 2: Separation. Anxiety and anger.* New York: Basic Books.

Bowlby, J. (1975). *Bindung.* [Attachment] Frankfurt: Fischer.

Bowlby, J. (1976). *Trennung.* [Separation] Frankfurt: Fischer.

Bowlby, J. (1983). *Verlust, Trauer und Depression.* [Loss, grief and depression] Frankfurt: Fischer.

Bowlby, J. (1987). Defensive Processes in the light of attachment theory. In D. P. Schwartz, J. L. Sacksteder & Y. Akabane (Eds.), *Attachment and the therapeutic process.* Madison: In-ternational Universities Press.

Bowlby, J. (1995). Bindung: Historische Wurzeln, theoretische Konzepte und klinische Relevanz. [Attachment: Historical roots, theoretical concepts and clinical relevance] In G. Spangler & P. Zimmermann (Eds.), *Die Bindungstheorie: Grundlagen, Forschung und Anwendung* (pp.17–27). Stuttgart: Klett-Cotta.

Brack, U. B. (Ed.). (1986). *Frühdiagnostik und Frühtherapie. Psychologische Behandlung von entwicklungs und verhaltensgestörten Kindern.* [Early diagnosis and early therapy. Psycho-logical treatment of children with developmental and behavior disorders] Weinheim: Psychologie Verlags Union.

Brehm, J. W. & Cohen, A. R. (1962). *Explorations in cognitive dissonance.* New York: Wiley.

Breier, A., Charney, D. S. & Heninger, G. R. (1986). Agoraphobia with panic attacks. *Archives of General Psychiatry, 43,* 1029–1036.

Broda, M., Koch, U. & Muthny, F. A. (1989). Bedarf und Möglichkeiten der psychologischen Intervention bei Dialyse- und Nierentransplantationspatienten. [Demand and possibilities of psychological intervention in dialysis and kidney transplant patients] In I. Hand & H.-U. Wittchen (Eds.), *Verhaltenstherapie in der Medizin* (pp. 262–274). Berlin: Springer-Verlag.

Brown, F. W., Golding, J. & Smith, G. R. (1990). Psychiatric comorbidity in primary care somatization disorder. *Psychosomatic Medicine, 52,* 445–451.

Brown, G. W. & Harris, T. O. (1978). *The origins of depression*. London: Tavistock.

Brown, J. D. (1993). Motivational conflict and the self: The double bind of low self-steem. In R. F. Baumeister (Ed.), *Self-esteem: The puzzle of low self-regard*. New York: Plenum Press.

Brown, J. D., Collins, R. L. & Schmidt, G. W. (1988). Self-esteem and direct versus indirect forms of self-enhancement. *Journal of Personality and Social Psychology, 55*, 445–453.

Brown, J. D., Novick, N. J., Lord, K. A. & Richards, J. M. (1992). When Gulliver travels: Social context, psychological closeness, and self-appraisals. *Journal of Personality and Social Psychology, 60*, 717–727.

Brown, J. W. & Jaffe, J. (1975). Hypotheses of cerebral dominance. *Neuropsychologia, 13*, 107–110.

Buck, R. (1982). Spontaneous and symbolic nonverbal behavior and the ontogeny of communication. In R. Feldman (Ed.), *The development of nonverbal behavior in children*. New York: Springer.

Buck, R. (1984). *The communication of emotion*. New York: Guilford.

Bühringer, G. & Küfner, H. (1996). Drogen und Medikamentenabhängigkeit. [Drug and medication dependency] In K. Hahlweg & A. Ehlers (Eds.), *Psychische Störungen und ihre Behandlungen* (pp. 513–588). Göttingen: Hogrefe.

Calhoun, K. S. & Atkeson, B. M. (1994). *Therapie mit Opfern von Vergewaltigung. Hilfen bei der Überwindung der psychischen und sozialen Folgen*. [Therapy with rape victims. Helping to cope with mental and social effects] Bern: Huber.

Campenhausen, C. von (1981). *Die Sinne des Menschen, Band 1: Einführung in die Psychophysik der Wahrnehmung*. [The human senses; Volume 1: Introduction into the psychophysics of perception] Stuttgart: Thieme.

Campos, J. J. & Barrett, K. C. (1984). Toward a new understanding of emotions and their development. In C. E. Ozard, J. Kagan & R. B. Zajonc (Eds.), *Emotions, cognitions, and behavior*. New York: Cambridge University Press.

Campos, J. J., Barrett, K. C., Lamb, M. E., Goldsmith, H. H. & Stenberg, C. (1983). Socioemotional development. In M. Haith & J. J. Campos (Eds.), *Handbook of child psychology, Vol. 2: Infancy and developmental psychobiology*. New York: Wiley.

Campos, J. J., Campos, R. G. & Barrett, K. C. (1989). Emergent themes in the study of emotional development and emotional regulation. *Developmental Psychology, 25*, 394–402.

Capitiano, J. P., Weissberg, M. & Reite, M. (1985). Biology of maternal behavior: Recent findings and implications. In M. Reite & T. Field (Eds.), *The psychobiology of attachment and separation*. London: Academic Press.

Carmon, A. & Nachshon, I. (1973). Ear asymmetry in perception of emotional nonverbal stimuli. *Acta Psychologica, 37*, 351–357.

Carnelley, K. B., Pietromonaco, P. R. & Jaffe, K. (1994). Depression, working models of others, and relationship functioning. *Journal of Personality and Social Psychology, 66*, 127–140.

Carver, C. S. & Scheier, M. F. (1981). *Attention and self-regulation: A control theory approach to human behavior*. New York: Springer.

Caspar, F. (1989). *Beziehungen und Probleme verstehen: Eine Einführung in die psychotherapeutische Plananalyse*. [Understanding relationships and problems: An introduction into psychotherapeutic plan analysis] Bern: Huber.

Caspar, F. (1994). *Plan Analysis. Toward optimizing therapy*. Seattle: Hogrefe Huber.

Caspar, F. M. (1995) *Hypothesenbildungsprozesse in psychotherapeutischen Erstgesprächen*. [The process of hypothesis formation in initial psychotherapeutic consultation] Postdoctoral thesis, Universität Bern.

Caspar, F. M. (1996). *Beziehungen und Probleme verstehen: Eine Einführung in die psychotherapeutische Plananalyse* [Understanding relationships and problems: An introduction into psychotherapeutic plan analysis] (2nd ed.). Bern: Huber.

Caspar, F. M. (1997). What goes on in a psychotherapist's mind? *Psychotherapy Research, 7,* 105–125.

Caspar, F. M. & Grawe, K. (1982). *Vertikale Verhaltensanalyse (VVA). Analyse des Interaktionsverhaltens als Grundlage der Problemanalyse und Therapieplanung* (Forschungsbericht No. 4). [Vertical behavior analysis. Analysis of interaction behavior as a basis for problem analysis and therapy planning (Research report No.4)] Universität Bern.

Caspar, F. & Grawe, K. (1992). Psychotherapie: Anwendung von Methoden oder ein heuristischer integrierender Produktionsprozess? [Psychotherapy: Application of methods or a heuristic integrated production process?] *Report Psychologie (7),* 10–22.

Caspar, F. & Grawe, K. (1996). Was spricht für, was gegen individuelle Fallkonzeptionen? – Überlegungen zu einem alten Problem aus einer neuen Perspektive. [What speaks in favor of an individual case conception, what speaks against it?- Thoughts on an old problem from a new perspective] In F. Caspar (Ed.), *Psychotherapeutische Problemanalyse* (pp. 65–85). Tübingen: dgvt.

Catlin, G. & Epstein, S. (1992). Unforgettable experiences: The relation of life events to basic beliefs about self and world. *Social Cognition, 10,* 189–209.

Chambless, D. L., Caputo, G. C., Bright, P. & Gallagher, R. (1984). Assessment of fear in agoraphobics: The body sensation questionnaire and the agoraphobics cognitions questionnaire. *Journal of Consulting and Clinical Psychology, 52,* 1090–1097.

Cialdini, R. B. & De Nicholas, M. E. (1989). Self-presentation by association. *Journal of Personality and Social Psychology, 57,* 626–631.

Cialdini, R. B., Borden, R. J., Thorne, A., Walker, M. R., Freeman, S. & Sloan, L. R. (1976). Basking in reflected glory: Three (football) field studies. *Journal of Personality and Social Psychology, 34,* 366–375.

Clarkin, J. F., Marziali, E. & Munroe-Blum, H. (1992). *Borderline personality disorder.* New York: Guilford.

Cloninger, C. R., Martin, R. L., Guze, S. B. & Clayton, P. J. (1990). The empirical structure of psychiatric comorbidity and its theoretical significance. In J. D. Maser & C. R. Cloninger (Eds.), *Comorbidity of mood and anxiety disorders.* Washington: Amnerican Psychiatric Press.

Cole, H. & Kobak, R. (1991). *Attachment and symptom reporting: Attentional processes in depression and eating disorder.* Unpublished manuscript. University of Delaware, Dept. of Psychology, Newark, De.

Collins, W. A. & Read, S. J. (1990). Adult attachment, working models and relationship quality in dating couples. *Journal of Personality and Social Psychology, 58,* 644–663.

Cooley, C. H. (1902). *Human nature and the social order.* New York: Scribner's.

Corteen, R. S. & Wood, B. (1972). Autonomic responses to shock associated to threat words. *Journal of Experimental Psychology, 94,* 308–113.

Craig, T. K. J., Boardman, A. P., Mills, K., Daly-Jones, O. & Drake, H. (1993). The south London somatization study I: Longitudinal course and the influence of early life experiences. *British Journal of Psychiatry, 163,* 579–588.

Craik, F. I. & Lockhart, R. S. (1972). Levels of processing: A framework for memory research. *Journal of Verbal Learning and Verbal Behavior, 11,* 671–684.

Cranach, M. von & Foppa, K. (Eds.). (1996). *Freiheit des Entscheidens und Handelns.* [Freedom of decision and action] Heidelberg: Asanger.

Creutzfeldt, O. D. (1983). *Cortex Cerebri. Leistung, strukturelle und funktionelle Organisation der Hirnrinde.* [Cerebral cortex. Performance, structural and functional organization of the cortex] Berlin: Springer.

Crick, F. & Koch, C. (1990). Towards a neurobiological theory of consciousness. *Seminars in the Neurosciences, 2,* 263–275.

Crits-Christoph, P. (1997). *The interpersonal interior of psychotherapy.* Presidential address. 28th annual meeting of the Society for Psychotherapy Research, Geilo, Norway.

Crits-Christoph, P., Barber, J. & Kurcias, J. S. (1993). The accuracy of therapist's interpretations and the development of the alliance. *Psychotherapy Research, 3,* 25–35.

Crits-Christoph, P., Cooper, A. & Luborsky, L. (1988). The accuracy of therapist's interpretations and the outcome of dynamic psychotherapy. *Journal of Consulting and Clinical Psychology, 56,* 490–495.

Cutting, J. (1992). The role of right hemisphere dysfunction in psychiatric disorders. *British Journal of Psychiatry, 160,* 583–588.

Cuntz, U., Pollmann, H. & Enck, P. (1994). Verhaltenstherapie bei Erkrankungen des Gastrointestinaltraktes. [Behavior therapy for patients suffering from gastrointestinal illness] In M. Zielke & J. Sturm (Eds.), *Handbuch stationäre Verhaltenstherapie* (pp. 619–631). Weinheim: Psychologie Verlags Union.

Dahl, H., Kächele, H. & Thomä, H. (Eds.). (1988). *Psychoanalytic process Research strategies.* Berlin: Springer.

Danish, S. J. & Kagan, N. (1971). Measurement of affective sensitivity: Toward a valid measure of interpersonal perception. *Journal of Counseling Psychology,* 51–54.

Davies, M. (1970). Blood pressure and personality. *Journal of Psychosomatic Research, 14,* 89–104.

DeCasper, A. J. & Fifer, W. (1980). Of human bonding: Newborns prefer their mother's voice. *Science, 208,* 1174–1176.

de Jong-Meyer, R., Schmitz, S., Ehlker, M., Greis, S., Hinsken, U., Sonnen, B. & Dickhöver, N. (1997). *Handlungsorientierte Interaktionsbeiträge in verschiedenen Therapien: Prozesssteuerung und Erfolgsrelevanz.* [Action-oriented interaction contributions in different therapies: Directing the process and success relevance] Manuscript submitted for publication. Münster: Psychologisches Institut I der Westfälischen Wilhelms-Universität.

De La Ronde, C. & Swann, W. B. (1993). Caught in the crossfire: Positivity and self-verification strivings among people with low self-esteem. In R. F. Baumeister (Ed.), *Self-esteem: The puzzle of low self-regard* (pp. 147–165).

De Ruiter, C. & Ijzendoorn, M. van (1992). Agoraphobia and anxious-ambivalent attachment: An integrative review. *Journal of Anxiety Disorders, 6,* 365–381.

De Shazer, S. (1985). *Keys to solution in brief therapy.* New York: Norton.

Denes-Raj, V. & Epstein, S. (1994). Conflict between intuitive and rational processing: When people behave against their better judgement. *Journal of Personality and Social Psychology, 66,* 819–82.

Deutsch, H. (1929). The genesis of agoraphobia. *International Journal of Psychoanalysis, 10,* 51–69.

DiClemente, R. J. & Peterson, J. L. (Eds.). (1994). *Preventing AIDS: Theories and methods of behavioral interventions.* New York: Plenum Press.

DiMatteo, M. R., Prince, L. M. & Hays, R. (1986). Nonverbal communication in the medical context: The physician-patient-relationship. In P. D. Blanck, R. Buck & R. Rosenthal (Eds.), *Nonverbal communication in the clinical context.* University Park and London: The Pennsylvania State University Press.

DiMatteo, M. R., Taranta, A., Friedman, H. S. & Prince, L. M. (1980). Predicting patient satisfaction from physicians' nonverbal communication skills. *Medical Care, 18,* 376–387.

Dixon, N. F. (1981). *Preconscious processing.* New York: Wiley.

Dohrenwend, B. S. & Dohrenwend, B. P. (Eds.). (1974). *Stressful life events: Their nature and effects.* New York: Wiley.

Dollard, J. & Miller, N. E. (1950). *Personality and psychotherapy: An analysis in terms of learning, thinking, and culture.* New York: McGraw-Hill.

Dolan, B. & Coid, J. (1993). *Psychopathic and antisocial personality disorders. Treatment and research issues.* London: Gaskell-The Royal College of Psychiatrists.

Dozier, M. (1990). Attachment organization and treatment use for adults with serious psychpathological disorders. *Develoment and Psychopathology, 2,* 47–60.

Dozier, M. & Kobak, R. (1992). Psychophysiology in adolescent attachment interviews. Converging evidence for deactivating strategies. *Child Develoment, 63,* 1473–1480.

Dozier, M., Stevenson, A. L., Lee, S. W. & Velligan, D. I. (1992). Attachment organization and familial over- involvement for adults with serious psychpathological disorders. *Development and Psychopathology, 3,* 476–489.

Dreyfus, H. L. & Dreyfus, S. E. (1986). *Mind over machine: The power of human intuition and expertise in the era of the computer.* New York: Free Press.

Ebbinghaus, H. (1885). *Über das Gedächtnis.* [Memory] Leipzig: Dunker.

Eccles, J. C. (1994). *Wie das Selbst sein Gehirn steuert.* [How the self directs the brain] München: Piper.

Ecker, D., Graf, B., Mempel, S., Scheidt, B. & Tempel-Griebe, H. (1994). Diagnostische Aspekte und gruppentherapeutische Erfahrungen bei der Behandlung sexuell missbrauchter und vergewaltigter Frauen. [Diagnostic aspects and group therapeutic experiences in the treatment of sexually abused and raped women] In M. Zielke & J. Sturm (Eds.), *Handbuch stationäre Verhaltenstherapie* (pp. 763–773). Weinheim: Psychologie Verlags Union.

Eckhorn, R. & Schanze, Th. (1991). Possible neural mechanisms of feature linking in the visual system: stimulus-locked and stimulus-induced synachronizations. In A. Babloyanz (Ed.), *Self-Organization, Emerging Properties and Learning.* New York: Plenum.

Eckhorn, R., Reitboeck, H. J., Arndt, M. & Dicke, P. (1990). Feature linking via synchronization among distributed assemblies: simulation of results from the cat visual cortex. *Neural Computation, 2,* 293–307.

Edelman, G. M. (1987). *Neural Darwinism. The theory of neuronal group selection.* New York: Basic Books.

Edelman, G. M. (1989). *The remembered present. A biological theory of consciousness.* New York: Basic Books.

Edelman, G. M. (1995). *Göttliche Luft, vernichtendes Feuer.* [Heavenly air, devastating fire] München: Piper.

Eimer, M. (1996 a). Kognitive Psychologie, Neurobiologie und das „Gehirn-Bewusstsein-Problem". [Cognitive psychology, neurobiology and the "brain consciousness problem"] In G. Roth & W. Prinz (Eds.), *Kopf-Arbeit.* Heidelberg: Spektrum Akademischer Verlag.

Eimer, M. (1996 b). Wahrnehmung und Aufmerksamkeit. [Perception and attention] In G. Roth & W. Prinz (Eds.), *Kopf-Arbeit.* Heidelberg: Spektrum Akademischer Verlag.

Ekman, P. (1971). Universals and cultural differences in facial expression of emotion. In J. P. Cole (1972). (Ed.), *Nebraska Symposion on emotion, 1971* (pp. 207–283). Lincoln: University of Nebraska Press.

Ekman, P. (1985). *Telling lies: Clues to the deceit in the marketplace, politics, and marriage.* New York: Norton.

Ekman, P. (1989). The argument and evidence about universals in facial expressions of emotion. In H. Wagner & A. Manstead (Eds.), *Handbook of social psychophysiology* (pp. 143–163). New York: Wiley.

Ekman, P. (Ed.). (1973). *Darwin and facial expression: A century of research in review.* New York: Academic Press.

Ekman, P. & Friesen, W.V. (1969). The repertoire of nonverbal behavior: Categories, origins, usage, and coding. *Semiotica, 1,* 49–98.

Ekman, P. & Friesen, W.V. (1974). Detecting deception from the body and face. *Journal of Personality and Social Psychology, 29,* 288–298.

Ekman, P. & Friesen, W.V. (1975). *Unmasking the face.* Englewood Cliffs, NJ: Prentice Hall.

Ekman, P. & Friesen, W.V. (1986). *FACS. Facial action coding system.* Palo Alto: Culting Psychologist Press.

Ekman, P., Friesen, W. V. & O'Sullivan, M. (1988). Smiles when lying. *Journal of Personality and Social Psychology, 54,* 1416–1426.

Ekman, P., Friesen, W.V. & Scherer, K. (1976). Body movement and voice pitch in deceptive interaction. *Semiotica, 16,* 23–27.

Elkin, I. (1994). The NIMH treatment of depression collaborative research program: Where we began and where we are. In A. E. Bergin & S. L. Garfield (Eds.), *Handbook of psychotherapy and behavior change.* New York: Wiley.

Ellis, A. (1962). *Reason and emotion in psychotherapy.* New York: Lyle Stuart.

Elsässer, K. (1996). *Verhaltenstherapeutische Unterstützung des Benzodiazepin-Entzugs.* [Behavior therapeutic support of withdrawal from benzodiazepene] Weinheim: Psychologie Verlags Union.

Emmelkamp, P. M. (1982). *Phobic and obsessive-compulsive disorders: Theory, research, and practice.* New York: Plenum.

Emmons, R. A. & King, L. A. (1988). Conflict among personal strivings: Immediate and long-term implications for psychological and physical well-being. *Journal of Personality and Social Psychology, 54,* 1040–1048.

Emmons, R. A., King, L. A. & Sheldon, K. (1993). Goal conflict and the self-regulation of action. In D. M. Wegner & J. W. Pennebaker (Eds.), *Handbook of mental control.* Englewood Cliff, NJ: Prentice Hall.

Engel, A. K. (1996). Prinzipien der Wahrnehmung: Das visuelle System. [Principles of perception: The visual system] In G. Roth & W. Prinz (Eds.), *Kopf-Arbeit.* Heidelberg: Sepktrum Akademischer Verlag.

Epstein, S. (1973). The self-concept revisited: Or a theory of a theory. *American Psychologist, 28,* 404–416.

Epstein, S. (1979). Natural healing processes of the mind: I. Acute schizophrenic disorganization. *Schizophrenia Bulletin, 5,* 313–321.

Epstein, S. (1983). The unconscious, the preconscious, and the self-concept. In J. Suls & A. Greenwald (Eds.), *Psychological perspectives on the self* (pp. 219–247). Hillsdale, NJ: Lawrence Erlbaum.

Epstein, S. (1987). Implications of cognitive self-theory for psychopathology and psychotherapy. In N. Cheshire & H. Thomae (Eds.), *Self, symptoms and psychotherapy.* New York: Wiley.

Epstein, S. (1989). Values from the perspective of cognitive-experiential self-theory. In N. Eisenberg, J. Reykowski & E. Staub (Eds.), *Social and moral values: Individual and societal perspectives* (pp. 3–22). Hillsdale, NJ: Lawrence Erlbaum.

Epstein, S. (1990). Cognitive-experiential self-theory. In L. A. Pervin (Ed.), *Handbook of personality:Theory and research* (pp. 165–192). New York: Guilford.

Epstein, S. (1991 a). Cognitive-experiential self-theory: An integrative theory of personality. In R. C. Curtis (Ed.), *The relational self: Theoretical convergences in psychoanalysis and social psychology* (pp. 111–137). New York: Guilford.

Epstein, S. (1991 b). The self-concept, the traumatic neurosis, and the structure of personality. In J. D. Ozer, M. Healy & A. J. Stewart (Eds.), *Perspectives in personality, Vol. 3A* (pp. 63–98). London: Jessica Kingsley.

Epstein, S. (1992). Constructive thinking and mental and physical well being. In L. Montada, S. H. Philipp & M. J. Lerner (Eds.), *Life crises and experiences of loss in adulthood* (pp. 385–409). Hillsdale, NJ: Erlbaum.

Epstein, S. (1993 a). Emotion and self-theory. In M. Lewis & J. Haviland (Eds.), *Handbook of emotions* (pp. 313–326). NewYork: Guilford.

Epstein, S. (1993 b). Implications of cognitive-experiential self-theory for personality and developmental psychology. In R. D. Parke, D. C. Funder, C. Tomlinson-Keasey & K. Widaman (Eds.), *Studying lives through time: Personality and development* (pp. 399–438). Washington, DC: American Psychological Association.

Epstein, S. (1993 c). Bereavement from the perspective of cognitive-experiential self-theory. In W. Strobe, M.S. Sroebe & R. O. Hansson (Eds.), *Handbook of bereavement: Theory, research, and intervention* (pp. 112–125). New York: Cambridge University Press.

Epstein, S. (1994). Integration of the cognitive and the psychodynamic unconscious. *American Psychologist, 49,* 709–724.

Epstein, S. & Katz, L. (1992). Coping ability, stress, productive load, and symptoms. *Journal of Personality and Social Psychology, 62,* 813–825.

Epstein, S., Lipson, A., Holstein, C. & Huh, E. (1992). Irrational reactions to negative outcomes: Evidence for two conceptual systems. *Journal of Personality and Social Psychology, 62,* 328–339.

Epstein, S. & Morling, B. (1995). Is the self motivated to do more than enhance and/or verify itself? In M. H. Kernis (Ed.), *Efficacy, agency, amd self-esteem* (pp. 9–29). New York: Plenum Press.

Erdelyi, H. (1993). Repression: The mechanism and the defense. In D. W. Wegner & J. W. Pennebaker (Eds.), *Handbook of mental control.*Englewood Cliffs, NJ: Prentice Hall.

Erdelyi, M. H. (1990). Repression, reconstruction, and defense: History and integration of the psychoanalytic and experimental framework. In J. L. Singer (Ed.), *Repression and dissociation* (pp. 1–32). Chicago: The University of Chicago Press.

Erickson, M. H. (1980). *The nature of hypnosis and suggestion.* New York: Irvington.

Erickson, R. F., Sroufe, L. A. & Egeland, B. (1985). The relationship between quality of attachment and behavior problems in pre-school in a high risk sample. In I. Bretherton & E. Waters (Eds.), *Growing points of attachment theory and research* (pp. 147–186). Monographs of the Society for Research in Child Development.

Erikson, E. H. (1959). *Identity and the life cycle. Selected papers.* New York: International University Press.

Erwin, K. T. (1996). *Group techniques for aging adults: Putting geriatric skills enhancement into practice.* Bristol, PA: Taylor & Francis.

Eysenck, H. J. (1987). Behavior therapy and neurosis. In H. J. Eysenck & I. Martin (Eds.), *Theoretical foundations of behavior therapy.* New York: Plenum.

Faber, F. R. & Haarstrick, R. (1989). *Kommentar Psychotherapie-Richtlinien. Gutachterverfahren in der Psychotherapie, Psychosomatische Grundversorgung.* [Commentary on psychotherapy guidelines. Expert evaluative procedures in psychotherapy, basic psychosomatic care] München: Jungjohann Verlagsgesellschaft.

Fabinger, A. A. & Fiedler, P. (1996). Somatoforme Störungen in der Zahn-, Mund- und Kieferheilkunde: Theoretische Einordnung, verhaltenstherapeutische Perspektiven und Fallbeschreibung. [Somatoform disorders in dentistry, periodontics and orthodontics: Theoretical review, behavioral therapeutic perspectives and case descriptions] *Verhaltensmodifikation und Verhaltensmedizin, 17,* 213–231.

Fairburn, C. G., Jones, R., Peveler, R. C., Carr, S. J., Solomon, R. A., O'Connor, M. E., Burton, J. & Hope, R. A. (1991). Three psychological treatments for bulimia nervosa. A comparative trial. *Archives of General Psychiatry, 48,* 463–469.

Fawzy, F. I. & Fawzy, N. W. (1994). A structured psychoeducational intervention for cancer patients. *General Hospital Psychiatry, 16,* 149–192.

Feather, N. T. (Ed.). (1981). *Expectations and actions: Expectancy-value models in psychology.* Hillsdale, NJ: Erlbaum.

Fenichel, O. (1945). *The psychoanalytic theory of neurosis.* New York: Norton.

Festinger, L. (1957). *A theory of cognitive dissonance.* Evanston, Ill.: Row, Peerson.

Fiedler, P. (1988). Existentielle Krisen und Krisenintervention. [Existential crises and crisis intervention] In G. Hörmann & F. Nestmann (Eds.), *Handbuch der psychosozialen Intervention* (pp. 114–127). Opladen: Westdeutscher Verlag.

Fiedler, P. (1995). *Persönlichkeitsstörungen.* [Personality disorders] (2nd ed.) Weinheim: Psychologie Verlags-Union.

Fiedler, P. (1996). Dissoziative, vorgetäuschte und Impulskontroll-Störungen. [Dissociative, factitious and impulse-control disorders] In J. Margraf (Ed.), *Lehrbuch der Verhaltenstherapie* (Volume 2, pp. 319–336). Heidelberg: Springer.

Fiedler, P. (1997). Therapieplanung in der modernen Verhaltenstherapie. Von der allgemeinen zur phänomen- und störungsspezifischen Behandlung. [Therapy planning in modern behavior therapy. From the general to phenomena-specific and disorder specific treatment] *Verhaltenstherapie und Verhaltensmedizin, 18,* 7–39.

Fiedler, P. & Mundt, Ch. (1996). Dissoziative Störungen, vorgetäuschte Störungen und Störungen der Impulskontrolle. [Dissociative disorders, factitious disorders and disorders of impulse control] In K. Hahlweg & A. Ehlers (Eds.), *Psychische Störungen und ihre Behandlungen* (pp. 355–436). Göttingen: Hogrefe.

Fiedler, P., Niedermeier, Th. & Mundt, Ch. (1986). *Gruppenarbeit mit Angehörigen schizophrener Patienten. Materialien für die therapeutische Arbeit mit Angehörigen und Familien.* [Group work with family members of schizophrenic patients. Materials for therapeutic work with family members] München, Weinheim: Psychologie Verlags Union.

Fiedler, P. & Standop, R. (1984). *Stottern. Ätiologie, Diagnose, Behandlung.* [Stuttering. Etiology, diagnosis, treatment.] (4th ed.) Weinheim: Psychologie Verlags Union.

Fiegenbaum, W. & Tuschen, B. (1996). Reizkonfrontation. [Stimulus confrontation] In J. Margraf (Ed.), *Lehrbuch der Verhaltenstherapie, Band 1.* Berlin: Springer.

Fiegenbaum, W., Freitag, M. & Frank, B. (1992 a). Kognitive Vorbereitung auf Reizkonfrontations-therapien. [Cognitive preparation in stimulus confrontation therapies] In J. Margraf & H. Brengelmann (Eds.), *Die Therapeut-Patient-Beziehung in der Verhaltenstherapie* (pp. 89–108). München: Röttger.

Fiegenbaum, W., Freitag, M. & Frank, B. (1992 b). Konfrontative Behandlung: Erfolg ohne Akzeptanz in der Praxis. [Confrontational treatment: Success without acceptance in the practice] *Verhaltenstherapie, 2 (2),* 1–17.

Fish, J. M. (1973). *Placebo therapy.* San Francisco: Jossey-Bass.

Fiske, S. T. & Taylor, S. E. (1991). *Social cognition.* (2nd ed.). Reading, MA: Addison-Wesley.

Flammer, A. (1990). *Erfahrung der eigenen Wirksamkeit. Einführung in die Psychologie der Kontrollmeinung.* [Experiencing your own effectiveness. Introduction to the psychology of controlled opinion] Bern: Huber.

Flohr, H. (1996). Ignorabimus? [Ignoramus?] In G. Roth & W. Prinz (Eds.), *Kopf-Arbeit.* Heidelberg: Spektrum Akademischer Verlag.

Fonagy, P., Steele, H., Steele, M., Leigh, K., Kennedy, R., Mattoon, G. & Target, M. (1994). Attachment, the reflective self, and borderline states. The predictive specifity of the adult attachment interview and pathological emotional development. In S. Goldberg, R. Muir & J. Kerr (Eds.), *Attachment theory: Social developmental and clinical perspectives.* Englewood Cliffs, NJ: Lawrence Erlbaum.

Ford, D. H. (1987). *Humans as self-constructing living systems.* Hillsdale, NJ: Erlbaum.

Ford, M. E. (1992). *Motivating humans.* Newbury Park, Ca.: Sage

Forster, P. M. & Govier, E. (1978). Discrimination without awareness. *Quarterly Journal of Experimental Psychology, 30,* 282–292.

Frank, J. (1961). *Persuasion and healing* (2nd ed.). Baltimore: The Johns Hopkins University Press.

Frank, J. D. (1971). Therapeutic factors in psychotherapy. *American Journal of Psychotherapy, 25,* 350–361.

Frank, J. D. (1973). *Persuasion and healing (rev. ed.)* (2nd ed.). Baltimore: John Hopkins University Press.

Frank, J. D. (1982). Therapeutic components shared by all psychotherapies. In J. H. Harvey & M. M. Parks (Eds.), *The master lecture series (Vol. 1): Psychotherapy resarch and behavior change* (pp. 9–37). Washington, DC: American Psychological Association.

Frank, J. D., Nash, E. H., Stone, A. R. & Imber, S. D. (1963). Immediate and long-term symptomatic course of psychiatric outpatients. *American Journal of Psychiatry, 120,* 429–439.

Freeman, A. & Reinecke, M. A. (1995). *Selbstmordgefahr? Erkennen und Behandeln: Kognitive Therapie bei suizidalem Verhalten.* [In danger of suicide? Recognition and treatment: Cognitive therapy for suicidal behavior] Bern: Huber.

Freud, A. (1936). *Das Ich und die Abwehrmechanismen.* [The ego and the mechanisms of defense] Wien: Internationaler Psychoanalytischer Verlag .

Freud, S. (1895/1959). Obsessions and phobias; their psychological mechanisms and their aetiology. In E. Jones (Ed.), *Sigmund Freud: Collected papers (Vol. 1)* (pp. 128–137). New York: Basic Books.

Freud, S. (1915/1957). Repression. In J. Strachey (Ed.), *The standard edition of the complete psychological works of Sigmund Freud, Vol. 14.* London: Hogarth.

Freud, S. (1915). Triebe und Triebschicksale. [Instincts and their vicissitudes] In *Collected works Vol. 10:* 209–232.

Freud, S. (1920). Jenseits des Lustprinzips. [Beyond the pleasure principle] In *Collected works Vol. 13:* 1–69.

Freud, S. (1926). Hemmung, Symptom und Angst. [Inhibition, symptoms and fears] In *Collected works Vol. 14:* 111–205.

Frick, R. W. (1993). *The cognitive psychology of intuition and flow.* Unpublished manuscript. Stony Brook, NY: State University of New York.

Friedman, H. S. & Riggio, R. E. (1981). The effect of individual differences in nonverbal epressiveness on the transmission of emotion. *Journal of Nonverbal Behavior, 6,* 96–104.

Frijda, N. H. (1986). *The emotions.* Cambridge: Cambridge University Press.

Frisch, I., Schwab, F. & Krause, R. (1995). Affektives Ausdrucksverhalten Gesunder und an Colitis erkrankter männlicher und weiblicher Erwachsener. [Affective expressive behavior of healthy male and female adults and those suffering from colitis] *Zeitschrift für Klinische Psychologie, 24,* 230–238.

Fromm, E. (1981). *Jenseits der Illusionen. Die Bedeutung von Marx und Freud.* [Beyond the illusions. The meaning of Marx and Freud] Stuttgart: Deutsche Verlagsanstalt.

Fürbringer-Lienhard, S. (1992). *Familientherapie. Grundkonzepte und ihre empirische Überprüfung.* [Family therapy. Fundamental concepts and their empirical testing] Unpublished Master's thesis. Institut für Psychologie der Universität Bern.

Galin, D. (1974). Implications of left-right cerebral lateralization for psychiatry: A neurophysiological context for unconscious processes. *Archives of General Psychiatry, 9,* 412–418.

Gallagher, S. (1986). Body image and body schema: A conceptual clarification. *Journal of Mind and Behavior, 7,* 541–554.

Garfield, S. L. (1992). Eclectic psychotherapy: A common factors approach. In J. C. Norcross & M. R. Goldfried (Eds.), *Handbook of psychotherapy integration* (pp. 169–201). New York: Basic Books.

Gasiet, S. (1980). *Menschliche Bedürfnisse. Eine theoretische Synthese.* [Human needs. A theoretical synthesis] Frankfurt am Main: Campus.

Gendlin, E. T. (1961). Experiencing: A variable in the process of psychotherapeutic change. *American Journal of Psychotherapy, 15,* 233–245.

Gendlin, E. T. (1978). *Focusing.* New York: Everest House.

Gerlinghoff, M. & Backmund, H. (1995). *Therapie der Magersucht und Bulimie.* [Therapy of anorexia and bulimia] Weinheim: Psychologie Verlags Union.

Goebel, G. (Ed.). (1992). *Ohrgeräusche. Psychosomatische Aspekte des komplexen Tinnitus.* [Noises in the ear. Psychosomatic aspects of complex tinnitus] München: Quintessenz.

Goldfried, M. R. & Robins, C. (1983). Self-schema, cognitive bias, and the processing of therapeutic experiences. In P. C. Kendall (Ed.), *Advances in cognitive-behavioral research and therapy.* New York: Academic Press.

Golding, J. M., Smith, G. R. & Kashner, T. M. (1991). Does somatization disorder occur in men? *Archives of General Psychiatry, 48,* 231–235.

Goldstein, A. J. & Chambless, D. L. (1978). A re-analysis of agoraphobia. *Behavior Therapy, 9,* 47–59.

Gollwitzer, P. M. (1987). Suchen, Finden und Festigen der eigenen Identität: Unstillbare Zielintentionen. [Seeking, finding and holding onto individual identity: Insatiable goal intentions] In H. Heckhausen, P. M. Gollwitzer & F. E. Weinert (Eds.), *Jenseits des Rubikon: Der Wille in den Humanwissenschaften* (pp. 176–189). Berlin: Springer.

Gollwitzer, P. M. & Heckhausen, H. (1987). *Breadth of attention and the counterplea heuristic: Further evidence on the motivational versus volitional mindset distinction.* Unpublished manuscript. München: Max-Planck-Institut für Psychologische Forschung.

Gollwitzer, P. M., Heckhausen, H. & Ratajczak, H. (1987). *From weighing to willing: Approaching a change decision through pre- and postdecisional mentation.* Unpublished manuscript. München: Max Planck Institut für Psychologische Forschung.

Goschke, T. & Koppelberg, D. (1991). The concept of representation and the representation of concepts in connectionist models. In W. Ramsey, D. Rumelhart & S. Stich (Eds.), *Philosophy and connnectionist theory* (pp. 129–162). Hillsdale, NJ: Erlbaum.

Goschke, T. (1996 a). Lernen und Gedächtnis: Mentale Prozesse und Gehirnstrukturen. [Learning and memory: Mental processes and brain structures] In G. Roth & W. Prinz (Eds.), *Kopf-Arbeit.* Heidelberg: Spektrum Akademischer Verlag.

Goschke, T. (1996 b). Gedächtnis und Emotion: Affektive Bedingungen des Einprägens, Behaltens und Vergessens. [Memory and emotion: Affective conditions of memorizing, retaining and forgetting] In D. Albert & K.-H. Stapf (Eds.), *Enzyklopädie der Psychologie Bd. II/4: Gedächtnis.* Göttingen: Hogrefe.

Grawe, K. (1976). *Differentielle Psychotherapie. Indikation und spezifische Wirkung von Verhaltenstherapie und Gesprächstherapie.* [Differential psychotherapy. Indication and specific effects of behavior therapy and client-centered therapy] Bern: Hans Huber.

Grawe, K. (Ed.). (1980 a). *Verhaltenstherapie in Gruppen.* [Behavior therapy in groups] München: Urban & Schwarzenberg.

Grawe, K. (1980 b). Die diagnostisch-therapeutische Funktion der Gruppeninteraktion in verhaltenstherapeutischen Gruppen. [The diagnostic-therapeutic function of group interaction in behavior therapy groups] In K. Grawe (Ed.), *Verhaltenstherapie in Gruppen* (pp. 88–223). München: Urban & Schwarzenberg.

Grawe, K. (1982). *Implikationen und Anwendungsmöglichkeiten der Vertikalen Verhaltensanalyse für die Sichtweise und Behandlung psychischer Störungen.* [Implications and application possibilities of vertical behavior analysis for the perspective on and treatment of mental disorders] Research report no. 1-1986. Psychologisches Institut der Universität Bern.

Grawe, K. (1985). Kulturelle und gesellschaftliche Funktionen einer Anwendungswissenschaft Psychotherapie. [Cultural and social functions of the applied science of psychotherapy] *Zeitschrift für personenzentrierte Psychologie und Psychotherapie, 4,* 355–377.

Grawe, K. (1986). *Schema-Theorie und interaktionelle Psychotherapie.* [Schema theory and interactional psychotherapy] Upublished research report no. 1986/1. Psychologisches Institut der Universität Bern.

Grawe, K. (1987). Psychotherapie als Entwicklungsstimulation von Schemata. Ein Prozess mit nicht voraussehbarem Ausgang. [Psychotherapy as developmental stimulation of schemata. A process with unforseeable outcomes] In F. Caspar (Ed.), *Problemanalyse in der Psychotherapie. Bestandsaufnahme und Perspektiven* (pp. 72–87). Tübingen: DGVT.

Grawe, K. (1988). Heuristische Psychotherapie. Eine schematheoretisch fundierte Konzeption des Psychotherapieprozesses. [Heuristic psychotherapy. A schema theory based conception of the psychotherapy process] *Integrative Therapie, 4,* 309–324.

Grawe, K. (1992). Komplementäre Beziehungsgestaltung als Mittel zur Herstellung einer guten Therapiebeziehung. [Shaping a complementary relationship as a tool for establishing a good therapeutic relationship] In J. Margraf & J. C. Brengelmann (Eds.), *Die Therapeut-Patient-Beziehung in der Verhaltenstherapie* (pp. 215–244). München: Röttger-Verlag.

Grawe, K. (1994). Psychotherapie ohne Grenzen – Von den Therapieschulen zur Allgemeinen Psychotherapie. [Psychotherapy without limits – from the therapy schools to general psychotherapy] *Verhaltenstherapie und psychosoziale Praxis, 26,* 357–370.

Grawe, K. (1995 a). Grundriss einer Allgemeinen Psychotherapie. [Outline of a general psychotherapy] *Psychotherapeut, 40,* 130–145.

Grawe, K. (1996). Klärung und Bewältigung. Über das Verhältnis der beiden wichtigsten Veränderungsprinzipien. [Clarification and mastery. The relation between the two most important principles of change] In H. Reinecker & D. Schmelzer (Eds.), *Verhaltenstherapie, Selbstregulation, Selbstmanagement.* Göttingen: Hogrefe.

Grawe, K. (1997 a). Research-informed psychotherapy. *Psychotherapy Research, 7,* 1–20.

Grawe, K. (1997 b). „Moderne Verhaltenstherapie" oder allgemeine Psychotherapie? ["Modern behavior therapy" or general psychotherapy?] *Verhaltenstherapie und Verhaltensmedizin, 18,* 137–159.

Grawe, K. & Baltensperger, C. (1998). Figurationsanalyse – ein Konzept und Computerprogramm für die Prozess- und Ergebnisevaluation in der Therapiepraxis. [Figuration analysis – a concept and computer program for evaluating process and outcome in the therapy practice] In A.-R. Laireiter & H. Vogel (Eds.), *Qualitätssicherung in der Psychotherapie und psychosozialen Versorgung. Ein Werkstattbuch.* Tübingen: DGVT-Verlag.

Grawe, K. & Braun, U. (1994). Qualitätskontrolle in der Psychotherapiepraxis. [Quality control in the psychotherapy practice] *Zeitschrift für Klinische Psychologie, 23 (4),* 242–267.

Grawe, K. & Caspar, F. (1984). Die Plananalyse als Konzept und Instrument für die Psychotherapieforschung. [Plan analysis as concept and instrument for psychotherapy research] In U. Baumann (Ed.), *Psychotherapieforschung. Makro- und Mikroperspektiven.* Göttingen: Hogrefe.

Grawe, K., Caspar, F. & Ambühl, H. (1990 a). Differentielle Psychotherapieforschung: Vier Therapieformen im Vergleich: Prozessvergleich. [Differential psychotherapy research: Four types of therapy in comparison: Process comparison] *Zeitschrift für Klinische Psychologie, 19 (4),* 316–337.

Grawe, K., Caspar, F. M. & Ambühl, H. (1990 b). Die Berner Therapievergleichsstudie: Wirkungsvergleich und differentielle Indikation. [The Bern therapy comparison study: Effectiveness comparison and differential indication] *Zeitschrift für Klinische Psychologie, 19 (4),* 338–361.

Grawe, K., Donati, R. & Bernauer, F. (1994). *Psychotherapie im Wandel – Von der Konfession zur Profession.* [Psychotherapy in transition – from confession to profession] Göttingen: Hogrefe.

Grawe, K. & Dziewas, H. (1978). Interaktionelle Verhaltenstherapie. [Interactional behavior therapy] *Mitteilungen der DGVT, Sonderheft 1.*

Grawe, K., Grawe-Gerber, M., Heiniger, B., Ambühl, H. & Caspar, F. (1996). Schematheoretische Fallkonzeption und Therapieplanung – Eine Anleitung für Therapeuten. [Schema theory case conception and therapy planning – a manual for therapists] In F. Caspar (Ed.), *Psychotherapeutische Problemanalyse* (pp. 189–224). Tübingen: dgvt.

Grawe-Gerber, M. (1992) *Psychotherapie aus interpersonaler Perspektive. Ein methodischer Beitrag zur Psychotherapie-Prozessforschung mit der „Structural Analysis of Social Behavior (SASB)".* [Psychotherapy from an interpersonal perspective. A methodological contribution on psychotherapy process research using the "Structural Analysis of Social Behavior (SASB)"] Unpublished dissertation, Bern: Institut für Psychologie der Universität.

Greenberg, L. S. (1986). Research strategies. In L. S. Greenberg & W.M. Pinsof (Eds.), *The psychotherapeutic process: a research handbook* (pp. 707–734). New York: The Guilford Press.

Greenberg, L. S., Elliott, R. K. & Lietaer, G. (1994). Research on experiential therapies. In A. E. Bergin & S. L. Garfield (Eds.), *Handbook of psychotherapy and behavior change, 4th ed..* New York: Wiley.

Greenberg, L. S., Rice, L. & Elliott, R. (1993). *Facilitating emotional change: The moment to moment process.* New York: Guilford.

Greenwald, A. G. (1980). The totalitarian ego: Fabrication and revision of personal history. *American Psychologist, 35,* 603–618.

Grosse Holtforth, M. & Grawe, K. (1997). *Computergestützte Schema- und Konsistenzanalyse.* [Computer-aided schema and consistency analysis] Unpublished computer programm. Universität Bern.

Grossmann, K. (1990). Entfremdung, Abhängigkeit ind Anhänglichkeit im Lichte der Bindungstheorie. [Alienation, dependency and devotion in light of attachment theory] *Praxis der Psychotherapie und Psychosomatik, 35,* 231–238.

Grossmann, K., Grossmann, K. E., Sprangler, G., Suess, G. & Unzne, L. (1985). Maternal sensitivity and newborn orientation responses as related to quality of attachment in Northern Germany. In I. Bretherton & E. Waters (Eds.), *Growing points in attachment theory and research* (pp. 233–278). Monographs of the Society for Research in Child Development.

Grossmann, K. & Grossmann, K. E. (1991). Attachment as an organizer of emotional and behavioral responses in a longitudinal perspective. In C. M. Parkes, J. Stevenson-Hinde & P. Marris (Eds.), *Attachment across the life cycle.* London: Tavistock.

Grossmann, K. E., August, P., Fremmer-Bombik, E., Friedl, E., Grossmann, A., Scheuerer-Englisch, H., Spangler, G., Stephan, C. & Suess, G. (1989). Die Bindungstheorie. Modell und entwicklungspsychologische Forschung. [Attachment theory. Model and developmental psychology research] In H. Keller (Ed.), *Handbuch der Kleinkindforschung.* Berlin: Springer.

Grüsser, O. J., Naumann, A. & Seeck, M. (1990). Neurophysiological and neuropsychological studies on the perception and recognition of faces and facial expressions. In Elsner G. & Roth N. (Eds.), *Brain, perception, cognition* (pp. 83–94). Stuttgart: Thieme.

Guidano, V. F. (1988). A systems, process-oriented approach to cognitive therapy. In K. S Dobson (Ed.), *Handbook of cognitive-behavioral therapies.* New York: Guilford.

Guidano, V. F. & Liotti, G. (1983). *Cognitive processes and emotional disorders.* New York: Guilford Press.

Guidano, V. F. & Liotti, G. (1985). A constructivist foundation for cognitive therapy. In M. J. Mahoney & A. Freeman (Eds.), *Cognition and psychotherapy.* New York: Plenum.

Gunnar, M. R., Brodersen, L., Nachmias, M., Buss, K. & Rigatuso, J. (1996). Stress reactivity and attachment security. *Developmental Psychobiology, 29,* 191–204.

Haan, N. (1977). *Coping and defending.* New York: Academic Press.

Haarstrick, R. (1976). Kommentierung der Psychotherapie-Vereinbarungen. [Commentary on conventions in psychotherapy] *Deutsches Ärzteblatt, 73,* 2084–2087.

Haase, R. F. & Tepper, D. T. (1972). Nonverbal components of empathic communication. *Journal of Counseling Psychology, 19,* 417–424.

Hacker, W. (1986). *Arbeitspsychologie: Psychische Regulation von Arbeitstätigkeiten.* [Psychology of work: Psychological regulation of different occupations] Bern: Huber.

Hafner, R. J., Badenoch, A., Fisher, J. & Swift, H. (1983). Spouse-aided versus individual therapy in persisting psychiatric disorders: A systematic comparison. *Family Process, 22,* 385–399.

Häfner, H. & Veiel, H. (1986). Epidemiologische Untersuchungen zu Angst und Depression. [Epidemiological examination of anxiety and depression] In H. Helmchen & M. Linden (Eds.), *Die Differenzierung von Angst und Depression* (pp. 65–74). Tro-pon-Symposion.

Hahlweg, K. (1994). Beziehungs- und Interaktionsstörungen. [Relationship and interaction disorders] In H. Reinecker (Ed.), *Lehrbuch der Klinischen Psychologie* (2nd ed., pp. 435–458). Göttingen: Hogrefe.

Hahlweg, K. & Dose, M. (1998). *Schizophrenie.* [Schizophrenia] Göttingen: Hogrefe.

Hahlweg, K., Dürr, H. & Müller, U. (1995). *Familienbetreuung schizophrener Menschen. Ein ver-haltenstherapeutischer Ansatz zur Rückfallprophylaxe.* [Family caring for schizophrenics. A behavior therapy approach to relapse prevention] Weinheim: Psychologie Verlags Union.

Haley, J. (1963). *Strategies of psychotherapy.* New York: Grunde & Stratton.

Haley, J. (1976). *Problem solving therapy.* San Francisco: Jossey Boss.

Hamm, R. M. (1988). Clinical intuition and clinical analysis: Expertise and the cognitive continuum. In J. Dowie & A. Elstein (Eds.), *Professional judgement* (pp. 78–108). Cambridge, Ma.: Cambridge University Press.

Hammond, K. R. (1988). *Information models for intuitive and analytical cognition* (Tech. report No. 281). University of Colorado, Center for Research on Judgment and Policy.

Hand, I. (1992). Behavior therapy for OCD: Methods for therapy and their results. In I. Hand, W.K. Goodman & U. Evers (Eds.), *Obsessive-compulsive disorders. New research results* (pp. 157–180). Berlin: Springer.

Harrigan, J. A. & Rosenthal, R. (1986). Nonverbal aspects of empathy and rapport in physician-patient interaction. In R. Buck, P. D. Blanck & R. Rosenthal (Eds.), *Nonverbal communication in the clinical context.* University Park and London: The Pennsylvania State University Press.

Harris, T. & Bifulco, A. (1991). Loss of parent in childhood, attachment style, and depression in adulthood. In C. M. Parkes, J. Stevenson-Hinde & P. Marris (Eds.), *Attachment across the life cycle.* London: Routledge.

Hartung, J. (1990). *Psychotherapie phobischer Störungen. Zur Handlungs- und Lageorientierung im Therapieprozess.* [Psychotherapy of phobic disorders. Treatment and situation orientation in the therapy process] Wiesbaden: Deutscher Universitäts-Verlag, DUV.

Hartung, J. & Schulte, D. (1991). Anregung eines handlungsorientierten Kontrollmodus im Therapieprozess. [Ideas for an action-oriented control mode in the therapy process] In D. Schulte (Ed.), *Therapeutische Entscheidungen.* Göttingen: Hogrefe.

Hartung, J. & Schulte, D. (1994). Action and state orientation during therapy of phobic patients. In J. Kuhl & J. Beckmann (Eds.), *Volition and personality. Action versus state orientation* (pp. 217–231). Seattle: Hogrefe & Huber.

Hatfield, E., Cacioppo, J. T. & Rapson, R. T. (1992). Primitive emotional contagion. In M.S. Clark (Ed.), *Emotion and social behavior* (pp. 151–177). Newbury Park: Sage Publications.

Hautzinger, M. (1998). *Depression. Psychologie affektiver Störungen.* [Depression. Psychology of affective disorders] Göttingen: Hogrefe.

Hautzinger, M., de Jong-Meyer, R., Treiber, R., Rudolf, G. A. E. & Thien, U. (1996). Wirksamkeit kognitiver Verhaltenstherapie, Pharmakotherapie und deren Kombination bei nicht-endogenen, unipolaren Depressionen. [Effectiveness of cognitive behavior therapy, pharmacotherapy and the combination of the two with non-endogenous, uniploar depressions] *Zeitschrift für Klinische Psychologie, 25,* 130–145.

Hayek, F. H. (1952). *The Sensory Order – An Inquiry into the Foundations of Theoretical Psychology.* London: Wiley & Kegan Paul.

Haynes, J., Bastine, R., Link, G. & Mecke, A. (1993). *Scheidung ohne Verlierer.* [Divorce with no loser] München: Kösel.

Hazler, R. J. (1996). *Breaking the cycle of violence: Interventions for bullying and victimization.* Bristol, PA.: Taylor & Francis.

Hebb, D. (1949). *The organization of behavior.* New York: Wiley.

Hebb, D. O. (1958). A neuropsychological theory. In S. Koch (Ed.), *Psychology – A study of science* (pp. 622–643). New York: McGraw Hill.

Heckhausen, H. (1980). *Motivation und Handeln: Lehrbuch der Motivationspsychologie.* [Motivation and action: Textbook of motivation psychology] Berlin:Springer.

Heckhausen, H. (1987 a). Wünschen – Wählen – Wollen. [Wishing - Choosing - Wanting] In H. Heckhausen, P. M. Gollwitzer & F. E. Weinert (Eds.), *Jenseits des Rubikon: Der Wille in den Humanwissenschaften* (pp. 3–9). Berlin: Springer.

Heckhausen, H. (1987 b). Perspektiven einer Psychologie des Wollens. [Perspectives on a psychology of volition] In P. M. Heckhausen, H. Gollwitzer & F. E. Weinert (Eds.), *Jenseits des Rubikon: Der Wille in den Humanwissenschaften.* Berlin: Springer.

Heckhausen, H. (1987 c). Vorsatz, Wille und Bedürfnis: Lewins frühes Vermächtnis und ein zugeschütteter Rubikon. [Intention, will and need: Lewin's early legacy and a silted up Rubicon] In H. Heckhausen, P. M. Gollwitzer & F. E. Weinert (Eds.), *Jenseits des Rubikon: Der Wille in den Humanwissenschaften* (pp. 86–96). Berlin: Springer.

Heckhausen, H., Gollwitzer, P. M. & Weinert, F. E. (Eds.). (1987). *Jenseits des Rubikon: Der Wille in den Humanwissenschaften*. [Beyond the Rubicon: The will in the humanities] Berlin: Springer.

Heiniger, B., Grawe-Gerber, M., Ambühl, H. & Grawe, K. (1996). Schematheoretische Fallkonzeption und Therapieplanung. Ein elaboriertes Beispiel zum Leitfaden. [Schema theory case conception and therapy planning. An elaborated example as a guide] In F. Caspar (Ed.), *Psychotherapeutische Problemanalyse*. Tübingen: dgvt.

Henry, W.P., Schacht, T. E. & Strupp, H. (1986). Structural analysis of social behavior: Application to a study of interpersonal process in differential psychotherapy outcome. *Journal of Consulting and Clinical Psychology, 54,* 27–31.

Henry, W.P., Schacht, T. E. & Strupp, H. (1990). Patient and therapist introject, interpersonal process and differential psychotherapy outcome. *Journal of Consulting and Clinical Psychology, 58,* 768–774.

Henry, W.P., Strupp, H. H., Schacht, T. E. & Gaston, L. (1994). Psychodynamic approaches. In A. E. Bergin & S. L. Garfield (Eds.), *Handbook of psychotherapy and behavior change.* New York: Wiley.

Herzog, T., Hartmann, A. & Falk, C. (1996). Symptomorientierung und psychodynamisches Gesamtkonzept bei der stationären Behandlung der Anorexia Nervosa – Eine quasi-experimentelle Vergleichsuntersuchung von 40 Aufnahmeepisoden. [Symptom orientation and overall psychodynamic conception in inpatient treatment of anorexia nervosa – A quasi-experimental comparative study of 40 admittance episodes] *Psychotherapie, Psychosomatik und medizinische Psychologie, 46,* 11–22.

Herrle, J. & Kühner, Ch. (Eds.). (1994). *Depression bewältigen. Ein kognitiv-verhaltenstherapeutisches Gruppenprogramm nach P. M. Lewinsohn.* [Coping with depression. A cognitive-behavior therapy group program according to P.M. Lewinsohn] Weinheim: Psychologie Verlags Union.

Höger, R. (1992). Chaos-Forschung und ihre Perspektiven für die Psychologie. [Chaos research and its perspectives for psychology] *Psychologische Rundschau, 43,* 223–231.

Hoffmann, N. (1994). Verhaltenstherapie bei Zwangsstörungen. [Behavior therapy of compulsive disorders] *Psychotherapeut, 39,* 43–52.

Hogan, R. (1978). Toward a theory of empathic arousal and development. In M. Lewis & L. A. Rosenblum (Eds.), *The development of affect.* New York: Plenum Press.

Holender, D. (1986). Semantic activation without conscious identification. *Behavior and Brain Sciences, 9,* 1–66.

Hollen, B. (1996). Der problemanalytische Prozess in den Kognitiven Verhaltenstherapien. [The process of problem analysis in cognitive behavior therapies] In F. M. Caspar (Ed.), *Psychotherapeutische Problemanalyse* (pp. 173–188). Tübingen: dgvt-Verlag.

Holloway, W. & McNally, R. J. (1987). Effects of anxiety sensivity on the response to hyperventilation. *Journal of Abnormal Psychology, 96,* 330–334.

Holmes, D. S. (1990). The evidence for repression: An examination of sixty years of research. In J. L. Singer (Ed.), *Repression and dissociation* (pp. 85–102). Chicago: The University of Chicago Press.

Holroyd, K. A. & Creer, T. L. (Eds.). (1986). *Self-management of chronic disease: Handbook of interventions and research.* New York: Academic Press.

Hornsby, J. L. & Payne, F. E. (1979). A model of communication skills development for family practice residents. *Journal of Family Practice, 8,* 71–76.

Horowitz, L. M. (1994). Pschemas, psychopathology, and psychotherapy research. *Psychotherapy Research, 4 (1),* 1–17.

Horowitz, L. M., Rosenberg, S. E., Baer, B. A., Ureno, G. & Villasenor, V. S. (1988). Inventory of interpersonal problems: Psychometric properties and clinical applications. *Journal of Consulting and Clinical Psychology, 56,* 885–892.

Horowitz, L. M., Strauss, B. & Kordy, H. (1994). *Inventar zur Erfassung interpersonaler Probleme. Manual.* [Inventory for assessing interpersonal problems. Manual] Weinheim: Beltz.

Horowitz, L. M., Rosenberg, S. E. & Kalehzan, M. B. (1992). The capacity to describe other people clearly: A predictor of interpersonal problems in brief dynamic psychotherapy. *Psychotherapy Research, 2 (1),* 37–51.

Horowitz, M. J. (1991). *Person schemas and maladaptive interpersonal behavior.* Chicago: University of Chicago Press.

Horowitz, M. J. (1988 a). *Introduction to psychodynamics: A new synthesis.* New York: Basic Books.

Horowitz, M. J. (Ed.). (1988 b). *Psychodynamics and cognition.* Chicago: The University of Chicago Press.

Horowitz, M. J. (1989). Relationship schema formulation: Role-relationship models and intrapsychic conflict. *Psychiatry, 52,* 260–274.

Horowitz, M. J. & Eells, T. (1993). Case formulation using role-relationship model configurations: A reliability study. *Psychotherapy Research, 3,* 57–68.

Horowitz, M. J. & Znoj, H. (in press). Control process theory: A revision of the concept of defense mechanisms. *Archives of General Psychiatry.*

Horowitz, M.J., Znoj, H. & Stinson, C. (1996). Defensive control processes for coping with excessively emotional states of mind. In M. Zeidner & N. Endler (Eds.), *Handbook of Coping: Theory, Research, Applications* (pp. 532–553). New York: Wiley.

Howard, H. I., Kopta, S. M., Krause, M. S. & Orlinsky, D. E. (1986). The dose-effect relationship in psychotherapy. *American Psychologist, 41,* 159–164.

Howard, K. I., Lueger, R. J., Maling, M. S. & Martinovich, Z. (1992). A phase theory of psychotherapy. *Annual International Meeting of the Society for Psychotherapy Research,* Berkeley, USA.

Howard, K. I., Moras, K., Brill, P. L., Martinovich, Z. & Lutz, W. (1996). The evaluation of psychotherapy: Efficacy, effectiveness, patient progress. *American Psychologist, 51,* 1059–1064.

Hoyer, J. (1992). *Intrapsychische Konflikte und psychopathologische Symptombelastung.* [Intra-psychic conflicts and the burden of psychopathological symptoms] Regensburg: Roderer.

Hoyer, J., Frank, D. & Lauterbach, W. (1994). Intrapsychischer Konflikt und Ambiguitätstoleranz als Prädiktoren klinischer Symptombelastung auf latenter Ebene. [Intra-psychic conflict and tolerance of ambiguity as predictors of the burden of clinical symptoms at a latent level] *Zeitschrift für Klinische Psychologie, 23,* 117–126.

Hoyndorf, S., Reinhold, M. & Christmann, F. (1995). *Behandlung sexueller Störungen. Ätiologie, Diagnostik, Therapie: Sexuelle Dysfunktionen, Missbrauch, Delinquenz.* [Treating sexual disorders. Etiology, diagnosis, therapy: Sexual dysfunction, abuse, delinquency] Weinheim: Psychologie Verlags Union.

Hubel, D. H. & Wiesel, T. N. (1959). Receptive fields of single neurons in the cat's striate cortex. *Journal of Physiology, 48,* 574–591.

Hubel, D. H. & Wiesel, T. N. (1962). Receptive fields, binocular interaction and functional architecture in the cat's visual cortex. *Journal of Physiology, 160,* 106–154.

Hubel, D. H. & Wiesel, T. N. (1968). Receptive fields and functional architecture of monkey striate cortex. *Journal of Physiology, 195,* 215–243.

Hüsler, G. & Hemmerlein, G. (1996). *Leben auf Zeit. Ein Psychotherapiemanual für den Umgang mit HIV/Aids und anderen lebensbedrohlichen Krankheiten.* [Living against the clock. A psychotherapy manual for dealing with HIV/Aids and other life-threatening illnesses] Bern: Huber.

Izard, C. E. (1977). *Human emotions.* New York: Plenum.
Izard, C. E. (1978). On the ontogenesis of emotions and emotion-cognition relationships in infancy. In M. Lewis & L. Rosenblum (Eds.), *The development of affect* (pp. 389–413). New York: Plenum.

Jackson, E. (1968). *Communication, family, and marriage.* Palo Alto: Science and Behavior Books.
Jacobi, C., Thiel, A. & Paul, T. (1996). *Kognitive Verhaltenstherapie bei Anorexia und Bulimia nervosa.* [Cognitive behavior therapy of anorexia and bulimia nervosa] Weinheim: Psychologie Verlags Union.
Jaede, W., Wolf, J. & Zeller-König, B. (1996). *Gruppentraining mit Kindern aus Trennungs- und Scheidungsfamilien.* [Group training with children from separated and divorced families] Weinheim: Psychologie Verlags Union.
James, W. (1890). *Principles of psychology.* New York: Holt.
Janis, I. L. (1972). A perfect failure: The bay of pigs. In I. L. Janis (Ed.), *Victims of group think: A psychological study of foreign-policy decisions and fiascoes.* Boston: Houghton-Mifflin.
Jeger, P. (1996). *Reflektieren und Handeln.* [Reflecting and acting] Unpublished dissertation, Institut für Psychologie der Universität Bern.
Jensen, J. P., Bergin, A. E. & Greaves, D. W. (1990 a). The meaning of eclecticism: New survey and analysis of components. *Professional Psychology: Research and Practice, 21,* 124–130.
Jensen, J. P., Bergin, A. E. & Greaves, D. W. (1990 b). The meaning of eclecticism: New survey and analysis of components. *Professional Psychology: Research and Practice, 21,* 124–130.
Jensen, M. R. (1987). Psychobiological factors predicting the course of breast cancer. *Journal of Personality, 55,* 317–342.
Jochmus, I., Tieben-Heibert, A., Stein, L., Maiwald, G., Diekmann, L., Reichwald Klugger, E., Kom, R., Weck, K. & Schärer, K. (1982). *Psychosoziale Betreuung chronisch nierenkranker Kinder und Jugendlicher.* [Psychosocial care for children and adolescents with chronic kidney disease] Münster/Heidelberg: Universitäts-Kinderkliniken. (Nephrologische Abteilung der Universitäts-Kinderklinik, Robert-Koch-Straße 31, 48149 Münster).
Johnson, S. M. & Greenberg, L. S. (1985 a). Emotionally focused couples therapy: An outcome study. *Journal of Marital and Family Therapy, 11 (3),* 313–317.
Johnson, S. M. & Greenberg, L. S. (1985 b). Differential effects of experimental problem-solving interventions in resolving marital conflict. *Journal of Consulting and Clinical Psychology, 53,* 175–184.
Jourard, S. M. & Landsman, T. (1980). *Healthy personality: An approach from the viewpoint of humanistic psychology* (4th ed.). New York: Macmillan.
Joyce, A. S. (1992). *Assessing the correspondence of interpretation with the therapist's initial problem formulation.* Paper presented at the annual convention of the Society for Psychotherapy Research, Berkeley, Ca.
Jung, R. (1978). Perception, consciousness, and visual attention. In P. A. Buser & A. Rougeul-Buser (Eds.), *Cerebral correlates of conscious experience* (pp. 15–36). Amsterdam: Elsevier/North-Holland.
Jungnitsch, G. (1992). *Schmerz- und Krankheitsbewältigung bei rheumatischen Erkrankungen. Psychologische Hilfen im Einzel- und Gruppentraining.* [Coping with the pain and illness of rheumatism. Psychological help in individual and group training] München: Quintessenz.

Kandel, E. R. & Hawkins, R. D. (1992). The biological basis of learning and individuality. *Scientific American, 267,* 52–60.
Kanfer, F. H. (1987). Selbstregulation und Verhalten. [Self-regulation and behavior] In H. Heckhausen, P. M. Gollwitzer & F. E. Weinert (Eds.), *Jenseits des Rubikon: Der Wille in den Humnawissenschaften* (pp. 255–285). Berlin: Springer.

Kanfer, F. H. & Phillips, J. S. (1970). *Learning foundations of behavior therapy.* New York: Wiley.

Kanfer, F., Reinecker, H. & Schmelzer, D. (1991). *Selbstmanagement-Therapie.* [Self-management therapy] Berlin: Springer.

Kanfer, F. H. & Saslow, G. (1969). Behavioral diagnosis. In C. M. Franks (Ed.), *Behavior therapy: Appraisal and status* (pp. 417–444). New York: McGraw-Hill.

Karpel, M. A. (Ed.). (1986). *Family resources: The hidden partner in family therapy.* New York: Guilford.

Katan, A. (1951). The role of displacement in agoraphobia. *International Journal of Psychoanalysis, 32,* 41–50.

Kauss, D. R., Robbins, A. S., Abrass, I., Bakaitis, R. F. & Anderson, L. A. (1980). The long-term effectiveness of interpersonal skills training in medical schools. *Journal of Medical Education, 55,* 595–601.

Kelly, G. (1957). *The psychology of personal constructs, Vols. 1 and 2.* New York: Norton.

Kelso, J. A., Holt, K. G., Kugler, P. N. & Turvey, M.T. (1981). Patterns of human interlimb coordination emerge from the properties of non-linear limit cycle oscillatory processes: Theory and data. *Journal of Motor Behavior, 13,* 226–261.

Kelso, J. A. & Scholz, J. P. (1985). Cooperative phenomena in biological motion. In H. Haken (Ed.), *Complex systems: Operational approaches in neurobiology, physics, and computers* (pp. 124–149). Heidelberg: Springer.

Kelso, J. A., Scholz, J. P. & Schöner, G. (1986). Non-equilibrium phase transitions in coordinated biological motion: Critical fluctuations. *Physics Letters A, 118,* 279–284.

Kendler, K. S., MacLean, C., Neale, M., Kessler, R., Heath, A. & Eaves, L. (1991). The genetic epidemiology of bulimia nervosa. *The American Journal of Psychiatry, 148,* 1627–1637.

Kendon, A. (1982). The organization of behavior in a face-to-face interaction: Observations on the development of a methodology. In K. R. Scherer & P. Ekman (Eds.), *Handbook of methods in nonverbal behavioral research.* Cambridge: Cambridge University Press.

Kiesler, D. J. (1966). Some myths of psychotherapy research and the search for a paradigm. *Psychol. Bull., 65,* 110–136.

Kiesler, D. J. (1982 a). Interpersonal theory for personality and psychotherapy. In J. C. Anchin & D. J. Kiesler (Eds.), *Handbook of interpersonal psychotherapy* (pp. 3–24). New York: Pergamon.

Kiesler, D. J. (1982 b). Confronting the client-therapist relationship in psychotherapy. In J. C. Anchin & D. J. Kiesler (Eds.), *Handbook of interpersonal psychotherapy.* New York: Pergamon.

Kiesler, D. J. (1983). The 1982 interpersonal circle: A taxonomy for the complementary in human transactions. *Psychological Review, 90,* 185–214.

Kiesler, D. J. (1986). The 1982 interpersonal circle: An analysis of DSM-III personality disorders. In T. Millon & G. L. Klermann (Eds.), *Contemporary perspectives in psychopathology: Toward the DSM IV.* New York: Guilford.

Kiesler, D. J., Anchin, J. C., Perkins, M. J., Chirico, M. M., Kyle, E. M. & Federman, E. J. (1976). *The impact message inventory.* Richmond: Virginia Commonwealth University.

Kihlstrom, J. F. & Hoyt, I. P. (1990). Repression, dissociation, and hypnosis. In J. L. Singer (Ed.), *Repression and dissociation* (pp. 181–208). Chicago: The University of Chicago Press.

Killeen, P. R. (1989). Behavior as a trajectory through a field of attractors. In J. R. Brink & R. Haden (Eds.), *The computer and the brain. Perspectives on human and artificial intelligence* (pp. 53–82). Amsterdam: Elsevier.

Killeen, P. R. (1991). Behavioral geodesics. In D. S. Levine & S. J. Leven (Eds.), *Motivation, emotion, and goal direction in neural networks* (pp. 91–114). Hillsdale, NJ: Erlbaum.

King, L. A. & Emmons, R. A. (1991). The psychological, physical and interpersonal implications of emotional expression, conflict, and control. *European Journal of Personality, 5,* 131–150.

Kinnunen, P. (1996). *Flugangst bewältigen. Informationen zur Entstehung und Behandlung für Betroffene und Therapeuten.* [Coping with fear of flying. Information on the emergence and treatment for the afflicted and for therapists] Weinheim: Psychologie Verlags Union.

Kiresuk, Th. & Lund, S. (1979). Goal attainment scaling: Research, evalutation and utilization. In H. C. Schulberg & F. Baker (Eds.), *Program evaluation in health fields* (Vol. 2). New York: Human Sciences Press.

Kirkpatrick, L. & Epstein, S. (1992). Cognitive-experiential self-theory and subjective probability: Further evidence for two conceptual systems. *Journal of Personality and Social Psychology, 63,* 534–544.

Kirsch, I. (1986). Response expectancy and phobic anxiety: A reply to Wilkins and Bandura. *American Psychologist, 41,* 1391–1393.

Kirsch, I. (1990). *Changing expectations: A key to effective psychotherapy.* Pacific Grove, CA: Brooks/Cole.

Kirsch, I., Tennen, H., Wickless, C., Saccone, A. J. & Cody, S. (1983). The role of expectancy in fear reduction. *Behavior Therapy, 14,* 520–533.

Klepsch, R., Hand, I., Wlazlo, E., Kaunisto, E. & Friedrich, B. (1989). Pathologisches Spielen. [Pathological games] In I. Hand & H.-U. Wittchen (Eds.), *Verhaltenstherapie in der Medizin* (pp. 313–326). Berlin: Springer.

Klerman, G. K., Weissman, M.M., Rounsaville, B. J. & Chevron, E. S. (1984). *Interpersonal psychotherapy of depression.* New York: Basic Books.

Klinger, E. (1977). *Meaning and void: Inner experience and the incentives in people's lives.* Minneapolis: University of Minnesota Press.

Knowlton, B. J., Ramus, S. J. & Squire, L. R. (1992). Intact artificial grammar learning in amnesia: Dissociation of classification learning and explicit memory for specific instances. *Psychological Science, 3,* 172–179.

Kolb, B. & Wishaw, I. Q. (1996). *Neuropsychologie* [Neuropsychology] (2nd ed.). Heidelberg: Spektrum Akademischer Verlag.

Konorski, J. (1967). *Integrative activity of the brain.* Chicago: The University of Chicago Press.

Kornhuber, H. H. & Deecke, L. (1965). Hirnpotentialänderungen bei Willkürbewegungen und passiven Bewegungen des Menschen: Bereitschaftspotential und reafferente Potentiale. [Changing brain potentials through voluntary and passive movements of the person: Activation potential and re-afferent potential] *Pflügers Archiv für Gesamte Physiologie, 284,* 1–17.

Krause, R. (1997). *Allgemeine psychoanalytische Krankheitslehre. Band 1: Grundlagen.* [General psychoanalytic theory of illness. Volume 1: Fundamentals] Stuttgart: Kohlhammer.

Krause, R., Steimer, E., Sänger-Alt, C. & Wagner, G. (1989). Facial expressions of schizophrenic patients and their interaction partners. *Psychiatry: Interpersonal and biological processes, 52,* 1–12.

Kryspin-Exner, I. (1988). Klinische Neuropsychologie und Verhaltenstherapie. [Clinical neuropsychology and behavior therapy] *Verhaltensmodifikation und Verhaltensmedizin, 9,* 97–118.

Kuhl, J. (1983). *Motivation, Konflikt und Handlungskontrolle.* [Motivation, conflict and action control] Heidelberg: Springer.

Kuhl, J. (1987 a). Action control: The maintenance of motivational states. In F. Halish & J. Kuhl (Eds.), *Motivation, intention, and volition* (pp. 288–306). New York: Springer.

Kuhl, J. (1987 b). Motivation und Handlungskontrolle: Ohne guten Willen geht es nicht. [Motivation and action control: Without good will it does not happen] In H. Heckhausen, P. M. Gollwitzer & F. E. Weinert (Eds.), *Jenseits des Rubikon: Der Wille in den Humanwissenschaften* (pp. 101–120). Berlin: Springer.

Kuhl, J. (1994). A theory of action and state orientation. In J. Kuhl & J. Beckmann (Eds.), *Volition and personality: Action versus state orientation.* Seattle: Hogrefe.

Kuhl, J. & Beckmann, J. (1994). *Volition and personality. Action versus state orientation.* Seattle: Hogrefe & Huber.

Kuhl, J. (1996). Wille, Freiheit, Verantwortung: Alte Antinomien aus experimentalpsychologischer Sicht. [Volition, freedom, responsibility: Old antinomies from the experimental psychology perspective] In M. von Cranach & K. Foppa (Eds.), *Freiheit des Entscheidens und Handelns: Ein Problem der nomologischen Psychologie* (pp. 179–211). Heidelberg: Asanger.

Kuhn, T. S. (1962). *The structure of scientific revolutions.* Chicago: University of Chicago Press.

Labov, W. & Fanshel, D. (1977). *Therapeutic discourse.* New York: Academic Press.

Lader, M. H. (1967). Palmar skin conductance measures in anxiety and phobic states. *Journal of Psychosomatic Research, 11,* 271–281.

Läderach, M. & Verdun, R. (1995) *Das Konstrukt des Schemas in Psychologie und Psychotherapie.* [The schema construct in psychology and psychotherapy] Unpublished Master's thesis, Bern.

Lauterbach, W. (1990). Intrapersonal conflict, life stress, and emotion. In C. D. Spielberger, I. G. Sarason, J. Strelau & M. T. Brebner (Eds.), *Stress and anxiety* (pp. 85–92). New York: Hemisphere.

Lauterbach, W. (1996). The measurement of personal conflict. *Psychotherapy Research, 6,* 213–225.

Lauth, G. W. & Schlottke, P. (1993). *Training mit aufmerksamkeitsgestörten Kindern.* [Training with ADD affected children] Weinheim: Psychologie Verlags Union.

Lazarus, A. A. (1992). Multimodal therapy: Technical eclecticism with minimal integration. In J. C. Norcross & M. R. Garfield (Eds.), *Handbook of psychotherapy integration* (pp. 231–263). New York: Basic Books.

Lazarus, R. S. (1982). The costs and benefits of denial. In S. Breznitz (Ed.), *The denial of stress* (pp. 1–30). New York: International Universities Press.

Lazarus, R. S. (1991). *Emotion and adaptation.* New York: Oxford University Press.

Lazarus, R. S. & Folkman, S. (1984). *Stress, appraisal, and coping.* New York: Springer.

Leary, T. (1957). *Interpersonal diagnosis of personality.* New York: Ronald Press.

LeBow, M. D. (1991). *Adipositas. Psychotherapie und Nachbehandlung von Übergewicht bei Erwachsenen.* [Adipositis. Psychotherapy and follow-up treatment of obesity in adults] Bern: Huber.

Le Doux, J. E. (1989). Cognitive-emotional interactions in the brain. *Cognition and Emotion, 3,* 267–289.

Leplow, B., Bamberger, D., Möbius, T. & Ferstl, R. (1993). Verhaltenstherapeutische Gruppenprogramme bei Parkinsonpatienten. [Behavior therapy group program for parkinsons patients] *Therapiewoche Neurologie und Psychiatrie, 7,* 59–68.

Leventhal, H. (1980). Toward a comprehensive theory of emotion. In L. Berkowitz (Ed.), *Advances in experimental social psychology* (pp. 140–207). New York: Academic Press.

Leventhal, H. (1984). A perceptual motor theory of emotion. In K. R. Scherer & P. Ekman (Eds.), *Approaches to emotion* (pp. 271–291). Hillsdale, NJ: Erlbaum.

Leventhal, H. & Scherer, K. (1987). The relationship of emotion and cognition: A functional approach to a semantic controversy. *Cognition and Emotion, 1,* 3–28.

Lewicki, P. (1986). Processing information about covariation that cannot be articulated. *Journal of Experimental Psychology: Learning, memory and cognition, 12,* 135–146.

Lewin, K. (1934). Der Richtungsbegriff in der Psychologie. [Principles of topological psychology] *Psychologische Forschung, 19,* 249–299.

Lewin, K. (1935). *A dynamic theory of personality: Selected papers.* New York: McGraw-Hill.

Lewin, K. (1936). *Principles of topological psychology.* New York: McGraw-Hill.

Lewin, K. (1946). Behavior and development as a function of the total situation. In L. Carmichael (Ed.), *Manual of child psychology* (pp. 791–844). New York: Wiley.

Lewin, K. (1951/1963). *Field theory in social science.* Bern: Huber.

Lewinsohn, P. H. (1974). A behavioral approach to depression. In R. J. Friedman & M.M. Katz (Eds.), *The psychology of depression: Contemporary theory and research.* Washington, DC: Winston Wiley.

Lewinsohn, P. M. (1976). The use of activity schedules in the treatment of depressed individuals. In C. E. Thoresen & J. D. Krumboltz (Eds.), *Counseling methods* New York: Holt, Rinehart & Winston.

Ley, R. G. & Bryden, M. P. (1982). A dissociation of right and left hemispheric effects for recognizing emotional tone and verbal content. *Brain and Cognition, 1,* 3–9.

Libet, B. (1978). Neuronal vs. subjective timing for a conscious sensory experience. In P. A. Buser & A. Rougeul-Buser (Eds.), *Cerebral correlates of conscious experience* (pp. 69–82). Amsterdam: Elsevier/North-Holland.

Libet, B., Gleason, C. A., Wright, E. W. & Pearl, D. K. (1983). Time of conscious intention to act in relation to onset of cerebral activity (readiness-potential). *Brain, 106,* 623–642.

Linehan, M. M. (1987). Dialectical behavior therapy for borderline personality disorders. *Bulletin of the Menninger Clinic, 51,* 261–276.

Linehan, M. (1993 a). *Cognitive behavioral treatment of borderline personality disorder.* New York: Guilford.

Linehan, M. (1993 b). *Skills training manual for treating borderline personality disorder.* New York: Guilford.

Liotti, G. (1988). Attachment and cognition: A guideline for the reconstruction of early pathogenic experiences in cognitive psychotherapy. In C. Perris, M. Blackburn & H. Perris (Eds.), *Cognitive psychotherapy. Theory and practice* (pp. 62–79). Berlin: Springer.

Liotti, G. (1991). Insecure attachment and agoraphobia. In C. M. Parkes, J. Stevenson-Hinde & P. Marris (Eds.), *Attachment across the life cycle* (pp. 216–233). London: Routledge.

Livingstone, M. S. & Hubel, D. H. (1988). Segregation of form, color, movement, and depth: Anatomy, physiology, and perception. *Science, 240,* 740–749.

Loftus, E. F. & Loftus, G. R. (1980). On the permanence of stored information in the human brain. *American Psychologist, 35,* 409–420.

Loftus, E. F. & Marburger, W. (1983). Since the eruption of Mt. St. Helens, has anyone beaten you up? Improving the accuracy of retrospective reports with landmark events. *Memory and Cognition, 11,* 114–120.

Lorenzer, A. (1970). *Sprachzerstörung und Rekonstruktion. Vorarbeiten zu einer Metatheorie der Psychoanalyse.* [Speech disorders and reconstruction. Preparation of a meta-theory of psychoanalysis] Frankfurt am Main: Suhrkamp.

Lorenzer, A. (1974). *Die Wahrheit der psychoanalytischen Erkenntnis. Ein historisch-materialistischer Entwurf.* [The truth of psychoanalytic knowledge. A historical materialism outline] Frankfurt am Main: Suhrkamp.

Luborsky, L. (1977). Measuring a pervasive psychic structure in psychotherapy: The core conflictual relationship theme. In N. Freedman & S. Grands (Eds.), *Communication structures and psychic structures.* New York: Plenum.

Luborsky, L. (1984). *Principles of psychoanalytic psychotherapy. A manual for supportive-expressive treatment.* New York: Basic Books.

Luborsky, L., Albani, C. & Eckert, R. (1991). *Manual zur ZBKT-Methode (deutsche Übersetzung mit Ergänzungen der Ulmer ZBKT-Arbeitsgruppe).* [Manual on the ZBKT method (German translation with a supplement from the Ulmer ZBKT-working group] Abteilung Psychotherapie, Universität Ulm.

Luborsky, L., Bachrach, H., Graff, H., Pulver, S. & Christoph, P. (1979). Preconditions and consequences of transference interpretations: A clinical quantitative inverstigation. *Journal of Nervous and Mental Disease, 167,* 391–401.

Luborsky, L. & Barber, J. P. (1994). Perspectives on seven transference related measures applied to the interview with Ms. Smithfield. *Psychotherapy Research, 4,* 152–154.

Luborsky, L. & Crits-Christoph, P. (Eds.). (1990). *Understanding transference: The CCRT method.* New York: Basic Books.

Luborsky, L., Popp, C. & Barber, J. P. (1994). Common and special factors in different transference-related measures. *Psychotherapy Research, 4,* 277–286.

Mackintosh, D. J. (1983). *Conditioning and associative learning.* New York: Oxford University Press.

MacLean, P. D. (1970). The limbic brain in relation to psychoses. In P. H. Black (Ed.), *Physiological correlates of emotion.* New York: Academic Press.

Main, M. (1991). Metacognitive knowledge, metacognitive montitoring, and singular (coherent) vs. multiple (incoherent) models of attachment: Findings and directions for future research. In C. M. Parkes, J. Stevenson-Hinde & P. Marris (Eds.), *Attachment across the life cycle.* London: Tavistock.

Main, M., Kaplan, N. & Cassidy, J. (1985). Security in infancy, childhood and adulthood: A move to the level of representation. In I. Bretherton & E. Waters (Eds.), *Growing points in attachment theory and research* (pp. 66–104). Monographs of the Society for Research in Child Development.

Malatesta, C. Z. (1990). The role of emotions in the development and organization of personality. In R. A. Thompson (Ed.), *Socioemotional development.* Nebraska: University Press, 3–56.

Malatesta, C. Z. & Haveland, J. M. (1982). Learning display rules (The socialization of emotion expression in infancy). *Child Development, 53,* 991–1003.

Malsburg, C. von der (1981). *The correlation theory of brain function* (Internal Report No. 81–2). Max-Planck-Institute for Biophysical Chemistry Göttingen.

Mandler, J. (1975). *Mind and emotion.* New York: Wiley.

Marcel, A. J. (1983 a). Conscious and unconscious perception: Experiments on visual masking and word recognition. *Cognitive Psychology, 15,* 197–237.

Marcel, A. J. (1983 b). Conscious and unconscious perception: an approach to the relation between phenomenal experience and perceptual processes. *Cognitive Psychology, 15,* 238–300.

Marcia, J. E. (1980). Identity in adolescence. In J. Adelson (Ed.), *Handbook of adolescent psychology.* New York: Springer.

Margraf, J. (Ed.). (1996). *Lehrbuch der Verhaltenstherapie.* [Textbook of behavior therapy] Berlin: Springer.

Margraf, J. & Schneider, S. (1990). *Panik, Angstanfälle und ihre Behandlung* [Panic, anxiety attacks and their treatment] (2nd ed.). Berlin: Springer.

Markowitsch, H. J. (1992). *Neuropsychologie des Gedächtnisses.* [Neuropsychology of memory] Göttingen: Hogrefe.

Maser, J. D. & Cloninger, C. R. (Eds.). (1990). *Comorbidity of mood and anxiety disorders.* Washington: American Psychiatric Press.

Maslow, A. H. (1954). *Motivation and personality.* New York: Harper.

Matarazzo, R. G. (1978). Research on the teaching and learning of psychotherapeutic skills. In A. E. Bergin & S. L. Garfield (Eds.), *Handbook of psychotherapy and behavior change.* New York: Wiley.

Mathe, A. A. & Knapp, P. H. (1971). Emotional and adrenal reactions to stress in bronchial asthma. *Psychosomatic Medicine, 33,* 323–340.

Maturana, H. R. & Varela, F. G. (1980). *Autopoiesis and cognition.* Boston: Reidel.

McClelland, D. C. (1958). Methods of measuring human motivation. In J. W. Atkinson (Ed.), *Motives in fantasy, action, and society* (pp. 7–42). Princeton, NJ: Van Nostrand.

McClelland, D. C. (1985). How motives, skills and values determine what people do. *American Psychologist, 40,* 812–825.

McClelland, D. C. (1989). Motivational factors in health and disesase. *American Psychologist, 44,* 675–683.

McDougall, W. (1932). *The energies of men.* London: Methuen.

McGoldrick, M. & Gerson, R. (1990). *Genogramme in der Familienberatung.* [Genograms in family counseling] Bern: Huber.

McGuffin, P. & Thapar, A. (1992). The genetics of personality disorder. *British Journal of Psychiatry, 160,* 12–23.

McMahon, T. A. (1984). *Muscles, reflexes, and locomotion.* Princeton, NJ: Princeton University Press.

McReynolds, P. (1990). The nature and logic of intrapsychic conflict. In C. D. Spielberger, I. G. Sarason, J. Strelau & J. M.T. Brebner (Eds.), *Stress and anxiety.* New York: Hemisphere.

Mead, G. H. (1934). *Mind, self, and society.* Chicago: University of Chicago Press.

Meichenbaum, D. W. (1977). *Kognitive Verhaltenstherapie.* [Cognitive behavior therapy] München: Pfeiffer.

Meichenbaum, D. W. (1994). *A clinical handbook/practical therapist manual for assessing and treating adults with post-traumatic stress disorder (PTSD).* Waterloo, Ontario: Institute Press.

Menzel, R. & Roth, G. (1996). Verhaltensbiologische und neuronale Grundlagen des Lernens und des Gedächtnisses. [Behavioral biology and neuronal foundations of learning and memory] In G. Roth & W. Prinz (Eds.), *Kopf-Arbeit.* Heidelberg: Spektrum Akademischer Verlag.

Merten, J. (1996). *Affekte und die Regulation nonverbalen interaktiven Verhaltens.* [Affect and the regulation of nonverbal interactive behavior] Bern: Peter Lang.

Metzinger, T. (Ed.). (1996). *Bewusstsein: Beiträge aus der Gegenwartphilosophie* [Consciousness: Reports from contemporary philosophy] (2nd ed.). Paderborn: Schöningh.

Meyer, A.-E. (Ed.). (1981). The Hamburg short psychotherapy comparison experiment. *Psychotherapy and Psychosomatics, 35,* 81–207.

Meyer, A.-E., Richter, R., Grawe, K., Schulenburg, J. M. Graf von & Schulte, B. (1991). *Forschungs-gutachten zu Fragen eines Psychotherapeutengesetzes.* [Research expertise on questions of psychotherapy regulations] Universitäts-Krankenhaus Hamburg-Eppendorf.

Miller, G. A. (1956). The magical number seven, plus minus two: Some limits on our capacity for processing information. *Psychological Review, 63,* 81–97.

Miller, G. A. (1962). *Psychology: The science of mental life.* New York: Harper and Row.

Miller, G. A., Galanter, E. & Pribram, K. H. (1960/1973). *Plans and the structure of behavior.* New York/Stuttgart: Holt/Klett.

Mineka, S. (1985). Animal models of anxiety-based disorders: Their usefulness and limitations. In A. Tuma & J. Maser (Eds.), *Anxiety and anxiety disoders* (pp. 199–244). Hillsdale, NJ: Erlbaum.

Mineka, S. (1987). A primate model of phobic fears. In H. J. Eysenck & I. Martin (Eds.), *Theoretical foundations of behavior therapy* (pp. 81–111). New York: Plenum.

Mineka, S., Davidson, M., Cook, M. & Keir, R. (1984). Observational conditioning of snake fear in rhesus monkeys. *Journal of Abnormal Psychology (93),* 355–372.

Minsky, M. (1975). A framework for representing knowledge. In P. H. Winston (Ed.), *The psychology of computer vision* (pp. 211–277). New York: McGraw-Hill.

Minuchin, S. (1967). *Families of the slums. An exploration of their structure and treatment.* New York: Basic Books.

Minuchin, S. (1974). *Families and family therapy.* Cambridge, Mass.: Harvard University Press.

Minuchin, S., Rosman, B. & Baker, L. (1978). *Psychosomatic families. Anorexia nervosa in context.* Cambridge, MA: Harvard University Press.

Moray, N. (1959). Attention in dichotic listening. Affective cues and the influence of instructions. *Quarterly Journal of experimental Psychology, 11,* 56–60.

Mowrer, O. H. (1960). *Learning theory and behavior.* New York: Wiley.

Mühlig, S. (1997). *Schmerz und Schmerzbehandlung bei Kindern und Jugendlichen.* [Pain and pain treatment in children and adolescents] Weinheim: Psychologie Verlags Union.

Murray, H. A. (1938). *Explorations in personality.* New York: Oxford University Press.

Murray, H. A. (1943). *Thematic apperception test manual.* Cambridge: Harvard University Press.

Murray, H. A. (1951). Toward a classification of interaction. In T. Parsons & E. A. Shils (Eds.), *Toward a general theory of action* (pp. 434–464). Cambridge: Harvard University Press.

Nacht, S. (1964). Silence as an integrative factor. *International Journal of Psychoanalysis, 45,* 299–303.

Neisser, U. (1974). *Kognitive Psychologie.* [Cognitive psychology] Stuttgart: Klett.

Neisser, U. (1976). *Cognition and reality. Principles and implications of cognitive psychology.* San Francisco: Freeman.

Nisbett, R. E. & Wilson, T. (1977). Telling more than we can know: Verbal reports on mental processes. *Psychological Review, 84,* 231–259.

Nisbett, R. E. & Ross, L. (1980). *Human inference and shortcomings of social judgement.* Englewood Cliffs, NJ: Prentice Hall.

Norcross, J. C. (1986 a). Eclectic psychotherapy: An introduction and overview. In J. C. Norcross (Ed.), *Handbook of eclectic psychotherapy.* New York: Brunner/Mazel.

Norcross, J. C. (1986 b). *Handbook of eclectic psychotherapy.* New York: Brunner/Mazel.

Norcross, J. C., Alford, B. A. & DeMichele, J. T. (1992 a). The future of psychotherapy: Delphi data and concluding observations. *Psychotherapy, 29,* 150–158.

Norcross, J. C., Alford, B. A. & DeMichele, J. T. (1992 b). The future of psychotherapy: Delphi data and concluding observations. *Psychotherapy, 29,* 150–158.

Norcross, J. C. & Goldfried, M. R. (1992). *Handbook of psychotherapy integration.* New York: Basic Books.

Norcross, J. C. & Newman, C. F. (1992 a). Psychotherapy integration: setting the context. In J. C. Norcross & M. R. Goldfried (Eds.), *Handbook of psychotherapy integration* (pp. 3–45). New York: Basic Books.

Norcross, J. C. & Newman, C. F. (1992 b). Psychotherapy integration: Setting the context. In J. C. Norcross & M. R. Goldfried (Eds.), *Handbook of psychotherapy integration* (pp. 3–45). New York: Basic Books.

Oesterreich, R. (1981). *Handlungsregulation und Kontrolle.* [Action regulation and control] München: Urban & Schwarzenberg.

OPD Working Group (Ed.) (2001). *Operationalized psychodynamic diagnostics - Foundations and manual.* Seattle: Hogrefe & Huber

Orlinsky, D. E. (1994). "Learning from many masters." Ansätze zu einer wissenschaftlichen Integration psychotherapeutischer Behandlungsmodelle. ["Learning from many masters." Approaches to the scientific integration of psychotherapy treatment models] *Psychotherapeut, 39,* 2–9.

Orlinsky, D. E., Grawe, K. & Parks, B. (1994). Process and outcome in psychotherapy – noch einmal. [Process and outcome in psychotherapy – once again] In A. E. Bergin & S. L. Garfield (Eds.), *Handbook of psychotherapy and behavior change.* New York: Wiley.

Orlinsky, D. E. & Howard, K. I. (1986). Process and outcome in psychotherapy. In A. E. Bergin & S. L. Garfield (Eds.), *Handbook of psychotherapy and behavior change* (3rd ed.). New York: Wiley.

Oswald, I., Taylor, A. M. & Treisman, M. (1960). Discrimination response to stimulation during human sleep. *Brain, 83,* 440–453.

Oswald, W.D. & Gunzelmann, T. (Eds.). (1995). *Kompetenztraining. Ein Programm für Seniorengruppen (Das SIMA-Projekt).* [Competency training, A program for seniors groups (The SIMA project)] Göttingen: Hogrefe.

Oswald, W.D. & Rödel, G. (Eds.). (1995). *Gedächtnistraining. Ein Programm für Senioren (Das SIMA-Projekt).* [Memory training, A program for seniors (The SIMA project)] Göttingen: Hogrefe.

Ovesey, L. (1966). The phobic reaction: A psychodynamic basis for classification and treatment. In G. Goldman & D. Shapiro (Eds.), *Development of psychoanalysis at Columbia University* (pp. 41–68). New York: Academic Press.

Paivio, A. (1986). *Mental representations. A dual-coding approach.* New York: Oxford University Press.

Paivio, A. (1991). Dual coding theory. Retrospect and current status. *Canadian Journal of Psychology, 45,* 255–287.

Panksepp, J. (1989). The psychobiology of emotions. The animal side of human feelings. *Experimental Brain Research, 18,* 31–55.

Pascual-Leone, J. & Johnson, J. (1991). Psychological unit and its role in task analysis: A reinterpretation of object permanence. In M. Chandler & M. Chapman (Eds.), *Criteria for competence: Controversies in the assessment of children's abilities.* Hillsdale, NJ: Lawrence Erlbaum.

Patrick, M., Hobson, R. P., Castle, D., Howard, R. & Maugham, B. (1994). Personality disorder and the mental representation of early social experience. *Development and Psychopathology, 6,* 375–388.

Peak, H. (1955). Attitude and Motivation. In M. R. Jones (Ed.), *Nebraska symposion on motivation* (pp. 149–189). Lincoln: University of Nebraska Press.

Perls, F. S., Hefferline, R. & Goodman, P. (1979). *Gestalttherapy* (German translation, 1979, Klett-Cotta). New York: Julian Press.

Perrett, D. I., Mistlin, A. J. & Chitty, A. J. (1987). Visual neurons responsive to faces. *TINS, 10,* 358–364.

Perrett, D. I., Smith, P. A., Potter, D. D., Mistlin, A. J., Head, A. S., Milner, A. D. & Jeeves, M.A. (1984). Neurons responsive to faces in the temporal cortex: studies of functional organization, sensitivity to identity and relation to perception. *Human Neurobiology, 3,* 197–208.

Perrig, W.J. (1990). Implizites Wissen: Eine Herausforderung für die Kognitionspsychologie. [Implicit knowledge: A challenge for psychology of cognition] *Schweizerische Zeitschrift für Psychologie, 49 (4),* 234–249.

Perrig, W., Wippich, W. & Perrig-Chiello, P. (1993). *Unbewusste Informationsverarbeitung.* [Unconscious information processing] Bern: Huber.

Perring, C., Oatley, K. & Smith, J. (1988). Psychiatric symptoms and conflict among personal plans. *British Journal of Medical Psychology, 61,* 167. 177.

Perruchet, L. R. & Pacteau, C. (1990). Synthetic grammar learning: Implicit rule abstraction or explicit fragmentary knowledge? *Journal of Experimental Psychology: General, 119,* 264–275.

Perry, C. (1991). Assessing psychodynamic patterns using the ideographic conflict formulation (ICF) method. In N. Miller, L. Luborsky & J. Docherty (Eds.), *Doing research on psychodynamic therapy.* New York: Basic Books.

Petermann, F. (Ed.). (1995 a). *Asthma und Allergie. Verhaltensmedizinische Grundlagen und Anwendungen.* [Asthma and allergies. Behavioral medicine fundamentals and applications] Göttingen: Hogrefe.

Petermann, F. (Ed.). (1995 b). *Diabetes mellitus. Sozial- und verhaltensmedizinische Ansätze.* [Diabetes mellitus. Social and behavior medicine approaches] Göttingen:Hogrefe.

Petermann, F. (1996). *Lehrbuch der Klinischen Kinderpsychologie.* [Textbook of clinical child psychology] Göttingen: Hogrefe.

Petermann, F., Jugert, G., Tänzer, U. & Verbeck, D. (1997). *Sozialtraining in der Schule.* [Social training in school] Weinheim: Psychologie Verlags Union.

Petermann, F., Noeker, M. & Bode, U. (1987). *Psychologie chronischer Krankheiten im Kindes- und Jugendalter.* [Psychology of chronic illnesses in childhood and adolescence] Weinheim: Psychologie Verlags Union.

Petry, J. (1996). *Psychotherapie des Glücksspiels.* [Psychotherapy of gambling] Weinheim: Psychologie Verlags Union.

Piaget, J. (1937). *La construction du réel chez l'enfant* [The construction of reality in children] Neuchâtel: Delachaux et Niestlé.

Piaget, J. (1976). *Die Äquilibration der kognitiven Strukturen.* [The equilibration of cognitive structures] Stuttgart: Klett.

Piaget, J. (Ed.). (1981). *Jean Piaget über Jean Piaget. Sein Werk aus seiner Sicht.* [Jean Piaget on Jean Piaget. His work from his own perspective] München: Kindler.

Pilkonis, P. A., Heape, C. & Proietti, J. M. (1991). Adult attachment styles, personality disorder, and treatment outcome in depression. *Annual meeting of the North American Society for Psychotherapy Research,* Panama City.

Piper, W.. E., Azim, F. A., Joyce, S. A. & McCallum, M. (1991). Transference interpretations, therapeutic alliance and outcome in short-term individual psychotherapy. *Archives of General Psychiatry, 48,* 946–953.

Pitman, R. K. (1987). A cybernetic model of obsessive-compulsive psychopathology. *Comprehensive Psychiatry, 28,* 334–343.

Popper, K. R. & Eccles, J. C. (1982). *Das Ich und sein Gehirn.* [The self and its brain] München: Piper.

Posner, M. I. & Dehaene, S. (1994). Attentional networks. *TINS, 17,* 75–79.

Posner, M., Klein, R., Summers, J. & Buggie, S. (1973). On the selection of signals. *Memory and Cognition, 1,* 2–12.

Powers, W. T. (1973). *Behavior: The control of perception.* New York: Aldine.

Powers, W. T. (1989). *Living control systems: Selected papers of William T. Powers.* Gravel Switch, KY: Control Systems Group.

Powers, W. T. (1992). *Living control sytems II: Selected papers of William T. Powers.* Gravel Switch, KY: Control Systems Group.

Prigogine, I. (1977). *Self organization in nonequilibrum systems: From dissipative structures to order through fluctuations.* New York: Wiley.

Prinz, W. (1996). Bewusstsein und Ich-Konstitution. [Consciousness and self-constitution] In G. Roth & W. Prinz (Eds.), *Kopf-Arbeit.* Heidelberg: Spektrum Akademischer Verlag.

Prioleau, L., Murdoch, M. & Brody, N. (1983). An analysis of psychotherapy versus placebo studies. *The Behavioral and Brain Sciences, 6,* 275–310.

Prochaska, J. O., Norcross, J. D. & DiClemente, C. C. (1994). *Changing for good.* New York: Avon Books.

Queisser, H. R., Armstrong, H. E., Smith, W.R. & Davis, G. R. (1980). Psychoeducational skills training for individuals with epilepsy. In D. Upper & S. M. Ross (Eds.), *Behavioral group therapy 1980* (pp. 219–234). Champaign: Research Press Company.

Rachman, S., Craske, M., Tallman, K. & Solyom, C. (1986). Does escape behavior strengthen agoraphobic avoidance? *Behavior Therapy, 17,* 366–384.

Reber, A. S. (1989). Implicit learning and tacit knowledge. *Journal of Experimental Psychology: General, 118,* 219–235.

Reinecker, H. (1991). *Zwänge. Diagnose, Theorien und Behandlung.* [Compulsions. Diagnosis, theories and treatment] Bern: Huber.

Reinecker, H. (1993). *Phobien.* [Phobias] Göttingen: Hogrefe.

Reinecker, H. (1994 a). *Lehrbuch der Klinischen Psychologie* [Textbook of clinical psychology] (2nd ed.). Göttingen: Hogrefe.

Reinecker, H. (1994 b). Soziale und spezifische Phobien. [Social and specific phobias] In H. Reinecker (Ed.), *Lehrbuch der Klinischen Psychologie* (2nd ed., pp. 91–116). Göttingen: Hogrefe.

Reiss, S., Peterson, R. A., Gursky, D. M. & McNally, R. J. (1986). Anxiety sensitivity, anxiety frequency and the prediction of fearfulness. *Behavior, Research, and Therapy, 24,* 1–8.

Reitboeck, H. J. (1983). A multi-electrode matrix for studies of temporal signal correlations within neural assemblies. In H. Flohr, E. Basar, H. Haken & A. J. Mandell (Eds.), *Synergetics of the brain.* Berlin: Springer.

Renken, B., Egeland, B., Marvinney, D., Mangelsdorf, S. & Sroeufe, L. A. (1989). Early childhood antecedents of aggression and passive-withdrawal in early elementary school. *Journal of Personality, 57,* 257–281.

Renneberg, B. (1996). Verhaltenstherapeutische Gruppentherapie bei Patienten mit selbstunsicherer Persönlichkeitsstörung. [Behavioral group therapy with patients suffering from avoidant personality disorder] In B. Schmitz, T. Fydrich & K. Limbacher (Eds.), *Persönlichkeitsstörungen: Diagnostik und Psychotherapie.* Weinheim: Psychologie Verlags Union.

Rescorla, R. A. (1988). Pavlovian conditioning: It's not what you think it is. *American Psychologist, 43,* 151–160.

Rief, W. & Hiller, W. (1998). *Somatisierungsstörungen und Hypochondrie.* [Somatization disorders and hypochondria] Göttingen: Hogrefe.

Rief, W. & Hiller, W. (1992). *Somatoforme Störungen. Körperliche Symptome ohne organische Ursache.* [Somatoform disorders. Physical symptoms with no organic cause] Bern: Huber.

Rief, W., Schaefer, S., Hiller, W. & Fichter, M. M. (1992). Lifetime diagnoses in patients with somatoform disorders: which came first? *European Archives of Psychiatric and Clinical Neuroscience, 241,* 236–240.

Rief, W., Stock, C. & Fichter, M. M. (1991). Das Anti-Diät-Programm als integrativer Therapiebaustein bei anorektischen, bulimischen und adiposen Patienten. [The anti-diet program as an essential, integrative part in the therapy with anorexic, bulimic and obese patients] *Verhaltenstherapie, 1,* 47–54.

Riemann, D. & Backhaus, J. (1996). *Behandlung von Schlafstörungen. Ein psychologisches Gruppenprogramm.* [Treatment of sleep disorders. A psychological group program] Weinheim: Psychologie Verlags Union.

Riggio, R. E. & Friedman, H. S. (1982). The interrelation of self-monitoring factors, personality traits, and nonverbal social skills. *Journal of Nonverbal Behavior, 7,* 33–45.

Robbins, A. S., Kauss, D. R., Heinrich, R., Abrass, L., Dreyer, J. & Clyman, B. (1979). Interpersonal skills training: Evaluation in an internal medicine residency. *Journal of Medical Education, 54,* 885–894.

Roberts, A. R. (1995). *Crisis intervention and time-limited cognitive treatment.* Thousand Oaks, CA: Sage.

Roder, V., Brenner, H. D., Kienzle, N. & Hodel, B. (1992). *Integriertes psychologisches Therapieprogramm für schizophrene Patienten* [Integrated psychological therapy program for schizophrenic patients] (IPT, 2nd ed.). Weinheim: Psychologie Verlags Union.

Rogers, C. R. (1951). *Client-centered psychotherapy.* Boston: Houghton Mifflin.

Rolls, E. T. (1984). Neurons in the cortex of the temporal lobe and in the amygdala of the monkey with responses selective for faces. *Human Neurobiology, 3,* 209–222.

Rosenthal, R. (1969). Interpersonal expectations: Effects of the experimenter's hypothesis. In R. Rosenthal & R. L. Rosnow (Eds.), *Artifact in behavioral research* (pp. 181–277). New York: Academic Press.

Rosenthal, R. & Benowitz, L. I. (1986). Sensitivity to nonverbal communication in normal, psychiatric, and brain-damaged samples. In P. D. Blanck, R. Buck & R. Rosenthal (Eds.), *Nonverbal communication in the clinical context.* University Park and London: The Pennsylvania State University Press.

Rosenthal, R., Hall, J. A., DiMatteo, M. R., Rogers, P. L. & Archer, D. (1979). *Sensitivity to nonverbal communication: The PONS test.* Baltimore: The Johns Hopkins University Press.

Rosenthal, R. & Rubin, D. B. (1978). Interpersonal expectancy effects: The first 345 studies. *Behavioral and Brain Sciences, 3,* 377–415.

Roth, G. (1995). *Das Gehirn und seine Wirklichkeit* [The brain and its reality] (3rd ed.). Frankfurt: Suhrkamp.

Roth, G. (1996). Das Gehirn des Menschen. [The human brain] In G. Roth & W. Prinz (Eds.), *Kopf-Arbeit.* Heidelberg: Spektrum Akademischer Verlag.

Roth, G. & Prinz, W. (1996). *Kopf-Arbeit.* [Head work] Heidelberg: Spektrum Akademischer Verlag.

Roth, L. H. (Ed.). (1987). *Clinical treatment of the violent person.* New York: Guilford.

Rotter, J. B. (1954). *Social learning and clinical psychology.* Englewood Cliffs, NJ: Prentice Hall.

Rotter, J. B. (1966). General expectancies for internal vs. external control of reinforcement. *Psychological Monographs, 80.*

Roweck, M. (1990) *Intraindividuelle Konfliktveränderung bei Alkoholkranken im Therapieverlauf.* [Intra-individual conflict change among alcoholics in the course of therapy] Unpublished Master's thesis, Joh.-Wolfgang-Goethe-Universität Frankfurt.

Ruesch, J. & Bateson, G. (1951). *Communication: The social matrix of psychiatry.* New York: Norton.

Ryle, A. (1990). *Cognitive-analytic therapy: Active participation in change.* Chichester: Wiley.

Sachse, R. (1992). *Zielorientierte Gesprächstherapi*e. [Goal-oriented client-centered therapy] Göttingen: Hogrefe.

Sachse, R. (1996). *Praxis der Zielorienten Gesprächspsychotherapie.* [The practice of goal-oriented client-centered therapy] Göttingen: Hogrefe.

Sachse, R. (1997). Zielorientierte Gesprächspsychotherapie bei Klienten mit psychosomatischen Störungen. [Goal-oriented client-centered therapy for patients with psychosomatic disorders] *Gesprächspsychotherapie und personenzentrierte Beratung,* 90–107.

Sacks, O. (1987). *Der Mann, der seine Frau mit einem Hut verwechselte.* [The man who mistook his wife for a hat] Reinbek: Rowohlt.

Safer, M. & Leventhal, H. (1977). Ear differences in evaluating emotional tone of voice and verbal content. *JEP: Human Perception and Performance, 3,* 75–82.

Safran, J. D. & Segal, Z. V. (1990). *Interpersonal process in cognitive therapy.* New York: Basic Books.

Saigh, P. A. (Ed.). (1995). *Posttraumatische Belastungsstörungen.* [Post-traumatic stress disorders] Bern: Huber.

Salkovskis, P. M. (1996). Somatoforme Störungen. [Somatoform disorders] In K. Hahlweg & A. Ehlers (Eds.), *Psychische Störungen und ihre Behandlungen* (pp. 308–354). Göttingen: Hogrefe.

Sampson, H. & Weiss, J. (1986). Testing hypotheses: the approach of the Mount Zion Psychotherapy Research Group. In L. S. Greenberg & W. Pinsof (Eds.), *The psychotherapeutic process: a research handbook* (pp. 591–613). New York: Guilford Press.

Sanderson, W.C., DiNardo, P. A., Rapee, R. M. & Barlow, D. H. (1990). Syndrome comorbidity in patients diagnosed with a DSM-III-R anxiety disorder. *Journal of Abnormal Psychology, 99,* 308–312.

Sanson-Fisher, R. W. & Poole, A. D. (1978). Training medical students to empathize: An experimental study. *Medical Journal of Australia, 1,* 473–476.

Savin-Williams, R. C. & Jacquish, G. A. (1981). The assessment of adolescent self-esteem. A comparison of methods. *Journal of Personality, 49,* 324–335.

Schacter, D. L. (1987). Critical review: Implicit memory; history and current status. *Journal of Experimental Psychology: Learning, Memory, and Cognition, 13,* 501–518.

Schacter, D. L. & Graf, P. (1986). Effects of elaborative processing on implicit and explicit memory for new associations. *Journal of Experimental Psychology: Learning, Memory, and Cognition, 12,* 432–444.

Schank, R. C. & Abelson, R. P. (1977). *Scripts, plans, goals, and understanding: an inquiry into human knowledge structures.* Hillsdale: Erlbaum.

Scheflen, A. (1974). *Körpersprache und soziale Ordnung.* [Body language and social order] Stuttgart: Klett.

Scheidt, C. E. & Waller, E. (1996). Bindungsrepräsentationen als psychobiologische Regulatoren? Ein bindungstheoretischer Ansatz psychosomatischer Forschung am Beispiel des spamodischen Torticollis. [Attachment representations as psychobiological regulators? An attachment-theory approach of psychosomatic research, the example of spasmodic torticollis] *19. Werkstatt empirische Forschung in der Psychoanalyse* (19th Workshop of empirical research of psyhcoanalysis). Ulm.

Scherer, K. R. (1984). On the nature and functions of emotions: A component process approach. In K. R. Scherer & P. Ekman (Eds.), *Approaches to emotion* (pp. 293–317). Hillsdale, NJ: Lawrence Erlbaum.

Schiepek, G., Kowalik, Z. J., Schütz, A., Köhler, M., Richter, K., Strunk, G., Mühlnichel, W. & Elbert, T. (1997). Psychotherapy as a chaotic process I: Coding the client-therapist interaction by means of sequential plan analysis and the search for chaos: A stationary approach. *Psychotherapy Research, 7,* 173–194.

Schiffman, H. R. (1976). *Sensation and perception. An integrated approach.* New York: Wiley.

Schlenker, B. R. (1980). *Impression management: The self-concept, social identity, and interpersonal relations.* Monterey, CA: Brooks/Cole.

Schlenker, B. R. (1985). Identity and self-identification. In B. R. Schlenker (Ed.), *The self and social life* (pp. 65–99). New York: McGraw-Hill.

Schmalbach, S. (1996). Ausbildung in Allgemeiner Psychotherapie am Beispiel des Curriculums Post-graduate Weiterbildung Psychotherapie der Universität Bern. [Training in general psychotherapy, the example of the Bern University post-graduate psychotherapy further education curriculum] Unpublished lecture manuscript, *Kongress für Klinische Psychologie und Psychotherapie der DGVT,* Berlin.

Schmidt, S. & Strauss, B. (1996). Die Bindungstheorie und ihre Relevanz für die Psychotherapie. Teil 1: Grundlagen und Methoden der Bindungsforschung. [The attachment theory and its relevance for psychotherapy. Part 1: Fundamentals and methods of attachment research] *Psychotherapeut, 41,* 139–150.

Schneider, R. & Margraf, J. (1998). *Agoraphobie.* [Agoraphobia] Göttingen: Hogrefe.

Schneider, W. & Shiffrin, R. M. (1977). Controlled and automatic human information processing: (1) Detection, search, and attention. *Psychological Review, 84,* 1–66.

Scholz, H. (1996). *Syndrombezogene Alkoholismustherapie.* [Syndrome-related alcoholism therapy] Göttingen: Hogrefe.

Scholz, J. P., Kelso, J. A. & Schöner, G. (1987). Nonequilibrium phase transitions in coordinated biological motion: Critical slowing down, and switching time. *Physics Letters A, 123,* 390–394.

Schulte, D. (1974). Der diagnostisch-therapeutische Prozess in der Verhaltenstherapie. [The diagnostic-therapeutic process in behavior therapy] In D. Schulte (Ed.), *Diagnostik in der Verhaltenstherapie* (pp. 60–73). München: Urban & Schwarzenberg.

Schulte, D. (1993). Wie soll Therapieerfolg gemessen werden? [How should therapy success be measured] *Zeitschrift für Klinische Psychologie, 22,* 374–393.

Schulte, D. (1996). *Therapieplanung.* [Therapy planning] Göttingen: Hogrefe.

Schulte, D., Hartung, J. & Wilke, F. (1996). Handlungskontrolle der Angstbewältigung. Was macht Reizkonfrontationsverfahren so effektiv? [Action control and the mastering of fear. What makes stimulus confrontation experiences so effective?] *Zeitschrift für Klinische Psychologie, 26,* 118–128.

Schulz, H.-C. & Hilgenfeldt, S. (1994). Experimente zum Chaos. [Experiments in chaos] *Spektrum der Wissenschaft, 1/94,* 72–81.

Schulz, P. & Hellhammer, D. (1992). Psychologische Aspekte chronischer Krankheiten. [Psychological aspects of chronic illnesses] In H. Reinecker (Ed.), *Lehrbuch der Klinischen Psychologie* (2nd ed., pp. 565–590). Göttingen: Hogrefe.

Schwartz, G. (1990). Psychobiology of repression and health. A systems approach. In J. L. Singer (Ed.), *Repression and dissociation.* Chicago: The University of Chicago Press.

Schwartz, G. E. (1983). Disregulation theory and disease: Applications to the repression/cerebral disconnection/cardiovascular disorder hypothesis. *International Review of Applied Psychology, 32,* 95–118.

Seligman, M. E. (1971). Phobias and preparedness. *Behavior Therapy, 2,* 307–320.

Seligman, M. E. & Maier, S. F. (1967). Failure to escape traumatic shock. *Journal of Experimental Psychology, 74,* 1–9.

Selvini-Palazzoli, M., Boscolo, L., Cecchin, G. & Prata, G. (1977). *Paradoxon und Gegenparadoxon.* [Paradoxes and counter-paradoxes] Stuttgart: Klett-Cotta.

Shallice, T. (1972). Dual functions of consciousness. *Psychological Review, 79,* 383–393.

Shallice, T. (1978). The dominant action system; an information-processing approach to consciousness. In K. S. Hope & J. L. Singer (Eds.), *The stream of consciousness: Scientific investigations into the flow of human experience.* New York: Plenum.

Shapiro, A. K. (1971). Placebo effects in medicine, psychotherapy and psychoanalysis. In A. E. Bergin & S. L. Garfield (Eds.), *Handbook of psychotherapy and behavior change* (pp. 439–473). New York: Wiley.

Shapiro, A. K. & Morris, L. A. (1978). The placebo effect in medical and psychological thera-pies. In A. E. Bergin & S. L. Garfield (Eds.), *Handbook of psychotherapy and behavior change*. New York: Wiley.

Shapiro, D. (1995). Finding out how psychotherapy works. *Psychotherapy Research, 5,* 1–17.

Shapiro, D. A. (1981). Comparative credibility of treatment rationales: Three tests of expect-ancy theory. *British Journal of Clinical Psychology, 20,* 111–122.

Shevrin, H. (1988). Unconscious conflict: A convergent psychodynamic and electrophysiological approach. In M.J. Horowitz (Ed.), *Psychodynamics and cognition* (pp. 117–168). Chicago: University of Chicago Press.

Shevrin, H. (1990). Subliminal perception and repression. In J. L. Singer (Ed.), *Repression and dissociation* (pp. 103–120). Chicago: The University of Chicago Press.

Shevrin, H. & Dickman, S. (1980). The psychological unconscious: A necessary assumption for all psychological theory? *American Psychologist, 35,* 421–434.

Shiffrin, R. M. & Schneider, W. (1977). Controlled and automatic human information process-ing II. Perceptual learning, automatic attending, and a general theory. *Psychological Re-view, 84,* 127–190.

Shoham-Salomon, V., Avner, R. & Neeman, K. (1989). "You're changed if you do and changed if you don't." Mechanisms underlying paradoxical interventions. *Journal of Consulting and Clinical Psychology, 57,* 590–598.

Shoham-Salomon, V. & Hannah, M. T. (1991). Client-treatment interaction in the study of differential change processes. *Journal of Consulting and Clinical Psychology, 59,* 217–225.

Shoham-Salomon, V. & Rosenthal, R. (1987). Paradoxical intervention: A meta-analysis. *Jour-nal of Consulting and Clinical Psychology, 55,* 22–27.

Siber, J. L. & Sincoff, J. B. (1990). Summary: Beyond repression and the defenses. In J. L. Singer (Ed.), *Repression and dissociation* (pp. 471–496). Chicago: The University of Chi-cago Press.

Siever, L. J. & Davis, K. L. (1991). A psychobiological perspective on the personality disor-ders. *American Journal of Psychiatry, 148,* 1647–1658.

Silberschatz, G. (1986). Testing pathogenic belief. In H. Sampson, J. Weiss and the Mount Zion Psychotherapy Research Group (Eds.), *The psychoanalytic process: theory, clinical obser-vation, and empirical research* (pp. 256–266). New York: Guilford.

Silberschatz, G., Curtis, J. T., Fretter, P. B. & Kelly, T. J. (1988). Testing hypotheses of psycho-therapeutic change processes. In H. Dahl, H. Kächele & H. Thomä (Eds.), *Psychoanalytic process research strategies* (pp. 128–145). New York: Springer.

Silberschatz, G., Fretter, P. B. & Curtis, J. T. (1986). How do interpretations influence the process of psychotherapy? *Journal of Consulting and Clinical Psychology, 54,* 646–652.

Singer, J. L. (1990 a). Preface: A fresh look at repression, dissociation, and the defenses as mechanisms and as personality styles. In J. L. Singer (Ed.), *Repression and dissociation*. Chicago: The University of Chicago Press.

Singer, J. L. (Ed.). (1990 b). *Repression and dissociation*. Chicago: The University of Chicago Press.

Skinner, B. F. (1957). *Verbal behavior.* New York: Appleton Century Crofts.

Skinner, B. F. (1969). *Contingencies of reinforcement.* New York: Appleton-Century Crofts.

Sloane, E. R. B., Staples, F. R., Cristol, A. H., Yorkston, N. J. & Whipple, K. (1975). *Psycho-therapy versus behavior therapy*. Cambridge: Harvard University Press.

Smith, G. R. (1991). *Somatization disorder in the medical setting*. Washington: American Psy-chiatric Press.

Smith, E. (1997). *Emotionalität und Entwicklung. Eine Untersuchung der Zusammenhänge zwischen objektivem Geschehen und subjektivem Erleben in emotional belastenden Psychotherapiesitzungen.* [Emotionality and development. A study of the connection be-tween objective actions and subjective experience in emotionally fraught psychotherapy sessions] Unpublished Master's thesis. Institut für Psychologie der Universität Bern.

Smith, G. R., Monson, R. A. & Ray, D. C. (1986). Patients with multiple unexplained symptoms. *Archives of Internal Medicine, 146,* 69–72.

Snyder, D. K. & Wills, R. M. (1989). Behavioral versus insight-oriented marital therapy: Effects on individual and interpersonal functioning. *Journal of Consulting and Clinical Psychology, 57,* 39–46.

Snyder, D. K., Wills, R. M. & Grady-Fletcher, A. (1991). Long-term effectiveness of behavioral versus insight-oriented marital therapy: A 4-year follow-up-study. *Journal of Consulting and Clinical Psychology, 59,* 138–141.

Southworth, S. & Kirsch, I. (1988). The role of expectancy in exposure-generated fear reduction in agoraphobia. *Behaviour Research and Therapy, 26,* 113–120.

Speckens, A. E. M., Hemert, A. M. van, Bolk, J. H., Rooijmans, H. G. M. & Hengeveld, M. W. (1996). Unexplained physical symptoms: outcome, utilization of medical care and associated factors. *Psychological Medicine, 26,* 745–752.

Sperling, M. B., Sharp, J. L. & Fisher, P. (1991). On the nature of attachment in a borderline population: A preliminary investigation. *Psychological Reports, 68,* 543–546.

Spitz, R. (1946). Anaclitic depression. *Psychoanalytic Study of the Child, 2,* 313–342.

Sroufe, L. A. (1979). Socioemotional development. In J. D. Osofsky (Ed.), *Handbook of infant development.* New York: Wiley.

Sroufe, L. A. (1984). The organization of emotional development. In K. R. Scherer & P. Ekman (Eds.), *Approaches to emotion.* Hillsdale, NJ: Erlbaum.

Stangier, U., Gieler, U. & Ehlers, A. (1996). *Neurodermitis bewältigen.* [Coping with neurodermatitis] Heidelberg: Springer.

Steele, C. M. (1988). The psychology of self-affirmation: Sustaining the integrity of the self. In L. Berkowitz (Ed.), *Advances in experimental social psychology, Vol. 21* (pp. 261–302). New York: Academic Press.

Steil, R. & Ehlers, A. (1996). Die Posttraumatische Belastungsstörung. Eine Übersicht. [Post-traumatic stress disorder. An overview] *Verhaltens-modifikation und Verhaltensmedizin, 17,* 169–212.

Steimer-Krause, E. (1994). Nonverbale Beziehungsregulation in Dyaden mit schizophrenen Patienten. Ein Beitrag zur Übertragungs-Gegenübertragungsforschung. [Nonverbal interaction regulation in dyads with schizophrenic patients. A report on transference and countertransference research] In U. Streeck & K. Bell (Eds.), *Psychoanalyse schwerer psychischer Erkrankungen* (pp. 209–229). München: Pfeiffer.

Steimer-Krause, E., Krause, R. & Wagner, G. (1990). Prozesse der Interaktionsregulierung bei schizophrenen und psychosomatisch erkrankten Patienten – Studien zum mimischen Verhalten in dyadischen Interaktionen. [Process of interaction regulation with schizophrenics and psychosomatic patients – Studies on facial behavior in dyadic interaction] *Zeitschrift für Klinische Psychologie, 19,* 32–49.

Steklis, H. D. & Kling, A. (1985). Neurobiology of affiliative behavior in nonhuman primates. In M. Reite & T. Field (Eds.), *The psychobiology of attachment and separation.* London: Academic Press.

Stern, D. N. (1985). *The interpersonal world of the infant: A view from psychoanalysis and developmental psychology.* New York: Basic Books.

Stern, D. (1992). *Die Lebenserfahrung des Säuglings.* [The life experience of infants] Stuttgart: Klett-Cotta.

Stiles, W. B., Shapiro, D. A. & Elliott, R. (1986). Are all psychotherapies equivalent? *American Psychologist, 41,* 165–180.

Stone, J. & Dreher, B. (1979). Parallel processing of information in the visual pathways. A general principle of sensory coding? *TINS, 5,* 441–446.

Stone, J., Dreher, B. & Leventhal, H. (1979). Hierarchical and parallel mechanisms in the organization of visual cortex. *Brain Research Reviews, 1,* 345–394.

Strauss, B. & Schmidt, S. (1997). Die Bindungstheorie und ihre Relevanz für die Psychotherapie. Teil 2: Mögliche Implikationen der Bindungstheorie für die Psychotherapie und die Psychosomatik. [Attachment theory and its relevance for psychotherapy. Part 2: Possible implications of attachment theory for psychotherapy and psychosomatics] *Psychotherapeut, 42,* 1–16.

Strauss, E. & Moscowitch, M. (1981). Perception of facial expressions. *Brain and Language, 13,* 308–332.

Strauss, E. (1986). Cerebral representation of emotion. In P. D. Blanck, R. Buck & R. Rosenthal (Eds.), *Nonverbal communication in the clinical context.* University Park and London: The Pennsylvania State University Press.

Strehl, U. & Birbaumer, N. (1996). *Verhaltensmedizinische Intervention bei Morbus Parkinson.* [Behavioral medicine intervention for Morbus Parkinson] Weinheim: Psychologie Verlags Union.

Stricker, G. & Gold, J. R. (Eds.). (1993). *Comprehensive handbook of psychotherapy integration.* New York: Plenum Press.

Strupp, H. H. & Binder, J. (1984). *Psychotherapy in a new key. A guide to time-limited dynamic psychotherapy.* New York: Basic Books.

Strupp, H. H. & Hadley, S. W. (1979). Specific vs. nonspecific factors in psychotherapy. A controlled study of outcome. *Archives of General Psychiatry, 36,* 1125–1136.

Stuhr, U. (1997). *Therapieerfolg als Erfolg.* [Success in therapy as success] Heidelberg: Asanger.

Stunkard, A. J. & Wadden, T. A. (1993). *Obesity: Theory and therapy.* New York: Raven.

Süllwold, L., Herrlich, J. & Volk, S. (1994). *Zwangskrankheiten. Psychobiologie, Verhaltenstherapie, Pharmakotherapie.* [Compulsions. Psychobiology, behavior therapy, pharmacotherapy] Stuttgart: Kohlhammer.

Sullivan, H. S. (1953). *The interpersonal theory of psychiatry.* New York: Norton Press.

Sullivan, H. S. (1954). *The psychiatric interview.* New York: Norton.

Swann, W.B. (1990). To be adored or to be known. The interplay of self-enhancement and self-verification. In R. M. Sorrentino & E. T. Higgins (Eds.), *Motivation and cognition, Vol. 2* (pp. 408–448). New York: Guilford.

Swann, W.B. (1992). Seeking truth, finding despair: Some unhappy consequences of a negative self-concept. *Current Directions in Psychological Science, 1,* 15–18.

Swartz, M., Blazer, D. G., Woodbury, M. A., George, L. K. & Manton, K. G. (1987). A study of somatization disorder in a community population using grade of membership analysis. *Psychiatric Developments, 3,* 219–237.

Swartz, M., Landerman, R., George, L., Blazer, D. & Escobar, J. I. (1990). Somatization disorder. In L. N. Robins & D. Regier (Eds.), *Psychiatric disorders in America.* New York: Free Press.

Talley, P. F., Strupp, H. & Butler, S. F. (Eds.). (1994). *Psychotherapy research and practice: Bridging the gap.* New York: Basic Books.

Tausch, R. & Tausch, A.-M. (1971). *Gesprächstherapie. Einfühlsame hilfreiche Gruppen- und Einzelgespräche in Psychotherapie und alltäglichem Leben.* [Client-centered therapy. Sensitive, helpful group and individual settings in psychotherapy and everyday life.] Göttingen: Hogrefe.

Taylor, S. E. & Brown, J. D. (1988). Illusion and well-being: A social-psychological perspective on mental health. *Psychological Bulletin, 103,* 193–210.

Tesser, A. (1988). Toward a self-evaluation maintenance model of social behavior. In L. Berkowitz (Ed.), *Advances in experimental social psychology, Vol. 21* (pp. 181–227). New York: Academic Press.

Teusch, L. (1995) *Gesprächspsychotherapie in Kombination mit verhaltenstherapeutischer Reizkonfrontation bei Panikstörungen mit Agoraphobie. Grundlagen und klinisch-experimentelle Überprüfung.* [Client-centered therapy in combination with behavior therapy stimulus confrontation in panic disorders with agoraphobia. Fundamentals and clinical-experimental testing] Postdoctoral thesis, Gesamthochschule Essen.

Teusch, L. & Finke, J. (1993). *Krankheitslehre der Gesprächspsychotherapie.* [Client-centered therapy and its theory of illness] Heidelberg: Asanger.

Teusch, L. & Finke, J. (1995). Die Grundlagen eines Manuals für die gesprächspsychotherapeutische Behandlung bei Panik und Agoraphobie. [The fundamentals of a manual for client-centered therapy of panic and agoraphobia] *Psychotherapeut, 40,* 88–95.

Thelen, E. & Smith, L. (1995). *A dynamic systems approach to the development of cognition and action* (2nd ed.). Cambridge, MA: The MIT Press.

Thelen, E. & Ulrich, B. D. (1991). Hidden skills: A dynamic systems analysis of treadmill stepping during the first year. *Monographs of the Society for Resarch in Child Development, Serial No. 223, 56.*

Thommen, B., Ammann, R. & Cranach, M. von (1988). *Handlungsorganisation durch soziale Repräsentationen: Welchen Einfluss haben therapeutische Schulen auf ihre Mitglieder?* [Action-organization through social representations: What influence do therapy schools have on their adherents?] Bern: Huber.

Thomson, G. (1986). Agoraphobia: The etiology and treatment of an attachment/separation disorder. *Transactional Analysis Journal, 16,* 11–17.

Thurmaier, F., Engl, J., Eckert, V. & Hahlweg, K. (1992). Prävention von Ehe- und Partnerschafts-störungen EPL (Ehevorbereitung: Ein partnerschaftliches Lernprogramm). [Prevention of marital and partner disorders EPL (Marriage preparation: a partnership learning program)] *Verhaltenstherapie, 2,* 116–124.

Todt, D. (1995). Verhaltensbiologische Aspekte der Entwicklung sozialer Bindungen auf vormenschlicher Stufe. [Aspects of behavior biology for the development of social attachments at the pre-human stage] In G. Spangler & P. Zimmermann (Eds.), *Die Bindungstheorie – Grundlagen, Forschung und Anwendung.* Stuttgart: Klett-Cotta.

Tolman, E. C. (1951). A psychological model. In T. Parsons & E. Shils (Eds.), *Toward a general theory of action* (pp. 279–361). Cambridge: Harvard University Press.

Tolman, E. C. (1952). A cognition motivation model. *Psychological Review, 59,* 389–400.

Tomkins, S. S. (1962, 1963). *Affect, imagery, consciousness, Vols. 1 and 2.* New York: Springer.

Tomkins, S. S. (1970). Affect as the primary motivational system. In M. B. Arnold (Ed.), *Feelings and emotions* (pp. 101–110). New York: Academic Press.

Tomkins, S. S. (1981). The quest for primary motives: Biography and autobiography of an idea. *Journal of Personality and Social Psychology, 41,* 306–329.

Tomkins, S. S. (1991). *Affect imagery and consciousness, Vol. 3.* New York: Springer.

Tori, C. & Worell, L. (1973). Reduction of human avoidant behavior: A comparison of counter-conditioning, expectancy and cognitive information approaches. *Journal of Consulting and Clinical Psychology, 41,* 269–278.

Totman, R. G. (1979). *Social causes of illness.* London: Souvenir Press.

Townsend, J. T. & Busemeyer, J. R. (1989). Approach-avoidance: Return to dynamic decision behavior. In C. Izawa (Ed.), *Current issues in cognitive processes* (pp. 107–133). Hillsdale, NJ: Erlbaum.

Treisman, A. M. (1986). Features and objects in visual processing. *Scientific American, 255,* 106–115.

Treisman, A. M., Squire, R. & Green, G. (1974). Semantic processing in selective listening? A replication. *Memory and Cognition, 2,* 641–646.

Tschacher, W. (1997). *Prozessgestalten.* [Process shaping] Göttingen: Hogrefe.

Tschacher, W. & Grawe, K. (1996). Selbstorganisation in Therapieprozessen – Die Hypothese und empirische Prüfung der „Reduktion von Freiheitsgraden" bei der Enstehung von Therapiesystemen. [Self-organization in therapeutic processes – The hypothesis and empirical testing of the "reduction in degrees of freedom" with the emergence of therapy systems] *Zeitschrift für Klinische Psychologie, 25,* 55–60.

Tschacher, W., Scheier, C. & Grawe, K. (1997). *Order and pattern formation in psychotherapy* (Research report No. 96–3). Psychiatrische Universitätsklinik Bern.

Tucker, D. M. (1986). Neural control of emotional communication. In P. D. Blanck, R. Buck & R. Rosenthal (Eds.), *Nonverbal communication in the clinical context.* University Park and London: The Pennsylvania State Univesity Press.

Tulving, E. (1972). Episodic and semantic memory. In E. Tulving & W. Donaldson (Eds.), *Organization of memory* (pp. 381–403). New York: Academic Press.

Tulving, E., Schacter, D. L. & Stark, H. A. (1982). Priming effects in word-fragment completion are independent of recognition memory. *Journal of Experimental Psychology: Learning, memory and cognition, 8,* 336–342.

Turkat, I. D. (1996). *Die Persönlichkeitsstörungen. Ein Leitfaden für die klinische Psychologie.* [Personality disorders. A guide for clinical psychology] Bern: Huber.

Turkewitz, G., Gordon, E. & Birch, H. (1965). Head turning in the human neonate; Spontaneous patterns. *The Journal of Genetic Psychology, 107,* 143–158.

Tuschen, B. (1996). Störungsorientierte Diagnostik: Neue Akzente bei der Problem- und Verhaltens-analyse. [Disorder-oriented diagnostics: New accents in problem and behavior analysis] In F. M. Caspar (Ed.), *Psychotherapeutische Problemanalyse* (pp. 133–154). Tübingen: dgvt-Verlag.

Tversky, A. & Kahnemann, D. (1974). Judgment under uncertainty: Heuristics and biases. *Science, 185,* 1124–1131.

Ulich, D. (1992). *Sozialisations- und Erziehungseinflüsse in der emotionalen Entwicklung* (Augsburger Berichte zur Entwicklungspsychologie und Pädagogischen Psychologie No. 58). [The influence of socialization and education on emotional development (Augsburg report on developmental psychology and pedagogical psychology No. 58.)] Universität Augsburg.

Ullman, L. P. & Krasner, L. (1969). *A psychological approach to abnormal behavior.* Engelewood Cliffs, NJ: Prentice Hall.

Ullrich, R. & Ullrich, R. (1978). *Das Emotionalitätsinventar als Befindlichkeitsmass. Testmanual EMI-B.* [The emotionality inventory as a measure of well-being. Test manual EMI-B] München: Pfeiffer.

Vaillant, G. (1977). *Adaptation to life.* Boston: Little, Brown.

Valins, S. & Ray, A. A. (1967). Effects of cognitive desensitization on avoidance behavior. *Journal of Personality and Social Psychology, 7,* 345–350.

Vallacher, R. R. & Wegner, D. M. (1985). *A theory of action identification.* Hillsdale, NJ: Erlbaum.

Vallacher, R. R. & Wegner, D. M. (1987). What do people think they're doing? Action identification and human behavior. *Psychological Review, 94,* 3–15.

Van den Bergh, O., Vrana, S. & Eelen, P. (1990). Letters from the heart: Affective categorization of letter combinations in typists and nontypists. *Journal of Experimental Psychology: Learning, Memory and Cognition, 16,* 1153–1161.

Varela, F. J., Thompson, E. & Rosch, E. (1991). *The embodied mind: Cognitive science and human experience.* Cambridge, MA, US: MIT Press.

Vogel, G. (1993). *Planung und Improvisation im Therapieprozess. Eine Analyse mikrotherapeutischer Entscheidungsprozesse.* [Planning and improvisation in the therapeutic process. An analysis of micro-therapeutic decision processes] Münster: Waxmann.

Vogelsang, M. (1996). Ein Modell kognitiv-behavioraler Gruppentherapie bei dependenten Persönlichkeitsstörungen. [A model of cognitive-behavioral group therapy for dependent personality disorders] *Verhaltensmodifikation und Verhaltensmedizin, 17,* 233–249.

Volpert, W. (1983). Das Modell der hierarchisch-sequentiellen Handlungsorganisation. [The model of hierarchic-sequential action organization] In W. Hacker, W. Volpert & M. von Cranach (Eds.), *Kognitive und motivationale Aspekte der Handlung.* Bern: Huber.

Vroom, V. H. (1964). *Work and motivation.* New York: Wiley.

Wachtel, P. L. (1977). *Psychoanalysis and behavior therapy. Toward an integration.* New York: Basic Books.

Wachtel, P. L. (1980). Transference, schema, and assimilation. The relevance of Piaget to the psychoanalytic theory of transference. *Annals of Psychoanalysis, 8,* 59–76.

Wallerstein, R. S. (1986). *Forty-two lives in treatment: A study of psychoanalysis and psychotherapy.* New York: Guilford.

Wallerstein, R. S. (1989). The psychotherapy research program (PRP) of the Menninger Foundation: An overview. *Journal of Consulting and Clinical Psychology, 57,* 195–205.

Warrington, E. K. & Weiskrantz, I. (1970). Amnesic syndrome: Consolidation of retrieval? *Nature, 228,* 629–630.

Watson, M., Pettingale, K. W. & Greer, S. (1984). Emotional control and autonomic arousal in breast cancer patients. *Journal of Psychosomatic Research, 28,* 467–474.

Watzl, H. & Rist, F. (1996). Schizophrenie. [Schizophrenia] In K. Hahlweg & A. Ehlers (Eds.), *Psychische Störungen und ihre Behandlungen* (pp. 1–154). Göttingen: Hogrefe.

Watzlawick, P., Beavin, J. H. & Jackson, D. D. (1969). *Menschliche Kommunikation. Formen, Störungen, Paradoxien.* [Human communication. Forms, disorders, paradoxes] Bern: Huber.

Wedel, S. & Grawe, K. (1980). Die differentiellen Effekte eines standardisierten Assertiveness-Trainings in Gruppen bei neurotisch gehemmten psychiatrischen Patienten. [The differential effects of a standardized assertiveness training in groups of neurotically inhibited psychiatric patients] In R. Ullrich, R. Ullrich de Muynck, K. Grawe & D. Zimmer (Eds.), *Soziale Kompetenz, Band 2.* München: Pfeiffer.

Wegner, D. M. & Pennebaker, J. W. (1993). *Handbook of mental control.* Englewood Cliffs, NJ: Prentice Hall.

Weiffenbach, O., Gänsicke, M., Faust, G. & Maier, W. (1995). Psychische und psychosomatische Störungen in der Allgemeinarztpraxis. [Mental and psychosomatic disorders in the general medical practice] *Münchner Medizinische Wochenschrift, 137,* 528–534.

Weinberger, D. A. (1990). The construct validity of repressive coping style. In J. L. Singer (Ed.), *Repression and dissociation* (pp. 337–386). Chicago: The University of Chicago Press.

Weiss, E. (1964). *Agoraphobia in the light of ego psychology.* New York: Grune & Stratton.

Weiss, J., Sampson, H. & the Mount Zion Psychotherapy Research Group (1986). *The psychoanalytic process: Theory, clinical observation, and research.* New York: Guilford.

Werner, H. (1948). *Comparative psychology and mental development.* Chicago: Follett.

Wicklund, R. A. & Gollwitzer, P. M. (1982). *Symbolic self-completion.* Hillsdale, NJ: Erlbaum.

Wienberg, G. (Ed.). (1995). *Schizophrenie zum Thema machen. Psychoedukative Gruppenarbeit mit schizophren oder schizoaffektiv erkrankten Menschen. Grundlagen und Praxis.* [Making schizophrenia a subject. Psycho-educative group work with schizophrenics or schizoaffective persons. Fundamentals and practice] Bonn: Psychiatrie Verlag.

Wile, D. B. (1984). Kohut, Kernberg, and accusatory interpretations. *Psychotherapy, 21,* 353–264.

Wilfley, D. E., Agras, W.S., Telch, C. F., Rossiter, E. M. and others (1993). Group cognitive-behavioral therapy and group interpersonal psychotherapy for the non-purging bulimic individual: A controlled comparison. *Journal of Consulting and Clinical Psychology, 61,* 296–305.

Willi, J (1975). *Die Zweierbeziehung.* [The partnership] Hamburg: Rowohlt.

Williams, J. M., Watts, F. M., MacLeod, C. & Mathews, A. (1988). *Cognitive psychology and emotional disorders.* New York: Wiley.

Wittling, W. (1990). Neuropsychologische Störungen. [Neuropsychological disorders] In H. Reinecker (Ed.), *Lehrbuch der Klinischen Psychologie* (2nd ed., pp. 527–566). Göttingen: Hogrefe.

Wittmann, H. B., Glier, B. & Spörkel, H. (1994). Verhaltensmedizinische Intervention bei entzündlichen Darmerkrankungen (Morbus Crohn, Colitis ulcerosa). [Behavioral medicine interventions for inflamed stomach illnesses (Crohn's disease, ulcerative colitis)] In M. Zielke & J. Sturm (Eds.), *Handbuch stationäre Verhaltenstherapie* (pp. 632–639). Weinheim: Psychologie Verlags Union.

Wolpe, J. (1958). *Psychotherapy by reciprocal inhibition.* Stanford, Ca.: Stanford University Press.

Wong, S. E., Slama, K. M. & Liberman, R. P. (1987). Behavioral analysis and therapy for aggressive psychiatric and developmentally disabled patients. In L. H. Roth (Ed.), *Clinical treatment of the violent person* (pp. 20–53). New York: Guilford.

Wortman, C. B. & Brehm, J. W. (1975). Responses to uncontrollable outcomes. In L. Berkowitz (Ed.), *Advances in experimental social psychology, Vol. 8* (pp. 277–336). New York: Academic Press.

Yalom, I. (1974). *The theory and practice of group psychotherapy.* New York: Basic Books.
Yates, J. (1985). The content of awareness as a model of the world. *Psychological Review, 92,* 249–284.
Young, J. E. (1994). *Cognitive therapy for personality disorders: A schema-focused approach* (2nd ed.). Sarasota, FL: Professional Resource Press.
Young, P. & Yamane, S. (1993). Sparse population coding of faces in the inferotemporal cortex. *Science, 256,* 1327–1332.

Zahn-Waxler, C., Robinson, J. & Emde, R. N. (1992). The development of empathy in twins. *Developmental Psychology, 28,* 1038–1047.
Zajonc, R. B. (1968). Cognitive theories in social psychology. In G. Lindzay & E. Aronson (Eds.), *Handbook of social psychology, Vol. I.* Reading, MA: Addison-Wesley.
Zaudig, M. (1995). *Demenz und „leichte kognitive Beeinträchtigungen" im Alter.* [Dementia and "light cognitive interference" with age] Bern: Huber.
Zimmer, D. (1996). Funktionelle Sexualstörungen. [Functional sexual disorders] In K. Hahlweg & A. Ehlers (Eds.), *Psychische Störungen und ihre Behandlungen* (pp. 723–798). Göttingen: Hogrefe.
Znoj, H., Horowitz, M. J., Bonanno, G. A., Marcker, A. & Stinson, C. (in press a). Control processes in bereavement: A new observer measure for coping with severe emotional distress. *Behaviour Research and Therapy.*
Znoj, H., Horowitz, M. J., Field, M., Bonanno, G. A. & Maercker, A. (in press b). Emotional regulation: The sense of control questionnaire. *Psychosomatic Medicine.*
Zuckerman, M., DePaulo, B. M. & Rosenthal, R. (1981). Verbal and nonverbal communication of deception. In L. Berkowitz (Ed.), *Advances in experimental social psychology, Vol. 14.* New York: Academic Press.
Zuckerman, M., DePaulo, B. M. & Rosenthal, R. (1986). Humans as deceivers and lie detectors. In P. D. Blanck, R. Buck & R. Rosenthal (Eds.), *Nonverbal communication in the clinical context.* University Park and London: The Pennsylvania State University Press.
Zwilgmeier, K. (1981). *Stufen des Ich. Bewusstseinsentwicklung in Gesellschaft und Kultur.* [Levels of the self. development of consciousness in society and culture] Fellbach: Bonz.

Author Index

Subject Index